677
2

D1622670

Property of
CUAdrama

Donated By

Property of
CUAdrama

SPACKENKILL SCHOOL LIBRARY
11 CROFT ROAD
POUGHKEEPSIE, N.Y. 12603

NATURAL AND MANMADE
TEXTILE FIBERS

Books by GEORGE E. LINTON

CALLAWAY MILLS TEXTILE DICTIONARY (co-author)

CHEMISTRY AND TEXTILES FOR THE LAUNDRY INDUSTRY
(co-author)

DAN RIVER MILLS DICTIONARY OF TEXTILE TERMS (co-author)

INTRODUCTION TO TEXTILES

MODERN TEXTILE DICTIONARY

STANDARD TEXTILE FABRICS

TEXTILES: CARE AND TESTING

APPLIED TEXTILES

APPLIED BASIC TEXTILES

NATURAL AND MANMADE TEXTILE FIBERS

NATURAL AND MANMADE TEXTILE FIBERS

Raw Material to Finished Fabric

BY

GEORGE E. LINTON Ph.D.

PROFESSOR EMERITUS, TEXTILE DEPARTMENT, FASHION INSTITUTE;
TEXTILE EDITOR FOR *AMERICAN FABRICS MAGAZINE*, NEW YORK CITY

FIRST EDITION

Fully Illustrated

DUELL, SLOAN AND PEARCE   NEW YORK

SPACKENKILL SCHOOL LIBRARY
11 CROFT ROAD
POUGHKEEPSIE, N.Y. 12603

COPYRIGHT © 1966 BY GEORGE E. LINTON

All rights reserved. No part of this book in excess
of five hundred words may be reproduced in any form
without permission in writing from the publisher.

First edition

DUELL, SLOAN & PEARCE
AFFILIATE OF
MEREDITH PRESS

Library of Congress Catalog Card Number: 65-24856

MANUFACTURED IN THE UNITED STATES OF AMERICA FOR MEREDITH PRESS

VAN REES PRESS • NEW YORK

To

The American Association for Textile Technology, Inc., New York City, whose objectives are to encourage mutual understanding in the fields of technology and marketing; the advancement of textile technology in all of its branches; cooperation with established facilities for textile education; and the interchange and dissemination of professional knowledge among the members and with other industry groups.

Foreword

Textile fibers, and the textiles and clothing made from them, rank as one of the three major essentials of mankind, and the textile industry is rated second among the twenty-two major industries in the United States with regard to the number of persons employed. Why then, does the average consumer know comparatively little concerning textiles, especially the textile fibers, both natural and manmade?

Among the reasons are:

(1) There is little, if any, carding, spinning, and weaving done in the home in this country.

(2) Knowledge of textile fibers, filaments, and the fabrics made from them, along with their characteristics and properties, is not widely disseminated.

(3) Most testing procedures, both chemical and physical, in terms of performance are of comparatively recent origin.

(4) Textile terminology as applied to fibers, filaments, and fabrics is often misused or misunderstood and seems to be in a continuing state of flux.

(5) Many students and teachers of textile subjects in secondary and higher institutions of learning are unable to acquire an overall mastery of the subject because of a lack of sources and proper organization of textile fibers and fabrics for educational and business purposes.

As one who has devoted many years to the problems of indoctrinating students, teachers, textile-mill trainees, home economics groups, and the general public with the knowledge covered in this effort, I find that this book, devoted solely to the natural and the manmade textile fibers, including characteristics and properties, the terminal uses of these fibers, the fabrics in which they are used to clothe mankind, and the types of clothing made from them, is most gratifying. Dr. Linton in this book has organized his material into a splendid sequence in excellent detail that should have much appeal to the layman, student, textile technologist, home economist, mill trainee, and the person employed in the various fields of the great merchandising world.

He has set down in black and white the essential information that one should study to become better versed in the textile fiber kingdoms. His text is well written and succinct, so that any reader interested in the subject will find the time spent well worth while. This book is bound to be of great interest to the reader, whether student or layman, textile technologist or casual reader. The book should be on the desk of every textile executive or in the library of those who desire concrete information on the textile fibers, their end uses, and their great impact in the textile and clothing industries.

CAMERON A. BAKER,
Director of Research and Development,
Better Fabrics Testing Bureau, Inc.,
New York City

Acknowledgments to Technical Advisers

The author is pleased to make sincere acknowledgment to all those whose aid, cooperation, guidance, and patience have aided him to make this book possible. Special acknowledgment is due to the following:

Paul Askew, Singer Company, Inc., Cobble Division, Chattanooga, Tennessee.

Matthew J. Babey, Atlas Electric Devices Company, Inc., Chicago, Illinois.

Cameron A. Baker, Director of Research and Development, Better Fabrics Testing Bureau, 101 West 31st Street, New York City.

Professor Rosa Balenzano, Art Department, Fashion Institute, New York City.

H. D. Barker, Ph.D., Division of Cotton and Other Fiber Crops, U.S. Department of Agriculture, Washington, D.C.

Allen F. Barney, Director Public Relations, Saco-Lowell Shops, Division of Maremont Corporation, Easley and Greenville, South Carolina.

John Bosshard and Staff, Fabric Development Department, American Viscose Company, Division of FMC Corporation, 350 Fifth Avenue, New York City.

Technical Staff, The Chemstrand Corporation, 350 Fifth Avenue, New York City.

Technical Staff, Eastman Chemical Products, Inc., 260 Madison Avenue, New York City.

Dr. Victor L. Erlich, Vice-President, Reeves Brothers, Inc., 1071 Sixth Avenue, New York City.

Ephraim Freedman, Director of the Bureau of Standards, R. H. Macy & Company, Inc., Herald Square, New York City.

Raymond Gagnon, Director of the School of Textiles, International Correspondence Schools, Scranton, Pennsylvania.

James L. Giblin, Dean, Southeastern Massachusetts Technological Institute, North Dartmouth, Massachusetts.

Ned Glattauer, Director, Production Department, Duell, Sloan & Pearce, a Division of Meredith Press, Inc., New York City.

James H. Grant, Advertising Manager, Draper Corporation, Hopedale, Massachusetts.

Joseph C. Hirsch and Fred Simmons, Stylists, Manchester Mills, Inc., 1290 Sixth Avenue, New York City.

Stanley B. Hunt and Charles Whitehead, *Textile Organon*, Textile Economics Bureau, Inc., 10 East 40th Street, New York City.

Aubrey D. Kelley, Vice-President (retired), George W. Elbogen & Company, Inc., 450 Park Avenue South, New York City.

Edward E. Kuhnel, Secretary, Clupak, Inc., 530 Fifth Avenue, New York City.

Cecil Lubell, Executive Editor for American Fabrics Magazine, 24 East 38th Street, New York.

Harry E. Mahler, Manager of Industrial Fabric Sales and Development, Owens-Corning Fiberglas Corporation, 717 Fifth Avenue, New York City.

George D. Maynard, Jr., Refined Products Company, Inc., Lyndhurst, New Jersey.

Professor Robert A. McWilliams, Textile Division of the Industrial Arts Department, State University College, Oswego, New York.

Christopher J. Moroney, Sales Promotion Manager, Sanforized Division of Cluett, Peabody & Company, Inc., 530 Fifth Avenue, New York City.

Mitchell J. Rudolf, Director of Standards, Supima Associates of America, 350 Fifth Avenue, New York City.

Charles Rutledge and Staff, Fiber Products Division of E. I. du Pont de Nemours & Company, Inc., Wilmington, Delaware.

William C. Segal, Publisher, and Miss Cora Carlyle, Fashion Coordinator for American Fabrics Magazine, 24 East 38th Street, New York City.

Lester H. Senholzi, Manager of the Greige Goods Department, Eastman Chemical Products Company, Inc., 260 Madison Avenue, New York City.

Charles Sinatra, Director of Photography and Visual Aids, American Viscose Company, Division of FMC Corporation, 350 Fifth Avenue, New York City.

Jacob Solinger, Consultant for the Apparel Trades, 601 West 115th Street, New York City.

Chester A. Strodl, Textile Fibers Division, Union Carbide Chemicals Company, 270 Park Avenue, New York City.

J. Vernon Wallace, Director Industrial Relations, Bibb Manufacturing Company, Inc., Macon, Georgia.

Robert Ward, Director Audio-Visual Services, National Cotton Council, Memphis, Tennessee.

Edwin Wilkinson, President of the National Association of Wool Manufacturers, 386 Fourth Avenue, New York City.

Textile Faculty of the Fashion Institute, 227 West 27th Street, New York City: Professors José Alvarodiez, Edna S. Brodie, Allen C. Cohen, Howard Essig, Giles Hopkins, Ray McCaughey, Joseph J. Pizzuto, Arthur Price, Joseph Samuels; Technologist, Joseph Garafolo.

Special Acknowledgment to the Apparel and Clothing Department of the Fashion Institute: Professors Ernestine Kopp (Chairman), Adelaide Manno, Renné Rolfo, Edmund Roberts, Josephine Watkins.

ZEALOUS AID IN THE PREPARATION OF THE MANUSCRIPT

Art Work: Professor Rosa Balenzano.
Typing: Margaret M. Linton, Marion L. O'Brien.

Acknowledgments to Companies and Agencies

COTTON

Bibb Manufacturing Company, Inc., Macon, Georgia.
Bradford Dyeing Association (U.S.A.), New York City.
Cluett, Peabody & Co., Inc., New York City.
Dan River Mills, Inc., New York City.
National Cotton Council, Memphis, Tennessee.
West Point-Pepperell, Inc., West Point, Georgia, and New York City.
Whitin Machine Works, Division of White Consolidated Industries, Inc., Whitinsville, Massachusetts.

EDUCATIONAL INSTITUTIONS

Fashion Institute, New York City.
Philadelphia College of Textiles and Science, Germantown, Pennsylvania.

FLAX-LINEN

The Irish Linen Guild, New York City.

GOVERNMENT AGENCIES

Bureau of Census, U.S. Department of Labor, Washington, D.C.
Farm Security Administration, Washington, D.C.
U.S. Department of Agriculture, Washington, D.C.
U.S. Department of Commerce, Washington, D.C.

MANMADE FIBERS AND FILAMENTS, CELLULOSIC TYPES

American Enka Corporation, 350 Fifth Avenue, New York City.
American Viscose Company, FMC Corporation, 350 Fifth Avenue, New York City.
Fibers Division, Beaunit Corporation, 261 Madison Avenue, New York City.
Celanese Fibers Company, A Division of Celanese Corporation of America, 522 Fifth Avenue, New York City.
Courtaulds (Alabama), Inc., 600 Fifth Avenue, New York City.
E. I. du Pont de Nemours & Co., Inc., Wilmington 98, Delaware.
Fair Haven Mills, Inc., Fair Haven, Vermont.
Industrial Rayon Corporation, A Division of Midland-Ross Corporation, 500 Fifth Avenue, New York City.
Mohasco Industries, Inc., New Bedford Rayon Division, 295 Fifth Avenue, New York City.
Tennessee Eastman Company, A Division of Eastman Kodak Company, 260 Madison Avenue, New York City.

MANMADE FIBERS AND FILAMENTS, NON-CELLULOSIC TYPES

Acrylic

American Cyanamid Company, Fibers Division, 30 Rockefeller Plaza, New York City.
The Chemstrand Corporation, 350 Fifth Avenue, New York City.
The Dow Chemical Company, James River Division, Textile Fibers Department, Williamsburg, Virginia, and 45 Rockefeller Plaza, New York City.
E. I. du Pont de Nemours & Co., Inc., Wilmington 98, Delaware.

Modacrylic

Tennessee Eastman Company, Kingsport, Tennessee.
Union Carbide Chemicals Company (A Division of Union Carbide Corporation), Textile Fibers Department, 270 Park Avenue, New York City.

OTHER MANMADE FIBERS AND FILAMENTS

Glass Fibers

The Carborundum Company, Buffalo Avenue, Niagara Falls, New York.
Ferro Corporation, Fiber Glass Division, Fiber Glass Road, Nashville 11, Tennessee.
Johns-Manville Fiber Glass Inc., 1810 Madison Avenue, Toledo 1, Ohio.
Modiglass Fibers, Inc., Florham Park, New Jersey.
Owens-Corning Fiberglas Corporation, 717 Fifth Avenue, New York City.
Pittsburgh Plate Glass Company, Fiber Glass Division, One Gateway Center, Pittsburgh 22, Pennsylvania.

Metallic Fibers

The Dow Chemical Company, James River Division, Textile Fibers Department, Williamsburg, Virginia.
Fairtex Corporation, Liberty Life Building, Charlotte 2, North Carolina.
Malina Company, 125 West 41st Street, New York City.
Metal Film Company, Inc., 40 Worth Street, New York City.
Metlon Corporation, A Division of Acme Backing Corporation, 432 Fourth Avenue, New York City.
Multi-Tex Products Corporation, 56 Elm Street, Newark, New Jersey.
Nylco Products, Inc., 530 Main Street, Clinton, Massachusetts.
Standard Yarn Mills, Inc., 62–05 30th Avenue, Woodside 77, New York.

Nonwoven Fabrics

Curlator Corporation, Textile Division, East Rochester, New York.
E. I. du Pont de Nemours & Co., Inc., Wilmington 98, Delaware.

Nylon

Allied Chemical Corporation, 261 Madison Avenue, New York City.
American Enka Corporation, Enka, North Carolina.
Fibers Division, Beaunit Corporation, 261 Madison Avenue, New York City.
The Chemstrand Corporation, 350 Fifth Avenue, New York City.
Dawbarn Division, W. R. Grace & Company, Inc., Waynesboro, Virginia.
E. I. du Pont de Nemours & Co., Inc., Wilmington 98, Delaware, and 350 Fifth Avenue, New York City.
Firestone Plastics Company, A Division of The Firestone Tire & Rubber Company, 45 Rockefeller Plaza, New York City.
The National Plastic Products Company, Odenton, Maryland.
Southern Lus-Trus Corporation, Jacksonville, Florida.

Nytril

Celanese Corporation of America, New York City.

Olefin

Alamo Industries, Inc., Charlotte, North Carolina.
AviSun Corporation, New Castle, Delaware.
Dawbarn Division, W. R. Grace & Company, Inc., Waynesboro, Virginia.
Industrial Plastic Company, 216 Tingley Lane, Metuchen, New Jersey.
Industrial Rayon Corporation, Division Midland-Ross Corporation, 500 Fifth Avenue, New York City.
The National Plastic Products Company, Odenton, Maryland.
Reeves Brothers, Inc., 1071 Sixth Avenue, New York City.

Southern Lus-Trus Corporation, Jacksonville, Florida.
United States Rubber Company, Footwear & General Products Division, Royalene
    Yarn Department, 1230 Sixth Avenue, New York City.

Other Polyvinyl Fibers

E. I. du Pont de Nemours & Co., Inc., Wilmington 98, Delaware.

Polyester

American Enka Corporation, Enka, North Carolina.
Fibers Division, Beaunit Corporation, 261 Madison Avenue, New York City.
Chemstrand Corporation, New York City.
E. I. du Pont de Nemours & Co., Inc., Wilmington, Delaware.
Fiber Industries, Inc., Shelby, North Carolina.
Goodyear Tire & Rubber Company, Akron, Ohio.
IRC Fibers Division, Midland-Ross Corporation, Cleveland, Ohio.
National Plastic Products Company, Inc., (Vectra) Odenton, Maryland.

Saran

Dawbarn Division, W. R. Grace & Company, Inc., Waynesboro, Virginia.
Firestone Plastics Company, Hopewell, Virginia.
The National Plastics Products Company, Odenton, Maryland.
Southern Lus-Trus Corporation, Jacksonville, Florida.
The Dow Chemical Company, James River Division, Textile Fibers Department,
    Williamsburg, Virginia.

Spandex

American Cyanamid Company, Bound Brook, New Jersey.
E. I. du Pont de Nemours & Co., Inc., Wilmington, Delaware.
Firestone Tire & Rubber Company, Hopewell, Virginia.
Globe Manufacturing Company, Fall River, Massachusetts.
Interspan, Inc., International Stretch Products, Inc., New York City.
Polythane Corporation (Chemstrand Corporation), New York City.
United States Rubber Company, Textile Division, New York City.

Vinyon

American Viscose Company, Division FMC Corporation, 350 Fifth Avenue, New
    York City.

PUBLICATIONS

American Dyestuff Reporter, Howes Publishing Company, Inc., 44 East 23rd Street,
    New York City (bi-monthly; A.A.T.C.C.).
American Fabrics Magazine Quarterly, and *AF Encyclopedia of Textiles,* Doric Pub-
    lications, 24 East 38th Street, New York City.
America's Textile Reporter, 286 Congress Street, Boston 10, Massachusetts (weekly
    since 1887).
Fairchild Publications, 7 East 12th Street, New York City.
Modern Textiles Magazine, 303 Fifth Avenue, New York City (monthly).
Textile Industries Magazine, 1760 Peachtree Road, N.W., Atlanta 9, Georgia
    (monthly).
Textile Mercury and Argus, Mercury House, Acton Square, Salford, Manchester,
    England (weekly).
Textile Organon, Textile Economics Bureau, Inc., 10 East 40th Street, New York City
    (monthly). The basic source of data and statistics in textiles.
Textile Statistics Section for the Combined Textile Industries. Annual dictionary and
    directory for data, statistics, and concise information on all textile mills and plants
    in the United States.
Textile World, McGraw-Hill Publishing Company, Inc., 330 West 42nd Street, New
    York City (monthly).

The "Mercury" Dictionary of Textile Terms, published in 1950 by The Staff of *Textile Mercury and Argus.* An excellent source book which covers the textile fields in great detail.

The Story of Asbestos Textiles, Asbestos Institute, Philadelphia College of Textiles and Science, 3243 Schoolhouse Lane, Philadelphia 44, Pennsylvania.

TEXTILE ASSOCIATIONS

American Association of Textile Chemists & Colorists, 44 East 23rd Street, New York City.

American Association for Textile Technology, Inc., 1 Liberty Street, New York City.

American Society for Testing and Materials, Philadelphia, Pennsylvania.

TEXTILE TESTING

Alfred Suter Company, 200 Fifth Avenue, New York City.

Atlas Electric Devices Company, Chicago, Illinois.

Better Fabrics Testing Bureau, Inc., 101 West 31st Street, New York City.

Bureau of Standards, R. H. Macy & Company, Inc., Herald Square, New York City.

Hatch Textile Research, Inc., 23 East 26th Street, New York City.

United States Testing Company, Inc., 1415 Park Avenue, Hoboken, New Jersey.

WEAVING

Crompton Knowles Corporation, Worcester, Massachusetts.

Draper Corporation, Hopedale, Massachusetts.

Philadelphia College of Textiles and Science, Philadelphia 44, Pennsylvania.

WOOLENS AND WORSTEDS

Australian Government on Behalf of Wool Interests, Canberra, Australia.

Deering Milliken, Inc., 1045 Sixth Avenue, New York City, and Deering Milliken Research Corporation, Greenville and Spartanburg, South Carolina.

National Association of Wool Manufacturers, 386 Fourth Avenue, New York City.

Wool Bureau, 360 Lexington Avenue, New York City.

Contents

[xv]

Introduction

This book and its companion, *Applied Basic Textiles*, should meet the needs of:

(1) Students and teachers of textiles, apparel, home economics, and merchandising in all its varied aspects.

(2) Training departments of textile companies and department stores.

(3) Those engaged in industries allied with textiles and apparel—applied, general and specific.

The textile horizon has expanded greatly in the last few years, especially so because of the great rise of the manmade fibers and filaments, many of which have caused much influence on our present-day methods of living, both urban and suburban, as well as rural. Greater knowledge and more familiarity with all things textile, in their far-reaching branches, have become more or less a prime requisite among practically all consumers, both in and out of industry.

Textiles differ in four ways—raw material, construction, color, and finish. The latter three are fully covered in *Applied Basic Textiles*. The author feels that his previous work, *Applied Textiles*, which was printed in six editions, no longer fills the needs of the vast textile populace, from the highly skilled textile technologist to the consumer of textile products of all types. He has therefore divided the former *Applied Textiles* into two books, which made it possible for him to include all necessary new developments—of which there have been many of late—with the existing factual information in the textile field.

One of the basic reasons for two books is that a single volume would become unwieldy in handling; it would be too large. Another reason is that raw materials —fiber and filament—have reached untold bounds, greatly increasing their importance, prominence, and place in the industry. In recent years we have been confronted with a maze of newly created manmade fibers and filaments, especially since the close of World War II.

Incidentally, to support this contention, there are sixteen categories of manmade fibers in the decree of the Textile Fiber Products Identification Act of March 3, 1960, promulgated by the Federal Trade Commission, Washington, D.C. At the present time, approximately two hundred manmade fibers are produced in this country. There are about 1,000 fiber and trademark names. In addition, outside the United States, there are about 1,700 fiber and trademark names, a total of approximately 2,700 names. Thus the textile technologist, let alone the consumer, is often confused in the quagmire and story of manmade fibers and filaments. A continuous and close study on all new developments is necessary to keep abreast of the trends of the times in this fast-moving and exciting industry.

Manmade fibers, like fashion and style, seem to come and go about every other day. Comparatively few have made the grade to the point that they have become household words—acetate, rayon, Arnel, A-Acrilan, "Antron," Avril, Bemberg, Cantrece, Creslan, Fortisan, Fortrel; Dynel, Verel; nylon, "Dacron," Kodel,

Zefran, Vycron, Fiberglas, Lastex and Laton; Lamé, Lurex, "Lycra," Vyrene, Spandelle, Metlon, Mylar, Reevon, etc.

Thus "many are called but few are chosen." Because of excellent promotion, educational programs, fashion shows and the other types of advertising media, the following names are becoming more and more household words and a part of our daily language—names of companies such as these are known to about everyone: Alamo, Allied Chemical, Avisco, Beaunit, Celanese, Chemstrand, Courtaulds, Cyanamid, Dawbarn, Dow, Du Pont, Eastman, Enka, Fiberglas, Fiber Industries, Firestone, Industrial, National Plastic, Reeves, Union Carbide, U.S. Rubber, et al.

Those fibers which have survived and withstood the test of time in durability and performance have made a great impact upon the public, and they have had a devastating effect on the four major natural fibers as well—cotton, flax and linen, wool, and silk. The natural fibers, known as long as recorded history, will be with us always, but in a gradually declining degree of use and consumption. This decline began in the late 1940's.

Both the cellulosic and the non-cellulosic fibers have made fantastic gains since the close of World War II. Only rayon, acetate, and nylon were known prior to this conflict. Each year sees new records unfolded for both types in production and consumption, and per-capita usage. The natural fibers are given full and detailed coverage in this book. Their past glory, history, and continued usage cannot be brushed aside by any manner or means. They still thrive, but not nearly to the degree that they did prior to 1939–1940.

The greatest thing in the mind of man is an idea; the greatest thing in the hand of man is a tool with which to work. Generally speaking, two things are important to the performance and durability of any product, textile or otherwise. First, the quality of the raw material used, and, secondly, the skills, techniques, and aptitudes of every worker who has a hand in the creating of a product, from the raw material to the finished, commercial article ready for the market. One of the reasons for the rise of the manmade fibers is that research and development groups were able to develop raw materials which, as is known now by everyone, have proved their worth to the consuming public.

This book covers in a factual, succinct manner the story of man, natural textile fibers, and the manmade textile fibers. The history of these three is important to the reader so that he may know what transpired many years ago (apperception) and link it with the present-day conditions and status of the items covered in the book (perception). Other features include the properties and characteristics of the fibers, strong and weak points, methods of manufacture into commercial yarn, fabrication into a cloth, the finishing of the goods, and the end, or terminal, uses for the manipulation of the finished materials into items of apparel, home furnishings, or industrial uses. Standard or staple fabrics for each fiber covered is a part of the detailed study of each fiber category.

The book is profuse in illustrations furnished by leading companies for the respective segments of the book. Pictures, line-cuts, flow charts, animated drawings and sketches, tables, etc., are so profuse that it may be said "that he who runs may read."

It is hoped that it will enable the consumer to purchase in a more intelligent manner inner and outerwear, apparel and clothing of all types and kinds, home furnishings, decorative materials, etc. The characteristics and performance of the host of fabrics covered are explained, as far as possible, in language easily understandable to the consumer.

This book acquaints the student and the younger employees of today with the myriad possibilities for employment in the industry—as a worker, buyer, seller, merchandise person, clerk, converter, designer, stylist, fashion coordinator, fashion writer, advertising, colorist, and color illustrator. The book should be of value to the president of a company large or small, to other executives, and employees from department heads to secretaries.

It is believed that it will appeal to and command the attention of the serious-minded individual who is desirous of a worth-while education in the great field of textile fibers from raw material to the finished fabric. It may serve as a means for promotion for those willing to give time, attention, and thought pertinent to advancing up the rungs of the ladder in this great industry.

More than forty technical advisers and more than eighty textile companies have aided the author in making this effort possible. Every unit in this volume has been checked for accuracy and proper setup. The author acknowledges gratefully the excellent work performed by everyone who has had some part, small or large, in the creation of the book. Advice, suggestions, and constructive criticisms are much appreciated.

There has never been a perfect yard of cloth woven on a loom. By the same token, it may be stated that there has never been a perfect book printed, one that is flawless in all details. Realizing this, the author has made every effort to cover correctly all the salient features and high points relative to textile fibers from raw material to the finished fabric. To that end, he would appreciate any constructive criticism from any reader of the book who might take exception to some portion of the text, interpretation, statistics, information, etc., contained in this volume.

Some Thoughts on How to Appraise, Read, and Study a Textbook

(1) First of all, examine the book casually, thumb through it, and form a first impression of it; first impressions are often lasting in nature whether or not in time you find the book does have appeal for you.

(2) Note name of the publisher, its status in the book trade, the name of the author, and the date of publication.

(3) Read well the text on the book jacket to learn of the background of the author; note other books he has written. Does the author seem to have sufficient background to do the type of book in question?

(4) Read the introduction carefully to learn of the underlying philosophy of the author and obtain a good idea of the comprehensiveness of the book.

(5) Then examine the book in detail and form an opinion as to whether you deem it worthy of your attention and interest.

(6) Examine the index very carefully, a most important part in any good book. Note the cross-references, the breakdown of subterms under the major captions, and the general over-all view of this part of the book. The index is very important to a beginning student in any subject, technical or otherwise.

(7) The following high points should be noted by the reader: the units or chapters in the book, the sequence of the contents, its setup and continuity, and the inclusion of pictures, illustrations, half-tones, flow sheets, company credits given by the author, etc.

(8) Check the front material of the book for the list of contributors and companies who have aided the author in his work.

(9) Does the book have an appendix, a most important part of any worth-while textbook? Also check the bibliography with regard to source material.

(10) After a close examination of the book, satisfy yourself that the author has written in a clear, lucid, understanding manner. Does he know his subject? Does the book have an ease of reading for you?

(11) Is the book factual and does it contain a goodly amount of general, as well as specific, information? Any good book should appeal to a serious student and should serve his need to increase his knowledge. Or is the book one of the so-called "scissors-and-paste" type done by an author who is not well versed in the field, or by one trying to write a book outside his or her major field or background?

(12) Is the book set up with a self-study and self-testing program which will aid the student in digesting the text? Psychologists are agreed that we retain 10 per cent of what we read, 20 per cent of what we hear, 30 per cent of what we see, but 90 per cent of what we write or underline on paper.

Thus a textbook should also serve you as a workbook. Underline all the items that seem to hold a special interest for you. Underlining will aid in your retention of the basic material so essential for examination purposes. Use a red, blue or ordinary lead pencil for underlining; ink is not suggested.

(13) Compare the book at hand with comparable books done in the field. Analyze the books from all angles and then form your opinion as to which one will best serve your purpose. Textbooks, chiefly semitechnical and technical books, often are done by an author with a rather meager background. There has never been a book written and printed that is perfect in all details. Many books done by authors not too well trained in the particular subject contain misstatements, errors, faulty setup and sequence, etc.

(14) Any well-written textbook should serve the beginning student through to the semitechnical and full-fledged technologist. Any book is an investment for you. Make certain that the investment of your money in a book is for one written by an author who is definitely aware of and fully competent in all the details and ramifications necessary to produce a really worth-while book. It is also suggested that students consult with their teachers or professors on any book that they intend to study.

Testing Program

This book contains a program for self-testing and group-testing; practically every unit contains a testing program. In addition, comprehensive testing in textiles may be found, as follows:

NATURAL AND MANMADE
TEXTILE FIBERS

PART ONE

TABLE OF CONTENTS

Part 1—Unit 1

TOPIC: INTRODUCTION TO MAN, AND THE STORY OF FLAX AND LINEN, WOOL, AND COTTON

The earliest period known in the cultural evolution of man is the Stone Age, which was marked by the creation and use of stone weapons and work implements. It preceded the Bronze Age and is subdivided into the eras of the Eolithic, Paleolithic, and Neolithic Ages.

The Eolithic or Early Stone Age was characterized by the crudest of stone tools and weapons. The Paleolithic or Old Stone Age covered roughly a period of 500,000 to 1,000,000 years. Features of the era included chipped stone tools, axes, stone javelins, harpoons of bone or ivory, and the well-developed Magdalenian cave art.

The Neolithic Age, which continued in Europe from about 10000 to 2500 B.C., featured polished stone articles, pottery-making, bows and arrows, domestication of animals, some work in agriculture, the invention of the most useful of all things, the wheel, and some weaving. Even today there exist some primitive peoples who are still living in the throes of Neolithic culture.

SOME CLUES TO EARLY MAN

WHERE	WHEN	BY	AT
Java Man— Skull, leg bone, teeth	1891	Eugène Dubois	Neat Trinil, Java
Heidelberg Man— Lower jaw	1907	Otto Schoetensack	Mauer, Germany
Peking Man— Teeth, jaw, skull, etc.	1921	Anderson, Black, Pei, de Chardin, et al:	Chon Kon Tien, China
Rhodesian Man— Cranium, limb, and other bones	1921	T. Zwigeiaar	Broken Hill, Rhodesia,
Neanderthal Man— Skull and various skeletal parts	1856	Dr. Fuhlrott	Near Düsseldorf, Germany
Cro-Magnon Man— Skull and skeletal parts	1868	Berthonmeyrow and Dehmares; announced	Les Eyzies, Dordogne, France
Natchez Man— Pelvis	1846	Dr. Dickeson	Natchez, Mississippi, U.S.A.

Courtesy: The Academy of Natural Sciences of Philadelphia, Philadelphia, Pennsylvania; SKOA.

TEXTILES IN ANCIENT HISTORY, SCRIPTURE, AND LITERATURE

The history, scripture, and literature of ancient times have revealed considerable information about textiles, so much so that it is now possible to follow its history in a continuous manner to considerable degree.

Paleolithic man had acquired the arts of carding, spinning, weaving, twisting cords, plaiting, braiding, and sewing. Fine bone awls, bone needles, and bone implements of work with marks of binding cords on them have been uncovered in the drift strata.

Neolithic man cultivated the flax plant and made linen cloth, its product. Remains of spinning wheels, spindles, spinning whorls, weaver's weights, and various yarns and fabrics were brought to light in the great excavations of the life of the Swiss Lake Dwellers, discovered in the winter of 1853–54.

History has revealed that the first "thread" was used to make stretchable fabrics such as nets for fishing, hammocks for sleeping, drayage bags and receptacles for carrying things, and traps for hunting animals. Some of the fabrics from these old days were made of the leno or doup(e) weave construction, in addition to plain or twill-woven materials.

Knotting, netting, intertwining, interlacing, crocheting, etc., were used to make some of the foregoing items as well.

A GEOLOGICAL TIME SCALE

After the geological time scale of Dr. Kirtley Mather,
Professor of Geology, Harvard University,
Cambridge, Massachusetts

ERAS	PERIODS		MOUNTAIN-MAKING EPISODES	LIFE	YEARS B.C.
CENOZOIC	QUATERNARY	Recent	("The Great Ice Age")	Age of Man	25,000
		Pleistocene			
					2,000,000
	TERTIARY	Pliocene	Alps	Age of Mammals	
		Miocene			35,000,000
		Oligocene			
		Eocene			60,000,000
MESOZOIC	CRETACEOUS		Rocky Mountains	Age of Reptiles	
	JURASSIC		Sierra Nevada		
	TRIASSIC				205,000,000
PALEOZOIC	CARBONIFEROUS	Permian	Appalachians		300,000,000
		Pennsylvanian			
		Mississippian		Age of Fishes	
	DEVONIAN				
	SILURIAN		Scottish Highlands		450,000,000
	ORDOVICIAN				
	CAMBRIAN				
PROTEROZOIC			Younger Laurentians	Age of Invertebrates	600,000,000
ARCHEOZOIC			Older Laurentians		1,260,000,000

Courtesy: The Academy of Natural Sciences of Philadelphia, Philadelphia, Pennsylvania; SKOA.

Decoration and embellishments on woven fabrics were done by embroidery in the days of ancient Egypt. Linen, silk, wool, and metallic threads were used to decorate articles of clothing. Elaborately decorated clothing, apparel, and fabrics are still very important in present-day life throughout the world, from the colorful peasant and national costumes of different peoples to the most elegant attire of sophisticated society.

Needles of bronze, copper, gold, iron, and silver were found in excavations made in Egypt and show that needles were used there as far back as 8000 B.C. Thus the development of what we call clothing and apparel is one of the most fascinating aspects of man's progress. The early history of textiles fuses delightful and interesting speculation with historical knowledge as it unfolded with an almost geologic slowness. As man gradually worked his way to self-assertion, he greatly benefited from his almost childish curiosity and imitativeness. He became a persistent explorer in the realm of nature, and step by step began to recognize the natural sources and resources from which he could fashion and mold a more agreeable physical life.

A fragment of ancient fabric—be it cotton, linen, silk or wool—is mute evidence of man's tedious but steady advance from a semisavage state to a primitive form of civilization. Spread over the early eras, from the Neolithic Ages to dynastic Egypt, are countless such evidences of skill which are far older than recorded history.

Man's first clothes were wild animal pelts which he wrapped around his body from shoulder to knee, and fastened with a sharp thorn. He used a wide variety of convenient shrubs, barks, nettles, leaves, and other plant life for various purposes such as nets, snares, and baskets. These he used for hunting and fishing thousands of years before he began to use fibers for clothing.

During the long interval between the Stone Ages, man passed from a primitive hunting stage to an intermediate pastoral stage which preceded a permanent agricultural stage. During the pastoral interlude he domesticated sheep and goats, collected their fiber fleeces, often from bushes and shrubs, and pressed these fibers into a felted mass for practical purposes.

In time man learned to spin yarns from carded fibers. These animal fibers were then woven into cloth. Still later he discovered the vegetable fibers and began to make fabrics of cotton and flax. Flax, incidentally, was the first textile fiber known to mankind.

It may be said that in these early days there were four cultures and four fibers. By the time of the beginning of recorded history all four fibers—cotton, linen, silk, and wool—were being woven into cloth. In the East many tools were invented for spinning yarn and weaving fabrics. Ancient China, Egypt, India, and Mesopotamia produced fabrics which gave evidence of a "superior civilization," and early records of trade show how textiles were used as a means of exchange between different nations. As one civilization succeeded another in various parts of the world, special skills in fabricating textiles often became characteristic of different regions. The flimsy linens of Egypt, the flower silks of China, the "woven wind" of India and the fabulous brocades of Mesopotamia all spoke the language of artistically minded peoples.

Thus, silk originated in China and cotton was native to India, but flax and wool originated in what is known as the Near East. Here were the plains and the valleys so vital for plant life and livestock. Phoenicia, the sailor, Greece, the trader, and Rome, the warrior, attempted little manufacture, since all faced the ancient sea routes and could barter or make war for such goods as they required.

Egypt of the old dynasties, and Mesopotamia—with its succession of Sumerian, Chaldean, and Babylonian rulers—were inland empires, and both races of people had no great love for the sea. In contrast to the terrain of Greece and Rome or to the narrow sea coast of Phoenicia and Tyre, their lands were adapted to agriculture.

Scripture and ancient literature contained many references to sheep, shepherds, cotton, linen, wool, weaving, etc. In Genesis it is reported that "Abel was the keeper of the sheep; Cain, a tiller of the soil." There is a passage in Deuteronomy concerning the dispute between the children of Israel, who wore wool, and the Egyptians, who wore linen.

Legend has it that about 8,000 years ago, the Babylonians wore woolen robes. It has also been recorded that they were wearing robes of this type in 6000 B.C. Assyria, Babylonia, and Chaldea are believed to be the homeland of wool. There are many references to flax and linen in ancient writings. Linen, according to most writers who have done research in the field, was the first fiber known to man. Textiles of beauty and charm that were woven thousands of years before the coming of Christ have been found among the earliest ruins of Egypt, Mexico, and Peru, and in the cave dwellings of Arizona and New Mexico.

By 1500 B.C., India was raising cotton, spinning yarn, and making cloth. The ancient Laws of Manu specified that the sacrificial thread of the Brahmin had to be made of cotton (karpasi), and that the theft of cotton thread was punishable by fines, and that rice water (possibly the first starch) was used in weaving fabric.

It is recorded in 1451 B.C. that a lavish Babylonian garment tempted Achan of the tribe of Judah to preserve the spoils of Ai when Israel took the city under Joshua. About this time is recorded: "To Sisera a spoil of dyed garments, a spoil of garments of embroidery." (Judg. 5:30 R.V.)

It is also known that from 1292–1225 B.C., ramie was used in a fabric form to wrap Egyptian mummies. Ramie shroud fabric has been found in the tomb of Pharaoh Rameses II.

Homer, the great Greek poet (fl. 8th C. B.C.), gave attention to laces, embroideries, Sidonian dyes, and weaving. Describing Ulysses following Ajax, he wrote the following:

> As when some dapper girdled wife
> Near to her bosom holdeth
> The spindle whence she draweth out
> The rove beyond the sliver,
> So near Ulysses kept and trod
> The very prints of Ajax.

Scripture tells us that in 896 B.C., "Mesha, King of Moab, was a sheepmaster, and rendered unto the King of Israel an hundred thousand lambs, and an hundred thousand rams, with the wool." (II Kings 3:4.)

In 613 B.C., Tanaquil, wife of Tarquinius Priscus, is said to have been the first to weave straight tunic on a perpendicular loom. Varro, circa 50 B.C., asserted that he had seen, in the Temple of Janus, the wool still preserved on the distaff and spindle of Tanaquil. This tunic was worn for many centuries under the white toga by the younger Roman citizens.

In 474 B.C., hempen ropes were used on ships with which Hiero, King of Syracuse, gained a naval victory over the Etruscans, thereby winning control of the Tyrrhenian Sea.

Ptolemy II (309–247 B.C.) at the height of his career gave a great banquet, at which, wrote Callixenus of Rhodes, "Underneath two hundred golden couches were strewn purple carpets of the finest wool, with patterns on both sides; and there were handsomely embroidered rugs, very beautifully elaborated with figures. Besides this, thin Persian cloths covered all the center space where the guests walked, having the most accurate representations of animals embroidered upon them."

Ovid (43 B.C.–18 A.D.) in his *Metamorphoses* describes the processing of wool fibers as done in his day.

Closely allied with textiles and clothing is the story of the needle. Fifty thousand years ago a prehistoric cavewoman punched a hole through a fish bone, guided her animal sinew "thread" through it, and became the first person to use a needle. Primitive women sewed with needles of highly polished bone, ivory, thorn, and wood; each type, of course, had the all-important eye. The Babylonians around 5000 B.C. made better needles from bronze, copper, gold, and silver. Even Cleopatra sewed at home, using a needle of gold to decorate a silk garment for Mark Antony. And Egyptian surgeon-priests used golden needles to stitch up wounds.

Needles fashioned from precious metals spread from Egypt to Greece, Rome, and China. They remained a high luxury for centuries, until the fourteenth century, to be exact. Although the Chinese are credited with being the first to use steel needles, it was a native of Nuremberg, Germany, who, in 1370 worked out a practical method of drawing and cutting steel. The secret of making needles of durable steel was a valuable one. The Nurembergers guarded their secret well, so much so that it was two hundred years later before England produced its first steel needle.

Incidentally, there are today some 8,400 different machine needles. They range in size from one no thicker than a hair of the head for stitching almost invisible seams in filmy fabrics to sturdy ones to stitch heavy belting that turns the wheels of giant factory machines.

In the story of thread, some prehistoric man learned that by twisting fibers together, he could make a thread of any length or thickness. This was the type of thread used by the Swiss Lake Dwellers some 25,000 years ago. The first thread was spun by hand. It was a simple process of drawing out the fibers among themselves, held in the left hand, twisting them with the right hand and then winding them onto a spindle. Egyptian women were the first to use a distaff to hold the fibers and a spindle upon which to do the winding. Though ancient India had a crude spinning wheel, the rest of the ancient world relied on the distaff and spindle for thread. Besides linen thread for sewing, women spun embroidery wools, cotton, and silk.

Spinning was a slow, tedious process with these primitive tools, and while civilizations rose and fell, nobody did anything about speeding up spinning until the sixteenth century, when Henry VIII, king of England, had a spinning wheel imported from India. The spinning wheel replaced the distaff and spindle, but threadmaking remained a hand operation for the next two hundred years. And it was also a home industry.

During the fifteen-year span from 1764 to 1779, England revolutionized carding, spinning, and weaving, and some of the improvements and new ideas and inventions of British geniuses were fantastic in scope. Production increased all along the line from raw material to finished fabric. Textiles became a machine-operated industry and left the home. And in the development of thread America played an important part. Eli Whitney's cotton gin was invented in 1793 and patents were granted him in 1794. This was a great boon to all things cotton.

[6]

Better handling had to be done in all phases of endeavor in the textile and allied fields in order to keep supply and demand on equal footing.

Samuel Slater, "The Father of the Cotton Textile Industry" in the United States, at this time entered the thread picture. He opened the first successful cotton mill in America in Pawtucket, Rhode Island, in 1793. The building is now the well-known and very interesting Old Slater Mill Museum. His wife was the daughter of one of his partners, Oziel Wilkinson, with whose family Slater lived when he came to Providence and Pawtucket to begin his work in cotton. Samuel and Hannah Wilkinson were married October 2, 1791.

Linen thread was universally used at this time because of its tensile strength, but it was not smooth, even, and easy to manipulate. Hannah had worked with Samuel in his efforts from the time he came to Pawtucket in 1790. She had an inventive mind with a definite scientific bent. The question of thread was puzzling, and Hannah set about doing something about it. She began working and manipulating cotton yarns in her endeavor to convert them into suitable thread that would have strength, smoothness, and uniformity. She knew that two yarns of fine cotton yarn could be twisted together with the use of skill on her spinning wheel to give a single effect from this ply yarn. Finally, she plied two single ends of a 20s cotton together and applied twist to them so that she now had a cotton sewing thread of 2/20s yarn, or the equivalent of a 1/10s cotton thread. Thus, cotton thread was now a reality. It was not long before cotton thread outstripped linen thread in usage. Mrs. Samuel Slater introduced spool cotton to the world, and when the thread was made with the then highly prized Sea Island cotton raised off the islands of the Carolinas and Georgia, it was very strong, even, uniform, and a beautiful thread. This invention occurred in 1793, and by the end of the year, Samuel Slater began the manufacture of cotton thread. Thus, the wife of a great inventor, Samuel Slater, Hannah Wilkinson Slater, an inventor herself, sounded the death-knell for linen thread, the universal thread used everywhere up to that time.

We know that man first fastened things together by the use of thorns six thousand years ago—and probably even earlier than that. It was about that time man discovered metal. In the beginning bronze, copper, gold, and silver were used for ornaments, symbols, etc., and the first crude safety pins came into being to hold garments together. Only one fastener was used by the Mediterranean peoples to hold their garments or robes together, and pins and brooches were the only clothes fasteners until the Middle Ages. In the thirteenth century the English found that strings laced through eyelets down the front or the back drew a garment tightly and gave more protection against chilly weather conditions. While an improvement, it was not ideal. Buttons began to replace lacings in the fourteenth century. A German goldsmith found that cloth, jewels, and other materials could be mounted as buttons. There was beauty to them, they were practical, and the women liked them. Buttons soon became the rage in fastening clothing and afforded better fit to the apparel.

Incidentally, the belt buckle with the metal prong appeared in the sixteenth century, along with the hook and eye. Puritan fathers in the seventeenth century ordered their womenfolk to fasten all garments with the inexpensive hook and eye. "Buttons are a vanity," they said.

New England learned the art of wire-drawing in the latter part of the seventeenth century. Thus straight pins were born. People of affluence sought them eagerly, and not everyone could afford the prices asked. They had to be made in part by hand, which kept the price rather high, and actually they remained more or less of a luxury for two centuries. Finally a machine was developed that could manufacture straight pins in one operation, and the pin famine was soon over and everyone could now afford them.

The safety pin, as we know it today, was invented by Walter Hunt of sewing-machine fame in this country. This "miracle fastener" was an instant success and still lives a very useful life. Then came the snap fastener, an ideal item for fastening all types of garments. In 1891 another unique fastener appeared on the scene and its inventor, Whitcomb Judson, an American, recognized it at the time as the answer to "gaposis." The clasp then became known as the slide fastener. Following World War I, improvements were made on the device, and these led to a new word in our vocabulary—the "zipper."

LINEN

The story of flax, the plant, and linen, the product, begins with the Neolithic Age. During this period man cultivated flax and processed it into linen for practical use. Remains of spinning wheels, spindles, spinning whorls, weights used by weavers on their looms, and various yarns and fabrics, some of the latter constructed in a twill-weave formation, have been unearthed in the Lake Dwellings.

The ruins of the Swiss Lake Dwellers, discovered in the winter of 1853–54, offer sufficient proof that the art of textiles was apparently known in the earliest times of the Stone Age, the period of the mammoth and the cave bear. Yarns of linen and wool were unearthed at this time in the excavations. During the Later Stone Age period mankind selected the principal textile fibers and used them— quite some improvement over the earlier eras in history—in the arts of carding, spinning, and weaving.

The Egyptians revered the Nile River, which, for part of its 4,500-mile course, flows through this desert area, fertilizing the nearby shores and making them ideal for plant life. Here the flax plant was cultivated for the first time, about six thousand years ago. Mesopotamia, from a Greek word which means "the land between two rivers," nurtured a people who looked upon the Euphrates and Tigris Rivers as divine forces. These rivers flowed in widely separated parallel channels, emptying into the Persian Gulf, and the intervening fertile plains were ideal pasture lands.

It was in these ancient lands that men first began to twist together the fibers of animals and plants to make threads so as to fashion fishing nets, snares for trapping animals, and baskets for many practical purposes. Actually, strange as it may appear, weaving preceded spinning by many centuries. The idea of weaving may have been suggested by the nests of birds, the cones of wasps, or the webs of spiders, originally known as "spinders." There is not any record to apprise us of when and where man learned to weave.

By the time man was able to record his history on temple walls or tablets of clay, the origins of weaving had been so long forgotten that early writers ascribed it to various deities. Pliny (Secundus) in the second century A.D., asserted that the Egyptians invented weaving, and Athaneous, more specifically, accords the

[8]

honor to "Pythymias the Egyptian." Athaneous, however, is not taken too seriously by classical scholars.

In 1716 B.C., it is to be noted that ". . . Pharaoh took off his ring from his hand, and put it upon Joseph's hand, and arrayed him in vestures of fine linen." (Gen. 41:42.) Linen, according to most writers who have done research in the matter, is the oldest fiber known to man and was the first fiber to be spun and woven into fabric.

In 530 B.C., Amasis of Egypt sent Polycrates, Tyrant of Samos, corselets of interestingly twisted linen yarn and thread for use by his troops. In the years 69–63 B.C., linen awnings were used in the theater when Quintus Catulus dedicated the Temple of Jupiter in Rome. Pictures found at Beni Hassan, of pre-Theban origin, show flax workers engaged in processing flax fibers into linen cloth.

The earliest of linen fabrics were more of an interlacing of yarns at almost any angle rather than so-called "straight weaving" to make fabric. As far back as 6000 B.C., the Egyptians used a single bar loom as revealed by excavations in 1923. This gave rise to the famous loincloths worn by the Egyptians for centuries. They were the basic garment of these people for thousands of years. The Egyptians believed that flax was "the first thing made by the gods for the people of the earth."

Flax and the Nile River were more or less synonymous with the Egyptians, and the finest linens of antiquity originated in Egypt. Linen found in Egyptian tombs shows a range of spinning and weaving from coarse sail canvas and semi-fine mummy wrappings to linen cloths so fine that they have actually been drawn through a finger ring.

White was the Egyptian's symbol of purity and fit "to be the robes of the gods." Not until the invasion of Egypt by a succession of northern Semitic peoples did the ancient Egyptians color their textile fabrics. These northern peoples— who come from the same ethnic stock as the people of the Old Testament—had long clothed their bodies in entirety and this custom was adopted by the Egyptians, who then began to cast aside the ancient loincloth and its supplementary apron.

Probably because linen came from the protected inner section of the flax plant, this bast fiber was looked upon as less perishable than the other fibers—cotton and silk. Woolen fabrics were unknown to the Egyptians as far as is known. No excavating group has ever found anything which pertains to wool. Linen was endowed by the Egyptians with religious symbolism, a suitable cloth for the long journey to the hereafter, and it was used for mummy wrappings for both Pharaoh and slave.

A tremendous amount of linen fabric was used in ceremonial burials. We know that during the occupation of Egypt by the Arabs, for over two centuries the conquerors used pitch-filled Egyptian mummies for fuel, after they had recovered the linen wrappings for clothing.

The Mesopotamians also raised flax, but their fabrics never equaled those of the Egyptians. Living on the borders of Mesopotamia were the Hebrews. They, like the Mesopotamians, used wool, since they lived in a cooler climate. Readers of the Old Testament, however, recall that after their enforced long sojourn in Egypt they changed to the use of linen fabrics.

In time, as linen moved westward into the Mediterranean countries, notably

[9]

Greece and Rome, there arose what might be called the world's first "battle of the fibers." The Greeks and the Romans were wool-using, sturdy, seafaring peoples. It satisfied them and had done so for many centuries; they were fully acclimated to wool. Linen had a very difficult time before it was accepted, and the process was slow and tedious.

Aristophanes (448?–380? B.C.), the Greek dramatist, relates a rather amusing tale about some of the "die-hard" Grecian dowagers who scorned in no uncertain terms the "Egyptian innovation" of using a linen square as a handkerchief. They preferred to use the tails of small animals, especially those of foxes, as had been the custom with their worthy forebears.

Flax was without competition as vegetable fiber in Europe until the eighteenth century, when, after a brief but spirited struggle, cotton surpassed it as the supreme fiber in commerce. Flax and linen still produce "the cloth of kings," and linen still serves very well in some circles, in which it has not as yet been replaced or even threatened.

WOOL

Wool is probably the second-oldest fiber known to man. History is quite clear that its origins, as far as known, go back to around 4200 B.C. At this time sheep were kept in the Tel Asman or Great Hill region on the banks of the Euphrates River in Mesopotamia. The earliest known representation of sheep is in a mosaic of Ur, not far from the Iranian (Persian) Gulf. The time is dated about 3500 B.C. Around 3000 B.C., people in Britain wore crude forms of woolen garments. Babylonian weavers were well versed in wool weaving, as attested to by the splendid flounced robe of Ishtar, on the Annubanini stela. The dress of the Assyrians in this era was rather elaborate, all sculptures of the kings showing full robes and beautifully embroidered mantles. The Chaldeans were also rather adept in raising sheep and weaving woolen fabrics. These ancient Mesopotamian peoples considered wool weaving a master craft. Both inner and outer garments of wool were worn by all classes of people, and this afforded textile craftsmen to explore a broad field in fabric, color, and design.

The word "shepherd" comes from the Sanskrit root Av which means "to guard" and suggests the helpless character of domesticated sheep when exposed to danger, as well as the need for careful tending and guarding in contrast to cattle and most goats, who can well shift for themselves. Sheep are considered to be "about the dumbest of all animals" and this is borne out to some degree when the losses among flocks caught in blizzards are considered; often they will just stay where they happen to be and freeze to death in very cold climates. Keeping a flock healthy is quite a task. The patient shepherd is really patient; if not, the flock will get out of hand in a short span of time. Sheep need close attention and sometimes seem to crave it.

Laban was the Syrian father-in-law of Jacob (Gen. 24:29–60). The Bible gives us some specific information about his flocks. His sheep, as well as most of the flocks of his time, were entirely black. His chief shepherd and son-in-law was evidently what would be known today in sheep circles as a very scientific breeder. Jacob was the son of Isaac. Laban, Jacob, and Isaac were all breeders of sheep; they constantly augmented their sheep flocks and helped one another in breeding, and cross-breeding sheep with goats, which produced a short-lived stock and perpetuated the black fleece. Isaac is responsible for the statement that "the sheep be separated from goats." And here perhaps is the origin of our association of lambs with innocence and goats with evil.

Incidentally, sackcloth, worn in ancient times by Assyrians and Hebrews as a symbol of grief and penance, was a fabric made from goat hair. The coarse, varied-length fibers of the fleece were used for both warp and filling to give an irritating prickly feel to the goods, which were cut and sewn like a sack to fit the body rather snugly.

The shift from black sheep to brown, gray, and eventually to shades of mottled white took place gradually. One explanation of the Golden Fleece is that Odysseus had seen sheep with a light-brown fleece coat instead of the usual black fleece of the day. So slowly did the change in color cast develop that it required some eighteen hundred years to spread from the Syrian valleys, along the northern coast of Africa, to the Moorish sheep breeders of Spain in the eighth century A.D.

Even as recently as a century ago the Mother Goose rhyme was written, "Baa! Baa! Black Sheep, have you any wool?" And it is worthy of note that this survivor of outmoded breeding provides "three bags full."

In 1800 B.C., a representation of a fulling mill for treating woolen fabrics was found on the tomb of Usertesen II. Thus, finishing of fabrics was known to these ancients. By 1000 B.C., the Phoenicians were carrying on active trade in raw wool and many types of woven goods with the Spaniards in and around the port of Cádiz. By 715 B.C., wool dyeing was established as a craft in Rome. In 529 B.C., a purple Babylonian wool carpet was laid upon the tomb of Cyrus (r. 550–529 B.C.) "the Elder" or "the Great," founder of the Persian Empire.

Around 375 B.C., the noted Athenian general Iphicrates had his abode furnished with carpeting made of brilliantly colored wool.

By 200 B.C., the Romans were practicing scientific sheep raising and breeding. They developed the famous Tarentine breed of sheep, forerunner of the present-day merino breed, the highest and finest in quality in sheep fleece of any wool found in the world today. The Romans crossed Colchian rams imported from Greece with Italian-bred ewes to obtain their prized Tarentines.

Julius Caesar (100–44 B.C.) was much interested in sheep and wool, since woolen clothing was vital to his warring legions, especially in the colder climates of what is now Europe—Britain, Ireland, and nearby lands subjected to cold weather at times. He had an animal husbandry expert whose tenets in breeding and raising sheep are still in vogue and closely followed in some of our Land-Grant universities which have courses in animal husbandry. His name was Lucius Junius Columella, and his famous book is *De re rustica*. Born a Roman, he lived in sumptuous quarters in Cádiz and Córdoba. He was the "Leonardo da Vinci" of animal husbandry, especially when it came to studying sheep in their habitats. He crossed the Tarentine sheep with native white sheep of the wandering tribes, especially in the Mediterranean area, and with sheep raised in what is now Germany, France, and Belgium. In Spain he laid the foundation for Merino sheep, a breed that is the nonpareil of sheep. Incidentally, there are today only about 40 distinct breeds of sheep and about 210 cross-breeds of sheep. Columella in his teachings seems to have developed cross-breeding to a perfection.

The word "merino," taken from the Spanish, means "to move from pasture to pasture." Columella was the originator of the *reals,* or roads, set up during pasturage seasons. The longest of his roads in Spain was about four hundred miles in length. Reals are still used today in putting sheep out to pasture.

Husbandry men in Caesar's legions stationed in England taught the less civilized Britons the better ways of breeding sheep, improved the flocks, the methods of spinning, and the weaving of cloth. Traces of these soldiers are still to be found in Britain and Ireland. After there were no more Roman soldiers in Britain, the void they made was taken over by evangelizing monks. Chief among these Order Monks were the Benedictines and the Trappists (Cistercians). As early as 500 A.D., they had built monasteries and abbeys which became centers for large agricultural enterprises. These buildings were practically "cities within themselves." Monastery Wool is the name given to the wool obtained from their flocks of sheep, some of which numbered 8,000, 10,000, and more. For more than a thousand years the Roman Catholic Church was the Great English Shepherd. Most students know that their empires were destroyed and outlawed during the reign of six-times married ruler of England, Henry VIII (1491–1547), son of Henry VII.

Both lay and clerical brothers of the communities, and there were many of these in England, Scotland, and Ireland, devoted much of their time and energy to sheep raising. In the convents, the womenfolk of the neighborhood were taught wool sorting, blending and mixing, carding and spinning of the fibers, and the weaving of cloths on the loom. Married women were given the title of "wife," which is a derivation from the word "weaver." Single women were known as "spinsters." The abbot of the monastery was usually the fiscal agent, since the uneducated farmers who brought their wool to sell were not able to figure out the amounts due them. It can be said that Monastery Wool during this long era really put Britain on its feet and opened up world commerce for the people of the Isles, which in due time led to the expression, "the sun never sets on the British Empire." The wool was shipped all over Europe. Flanders, France, the great Italian city-states, and the provinces and principalities of what is now Germany, all bought wool from the monasteries. Stock piles for wool were established throughout Europe, and as fast as wool could be sheared from the sheep, it was on its way to the warehouses on the Continent.

In 1539, Henry suppressed 190 abbeys and monasteries in Britain, and Monastery Wool met its demise. The religious communities affected housed upward of fifty thousand people, and the income was around twelve million dollars annually. Britain now became wealthy, since its sales of wool were of great volume—so much so, that periodically laws were invoked, before and after 1539, to forbid exportation of wool and to induce textile workers from European nations to come there and ply their trades to build up British cloth manufactures. As a result of the invitations, along with unrest in many major countries on the Continent, Britain was able to corral many Flemish, French, and Italian weavers. These hundreds of artisans laid the foundation for a thriving wool industry, which for five centuries has made England outstanding as a textile center.

With the advent of the manmade fibers, wool has suffered in many ways and at present accounts for around 6 per cent of world fiber production. It began this decline in a limited way after World War I, when rayon, acetate, and, to some degree, nylon made their influence felt. Lighter-weight clothing has also affected the consumption of the fiber. For example, the day of 30–35 ounce-per-yard woolen cloths for overcoatings has passed. The heaviest fabric weight of woolen coatings today is around 22–24 ounces per yard.

Following World War II, the rash of more manmade fibers crippled seriously the use of the fiber of both woolens and worsteds. The acrylics, modacrylics, polyesters, and other types have joined with acetate, rayon, and nylon in further curbing the popularity of wool. The manmades now outstrip wool in usage in a ratio of about three to one.

COTTON

Cotton, often known as the "Universal Textile Fiber," and commercially the most valuable of all plant fibers, grows in tropical and subtropical climates. Cotton can be raised almost anywhere in these climates. For example, we could, if necessary, raise seven times as much cotton as we do at present; our annual cotton crop is around fourteen million bales of 478 pounds of fiber and 22 pounds of cooperage to make a 500-pound bale. The United States, in fiber consumption, shows that cotton is responsible for about 60 per cent of the total used.

It is not known when "King Cotton" was first woven into fabric. Like wool and linen, it was being converted into textiles long before man had learned to record his activities. Probably the first mention of cotton is found in the vague phrases of a dead language uncovered in Mohenjo-Daro, ancient Indus Valley site. This evidence seems to trace with reasonable certainty the actual use of cotton as early as 3000 B.C. Thus, cotton was used in India thirty centuries before Caesar invaded Britain, the nation that in time was to become the world's greatest developer and user of cotton, and producer of the world's finest cotton fabrics.

Behind the story of cotton lies the mystery of the people who lived along the banks of the Ganges River in India. They were the first to cultivate cotton. They are the ones who developed primitive tools which are the ancestors of the great carding frames, spinning machines, and power looms of today. For nearly five thousand years cotton textiles have been woven on small hand looms in India, a great cottage industry there. Calico, chintz, gingham, madras, and muslin all originally came from India.

The gossamer-like Indian muslins and gauzes were the most delicate cottons ever fashioned and made on a loom. The ancient weavers of India practiced a skill that has never been equaled or nearly equaled by modern man and his textile technology. The Indian cloths are known in history as "woven wind of India." Indian legend tells us that the ancient Hindus wore wonderful raiment of fine white cloth, which was woven of fibers from the "wool-bearing tree."

These zephyr muslins of Dacca, a city not too far from Calcutta, now in Pakistan, were said to be so fine in texture that when laid on the grass and wet with dew, they would become invisible. Some Dacca cloths were constructed with continuous threads said to have been two hundred miles long, spun from a single pound of lint cotton. Fabrics seventy yards long and one yard wide could be made from one pound of manipulated cotton. An ancient traveler speaks of Dacca muslins as "the work of fairies rather than of men."

There is an ancient story about a potentate in northern India who chided his daughter about her diaphanous gown, since it apparently revealed her shape and showed her to be in good form. The princess replied that she was actually wearing seven thicknesses of the fabric. This reminds one of "The Dance of the Seven Veils," and these Dacca fabrics also inspired Indian poetry and song.

Although no other natural fiber can be spun into yarn of such extreme fineness as the fiber of the cotton plant, yet cotton was the last of the "big four" textile fibers—cotton, linen, silk, and wool—to reach Europe.

Incidentally, to give one an idea of the yarn counts and diameters of the yarns used in these muslins, in terms used by textile technologists today, the yarn counts ranged from a 450s to a 600s cotton. The highest cotton counts in use today, and they are not seen too often, range from a 140s to a 160s yarn size—117,600 yards up to 134,400 yards in the one pound of spun cotton yarn. Pick count or texture in warp and filling began around 100 and sometimes ran as high as 300 or more ends and picks per square inch of fabric.

When King Solomon built his temple in 950 B.C., he used cotton hangings, and the fabric is supposed to have come from Egypt and Phoenicia. As both nations at this time had trade relations with India, it is presumed that the fabrics used were Indian. In early Hebrew times the land around Jericho became famous for its cotton and a town named Magog (the Cotton City) in Syria was an important caravan station and exchange.

Where did beautiful "quoton" come from? Local traders said it had been obtained from foreign traders whom they met in distant lands and with whom they exchanged goods. As trade increased in volume and thus became more dependent upon supply, traders pushed farther eastward in search of other beautiful fabrics. Finally they reached the mysterious land of Brahma located on a river. They reported that they saw "growing all around them trees with fruit of wool exceeding in beauty and goodness the wool from sheep." As late as the thirteenth century Marco Polo spoke of cotton "as vegetable wool growing on trees," and pictures of these "trees" made in Florence, Italy, showed a sheep's head at the end of each branch.

In 450 B.C., Herodotus (484?–424? B.C.), the historian, made several references to textiles. In Book II Ch. 106, he describes cotton: "The wild trees of that country (India) bear fleeces as their fruit, surpassing that of sheep in beauty and excellence, and the Indians use cloth made from this tree in wool." In Book IV there is a reference to hemp: "Hemp grows in Scythia; it is very like flax; only it is much coarser and a taller plant; some grows wild about the country, and some is cultivated. The Thracians make garments of it, which closely resemble linen." He also mentions the cotton drawers worn by the Indian contingent of Xerxes' invading armies, and the garments of the inhabitants of the Caucasus variegated with figures dyed with infusion of leaves. It was reported at the time that this craftsmanship had been practiced for more than a thousand years by the Indians.

Alexander the Great, at the time of the invasion of India in 327 B.C., expressed interest and surprise at the beautiful cotton prints made there. He also mentioned the flax and linen industries. Dating from these discoveries and findings, cotton became the main fabric for apparel along the shores of the Mediterranean Sea for the next three hundred years.

In the span of time from 69–63 B.C., cotton awnings were used by Lentulus Spinther at the Apollonaris Games held during the month of July.

In the first century of the Christian era, Arab traders brought calico, muslin, and comparable cotton cloths to ports on the Red Sea, which from there were brought to the centers in Europe. Cotton was introduced into Spain by the Moors in the ninth century. It was here that the first actual cultivation of cotton in all Europe began. The fibers were spun into yarn, and the yarn into cloth. It is believed that at this "late date" only India and Spain were weaving cotton fabric. The Spanish industries were local or provincial in character, and cotton was therefore little known outside of Spain. It was only after the opening of the water route to India, beginning in 1497, that cotton began to be used in other parts of western Europe.

The Era of Discovery, known to most students, was at hand, and it was not long before the use of cotton became known and appreciated in the rest of the Western world. Cotton was here to stay and it is still the greatest fiber of all and justly warrants the title of "the universal textile fiber."

TOPIC: Introduction to and the Story of Silk

The origins of silk are legendary. One legend tells us that around 5000 B.C., according to Chinese tradition, Foh-hi, the first emperor, had his people given instruction in silk culture (sericulture). In 4500 B.C., Babylonian carvings of Urnina show a figure clad in a fabric which reached from shoulder to ankle. Woolen fabrics were also used at this time and were similarly draped. Around 4400 B.C., carvings of Eannatum depicted men appearing in a kilt fringed above the knee, and apparently made of linen or silk.

During this era a daughter of the Third Emperor of China, while strolling through the palace grounds, observed a silkworm spinning its cocoon. The thought occurred to her that an insect could "wind or unwind" and do this to its advantage. The silkworm winds its filament (sericin or silk gum holding the two filaments emitted by the worm) by instinctive action. The cocoon can be unwound by treating it in a bowl of hot water, and when fully unwound will produce a filament that will range from 300 yards to 1,600 yards in filament length; the longer the filament, the finer will be the diameter of it, and the better the quality.

As a reward, a grateful people bestowed divine honors upon the observant princess and long worshiped her as "the Little Lady of the Silkworm." And well they might, since this observation laid the foundation of China's great wealth.

The Chinese retained a monopoly on sericulture for almost three thousand years. They were the only people who mastered the skill to raise the silkworm, obtain the filament by reeling it from the cocoon, spin or throw it, and weave the filaments into fabrics of beauty and charm.

Mulberry tree leaves provided food for silkworms in cultivating silk. Wild silk, now known as Tussah silk, is nourished by the leaves of several types of trees—the castor oil plant, cherry tree, etc.

Fibroin is the name given to the two filaments emitted by the worm when throwing or spinning; a single filament is called the brins; the brins, fibroin, and sericin combined are called the bave.

[15]

During the classical period of Greece and Rome, there was much speculation as to the origin of silk. It was a great mystery. The Chinese described the silk spinner as a "silkworm," and this allowed them to keep their secret, since no one in the then Western world even guessed or thought that the product came from the moth caterpillar.

Exposure of the guarded secret was threatened only once when knowledge of sericulture was brought to India through love, the romance of a Chinese princess and an Indian prince. The Indians, however, failed to take advantage of the opportunity because there were laws which forbade the killing of the female before it could emerge from the cocoon. Since nature was permitted to take its course, the cocoon was thus partially damaged and it was impossible to obtain the 300-to-1,600-yard lengths of filament when the cocoon was reeled in a basin of hot water. The Indians did not know how to manipulate the short strands of filament into yarn. Later, of course, sericulture was introduced into India, and in time that country became one of the world's leading producers of high-quality silk filament.

The Chinese were aware of the fact that cocoons which matured in the "wild state" produced a filament that was tinged brown, ecru, or yellow in color cast. They evolved a scientific routine for feeding their silkworms with the leaves from the white mulberry trees, the essence affording excellent nutriment for the silkworms. Thus, this true or cultivated silk was fed on leaves that were approximately the same age as the caterpillar, and the desired color for the filaments was therefore obtained. The cultivation of these cocoons would not present baffling problems to the modern scientist, yet it may be noted that few important improvements in sericulture have been proposed to refine these ancient practices of the Chinese.

Rather voluminous literature of the ancients testifies not only to the antiquity of the silk industry, but also to the importance of sericulture among the Chinese, especially through the aid of benefactors who were of noble, royal, and wealthy families. And the industry was guarded for many centuries before silk became known to the rest of the world. During that time China was known as a "closed nation." The rest of the world knew little or nothing about it. Despite this isolation, it is worthy of note that China was the first nation to use the compass, paper, porcelain, a movable type for printing, paper money, and gunpowder. These things were merely "rediscovered" in the Western world later on and were put to the practical uses which they now enjoy.

Aristotle (384–322 B.C.) made some very interesting comments on silk. He stated that the first silk fabric was worn by Pamphile, the daughter of Plates, and that the material had been woven on the isle of Cos. He made the first notation in the "New Western World" in literature in *Hist. anim.* v. 19 (17) 11 (6), wherein he made the statement that a "Great Worm that has horns differs very much from other types of insects and animals." The passage goes on to tell about the first change or metamorphosis in the life cycle of the silkworm, on to the egg stage, larva, pupa, and lastly the chrysalis, or "golden thing." He described the caterpillar stage, the Bombylius into the chrysalis, and stated that all these developments occur within six months. He mentioned the worm's encasing itself and the "spinning" of the continuous filament emitted from two openings underneath the mouth of the worm. These filaments, he stated, were spun by women after the reeling of the cocoon, a term which denotes the taking of continuous fiber or filament from a cocoon.

Legend has it that what Aristotle has left for posterity had been gleaned and derived from information acquired by the Greeks with Alexander the Great (356–323 B.C.), who was king of Macedonia and the conqueror of Asia. Alexander, it will be noted, covered very large areas in his campaigns and career. And, it stands to reason, as Aristotle mentioned, that silk must have been brought to Cos, where it was woven into gauzy, tissue-like fabrics, since the famous Cos Vestis was a fabric that revealed rather than covered the human female form.

Julius Caesar (100–44 B.C.), the Roman general, historian, and statesman, is said to have decreed a law whereby silk fabrics were to be banned altogether and that punishment would be meted out to anyone wearing any silken garb. Lucius Junius Columella, the great husbandryman of Caesar, knew of silk. He was a native of Cádiz, Spain, and his estates were in and around Córdoba. There may likely be something in the fact that because his main interest was sheep and wool, he persuaded Caesar to ban silk and silk materials. He may have thought that silk would make inroads into the woolen-cloth industry, and these cloths clothed the armies of Caesar. He was also of the opinion that silk was prohibitive in price and that its use would lead to extravagance and indolence. Another interesting note that hindered the silk industry was the belief or superstition that silk fabrics were of evil omen, thereby proving that superstition was as rampant then as at present.

In 75 B.C., Pompey (106–48 B.C.), Roman general and a member of the First Triumvirate, returned from China laden with beautiful silk fabrics. During this era silk was the leading fabric used by the affluent in Rome. In 54 B.C., silk was further introduced into Rome following the Parthian Wars. Marcus Antonius sent a delegation to Seres (ancient name for China) to arrange for the importation of silks to Rome. The mission was not fruitful, and Persia remained the source of supply for these desired Chinese silks.

Around the beginnings of the Christian era, raw silk began to form an important and costly item among the prized products from the East which gradually began to trickle into Rome. Allusions to silk and its sources had become rather common in classical literature, but although these references do show familiarity with the fabric, they are nevertheless inaccurate and vague as to the sources of silk and the manipulation of it into fabric. Even the great Pliny (23–79 A.D.) knew nothing more about the silkworm than that which could be learned from the mention of it in the descriptions given in the writings of Aristotle.

These silken treasures and textures that came to Rome were considered to be effeminate. For example, Aurelian (212?–275 A.D.) would not wear silk garb, nor would he permit his wife to bedeck herself with the fine gauzy textures. Silk, however, was worth its weight in gold, and notwithstanding its cost, it gradually met with favor and the industry commenced to grow and to prosper during this era.

It is believed that knowledge of the silk industry came from China by way of Korea to Japan in the early years of the third century A.D. The *Nihongi*, one of the ancient books of Japanese history, states that before 300 A.D., some Koreans were sent to China from Japan to obtain competent persons to teach the art of preparing silk so that it could be woven. The intricacies of weaving were, in due time, learned from the Chinese. These Koreans, according to the chronicle, returned to the court with four Chinese girls who were able to give excellent instruction in plain and figure weaving. In time a temple was erected to their memory in the province of Setsu. Japan put forth great efforts in the industry. But a secret cannot be kept forever. Knowledge traveled westward—first to India.

By this time, India saw the great possibilities of the industry. Times had changed, the laws were less severe, and it was now possible to manipulate the filament from the cocoon to finished fabric form. A Chinese princess is supposed to have taught the industry to the Indians, and legend has it that she secreted some eggs in her headdress, along with seeds of the mulberry trees, so that the trees, when grown, could afford the nutriment for the silkworms. Silk began to be on the upgrade in India from this time on.

The Indians, with their knowledge of the silkworm, established sericulture in the valley of the Brahmaputra River and in the tract lying between it and the Ganges River. From this arose the famous overland road from the Chinese Empire to the west for commerce and trade. It is almost certain that Persia and the states of central Asia acquired their first knowledge of the silkworm, its care and manipulation through this famous road. It had two routes to the west. The northern road began in either Peking or Shanghai and went to Sian, Lashikont, Baghdad, Damascus, Constantinople (Istanbul), and on to Rome. The southern route extended from Peking or Shanghai to Japan, Manila, Bombay, Aden, and Suez, with a possible stopover at Damascus and Constantinople, and on to Rome. This famous "Silk Road" is supposed to have been opened around 126 A.D. The road was closed in the ninth century, but was reopened in the thirteenth century, when Marco Polo followed it in order to get to Asia. However, the road did not receive its name until the nineteenth century, when Ferdinand von Richthofen, the noted German geographer of that century, gave it the name "The Silk Road."

For many centuries Damascus has been known in world history as a "clearing-house center," and it is still known as one of the great exchange and meeting places for the business world, especially in trading between East and West. The word "Damascus" comes from the Hebrew "Dammeseq" which is also related to the Arabic word *Dimushq*. This form, via the Greek and Latin and Italian, gives us the English word, "damask." It is also interesting to note that the Hebrew word *meshi* gave rise to the English word "mesh," which in ancient times referred to a silken-like gauze fabric.

Incidentally, it is believed that silkworms were first reared in Japan in 195 A.D., the year that Buddhism entered that country. Thus, for the first five centuries A.D., only China, Korea, Japan, India, Khotan and Persia, along with a few states in central Asia, knew how to raise silkworms and to manipulate the filament into fabric.

Coming to the time of Justinian (483–565 A.D.), the great Roman emperor of the East and the codifier of the Roman Laws—The Justinian Code—one begins to find that the attitude toward silk had changed. Justinian secured a monopoly in the manufacture of silk and in its trade and he placed all things silk under his aegis for guidance and decree. Looms were operated in his palace in Constantinople (Istanbul), and by entreaties to the Christian prince of Abyssinia, he endeavored to divert the trade from the Persian routes and was able to obtain Far Eastern silk in a more direct way. What Justinian left undone was completed by two Nestorian monks in the middle of the sixth century. Up to now the cost of imported fabrics had been still excessively high, supply was often not in keeping with the demand, the time element was too long. More people wanted silk.

In 552 these two Nestorian monks carried the secrets of silk, at the risk of their lives, to Constantinople. They began the rearing of silkworms, and so the silk industry was founded. These monks, who carried the secrets of silk in their canes, performed a great service to the then Western world. New types and varieties of silkworms were created, and in time an untold prosperity was to result from these humble beginnings, with many areas sharing in the rewards from the raising and manipulation of silk—all thanks to the lowly silkworm, about which there had been so much mystery through so many centuries.

These conditions were to last for more than twelve hundred years, and only since the eighteenth century has it been necessary to resort to the Far East again in the demand for supplies of silkworms. Times have changed since these beginnings, and in this so-called modern era nations are supposed to understand one another much better from the standpoint of internationalization of trade and commerce. Of course, war has from time to time disrupted all industries in all fields of endeavor. Silk, however, still marches on and is still "the fabric of milady."

Since the establishment of sericulture in western Europe, much progress has been made. The silken textures of Byzantium became well known, and at a later period the Saracens were complete masters of the industry and they spread silk both east and west.

Designs and motifs in silk fabrics became characteristic of the several peoples of the times. Colors and patterns in fabric were known as peculiar to this or that country, and this, to some degree, still prevails today. The Saracens in their reign of supremacy extended the industry far and wide, and many centers in Asia Minor were given over to it. The industry became deep rooted in Sicily, and extant cloths from there, with Saracenic design, are proof that silk had a solid footing in the Saracenic world.

Ordericus Vitalis, who died in the first half of the twelfth century, mentions that the Bishop of Saint Ervoul in Normandy had returned from Apulia and brought with him from this southern Italian region several large pieces of silk. Cuts were made from four of the fabrics and they were used to adorn his cathedral chanters. As time went on, the centers in Europe in the Middle Ages fostered the industry, and cloths made of silk always had an important and conspicuous place in the services of the Roman Catholic churches as vestments, hangings, some altar cloths, etc.

The student of history is familiar with the meteoric rise of Rome, Florence, Genoa, Milan, Pisa, Venice, Bologna, and several other cities of the Italian city-states, all of which now make up the present-day Italy, which has given the world more culture in all its meanings and phases than any other nation on earth. At the height of the trade and commerce in these "silk cities" it was found that the silk industry in its various branches was more profitable than any other business. The prominent families of the many city-states fostered the industry and became its patrons, with excellent results. Outstanding among the influential families of the era were the Colonna, Borgia, de' Medici, della Rovere, d'Este, Sforza, Visconti, and Orsini. Their silk garments were superb in all respects, and the richly woven fabrics, coats-of-arms, and other embellishments all tended to add to the beauty of a person, occasion, or event.

Many notable Spanish families also became patrons of the silk industry. In the thirteenth century, for example, there were over twelve thousand silk looms in Seville alone. All weaving in Spain was under Church supervision, and Cardinal Barberini, who later became Pope, made a great reputation for himself because he put the industry there on a level with Italy and France. The cathedrals and museums, monasteries and convents in Spain attest to his great work, since silks, tapestries, hangings, and altar cloths still extant are beautiful in motif and sturdy in construction and texture.

By the fourteenth century it may be stated that silk was becoming gradually more of a necessity than a luxury. The demand for silk was growing by leaps and bounds. The industry was spreading, and more people became quite interested in silk fabrics, garments, and even home furnishings. As nations conquered and developed, and as their cultures spread and became more deep rooted and nationalistic in scope, silk went right along with the changing times in its progress and uses.

In 1480, Louis XI of France became an avid patron of the industry in Tours. The founder of the silk industry of France, however, was the great Francis I. He lived from 1494 to 1547 and began his reign in 1515. Much of his early boyhood was spent in Savoy (Italy), where he received most of his education. His first acquaintance with silk came from reading of the travels of Marco Polo in the thirteenth century. As a boy in Italy, he saw the fine work being done in silk by the Italian artisans. He became much interested in silk. In time it became an obsession with him, so much so that when he became king, he induced a great many Italian silk workers to come to France. Many of them went to work in Lyons, St. Etienne, and other areas in that part of France. He was also interested in silk fashions.

Francis I is known in history as the "Father of the Silk Industry," and for over four hundred years Lyons has been the greatest "silk city" in the world. And, because of Francis' interest in fashion, Paris is still the leading fashion center and has been the world's leading couturier ever since.

About 1600 Olivier de Serres and Laffemas, somewhat against the will of the great Sully, obtained royal edicts favoring the growth of mulberry plantations and furthering cultivation of silk, thereby increasing the opportunity for employment of the peasants. The benefits, however, of these efforts were not realized until the time of Jean Baptiste Colbert (1619–83), the great French statesman and financier of Rheims. He encouraged people to take up the industry and gave premiums to them when their efforts were successful. This stimulation given to silk by Colbert made France more and more the world center of fashion and style, vogue and demand, motif and design, and the cut and quality of women's clothes to this day attest to his great efforts.

During the reign of Henry VI of England, the silk industry was receiving some recognition. He was born in 1421 and died in 1471. He ruled England twice, from 1422, including regency, to 1461, and from 1470 till his death in 1471. This very interesting monarch laid the foundation for later efforts to be expended in England in due time. Fruit of his work was borne in 1585, when a large body of Flemish weavers came to England from the Low Countries. This was at the time

[20]

when England was at war with Spain. The war did much to devastate the lands of the workers, and silk more or less passed into oblivion in England.

The cathedral city of Nantes in western France, located on the Loire River, is noted for the Edict of Nantes, which was a decree of Henry IV in 1598 which granted freedom of conscience to Protestants in that country. Incidentally, it was revoked in 1685 by Louis XIV. By the end of the seventeenth century, because of the religious strife in France, thousands of skilled workers had left for other shores. England profited greatly from the migrations. These Huguenots included many workers who knew how "to work" silk. The revocation of the Edict of Nantes was a terrible loss to France but a great gain for Germany, Switzerland, and Great Britain, among other nations.

Another interesting angle in the history of the silkworm is that Cortes appointed officials to introduce sericulture in what was then New Spain and is now Mexico, and part of our Southwest. This great explorer appointed his group in 1522 and decreed that they should oversee the planting of trees, import the eggs, and put the industry on a sound basis. The venture, of course, failed. Acosta, the Spanish chronicler of the times, recorded the happenings and mentioned its failure in his writings to the Spanish court.

James I (1566–1625) was the first of the Stuart rulers of England. He was also James VI of Scotland. He was king of England from 1603 to 1625 and of Scotland from 1567 to 1625. He is known in history as "the king with many irons in the fire." Silk was one of the irons. Textile workers who had come over from France settled for the most part in the then Spittlesfield area in London. In 1620, James formed an incorporation of silk throwsters in this city. He decreed that mulberry plantations be set up in England, Scotland, and Ireland, as well as in the American Colonies. Traces of mulberry trees can still be found in some of the early settlements in America. Those few trees still growing—gnarled, tangled, old and bent—can be found in Williamsburg, Jamestown, and Yorktown in Virginia; Princeton, New Jersey; Charleston, South Carolina, in and around Boston and Philadelphia, and in several places in Connecticut. They show the living efforts of the settlers to raise silkworms.

A memorable date in the history of the United States is 1607, the founding of the colony in Jamestown, Virginia. Two years later King James I tried to install sericulture as one of the occupations of the settlement. He attempted once more to bring the industry to the fore in 1619. His 1609 venture met with disaster by shipwreck, but his second one was more successful. The settlers began to show some interest in silk, and with the materials at hand, it was thought that success might be achieved. Bounties and premiums were offered to give the project some stimulus.

The following is a verse written at this time:

> Where worms and wood doe naturally abound,
> A gallant silken trade must there be found.
> Virginia excels the world in both—
> Envy nor malice can gaine say this troth.

But because of other extenuating circumstances at the time, the venture failed.

In the Prospectus of Laws of the Compagnie des Indes Occidentales, the cultivation of silk occupies a place among the glowing attractions offered to prospective settlers in the colonies and foreign possessions, but it was merely "a lure to disaster." Up to the time of the American Revolution bounties and rewards were still offered by the Home Office in London for work done in sericulture.

It is worthy of comment that the ever versatile Benjamin Franklin, along with other luminaries of his time, was interested in nursing along a filature into the healthy life in Philadelphia. It was believed that this city would show an interest in silk, but little resulted from the time, money, and effort expended. After the Revolution, when peaceful enterprise was again assured, bounties on silk were offered to the settlement in Gurleyville, Connecticut. This is the first instance recorded of bounties actually being paid to individuals.

Sericulture, however, never could take hold in the colonies, then or now. There were many factors militating against the success of it in the old colonial days— war, financial difficulties, disagreements with the mother country, and the fact that there were too many other, more important, items in the lives of the colonists that needed attention. Nevertheless, there were many efforts made here to raise the worms, but all met with failure. The climate and the soil were not conducive to silk raising, as well. It is much easier and more economical to buy silk from foreign nations than to try and raise it here.

In 1838, following the financial panic in the United States in 1837, there arose a great era of speculation of all types. It soon became a mania. The upset conditions in the nation caused people to seek out new ventures that would, of course, pay well. The order of things had to be changed. Sericulture received some attention since the previous reverses were known, and some were of the opinion that the time was now ripe for it to make real progress. Sericulture suddenly became a household word here and it was the most talked-of thing of the times. This hysterical mania grew in leaps and bounds chiefly because of efforts by Samuel Whitmarsh and his representatives of Philadelphia. This group reported the great capabilities of the South Sea Island mulberry trees (*Morus multicaulis*) for the feeding of silkworms.

So neatly was the question placed before the public that in almost no time at all many sections of the nation went "wild" over the chances of retrieving their losses by raising silkworms. It is a fact that plants and crops were displaced and sidetracked for the "new eighth wonder of the world." The Morus multicaulis tree seemed to be on the lips of all. Plantations were laid out to raise the trees. There was wild scrambling to get into the business venture in the beginning. It has been estimated that in one week in Pennsylvania $300,000 changed hands in the turnover in purchasing young trees. Trees were sold two and three times over and always at a profit. Prices advanced rapidly, and there was a ready market for the trees. Plants of a single-year growth were sold at one dollar per shrub in the height of the feverish excitement. But like all wildcat propositions the bubble soon burst, and by the end of 1839 the famous Morus multicaulis was found to be no golden tree but merely a drug on the market. Costly plantations were now uprooted and the tree was gone but surely not forgotten.

In 1865–66 California came forward with the well-known and time-worn bounty proposition to raise silk there, but the law was soon repealed since there was no interest evinced by the populace. Then, in 1872, after the Civil War, another attempt was made there, and it was thought that some of the veterans might become interested in silk. The bill never passed the Legislature.

The standards of living and the costs, when compared with those of other nations that raised the worms and the trees, made the wiser heads here see that it was cheaper and more economical to buy silk from abroad, especially from China and Japan.

A striking feature of this portion of the history of silk is the persistent effort put forth by the various "potentates" and rulers in stimulating silk raising within their domains—efforts to the present days in the British Colonial possessions, in the Americas, India, and some of the holdings of the Continental powers. It is the adage of "raise the raw material or commodity in the colonies and manufacture the product in the motherland." This is the philosophy that was one of the main reasons that brought on the War Between the States in America, 1861–65, "southern wealth and northern profit."

Despite the patronage, however, given sericulture by the powers that controlled and fostered it, little permanent success has ever been obtained except in China and Japan, and the standards of living there have made its success possible.

In truth, raw silk of commerce can only be profitably brought to the market where there is an abundance of very cheap labor. Thus, these seem to be the main reasons why nations which raise the product successfully can continue to do so without further competition—China, Japan, the Levant; India, Bengal, and Pakistan; and in some of the European countries where comparatively small yield is possible.

BRIEF STORY OF DENIER

Two great leaders in world history, incidentally, are responsible for the denier, the term used to figure the size and yarn data for silk filament and the manmade filaments and staple stock sizes and yarn counts. They lived about fifteen hundred years apart. The *denarius*, plural *denarii*, was a coin used before and during the time of Julius Caesar. Of small value, it was first made of silver, but copper and gold were used to mint the coins later on. The English coin, the penny (*d.*; plural, pence), and the American penny are descendants of the original denarii. The coin is mentioned several times in both the Old Testament and the New Testament. First used outside Rome during the time of Caesar's Gallic Wars in what is now France, the value of the denier was very little and is supposed to be worth about one-twelfth of the old-time French *sou*, although numismatists believe that it was worth about sixteen to twenty-four cents, according to the monetary standards of today. Its size is about that of the middle fingernail of a man. While of little monetary value today, it is a genuine collector's item among coin collectors. One in superb condition, face and obverse, may cost up to fifty dollars or more, and worn coins may run as high as twenty dollars.

Caesar, of course, lived for posterity, but his denier lapsed into oblivion soon after his death in 44 B.C. Little was heard of the denier until the time of Francis I, king of France from 1515–1547. Up to this time the old method for measurement in the relation between length and weight was the ell or aune, taken originally as the length measure for the human arm. This length was 45 inches in England, 46.69 inches in France, and 37.2 inches in Scotland. Tradition has it that Henry I (or Beauclerc) of England (1068–1135), the son of William the Conqueror, who reigned from the year 1100 after conquering Normandy until his death, corrected what he termed the false ell used by a merchant and decreed that as a standard for the future the ell be the length of his arm, the 45-inch length.

One of the first acts decreed when Francis ascended his throne was to abolish the old method of measuring yarn. Silk used 80 skeins of 120 aunes for a total length of 9,600 aunes. Francis invoked the system of weight in the terms of denier —i.e., the number of denier coins or weights necessary to balance the silk in question. The denier weight was 0.0531 grams. This method and procedure, used to the present day, in figuring denier in terms of grams is to find the weight in grams of 9,000 meters or 9,846 yards of yarn. For example, if 9,000 meters of silk or manmade filament yarns weigh 100 grams, the filament is known as a 100-denier yarn.

A gram is approximately 1/28th of one ounce, or 1/450th of one pound. Since there are 492.13 yards of filament used as a standard length in computations, and there are 7,000 grains in one pound, the length of the #1-denier is found by multiplying these two numbers together and then dividing by .771618, the standard grain weight of 1-denier. This results in a length of 4,464,528 yards in a 1-denier yarn—and this figure has been used for over four hundred years, since the time of Francis I.

Thus:

$$\frac{492.13,\ \text{standard length in yards times 7,000 grains in one pound}}{.771618,\ \text{standard grain weight of one denier}}\ \text{gives 4,464,528,}$$

the number of yards in one pound of a #1-denier yarn.

Thus the length of a #1-denier filament (yarn) would be about 2,500 miles long, or the distance from New York City to Phoenix, Arizona. Of course, a denier of this size is much too fine to allow ease of manipulation; hence the necessity of plying several denier filaments together for processing.

To find the yards of yarn per pound in any size denier, it is only necessary to divide the denier size given into the standard of 4,464,528 yards for the #1-denier.

The number of yards in one pound, for example, of a 30-denier yarn would be found in the following manner:

30)4,464,528(148,817.6 yards to the pound, or, in round numbers, a total of 150,000 yards to the pound.

The manmade fibers and filaments have had a rather devastating effect on the four major natural fibers—cotton, wool, linen, and silk, especially the last two. Man is constantly searching for new, better fibers which present new properties that prove of value to mankind. Natural fibers have always been plentiful, but it should be borne in mind that they were originally and basically designed by nature for use in clothing. Man had to use these four fibers as he found them, and has been using them since time immemorial. With the advent of the manmade fibers, the picture for textile fibers has been changed a great deal. These fibers have strength, resist abrasion, chafing and wear, have beauty, and give good performance in usage. Unlimited quantities of these quality fibers at satisfactory prices are obtainable, and they are not limited by crop yield, climate, disease, national or international conditions. As Ralph Waldo Emerson once wrote:

Give the past unto the wind
All before us lies the way!

The natural fibers, which satisfied man's needs for thousands of years, have undergone a revolution in the present century—the century of synthetics—"the

Synthetic Age." The impact and the inroads of the new manmade fibers have been substantial. Linen and silk have been affected very seriously, and it is extremely doubtful whether they will ever recover their former eminence in the textile sphere. Wool has lost much of its former prestige and usage but seems to be making a slow comeback. Only cotton seems to have held its place in the textile world. It still accounts for about 65 per cent of total fiber production throughout the world and in this country, but it is very doubtful if its position will become better; in fact, it may lose some ground in the years to come. The manmade fibers —cellulosic and non-cellulosic—account for about 29 per cent of total world production, while wool hovers around 9 per cent.

Silk, "the fabric of milady," and linen, "the cloth of kings," now have a combined total which is less than one-half of one per cent in annual world production of all textile fibers. All the natural fibers, however, are still with us, and let us hope they always will be, since each has its place in the great textile and apparel world even though their luster and romance may have been dimmed by the passage of time and the advent of the scientific era which introduced the manmade fibers to the world.

Part 1—Unit 3

TOPIC: THE HISTORY AND GRADES OF COTTON

Cotton, often called the universal textile fiber, is supposed to have originated in India. It is now grown in many areas in the temperate zones throughout the world. About twelve million bales are raised annually in the United States, each bale having a standard weight of 478 pounds, plus 22 pounds allowed for cooperage, thereby making the gross bale weight 500 pounds. Cotton burns quickly, leaves little ashes, and has the odor of burning paper. Under the microscope it is a flat, ribbon-like fiber with 150 to 300 turns of natural twist per inch—one of its greatest advantages for use in textiles.

Cotton is white, brownish-white, yellowish-white, or bluish-white; it is a soft, fibrous substance that surrounds the seeds of certain plants of the mallow family, called *Gossypium*. Cotton is the most important and versatile fiber known to mankind. It is used in innerwear, outerwear, accessories, decorative materials in the home, and in industry.

Cotton may be used to make cheap cheesecloth, tobacco cloth, or print material. It may be used to make fine drawnwork materials, whose price may run into hundreds of dollars in value. Fine cotton work is produced in Europe, where most of it comes from the religious schools in which the manipulation of cotton yarn, thread, and cloth has been taught for centuries.

The United States now produces about 35 per cent of the world production; India is the second-largest producer of the fiber. Brazil, Egypt, Central America, China, Mexico, and Peru are other noted producing areas.

In this country there is about twelve times as much cotton used per year as scoured wool. There is about three times as much cotton cloth produced annually, on a square-yard basis, as all other textile cloths combined.

Only 15 per cent of the available cotton-raising area is used for this purpose; hence, the supply can be readily taken care of by increased demands of industry.

Important Dates in the History of Cotton

Cotton was grown in pre-Inca Peru and in neighboring areas.

1800 B.C.: Cotton was raised and cotton cloth made in India.

800 A.D.: Records show that cotton was grown in Japan.

The Crusades spread knowledge of cotton throughout Europe, by way of Egypt, Persia, and the Far East.

Thirteenth-century England was noted for its candlewicks of cotton.

1492: Columbus found cotton in the Bahamas and took samples of Sea Island cotton to Spain. Knowledge of the fiber spread to other European nations.

1519: Pizarro and Cortes found "the white flower" growing in Mexico, Central America, and South America.

1520: Magellan found cotton being grown extensively in Brazil.

1641: The cotton industry was established in England. In this industry were heard the first rumblings of the Industrial Revolution.

1650: Cotton plantations were established in Virginia.

1701: To protect the wool growers, England forbade the use of cotton.

Eighteenth century: Brazil and West Indies were the world centers for cotton production. Slavery increased rapidly in the West Indies.

1758: South Carolina sent a few pounds of cotton to London.

1753–1838: Carter Burwell completed the famous Carter's Grove Plantation, six miles from Williamsburg, Virginia, by 1753. The plantation owned more than one thousand slaves who worked chiefly in indigo and rice production until around 1800, when cotton became "king," following the invention of the cotton gin by Eli Whitney in 1793.

The property was inherited by Burwell on the death of his mother, a daughter of the famous Robert "King" Carter, progenitor of one of the F.F.V.'s (First Families of Virginia). The Grove embraced some 300,000 acres of the colony's best lands.

The plantation remained in the family until 1838, when it was broken up to some degree and sold to private buyers. Carter's Grove, in its halcyon days, still retained the more than one thousand slaves, most of whom were used to work the cotton fields. The main house, still standing and now a show place, has been described as the "most beautiful house in America."

1775: Slaves constituted two-thirds of the population of the five southern colonies of the original thirteen colonies. They worked on products such as rice, indigo, and tobacco, while cotton was in the background because of the time and labor necessary to separate the lint fiber from the seeds, a tedious hand operation. Cotton was not a "revenue product" in the South at this time.

In 1778 Virginia forbade the importation of slaves into that state; Maryland followed suit in 1783. Without King Cotton, slavery would have withered and died in due time.

1793: Eli Whitney, a Yale graduate and native of Connecticut, built his famous cotton gin on "Mulberry Grove" Plantation, a plantation that had been given General Nathanael Greene by the state of Georgia in appreciation of his successful efforts during the American Revolution in winning the South for the colonies from the British Armies. By this time the General had died and the plantation was managed by his widow and Phineas Miller, who became the partner of Whitney in marketing the cotton engines (gins). Working on the plantation, about twenty miles north of Savannah on the river of that name, Whitney actually had his gin in operation in less than two weeks' time. It is one of the simplest and greatest inventions of all time.

1795: Because of the success of the cotton gin, about 6,000,000 pounds of cotton were raised in the United States. Slavery was definitely now on the rise, and the breeding of slaves became an actuality in the northernmost states of the South.

1820: Cotton production in the twenty-five years following the invention of the gin had a phenomenal rise to 125,000,000 pounds on an annual basis.

1860–61: The population of the South was 9,000,000 whites, 4,000,000 slaves, and 250,000 free slaves. Thus, King Cotton and slavery were bound to bring about the conflict between the States.

Cotton, slavery, and the wealth of the South, along with "northern profit" since all types of commodities, goods, equipment, etc., came from the North, especially from New England, New York, and Pennsylvania, had grown up together since 1820. The increase of plantations in the South was fabulous.

The book, *This Is the South,** by Robert West Howard, reveals that:

> ... in 1852, Samuel Hairston of Pittsylvania, Virginia, held between 1,600 and 1,700 slaves, managed another 1,000 belonging to his mother-in-law, and was said to have been worth between three and four million dollars. In fact, every southern state had at least one millionaire before the war, with their wealth based almost entirely on land, cotton, and slaves.
>
> By 1860 about one-fourth of the white adults in the South owned slaves. One hundred thousand of them were planters. The average planter held around one thousand acres of land and owned from 20 to 40 slaves, who were all engaged in producing the staple commodity, cotton, for sales purposes.
>
> A total of 30,400 whites owned from 20 to 40 slaves; 13,456 owned from 40 to 100; 1,980 owned from 100 to 200; 224 owned from 200 to 300; 74 owned 300 to 500; 13 owned from 500 to 1,000.

More than one thousand slaves were owned by at least three notables of the Confederacy—President Jefferson Davis, ex-President James K. Polk, eleventh president of the United States (1845–49), and General Wade Hampton of Columbia, South Carolina, leader of the famous cavalry, The Hampton Legion, during the war. The family still owns large cotton plantations in South Carolina and Mississippi, which pre-date the Civil War.

A year before hostilities began and up to the beginning of the war, a strong, healthy male slave sold for twelve to fifteen hundred dollars, and there were many sales at these prices. Prior to the war, cotton was produced in the South and manufactured into products mainly in the textile mills of New England; hence, the rise of the basic, classic statement of "southern wealth and northern profit."

In addition, the South also supplied the great cotton mills of the Lancashire area in England. The war stopped these shipments and crippled these mills to marked degree. Brazil then became a cotton country and aided much in supplying the British market, and has continued to do so to the present day, along with other major cotton-producing countries.

In 1861, cotton was the major source of revenue for the South and it had a value of around twenty-five million dollars in gold, about tenfold above the gold supply of the Confederacy. Cotton baleage in warehouses was around four and a half million bales. Thus, with a gigantic war on its hands, the blockade of all southern shipping ports, and not being able to export this commodity, the South was in a very poor position relative to its cotton. It can be stated, in retrospect, that cotton became a delusion and lost cause to the Confederacy, since these vast amounts of the staple had to remain at home. Cotton became such a drug on the market that the Confederacy actually had to deal with the northern textile companies by supplying them with cotton in return for meat, bacon, blankets, medicines, and other necessities. During the war, Memphis, Tennessee, was the great clearing house in cotton sales and purchases of sorely needed supplies. Memphis was more important to the South with outside activities, cotton, commerce, and

---

* *This Is the South,* edited by Robert West Howard, copyright © 1959, by Rand, McNally & Company, Chicago, Illinois.

trade than Nassau and the other islands that served as havens, when they could do so, for the blockade runners.

By the end of the war the stock supply of the four and a half million bales in the cotton bale inventory of 1861 showed the following: two and a half million bales had been destroyed to prevent capture by the enemy, one million bales got by the blockade, while the remaining one million bales were smuggled into the northern textiles areas and sold by the owners in the South, a private gain for the consignors of the cotton staple. Close students of the history of the Confederate States of America may agree that among the main reasons for the loss of the war were "over-democratization," economic supremacy of the North, its industrial production, greater manpower, more railroad mileage, and a better welded government, especially in matters of taxation—great factors that finally caused the Confederacy to lose the war.

Students interested in the history, economy, philosophy, and psychology of the Confederate States of America before, during, and after the war are referred to the following books:

Ante-bellum: Three Classic Writings on Slavery in the Old South, by George Fitzhugh and Hinton R. Helper, edited by Harvey Wish, Capricorn Books, G. P. Putnam's Sons, New York, 1960.

Rise of American Civilization, by Charles A. and Mary R. Beard, Macmillan Company, rev. ed., 1949.

The Slave States, by Frederick Law Olmsted, edited by Harvey Wish, Capricorn Books, G. P. Putnam's Sons, New York, 1959.

1920: Following World War I, the exodus of textile mills began from New England, New York, and Pennsylvania to the South. This change is still going on. The South has been raising the cotton, and had been manufacturing most of it; but the raising of cotton is gradually moving to the Southwest and the Pacific Coast, because in addition to cotton-cloth manufacture, the manmade fibers and the plants to process them are located there. New England is now a center of diversified industries, and Arizona, New Mexico, and southern California are now among the leading ten cotton-growing states or areas in the nation.

There are many reasons given for the rise of the South in cotton and manmade textiles, such as accessibility to markets, lower wages, improved living conditions, very good work by public relations agencies, less trouble with the unions than in the North, and tremendous investment of capital.

1935: Production reached over 18,000,000 bales, a banner year.

1936: The famous Rust Brothers, John and Mack, brought out their mechanical cotton picker, the best type to date. About four thousand previous attempts had been made to perfect a machine that could pick cotton in the field. Their invention has increased production greatly.

1946: During World War II, cotton was in the ascendancy, like all other major textile fibers. World production was 24,000,000 bales, with the United States raising 12,000,000 bales, or 50 per cent of the world total.

1960: Production figures in cotton bales are about the same as in 1946, both worldwide and in the United States. At the present time cotton production totals about 17,000,000,000 pounds and accounts for about 60 per cent of total fiber production, worldwide and national, with total per-capita consumption of 28 pounds out of a grand-total per-capita consumption of all textile fibers of 40 pounds. Incidentally, wool fibers make up about 6 per cent of the total production, manufactured fibers about 33 per cent, while all other fibers make up the remaining 1 per cent of production.

[28]

1964–65: The latest available figures for per-capita consumption of major textile fibers throughout the world reveal the following:

FIBER	PERCENTAGE OF TOTAL	PER CAPITA IN POUNDS
Cotton	59.40	22.5
Wool-Worsted	6.10	2.3
Acetate and Rayon	17.90	6.8
Other Manmade Fibers	15.20	5.8
All Other Fibers	1.40	n.a.
	100.00	37.4 pounds

The inroads made by manufactured fiber production on the natural fibers such as cotton, wool, worsted, linen, and silk since World War II have been considerable, and the latter fibers have all lost some ground to the manmade group. Because of great gains made for these newer fibers through performance, advertising, consumption, and comparison, the natural fibers have had to fight for their place in the textile sun; all have decreased to some degree, especially wool, worsted, linen, and silk. While consumption of cotton has also declined somewhat, it is still the world's universal textile fiber and is now doing very well at holding its own in production and usage. So much so that despite the many and varied, and at times fantastic, claims made for the newer fibers, a member of the New York Stock Exchange wrote this about cotton:

Cotton is truly a miracle fiber—it is older than recorded history, it is mothproof without treatment, it does not store up static electricity, and it does not melt. It will not vanish under chemical fumes as you walk down the street; it can be dyed any color or shade, and can be made colorfast. It can be treated so that it won't wrinkle. And cotton styling compares exceedingly well with that done in any other major textile fiber range of fabrics.

—J. J. Scanlan, New York Stock Exchange, New York City, New York.

Major World Cotton-Growing Areas

	NAME	LENGTH	GROWN IN
1.	Sea Island	1-½ to 2-in.	Mexico, Central American nations
2.	Egyptian	1-¼ to 1-¾ in.	Egypt
3.	Arizona	1-¼ to 1-¾ in.	Arizona, California, New Mexico
4.	Uplands	¾ to 1-1/16 in.	Carolinas, Tennessee, Louisiana, Alabama, Mississippi
5.	Peruvian	1-¼ to 1-½ in.	Peru, Arizona
6.	Indian	½ to ¾ in.	India
7.	Chinese	½ to ¾ in.	China, Japan

Differences Between Some Major "Rain-Grown" and "Irrigated" Cottons

"RAIN-GROWN COTTONS": UPLANDS, raised in the southern Cotton Belt Area in this country, is of short staple and has minimum strength; DELTA is raised in the Mississippi River Delta, has medium staple length and minimum strength; VALLEY COTTON is grown in the well-known Rio Grande River Valley, has medium staple and average length.

"IRRIGATED COTTONS": CALIFORNIA is raised in the great San Joaquin Valley, has medium fiber length and possesses extra strength; EGYPTIAN is grown along the great Nile River Valley, has an extra-long staple and extra strength; EL PASO is found in West Texas and New Mexico, is classed as a long staple cotton with extra strength. PIMA is raised in Arizona and New Mexico and gets its name from the famous Pima County in southern Arizona.

Thus it will be noted that irrigated cottons are better and stronger, and have greater staple lengths when compared with rain-grown cottons.

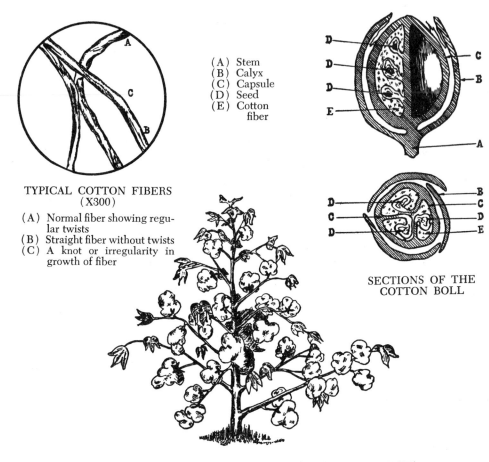

TYPICAL COTTON FIBERS
(X300)

(A) Normal fiber showing regular twists
(B) Straight fiber without twists
(C) A knot or irregularity in growth of fiber

(A) Stem
(B) Calyx
(C) Capsule
(D) Seed
(E) Cotton fiber

SECTIONS OF THE
COTTON BOLL

AMERICAN UPLAND COTTON SHRUB (AFTER DODGE)

COTTON BOLLS

Reprinted by permission from Textile Fibers, *fourth edition, by J. Merritt Matthews, published by John Wiley & Sons, Inc.*

SUPIMA: Certification mark that is registered property of the SuPima Association of America. Usage of the mark is controlled by means of a licensing agreement with the Association, and the mark can be applied only to wearing apparel and textile products made entirely of southwestern extra-long staple cotton fiber grown by members of the Association. About four thousand members grow this irrigated cotton from the controlled seed in Arizona, New Mexico, Texas, and California. The certification mark is written "SuPima." Many of the members are Indians of the Pima, Apache, Nez Percé, Ute, and neighboring tribes. Their knowledge of raising these choice staples is uncanny, and they achieve great success in their efforts. The term comes from the combination of the words "super" and "Pima"; hence, "SuPima." Maximum staple is $1\frac{7}{16}$ inches.

The Grades of Cotton

To raise anything in the vegetable kingdom, favorable soil and climatic conditions are vital. Color, strength, length, properties, and characteristics of cotton are naturally affected by these conditions. The American Cotton Grading Table (also used in many other countries) follows:

1. Middling fair.
2. Strict good middling.
3. Good middling.
4. Strict middling.
5. Middling—all grades of cotton are compared with this type.
6. Strict low middling.
7. Low middling.
8. Strict good ordinary.
9. Good ordinary.

What to Look for When Buying Raw Cotton

GRADE: The appearance of the cotton as to cleanliness, freedom from leaf, chaff, stains, dirt, and so on.

STAPLE: The average length of the bulk fibers, 1½ inches, etc. Staple also implies whether the cotton is harsh, crimpy, weak, strong, substantial, and so on.

IMPURITIES: The amount of sand, grit, and other ordinary impurities that are met with in dealing with the stock.

DAMPNESS: The determination whether the cotton has more than 6 or 7 per cent of dampness, the usual amount. Weather conditions will cause the moisture content to vary, and this point has to be closely watched.

TINGES AND OFF-SORTS: These may spoil a lot of cotton intended for some particular use. They are caused by the plants falling on the ground in rain, wind, sandstorms, and such.

OTHER POINTS: The fineness of fiber, amount of waste, feel, freedom from seeds, short and immature fibers, strength, cracked seeds, brightness.

Cotton Bales

TYPE	DIMENSIONS	WEIGHT
1. American	54 x 27 x 27 inches (variable)	500 lbs. over-all, 478 lbs. legal
2. Brazilian	50 x 20 x 16 inches	250 lbs.
3. Egyptian	50 x 20 x 30 inches	700 to 730 lbs.
4. Indian and Far East	50 x 20 x 16 inches	400 lbs.
5. Mexican	53 x 33 x 46 inches	500 lbs. approximately
6. Peruvian	45 x 25 x 20 inches	200 lbs. approximately

TESTING

1. What is the standard weight of a cotton bale in this country?
2. Give some reasons for the wide acceptance and use of cotton in apparel.
3. Take the statement, "Cotton is truly a miracle fiber, etc.," and identify the fiber alluded to in the entire statement.
4. Give the Cotton Grading Table, in order.
5. America produces what percentage of all world cotton?
6. Name five world cottons.

Part 1—Unit

TOPIC: Properties and Characteristics of Cotton

Cotton-staple fiber length runs from ½ inch to about 2 inches, with the choic length between 1 and 2 inches; about 60 per cent of American cotton range between ⅞ inch and 1¼ inches. Cotton has a very wide variety of uses, from infants clothing to work clothing to toweling. Its quality is determined by color, foreig matter present, staple length, and method of preparation by the cotton gin. Th color may be: extra white, white, spotted, tinged, yellow, stained. The foreig matter present refers to the parts of the plant and dirt present in the cotton.

Staple refers to the average length of the fiber. It indicates the suitability c cotton for particular uses. Fiber length or staple is determined by gradually re ducing a tuft of cotton—by pulling it out a number of times, until the individua fibers are drawn out, and then measuring it very accurately. Although mechanica devices exist for measuring cotton staple, most of the work is still done by hand b the clever cotton classers who can measure cotton fiber to the nearest sixteent of an inch with ease.

Staple cotton refers to cotton 1⅛ inches in length or longer. The character c cotton fibers refers to all qualities not included in grade and staple, such a strength, uniformity, spirability.

Cotton, Properties of

PHYSICAL CHARACTERISTICS

MICROSCOPICAL APPEARANCE: A flat, ribbonlike fiber which has from 150 to 300 natura turns of twist per inch.

LENGTH: ½ inch to 2 inches, or slightly longer.

DIAMETER: .0005 inch to .0009 inch.

COLOR: Ordinarily white; may be cream-colored or tinted brown.

LUSTER: In untreated condition has no pronounced luster.

STRENGTH: Intermediate between silk and wool. The single fiber will sustain a dea weight of 2 to 8 grams. Strength is temporarily increased when wet, and decrease when abnormally dried.

ELASTICITY: Not nearly as elastic as silk and wool. Spiral twists make it apparently mor elastic than linen.

CONDUCTIVITY OF HEAT: Better than silk or wool, not as good as linen.

HYGROSCOPIC MOISTURE: 6 to 7 per cent.

CAPILLARITY AND PENETRABILITY: It has capillarity because of its tubular structure

FIBER COMPOSITION: Formula is $C_6H_{10}O_5$, n or x times. Cellulose content varies from 90 per cent to about 96 per cent, water from 5 to 8 per cent, natural impuritie from 4 to 6 per cent.

CHEMICAL CHARACTERISTICS

EFFECT OF LIGHT: Loses strength.

MILDEW: Pure cotton is not attacked readily. Sized or treated with starches, flours, and gums, it will be affected by mildew in presence of dampness.

HEAT: Withstands high temperatures well. In dry atmosphere, it can be heated to 300° F. without injury. At 475° F., the fiber will turn brown and burn.

WATER: Boiling water does not affect the fiber.

MINERAL ACIDS: Concentrated acids such as hydrochloric, hydrofluoric, nitric, and sulfuric will destroy the fiber. Cold dilute acids will not injure the fiber if washed out or neutralized. Dilute solutions, 3 per cent or less, of these acids, if allowed to dry, cause the fiber to become tender, and in time will destroy cotton.

VOLATILE ORGANIC ACIDS: With formic or acetic acids there is no detrimental action.

NON-VOLATILE ACIDS: Oxalic acid will cause a high loss in tensile strength; a low loss with tartaric acid. Citric acid will tender the fiber, if not removed, and especially if heat is applied.

STRONG ALKALIES: With caustic soda, soda ash, there is no injury, even if concentrated, and even if the heat is applied when the oxygen is excluded. Concentrated solutions will mercerize cotton if it is under tension; otherwise the cotton will shrink.

WEAK ALKALIES: No injurious effect upon the fiber.

OXIDIZING AGENTS: Potassium permanganate, for example, will destroy cotton if not controlled.

METALLIC SALTS: Cotton has practically no affinity for metallic salts.

AFFINITY FOR DYESTUFFS: Less than that of silk and wool.

DYEING: Cotton is dyed by direct dyestuffs, sulfur dyes, basic dyes with a mordant, by coloring matter developed in the fiber, and by vat dyes.

BLEACHING AGENTS: Chlorine bleach or hypochlorites, when in cold, dilute solution will not injure the fiber. The bleach used, however, should be removed carefully, since heat and concentrated solutions will destroy the fiber.

OTHER OXIDATION BLEACHES: Hydrogen peroxide, sodium perborate, or potassium permanganate will not injure cotton, if properly controlled.

REDUCTION BLEACHES: Sulfurous acid (sulfur dioxide plus water) or hydrosulfites will cause no injury if controlled.

Other Properties and Characteristics of Cotton

Will shrink unless pre-shrunk.
Launders easily and well; much used in wash-and-wear garments.
Ideal for blending with other major fibers.
Is soft and comfortable next to the skin.
Stores well; no deterioration if well cared for.
Comfortable in warm weather.
Classed as a dead fiber; wool is a live fiber.
Available in large quantities.
Flexible; not broken when twisted.
Wrinkles easily but can be made wrinkle-resistant.
Crease-resistant finishes easily applied.
Makes excellent toweling because of absorbent properties.
Relatively inexpensive fiber.
Mercerized for added and permanent luster.
Lower quality yarns are carded; higher grade yarns are combed.
Said to have over ten thousand uses.
Can be spun to very high counts of yarn, 100s and higher.
Cool because of its power of absorption followed by evaporation.

TESTING

1. Define staple; cotton staple.
2. How is the fiber length of cotton determined?
3. List fifteen properties and characteristics of cotton.
4. Name ten cotton materials found in the home.
5. Why would cotton garments be ideal for children's wear? Infants' wear?
6. Name three colors of cotton.

TOPIC: Cotton-Cloth Manufacture

(1) PREPARATION: Testing of the soil for planting and cultivation. The question of irrigation is considered along with other local factors, such as rainfall, sandstorms, possible ,productiveness along the lines of "bales to be produced per acre," etc. Preparation begins in the deep South in early January and is usually completed in the northern cotton belt by the first of March. Incidentally, frost is one of the banes of the cotton planter, and climatic conditions are studied by the experienced grower from all angles.

(2) PLANTING: This commences around the middle of March and extends to about mid-April. Planters like to have all this work done around April 15. Constant care has to be given the plants as they begin to grow and thrive, especially during the hot summer months.

(3) PICKING: This depends very much on weather conditions; if favorable during the raising season, "first bales" will come into the market in July. Picking lasts until early September in the most southerly areas and will continue to about early or mid-November in other areas. Three harvestings are usually obtained from cotton, and it is not unlikely that it will be early December before the final picking has been completed. About 85 per cent of the crop is now picked by automatic cotton picker, a great advantage over the old-time hand-picking methods which had many obvious disadvantages.

(4) GINNING: This is the separation of the fiber from the seed; one-third of the weight is the cotton fiber while the other two-thirds consist of foreign waste matter such as leaves, pieces of pods, chaff, grit and grime, pebbles, etc. First-time ginning takes place on the plantation or at the "community gin." Usable fiber obtained in the ginning is called lint cotton, ideal for manufacture into products of apparel, decorative materials, and for use in industrial fabrics of many types.

(5) SECOND-TIME GINNING OR DE-LINTING: Cottonseed, after being separated from the lint cotton at the "community gin" or on the plantation, is sold to cotton dealers, who ship this seed in carload lots to the large "cotton cities" of the South: Memphis, Galveston, Houston, Little Rock, New Orleans, and several other centers. The rugged de-linting treatment separates the short, brown fibers that have clung tenaciously to the seeds and which were not removed in the first-time ginning. These fibers are known as linters and they sell for around fifteen cents or so per pound. Practically all linter stock is used in industry. Cotton can be said to be the "father of acetate and rayon," since it is this cellulosic fiber stock that serves as the basic raw material in their manufacture. Both rayon and acetate, although they use different processes in the manufacture into yarn, are cellulosic in nature; rayon is classed as a true cellulosic manmade fiber while acetate is known as a cellulose derivative, along with Arnel, which is a cellulose triacetate textile fiber.

(6) BALING: The compressing of ginned cotton into bale form. A legal United States bale of cotton weighs 478 pounds, and there is an allowance of 22 pounds for wrappings such as burlap, cord, cooperage; thus the American bale weighs about 500 pounds. Bale dimensions are usually 54 by 27 by 27 inches.

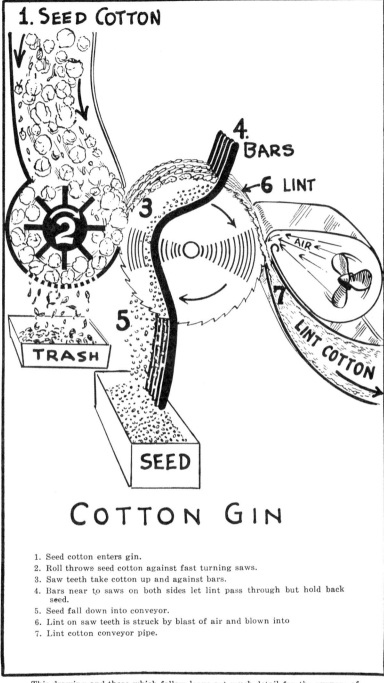

COTTON GIN

1. Seed cotton enters gin.
2. Roll throws seed cotton against fast turning saws.
3. Saw teeth take cotton up and against bars.
4. Bars near to saws on both sides let lint pass through but hold back seed.
5. Seed fall down into conveyor.
6. Lint on saw teeth is struck by blast of air and blown into
7. Lint cotton conveyor pipe.

This drawing and those which follow leave out much detail for the purpose of making more clear the basic principle of operation.

Pages 35-42 Courtesy Bibb Manufacturing Co., Inc., Macon, Georgia

BLENDING FEEDER

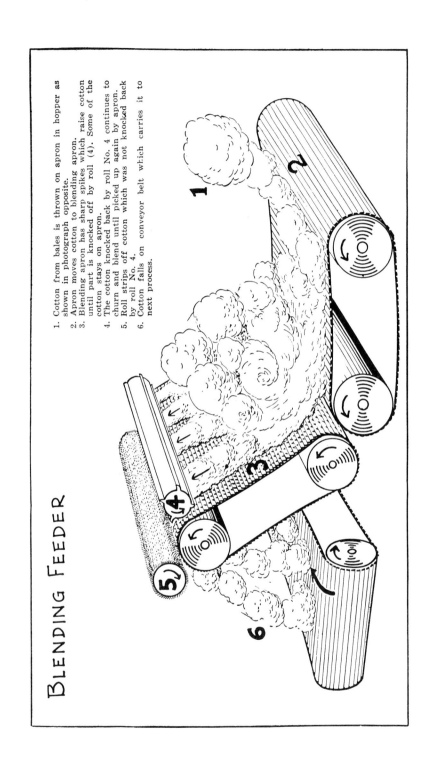

1. Cotton from bales is thrown on apron in hopper as shown in photograph opposite.
2. Apron moves cotton to blending apron.
3. Blending apron has sharp spikes which raise cotton until part is knocked off by roll (4). Some of the cotton stays on apron.
4. The cotton knocked back by roll No. 4 continues to churn and blend until picked up again by apron.
5. Roll strips off cotton which was not knocked back by roll No. 4.
6. Cotton falls on conveyor belt which carries it to next process.

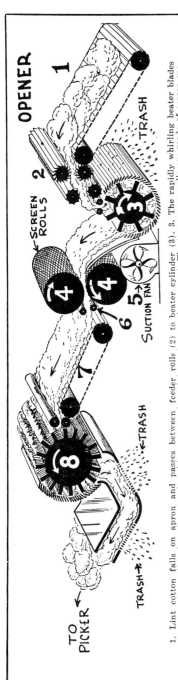

1. Lint cotton falls on apron and passes between feeder rolls (2) to beater cylinder (3). 3. The rapidly whirling beater blades each take off small tufts of cotton knocking out trash and loosening up the mass. 4. The two screen rolls are made of screen material and air is sucked out of them by the fan (5). This draws the cotton from the beater and condenses it on the surface of the screen rolls from which it is taken and passed on by the small rolls (6). The air suction through the cotton takes out dirt and trash. 7. The conveyor belt (7) passes the cotton to another type of beater. (Many types of beaters are used. Those shown are typical.) 8. From the beater the cotton passes to a conveyor which take it to the next machine which is the picker. (see below)

1. Cotton in a loose mass from the opener enters the picker which is a series of beaters (2) (2) and screen rolls (3) (3) similar to those described under opening, but gradually more refined. 4. At the final output of the beater and screen system the cotton has again been formed into a sheet or "lap." At this point the "evener" operates to feed more or less cotton as may be required to make the lap perfectly uniform as it is wound up into a "lap roll" (5) on the winding rolls (6). From this point the lap roll is taken to the carding process.

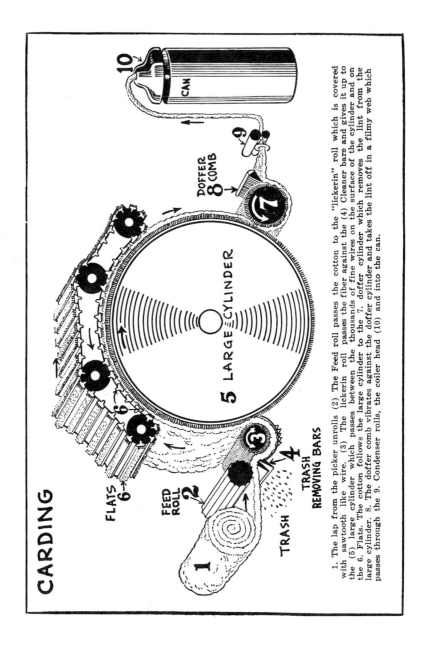

CARDING

1. The lap from the picker unrolls (2) The Feed roll passes the cotton to the "lickerin" roll which is covered with sawtooth like wire. (3) The lickerin roll passes the fiber against the (4) Cleaner bars and gives it up to the (5) large cylinder which passes between the thousands of fine wires on the surface of the cylinder and on the 6. Flats. The cotton follows the large cylinder to the 7. doffer cylinder which removes the lint from the large cylinder. 8. The doffer comb vibrates against the doffer cylinder and takes the lint off in a filmy web which passes through the 9. Condenser rolls, the coiler head (10) and into the can.

DRAWING

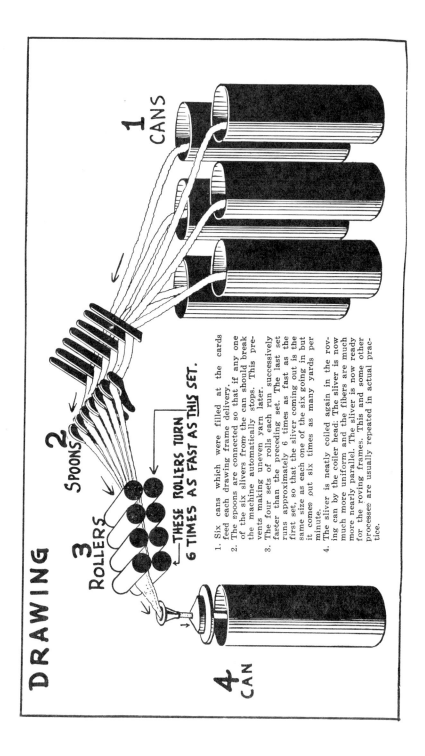

1 CANS

2 SPOONS

3 ROLLERS

← THESE ROLLERS TURN 6 TIMES AS FAST AS **THIS** SET.

4 CAN

1. Six cans which were filled at the cards feed each drawing frame delivery.
2. The spoons are connected so that if any one of the six slivers from the can should break the machine automatically stops. This prevents making uneven yarn later.
3. The four sets of rolls each run successively faster than the preceding set. The last set runs approximately 6 times as fast as the first set, so that the sliver coming out is the same size as each one of the six going in but it comes out six times as many yards per minute.
4. The sliver is neatly coiled again in the roving can by the coiler head. The sliver is now much more uniform and the fibers are much more nearly parallel. The sliver is now ready for the roving frames. This and some other processes are usually repeated in actual practice.

[39]

ROVING FRAMES

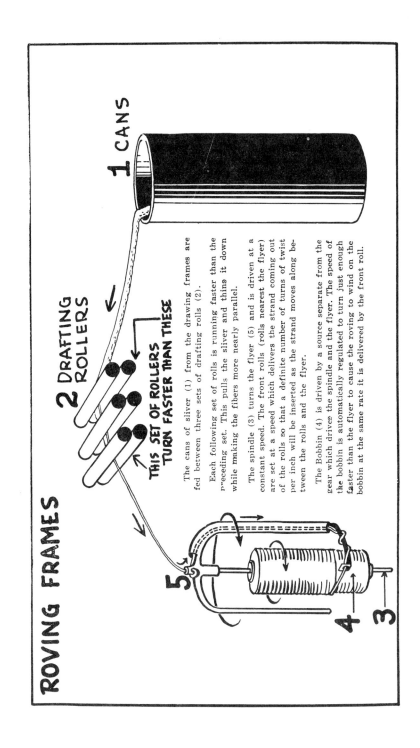

1 CANS

2 DRAFTING ROLLERS

THIS SET OF ROLLERS TURN FASTER THAN THESE

The cans of sliver (1) from the drawing frames are fed between three sets of drafting rolls (2).

Each following set of rolls is running faster than the preceding set. This pulls the sliver and thins it down while making the fibers more nearly parallel.

The spindle (3) turns the flyer (5) and is driven at a constant speed. The front rolls (rolls nearest the flyer) are set at a speed which delivers the strand coming out of the rolls so that a definite number of turns of twist per inch will be inserted as the strand moves along between the rolls and the flyer.

The Bobbin (4) is driven by a source separate from the gear which drives the spindle and the flyer. The speed of the bobbin is automatically regulated to turn just enough faster than the flyer to cause the roving to wind on the bobbin at the same rate it is delivered by the front roll.

SPINNING

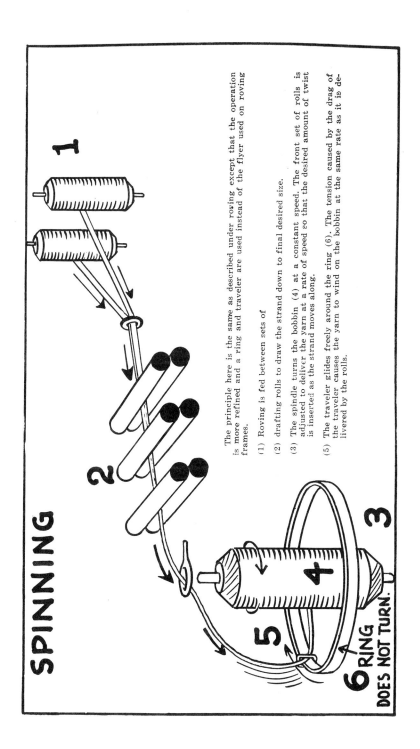

The principle here is the same as described under roving except that the operation is more refined and a ring and traveler are used instead of the flyer used on roving frames.

(1) Roving is fed between sets of

(2) drafting rolls to draw the strand down to final desired size.

(3) The spindle turns the bobbin (4) at a constant speed. The front set of rolls is adjusted to deliver the yarn at a rate of speed so that the desired amount of twist is inserted as the strand moves along.

(5) The traveler glides freely around the ring (6). The tension caused by the drag of the traveler causes the yarn to wind on the bobbin at the same rate as it is delivered by the rolls.

RING DOES NOT TURN.

TWISTING

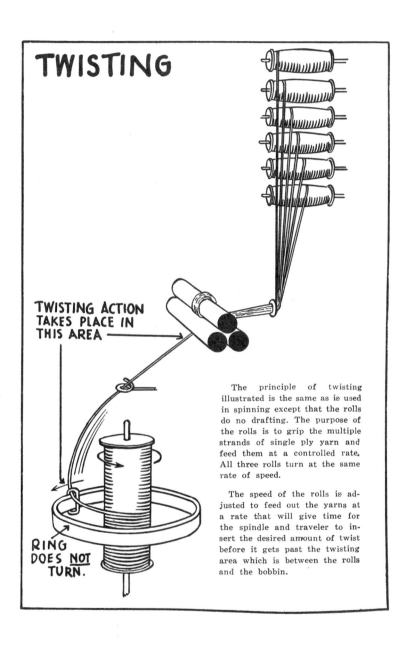

TWISTING ACTION
TAKES PLACE IN
THIS AREA

RING
DOES **NOT**
TURN.

The principle of twisting illustrated is the same as is used in spinning except that the rolls do no drafting. The purpose of the rolls is to grip the multiple strands of single ply yarn and feed them at a controlled rate. All three rolls turn at the same rate of speed.

The speed of the rolls is adjusted to feed out the yarns at a rate that will give time for the spindle and traveler to insert the desired amount of twist before it gets past the twisting area which is between the rolls and the bobbin.

Courtesy: Farm Security Adm.; U. S. Cotton Research Station, Stoneville, Miss.; Dan River Mills, Inc.

Hand picking cotton   Mechanical cotton picker

Baling cotton

Cotton gins

Courtesy: Dan River Mills, Inc.

Opening the bale
Breaking cotton lumps
Placing lap in card

Mixing bales
Cotton lap
Carding machine

Courtesy: Dan River Mills, Inc.

Breaker drawing frame	Sliver lap machine
Comb	Roving frame
Further drawing with some twisting	Spinning frame

Courtesy: Dan River Mills, Inc.

Twister	Warper
Warp beam dyeing	Slasher
Drawing-in	Weaving

Courtesy: Dan River Mills, Inc.

Singeing
Washing and Bleaching
Shearing

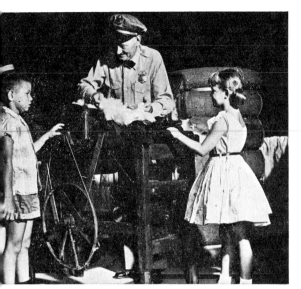

Eli Whitney's first commercial cotton gin, a priceless item. This gin was found in Wilkes County, Georgia, in 1934, after having been lost for 140 years. The original, pilot model of the Whitney cotton gin is believed to have been destroyed by fire. Officer Paul Partridge is explaining the cotton gin to Kay and Jon Cowan.

Courtesy: Robert E. Sibley, Director of Public Relations, The Citizens and Southern National Bank, Atlanta, Georgia

Modern cotton gin, which can process more cotton in a few minutes than Whitney's gin could in a full day.

Courtesy: National Cotton Council of America, Memphis, Tenn.

A modern cotton ginning plant.

Courtesy: National Cotton Council of America

(7) BREAKING: In the mill, after the cotton has been received, the breaker-picker or breaker-opener machines break up the lumps and clods of the compressed cotton as taken from the bale. Much loose waste matter is removed in the tumbling action, and there are also sets of fans which readily further open up the stock for manipulation. The last machine in the set is called the finisher-picker and it delivers the processed, opened cotton at the delivery end of the frame in a lap form. This lap is about forty inches wide and has a weight of about forty pounds. This stock is then ready to be presented to the carding machine.

(8) CARDING: Carding cleanses and further disentangles the fibers to a marked degree. Carding changes the bulk, raw stock into a sliver form, which is a loose rope-form of fibers about the size of a man's thumb and has a weight from 40 grains to about 60 grains per yard. No twisting is applied to the fibers in the carding frame. The sliver is soft, smooth, fluffy, and has a kindly feel; the fibers are clean and parallel.

> NOTE: Carded cotton, if it is to be used in a carded yarn, goes from the card directly to the first drawing frame and skips the sliver-lap, ribbon-lap, and combing frames.

(9) COMBING: This fine, detailed operation on the stock completes the cleansing of the fibers and removes the short, undesirable fibers, too short for combed yarns; these are known as cotton comber noil.

Combing sets the long, choice, desirable fibers into a silken-like strand or sliver form. The sliver-lap and the ribbon-lap frames have aided in obtaining this choice stock strand of fibers. Combed yarn, when compared with carded yarn, is superior in all respects, goes into higher-quality fabrics and commands a higher price for the particular article of clothing or apparel.

(10) DRAWING: Carded stock is run once or twice through the drawing frame in sliver form so as to double and redouble the stock form being manipulated. Combed stock is run from two to six times through the same drawing frame in order to increase the doublings and redoublings and to take care of attenuation, which is a gradual reducing of the diameter of the strand due to introduction of draft. This causes the fibers to be actually drawn among themselves to a longer and straighter finished length, which is made possible by the excess speed of the front rollers over the carrier rollers and the back or feeding-in rollers, which always go at the slowest speed. It should be kept in mind, however, that the actual individual fibers are not stretched at all; it is the drafting which causes the diminishing of the strand diameter while it is being manipulated in the frame.

(11) SLUBBER AND ROVING FRAMES: These follow the drawing frames in sequence. They condense the sliver into what is known as a slubbing formation. The diameter of slubbing may be compared with that of an ordinary lead pencil. The roving frame further condenses the slubbing until it takes on the form called roving. Its diameter may be compared with that of the lead in a lead pencil. Roving signifies that the form of fibers has been drawn, drafted, twisted, and set in order for the spinning frame. The word "roving" always signifies that the particular stock is "one step removed from being finished spun yarn."

(12) SPINNING: Cotton is spun on the ring frame or else on the mule spinning frame. Spinning is the final drawing, twisting, and the winding of the newly spun yarn onto some practicable device such as a cone, cop, spindle, tube, etc. Thus yarn is the final product of all the foregoing operations. This yarn is now of commercial value and ready for the market. Mule-spun yarn is softer and loftier; ring-spun yarn is wirier, usually has more turns-of-twist per inch in it, is generally spun to a finer diameter than mule-spun yarn, and can provide higher textures and pick count in woven goods.

Importance of Strength and Twist in Cotton Yarns

These two points are important in the spinning of practically any type of yarn. The following points are important relative to the spinning of cotton yarns:

(a) Fiber strength is 37 per cent of the strength of a yarn in the case of coarse and average cotton yarns. Generally speaking, average yarns are those of sizes below

50s (840 cotton standard times 50 yarn count gives 42,000 yards to the pound of yarn).

(b) Fiber fineness is very important in the manufacture of yarn, since it contributes up to 16 per cent of the yarn strength in average cotton yarn counts, and becomes increasingly important as the higher or finer yarn counts are spun on a spinning machine.

(c) When yarn sizes pass or go above 50s, the order is reversed, and the fineness becomes more important than the actual fiber strength.

(d) Maturity of the cotton is important to the fiber, the yarn, the fabric, the dyeing, printing, and finishing operations.

(e) The grade of cotton includes the staple length of the fiber or fibers, the amount of wastes, and the yarn sizes.

(f) The upper-half mean-average length of fiber is in the upper half of any sample of cotton under consideration.

(g) The mean average is the average length of all the fibers.

(h) The uniformity ratio of the mean is compared with the upper-half mean.

(i) The length and the uniformity coincide to 47 per cent in yarn strength. Uniformity is very important in the appearance of the spun yarn and for ease of handling.

The Laws of Machines

Pertinent to all types of machines, the laws here pertain to the drafting of cotton fibers, as well as to the drafting of any textile fibers being processed into yarn. The following information covers the functions of these laws:

(a) The work done on a machine is the INPUT and equals the product of the effort force and the effort distance.

(b) The work done by a machine is the OUTPUT and equals the product of the resistance and the resistance distance. Thus:

INPUT—E (Effort) times DE (Effort Distance).
OUTPUT—R (Resistance) times DR (Resistance Distance).

(c) Theoretically, INPUT should equal OUTPUT. Actually, INPUT is always greater than OUTPUT because some of the INPUT is used to overcome the friction on the machine. The energy lost turns into heat so that there is no violation of the law of the conservation of energy.

(d) Therefore, the laws of machines are: INPUT equals the useful work OUTPUT plus the losses caused by friction.

Cloth Manufacture

This includes weaving fabric on the loom, making knitted cloth on a knitting frame, and the manufacture of braided or plaited material on braiding, lace, or similar machines. Hundreds of materials are produced by each of these three methods of making commercially valuable products.

Gray, Grey, Greige, Griege Goods

Any fabric, irrespective of color, that has been woven on a loom but which has received no dry- or wet-finishing treatments or operations. Gray goods after being taken from the loom are taken to the perch for the chalk-marking of all blemishes and defects, no matter how small. These irregularities in cloth are removed in the finishing of the material as the gray goods are converted into the finished state.

Interpretation of Data on Approval Sample Labels

Interpretation of all data found on labels, pasted labels, tags, or tickets is important to anyone who comes in contact with an approval sample, head end, swatch of fabric, or a cut length from a bolt of goods. The following is a typical informational label from an approval sample:

BRADFORD DYEING ASSOCIATION (U.S.A.)
New York City

Description: All-spun-acetate and spun-rayon twill cloth.

Gray Width	47.00″	Finished Width	44.5″
Thread count	96 x 50	Weight	2.16 yds to lb
Maker	Erlanger	Our Style	16382
Maker's Style	7128	Date	January 23, 1965
Finish	Crease-resistant and calendered		

TESTING

1. What is the difference between first-time ginning and second-time ginning?
2. What is the purpose of carding fibers?
3. How does carding differ from combing?
4. Why do combed fabrics cost more than carded cloths of comparable nature?
5. Define sliver, slubbing, roving, yarn, ply-yarn.
6. Name the three operations in the spinning of roving into yarn.
7. Explain the principles of spinning yarn.
8. Discuss the importance of twist or lack of proper amount of twist per inch, in cotton yarns.
9. Discuss the principles of the laws of machines with the work on machines as to input and output.
10. Describe gray goods from the loom.
11. Differentiate among reed width, loom width or gray goods, and finished width of textile fabric.
12. Define the following terms found on labels used on approval samples—thread count, type of finish, weight of fabric.

Part 1—Unit 6

TOPIC: COTTON-CLOTH FINISHING

With the exception of heavy cotton fabrics such as canvas, duck, and webbing, practically all cotton cloths receive a number of finishing treatments. Many cottons are in an unbleached condition as they come from the loom in the gray- or greige-goods state. There is no appeal to the cloths, which are often soiled, contain varying portions of foreign matter such as specks, motes, and a host of other impurities; blemishes and flaws are also noted. There has probably never been a perfect yard of fabric woven on a loom. Fabrics are "made in the finishing," and "the fabric's the thing." Finished cloth must have "eye appeal and buy appeal," along with other assets, to make it salable. An unbleached cotton muslin or print cloth from the loom is not appealing to the eye. When finished, however, they may be bleached to the white, dyed or printed, may come in a desirable natural shade or color, and possess a very attractive finish for the surface effect.

Cambric, longcloth, lawn, dimity, percale, and sheeting in the finished state are white, smooth, and attractive. The change from gray or loom goods to the salable product is fantastic.

Finishing is really an art and a science in the making of fabrics which will be presentable to the consuming public. The resultant cloth may be fair, medium, good, or excellent in quality when made ready for usage. It is the converting of cloth from a state with a rather unsightly appearance to one that has consumer appeal. Finishing instructions have to be carried out to the letter, and discretion, judgment, and accuracy are paramount. There are three reasons for finishing materials:

(1) To give beauty and appeal to the goods for consumer purchase.
(2) To remedy all defects in the goods whether small or large.
(3) To add weight to the fabric sometimes in order to improve the "hand" or "feel"; or to apply certain finishing agents for providing some special attribute.

Finishing may be compared with the application of cosmetics to the face to improve the attractiveness of the wearer. Some persons can use cosmetics to advantage; for others it seems to do little or no good at all. Some can apply cosmetics with a good technique while others use them to a degree that "they seem to be put on with a spray and to remove them a chisel is needed to get them off." So it is with finished fabrics: finishing can usually do much for materials, but there are some cloths that are definitely not too well finished because of faulty application or because something has gone awry during the various finishing treatments given the goods.

Generally speaking, there are three types of finishes that cloth may have or be given:

1. MILL FINISH: A brand-new condition is given the finished fabric.
2. HOME LAUNDRY FINISH: The garments after laundering have to go through various treatments to "bring the cloth back to new." Each article, however, deteriorates after laundering until it reaches "the point of no return."
3. COMMERCIAL LAUNDRY: Its function is "to bring soiled garments to the cleansed state so that further wear is possible."

A fabric from the textile plant has either a temporary, a permanent, or a durable finish. The price paid for the materials and ingredients used, and the end use of the fabric, govern the type of finish to be applied. After all is said and done, anything that is made to be sold depends on the consumer—YOU:

> Jobs depend on Sales,
> Sales depend on Price,
> Price depends on Cost,
> Cost depends on YOU.

The consumer pays for any product, whether it is a process or a product, and the price has to be "right." The foregoing philosophy holds true especially when buying finished goods or articles.

MAJOR FINISHING TREATMENTS ON COTTON FABRICS

In the finishing of all types of fabric, cotton and otherwise, there are four terms that should be understood by the reader. These follow:

(1) DRY-FINISHING OPERATIONS: Those processes in which the cloth is handled in a dry condition. These include perching, measuring, burling, specking, mending, sewing; calendering, brushing, cropping, friction calendering, glazing, napping, shearing, gassing or singeing, Schreinerizing, et al.
(2) WET-FINISHING OPERATIONS: General term for those finishing processes in which the material is immersed in, or becomes wet with, water, or any other liquid or solution. Examples include bleaching, dyeing, printing, fulling, milling, scouring, soaping, shrinking, crabbing, sponging, decating, waterproofing, mercerizing, sizing or starching, Sanforized, Rigmel, etc.

Courtesy: Bradford Dyeing Association; Cluett, Peabody & Company, Inc.

Tentering   Calendering

Sanforized—controlled compressive shrinking

(3) BASIC FINISH: One that alters or improves in some manner the texture or surface appearance or effect of a fabric. Examples include mercerizing, calendering, friction calendering, glazing, moiré or watermarked, napping, shearing, cropping, embossing, chasing, beetling, et al.

(4) FUNCTIONAL FINISH: One that alters or improves the wearability or performance of a fabric or garment to give protection or a longer life to the article and thereby enhance consumer demand. Examples include absorbency, crease resistance, crease retention, fire resistance, laundryproofing, mildew resistance, durability, shower repellency, et al.

WET-FINISHING TREATMENTS

BLEACHING: Bleaching removes natural and other types of impurities and blemishes of various types from the goods, takes out coloring matter that might be present, and makes the cloth white, or very nearly white. It also provides for better and clearer dyeing or printing of the material. It aids in the affinity of the dyestuff in the dye bath to give better or improved color effect. It is possible to bleach practically any of the major textile fabrics seen today.

DYEING: The process of coloring fibers or fabrics with either natural or synthetic dyes. There are today about eight thousand different dyestuffs on the market and there is a marked difference in their resistance to heat, acids, alkalies, absorbency, fastness, gas-fading, ironing, perspiration, sunlight, cleaning agents, solubility, application, etc.

PRINTING: The producing of motifs, designs, or patterns of one or more colors (up to sixteen are possible) onto fabric. There are several methods in use today, including direct, discharge, blotch, and resist, which are really techniques used in the application of the color to the goods; actual methods of printing include block, screen or stencil, and roller.

ABERDEEN: Slightly starched finish given to sheeting that has been dyed black for use as lining.

BACK-FILLING: Usually applied to low-grade, low-cost cloth to provide a better appearance. Only one side of the goods is affected by the process. The filling solution is composed of varying amounts of the following ingredients—corn starch, talc, China clay, and tallow. Other starches are often added to the solution when deemed necessary. The mixture is usually heavy and rather thick. Application is done by a starch mangle. In filling dyed goods, the compound is always colored to resemble closely the shade of the fabric itself. Care must be taken to see that this filling starch does not work to the surface of the goods. It is advantageous to calender the cloth heavily prior to the starching process, since this presses the threads or yarns closer together and, at the same time, flattens them out, thereby preventing the starch from easily coming through to the face of the goods.

BLUE-WHITE: Used on cottons to give a distinctive finish. It is obtained by the use of a small amount of bluing to the bleached fabric so as to neutralize the yellowish effect which often occurs when running cloth through the various treatments in the Wet-Finishing Department in the mill. Storage of cloth from time to time, on its way through the mill, will cause this yellowish cast or shade to appear. This is an undesirable cast; hence, the use of more of the desirable blue-white treatment or finish.

BRADESTA: An anti-static pilling-resistant finish used for "Dacron" polyester and cotton blends. Trademark of Bradford Dyeing Association (U.S.A.), New York City.

BRADLUSTRA: Durable finish which imparts improved hand and a permanent in-grained luster to high-quality cottons. Trademark of Bradford Dyeing Association (U.S.A.), New York City.

DUPLEX PRINTED: A method for printing the same or some other motif or pattern on the back of the goods after the face of the cloth has been printed with color. Two operations are necessary in the printing. It finds use in simulating woven stripes and designs in certain cloths used for decorative purposes. Also known as register printing, this type of cloth can be classed as a reversible. Some rough-and-ready shirting and sportswear blouses, shirts, and jackets are duplex printed.

ELASTIC DUCK: A very firm, starched finish applied to cotton sheeting, dyed black or some other dark shade for use in lining.

FRENCH: Similar to the dull finish, it gives a slightly starched appearance on some cottons. Little or no luster is seen on the goods.

FULL BLEACHED: This implies that the material has received at least one boiling in the alkali bath or baths, and that bleaching has taken place in the bleaching powder bath.

FULL OR DOUBLE MERCERIZED FINISH: This signifies that the fabric has received full-strength mercerizing immersion—25 to 55 degrees, Twaddle Thermometer, bath of caustic soda, cold. There is no marked increase in mercerization above the 55-degree mark on the thermometer.

MERCERIZED: Achieved by running goods through a tentering frame at high-speed velocity, the cloth being submerged in a solution in a frame vat so that it will take on the silken finish. Results obtained from mercerizing cotton cloth include increased strength, improved luster, more cylindrical diameter in the yarn when compared with non-mercerized yarn, better affinity for dyestuffs, better uniformity and evenness, and only about seven-tenths as much dyestuff needed to give good results in dyeing when compared with non-mercerized dyed cloth. Final diameter of the yarn is finer in the finished cloth. Discovered by accident in 1844 by John Mercer, English scientist and chemist, whose experiment was to find some way whereby the affinity of dyestuff to cotton cloth could be increased. His accidental findings are considered one of the great phenomena in textile science.

PLISSÉ: Cotton, acetate, or rayon fabric treated in a striped motif, or in spot formation, with a caustic-soda solution which shrinks parts of the goods to provide the crinkled or pleated effect (plissé). The effect may or may not be removed after washing; this depends on the quality of the fabric or garment. Ironing, if done, should take place after the fabric is thoroughly dry in order to smooth out double thicknesses such as hems.

PRE-SHRUNK: Fabrics or garments which have received a pre-shrinking treatment. Often done on cottons to remove the tendency for cloth to shrink when washed or laundered. Worsteds and woolens are also shrunk before cutting the fabric for use in a garment to prevent further shrinkage. The percentage of residual shrinkage must be indicated on the label of the goods or garments thus treated.

REPELLENT TREATMENTS: Any one of a great number of treatments that may be applied to fabrics and garments to make them repellent to moths, water, mildew, moisture, perspiration, etc. They may or may not be durable in nature. Some disappear after the first washing and laundering, others will give good service, at times almost to the point of permanency. A very few may be classed as permanent.

RIGMEL, RIGMEL SHRUNK: Trademark of the Bradford Dyeing Association (U.S.A.) for a stabilization process which also affords luster and a soft, mellow hand to fabrics such as cotton shirting and dress fabrics. The method controls shrinkage to within 1 per cent of the length or the width of the material; in fact it can be controlled to within one-quarter inch per yard in both directions.

SANFORIZED: A checked standard of shrinkage. The trademark is applied to fabrics that have been shrunk by the compressive shrinkage process and indicates that the residual shrinkage of the fabric is less than 1 per cent and that tests have been made by the trademark owner to insure that the shrinkage conforms to the 1-per cent standard.

The trademark owner, Cluett, Peabody & Company, Inc., permits the use of the "Sanforized" label on compressive pre-shrunk fabrics wherever the following conditions have been met:

(1) The residual shrinkage in the fabric, that is, the amount of shrinkage left after shrinking, does not exceed 1 per cent by the U. S. test method, CCC-T-191a.

(2) Tests to determine residual shrinkage have been checked and approved by the trademark owner.

SANFORIZED PLUS: A Cluett, Peabody & Company, Inc., trademark which signifies a regularly checked standard of wash-and-wear performance. Fabrics so labeled have met the rigid test requirements for shrinkage, smoothness after washing, crease recovery, tensile strength, and tear strength as prescribed by The Sanforized Company of the parent company.

SHRINKAGE CONTROL: During weaving and certain procedures in finishing, the cloth is held under tensions which, when released, will allow the goods to contract or shrink. The production of serviceable goods necessitates the dimensional stabilization of the material to prevent this shrinkage from occurring during consumer use. The potential shrinkage is determined and then actually duplicated in the finishing process. Cotton fabrics identified by trade names Rigmel-Shrunk (Bradford Dyeing Association) or Sanforized (Cluett, Peabody & Company, Inc.) are mechanically manipulated to achieve planned dimensions that allow anticipation of residual shrinkage of less than 1 per cent.

SIZING, SIZED, STARCHING, STARCHED: These terms are used interchangeably and refer to the application of a size or starch to warp yarn to increase strength and smoothness and to add weight to the gray goods from the loom. Sizing may be applied to yarn in hank or ball warp form, or on the slasher or dresser frames. Sizing mixtures may be made from a number of starches, such as those obtained from potato peelings, oyster shells, cassava, barley, corn, sago, wheat, rice, gum tragacanth, Irish moss, British gum, et al.

They are also applied to fabrics and garments. Many of these are starched before being sold over the counter in the department store, or sent to the cutting-up house to be made into finished garments.

STARCHLESS: A cotton fabric, for example, finished and "starchless" since there is not any starch to wash out or replace. Features of the finish include absence of lint, non-sleazy appearance, and no fuzzy fiber surface after washing, laundering, or being exposed to moisture.

TENTERING: A machine that dries and stretches cloth to its finished width, and straightens the weave by the action of two diverging endless chains. Each chain is equipped with a series of clips that hold an edge of the cloth and convey it over gas flames or through a hot-air drying compartment.

UNBLEACHED: Many fabrics, especially cottons, in the trade come in an unbleached or natural condition. Materials of this type have a sort of "creamy" or somewhat "dirty" white color cast and much foreign matter is often seen in them—burs, nips, nebs, specks, et al. These cloths are stronger than full-bleached fabrics. Examples of unbleached goods include canvas, duck, unbleached muslin, osnaburg, cretonne, sheeting, some toweling (cotton and linen), and some moleskin and comparable fabric used for pocket lining.

WASHABLE: Fabrics which will not fade or shrink when they are washed. The term should always be qualified by careful directions in methods of handling based on laboratory tests. Not to be confused with "WASH-AND-WEAR."

"WASH-AND-WEAR": This type of garment is one that can be washed by hand or in a washing machine at the warm-water setting. When drip-dried it retains creases or pleats, and recovers sufficiently from wrinkles to need little, if any, ironing. Washing temperatures should range between 95° F. and 110° F.

WASHFASTNESS: A term that seems to cause considerable confusion, especially among consumers. The term is applied, rather loosely at times, to fabrics or garments which can be washed and laundered. Much depends on the actual item or article before the term should be applied.

DRY-FINISHING TREATMENTS

In some circles these finishing treatments or processes are referred to as mechanical treatments, depending, of course, on the particular operation in finishing of the goods. Major finishes in the group follow:

BEETLING: Provides a flattened appearance to the cloth by the use of beetlers or fallers. The spaces between the warp and the filling, in this mechanical treatment, are covered up and tend to produce a high gloss on the material. The term "beating-out" or "beetling-out" is used often in speaking of the appearance of the fabric. Beetling gives a better linen-like finish than any other used on cotton cloth.

As the cloth is slowly wound onto a roller, the fallers or hammers, which are heavy metal devices, strike the top layer of the cloth with great force and cause the goods to take on a "thready appearance." There is also a sort of moiré or watermarked effect seen on the material caused by the beating of the goods in the layer formation. Several cottons are given this treatment which is not very durable when the fabric or garment is in use.

CALENDERED: The calender machine consists essentially of a set of heavy rollers mounted on vertical frames and arranged to pass the cloth between the rollers. The frame may have from two to ten rollers, or bowls, some of which can be heated. By the use of different combinations of heat, pressure, type and number of rollers, surface friction, etc., it is possible to produce a wide assortment of finished effects, especially on cottons and rayons.

The number of rollers may vary as well as the manner in which the cloth is run through the frame. Some calender finishes are chased, friction, glazed, watermarked or moiré, et al.

CAMBRIC: Gives a brighter and firmer finish to cottons than the muslin finish. The cloth has to be well-singed and calendered, and may or may not be pure or back-filled.

CHASED: Beetled effects may be simulated on cottons with this finish; inexpensive treatment for inexpensive cloths. Many cotton staples receive this finish, which is not lasting in nature. The yarns in the cloth are not all of the "same height," and this causes lines of bright-and-dim effects observed when the rays of light strike the goods. The cloth is "threaded" so that several layers of fabric can be passed through between the chasing rollers at the same time. From four to as many as sixteen layers of material may be manipulated at one time.

DE LUXE: This affords cottons a high Schreiner, luster finish. The rollers used for this type of finish may have as many as 360 grooves or gouged lines to the inch. Venetians and other lining materials are often given this finish. De Luxe is actually a heavy Schreiner finish.

DULL: Applied to cottons, the goods are sent directly to the frames to obtain the desired finished width, and then go to the "making-up room" for folding. The finish is produced on the goods with or without the tentering treatment, and is given a very slight-heated calendering. This finish is often given cambric and comparable fabrics that are to be used for lining.

DUVETYNE, SUEDE, FELTED: In a finish of this category, the cloth is napped on one or both sides, and it is then sheared and brushed carefully in order to obtain the necessary closely cropped nap that is characteristic of the finish.

EMBOSSED: A popular effect made on cloth by passing it between a series of rollers, each set having one smooth and one embossed roller. These metallic rollers are heated so as to give better results. The embossed rollers have been engraved with suitable patterns, which will be reproduced on the fabric and give the appearance of a raised or embossed surface to the goods. Motifs may be birds, "tear drops," foliage, scrollwork, figures, pastoral scenes, etc.

Embossing is often applied to certain fabrics, and can be used effectively on velvets and other pile fabrics to bring about the desired effects. The impression seen on some embossed cloths more or less resemble genuine Jacquard woven effects.

FLANNEL: Usually a cotton or rayon fabric slightly napped on both sides to resemble woolen fabric used for some dressgoods, blanketing, coating, etc.

FRAMED: The cloth is "framed" or held out to as near the finished width as possible. Many cottons are finished this way—organdy, voile, dimity, lawn, nainsook, batiste, pajama checks, et al.

FRICTION CALENDER: A very bright, shiny finish used on lining twills, sateen, silesia, messaline, and binding finish cloths. Brought about by the one calender roller going at a slightly increased speed over the other roller in the set. Rollers may or may not be heated.

FROSTING: A slight luster is given to fabric by the Schreiner method at low temperature. Used solely on cottons. (See SCHREINER FINISH.)

GASSING: The process of burning off protruding fibers from yarns and cloths by passing them over a gas flame or heated copper plates. This gives the fabric a smooth surface which is very necessary for fabrics to be printed, and for those where a very smooth, inviting hand is desired. Also called singeing. (See SINGEING.)

GLAZED: This finish provides luster, sheen, shine or polish to some fabrics. It is done by friction calendering and the depth and the life of the finish depends on ingredients used and the settings on the machine. Some fabrics have durable finish while others will not withstand laundering. Chintz is an example of glazed fabric.

MOIRÉ, WATERMARKED: A finish given cotton, silk, acetate, rayon, nylon, etc., where bright-and-dim effects are observed. This popular finish is achieved by passing the fabric between engraved rollers which press the particular motif into the goods, causing the crushed and the uncrushed parts to reflect light differently.

NAPPING: Producing a nap or fuzziness by lifting the short or the loose fibers to the surface of the material. Done by means of rollers clothed with fine, pressed steel wire or by a teasled roller which "scrapes" the surface of the cloth to raise the nap.

SCHREINER FINISH: The natural luster of many cloths, such as cottonback sateen, sateen, muslin, linene, linon, and lining is enhanced by a method of milling or pounding called "Schreinerizing." The material is subjected to the physical action of a roller, usually made of steel, with a great many fine lines per inch engraved on it. The roller flattens the threads in the cloth and imprints onto the surface a series of ridges, so fine that it is necessary to use a microscope to see the fineness of the work.

These very fine lines reflect the rays of light and bring out the appearance by which the cloth is characteristically known. Some of the finishes allied with schreinerizing are frost-schreinerization, imitation schreinerization, imitation mercerization, bloom finish.

SINGEING: This treatment will produce smoothness on the material. Protruding fibers, lint, and fuzz are removed by singeing without injury to the goods, by passing the cloth rapidly over gas jets or electric plates. (See GASSING.)

TESTING

1. Define the following terms used in finishing of fabrics: (1) mill finish; (2) dry finishing; (3) wet finishing; (4) basic finish; (5) functional finish.
2. Name and give the functions of three wet-finishing treatments; of three mechanical or dry-finishing treatments.
3. Differentiate between dyeing and printing.
4. Name four fabrics that are usually dyed and not printed.
5. Name four printed materials.
6. Why is the Sanforized method so popular for finishing many fabrics?
7. List three advantages derived from mercerizing goods.
8. Compare a seersucker fabric with one that has been given a plissé finish.

9. Differentiate between mercerized cloth and one that has been given a schreinerized finish.
10. What is meant by a Sanforized Plus finish on fabrics?
11. Differentiate among a washable fabric, a "wash-and-wear" fabric, and one that uses the term "washfastness" on the label attached to the goods.

PROTECTIVE OR SPECIAL TREATMENTS AND FINISHES

These include a number of processes, treatments, and finishes applied to fabrics and/or garments, made from many of the major fibers, to afford better performance or protection to the cloth, the garment, and/or the consumer. Included in this category would be the following:

ABSORBENCY: The result of treating fabric with chemicals so as to give it greater and quicker water-absorption properties.

BRADPERMA CMI: A chlorine-resistant wash-and-wear finish for fabrics made of cotton. Trademark of Bradford Dyeing Association (U.S.A.), Westerly, Rhode Island, and New York City.

CHLORINE RETENTIVE: Resin finishes or treatments given cotton, rayon, nylon, and other fabrics may cause the goods to retain certain and varying amounts of chlorine. This is later removed by hot calendering or pressing, which will often cause degradation and/or discoloration.

CREASE RESISTANCE: Often referred to as C.R.F. (Crease-Resistant Finish), it is applied by the use of synthetic resins or other chemicals on material to cause it to resist and then recover, if need be, from wrinkling.

CREASE RETENTION: The ability of a cloth to retain a fold or pleat that has been created purposely, usually by a heat treatment. The heat-setting of the thermoplastic fibers used in textiles will cause creases to become permanently set.

DETERGENT: This is not a treatment or a finish; it is an ingredient, a cleansing agent or solvent much used in finishing fabrics. Originally, it meant a soap, a water softener, or a "soap-saver." The term now means a set of washing products known as "synthetic detergents," ideal for use in washing, cleansing, and placing the goods in a better, more workable condition. The term "detergent" is now disassociated from soap. (*See* SOAP.)

DRYCLEANING: A method or process applied to garments which cannot be laundered. Organic solvents such as carbon tetrachloride, $C\ Cl_4$, or certain mineral compounds are used to remove dirt, soil, and most spots and stains. Unaffected stains have to be removed by other special agents. Incidentally, perspiration is not removed in drycleaning of garments.

FIREPROOFING: A fabric to be fireproof must be 100 per cent fireproof, according to the Federal Trade Commission, Washington, D.C. If treated to prevent the spread of flame, the fabric is called fire-resistant. Some materials are treated with a chemical which will melt at a low melting point and cover the fabric with a non-flammable film. (*See* FIRE-RETARDANT.)

FIRE-RETARDANT: Fabrics treated with special chemical agents to make them retardant or resistant to fire. There is a wide range of fire-retardants on the market today.

HEAT-SETTING: Heat application will usually stabilize manmade-fiber fabrics so that they will not be altered in shape or size. Resins and heavy pressures are often resorted to in this work; a resin will be applied to the material, and the heat and the pressure will then insure the correct shape and width of the fabric.

IMPREGNATED: A cloth in which the interstices or minute openings in the texture among the interlacings of the warp and filling yarns are filled completely by some impregnating compound throughout the thickness of the goods, as distinguished from coated or sized materials, where the agent has been applied to the surface of the fabric and where the interstices are not completely filled in. (Definition of the A.S.T.M., Philadelphia, Pennsylvania.)

LACQUERING: Goods that have been treated chemically in order to produce a thin chemical film on the surface of the cloth; may also be applied as a motif or design onto a fabric. Not durable against drycleaning unless so stated.

LAUNDRYPROOF: Laboratory-tested fabrics and garments which will withstand laundering without loss of color or shrinking under ordinary washing conditions. The term can be applied only to items so tested.

MILDEW-RESISTANT: Treating textiles to make them impervious to mildew and mold; it is possible now to determine the amount of degradation or damage on a degree principle.

"PERMANENT FINISH": A comparatively much used term given a number of materials for which some particular claim is made. Examples could include moiré or water-marked effect on faille, taffeta, organdy and dimity; the smoothness on broadcloth; embossed fabrics, some crepe effects, glazed fabrics, etc. The term also implies cloths which are crease-resistant, shrinkage-resistant, and wear-resistant. In reality, however, the safer term to use is "Durable Finish." Actually, very few finishes truly qualify as being permanent for the life of the fabric or garment.

PERSPIRATION-RESISTANT: Said of fabrics or garments that resist acid or alkaline perspiration. Laboratory test results should be consulted prior to selling any fabric or garment as perspiration-resistant.

SANITIZED: A bacteriostatic type of finish which protects fabrics from deteriorating and having odor-causing effects of bacteria, mildew, and mold. Sold to licensees by the owner, Sanitized Sales Company, Inc., New York City.

SCOURING: It is not an actual finish but a most important process in finishing textiles, hence its inclusion: (1) To cleanse a fabric in totality or its surface by washing and an abrasion or rubbing treatment. (2) The use of detergents and soaps, as well as other cleaners, to remove dirt, grime, soil, and other foreign matter or particles. (3) To remove the sizing and tint used on warp yarn in weaving in the loom, and, in general, cleaning a fabric or yarn prior to dyeing. (4) The freeing of wool from yolk, suint, dirt, and all other foreign matter. It may be done by washing the stock with soap, alkali, by treating it with chemicals or solvents, or by naphthalating at below-freezing temperatures.

SHOWERPROOFING: Some materials are treated chemically and by the addition of a wax coating can be made to repel water. Cloth thus treated is more hygienic than non-porous rubber fabric, for example, since air cannot circulate through the latter.

SHOWER-REPELLENT: Sometimes referred to as splash-resistant, the term implies cloth that is resistant to light rain and showers. The process is such that washing or drycleaning gradually removes the finish-coating, thereby diminishing its effectiveness.

SILICONE: At times, a rather broad generic term for one of a class of organic compounds, based on the partial substitution of silicon for carbon. Obtained from silicon, a compound of sand, it is used to protect fabrics against spotting, staining, soiling, and wetting. It also finds much use as a softening agent in the finishing of fabrics.

SOAPING: Actually not a finish but a most important agent in finishing fabrics. Four types of soap find use in fabric finishing: (1) Hard Soap contains sodium compounds of fatty acids which harden under exposure to air. Used mainly in hard water washing. (2) Soft Soap contains potassium compounds which will absorb water and have the tendency to liquefy. (3) Neutral Soap contains compounds of olive oil or lard oil with potash, freely soluble and free from alkalies. (4) All-Purpose Soap is one in which mild alkaline-builders are added to improve cleansing and to soften water, and which often contains a brightener. Used mainly in the "family wash."

[60]

SOIL RETARDANT: Fabrics are treated with various chemical compounds to enable them to resist the effect of soil on materials. Applied to many materials and also much resorted to by textile companies to ascertain the results on yarns and fabrics actually buried in the ground, either for a short time to a year, or more.

SPOT-AND-STAIN-RESISTANT: Applied to materials to resist spots and stains. Many ingredients may be used for the purpose, depending upon the fiber or fibers used in the fabric or garment. A fabric should be laboratory-approved before any such claim is made.

SYNTHETIC DETERGENT: Not a finish but an important ingredient used in processing and finishing fabrics. The abbreviated form is known as "Syndet." It is a cleaning agent made from chemicals, usually hydrocarbons, sulfuric acid, and sodium carbonate. It comes in various forms—liquid, paste, powder, etc. Much used when rapid and thorough wetting of fabrics is desired. Varied concentrations are available for the many different processes used in finishing textiles.

TARNISH PREVENTION: Chemical treatment applied to some cloths wherein there is an inhibiting of the action of atmospheric gases and body reagents which would cause tarnishing. The type of treatment decides as to the final effectiveness of the agent used. Any claim to tarnish prevention should describe its effectiveness.

WATER-REPELLENT: Ability of a fabric to resist penetration by water, under certain conditions. Various types of tests are used, and these are conducted on samples before and after subjection to standard washing and drycleaning tests. Immersion, spray, spot, and hydrostatic methods may be used. Shower-resistant, rain-resistant, and waterproof factors are interpreted from the results of the testing.

WATER RESISTING: Fabric treated chemically to resist water, or it may be given a "wax-coating treatment" to make it repellent. Not to be confused with water-repellent; the terms, however, are often used interchangeably.

"ZELAN": A durable repellent finish; it is a finish and not the fabric or the garment. Fabrics treated with "Zelan" shed rain, snow, water, resist spots and stains with the exception of grease; resist perspiration, and wrinkle less easily. The treatment goes into the fibers and does not coat the weave formation. Air circulates normally, body heat and moisture can escape, and clothes are always comfortable. Not used on all-wool and all-acetate fabric. Product of E. I. du Pont de Nemours & Co., Inc., Wilmington, Delaware.

"ZE PEL": A fabric fluoridizer of E. I. du Pont de Nemours & Co., Inc., Wilmington, Delaware. This compound contains fluorine which aids in the formation of a shield or layer of film around textile fibers in a fabric to prevent spots and stains penetrating the fibers in a cloth, thereby making their removal an easy matter. Treatment with the product does not affect washfastness of dyes used in a material nor does it affect the "breathability" or strength of the fabric. It provides excellent protection against water and stains on garments.

"ZESET": A textile finish that imparts durable wrinkle- and shrink-resistance to cotton and viscose-rayon fabrics. Spun-rayon materials, many of which at present are not washable, when treated with "Zeset" can be laundered and bleached under the usual home conditions without serious loss of strength and discoloration often encountered in the case of home-bleached fabrics. Product of E. I. du Pont de Nemours & Co., Inc., Wilmington, Delaware.

TOPIC: EXAMINATION ON COTTON FROM FIELD TO FINISHING

TRUE-FALSE QUESTIONS   50 points

1. _____ Cotton is classed as a live vegetable fiber.
2. _____ Most cotton staple is more than 1½ inches in length.
3. _____ Most Egyptian cotton is more than 1 inch in staple length.
4. _____ All grades of cotton are compared with middling cotton for classing.
5. _____ Middling fair cotton is an ordinary staple.
6. _____ Over 50 per cent of American cotton is ⅞ inch to 1¼ inches in length.
7. _____ Cotton has from 150 to 300 turns of twist per inch in the fiber.
8. _____ The average length of a group of fibers is called staple.
9. _____ Cotton is a poor conductor of heat.
10. _____ Cotton is not flexible and breaks easily when twisted.
11. _____ Moisture content in cotton is from 6 to 7 per cent.
12. _____ Impurities in cotton range around 10 per cent.
13. _____ Cotton is classed as a cool fiber because of its power of absorption.
14. _____ Lower-quality cotton is always carded and combed.
15. _____ Non-elasticity is a property of the cotton fiber.
16. _____ Mildew will not attack cotton.
17. _____ Carding removes short fiber or noil in its functioning.
18. _____ Cotton linters cannot be used to manufacture yarn.
19. _____ Cotton will take a crease readily and keep it indefinitely.
20. _____ All cotton is now picked by automatic cotton-picking machines.
21. _____ The usable cotton fibers to be made into spun yarn are called lint.
22. _____ Cotton will become weaker when wet or damp.
23. _____ Waxy and fatty matter are not found in cotton.
24. _____ All cotton yarns must be carded.
25. _____ Chlorine can be used to bleach cotton.

MATCHING QUESTIONS   10 points

Place the number of your choice from the second column of words or terms on the blank line provided to the left where there is a definite link or match with the words or terms in the first column:

1. _____ Carding	1. One step removed from spun yarn
2. _____ Drawing of fibers	2. De-linting
3. _____ Slubbing	3. Revolving, tumbling action
4. _____ Brown in color	4. Cotton linters
5. _____ Not used in carding cotton	5. Result of drawing, twisting, and winding fibers
6. _____ Card lap	6. Greater in diameter than roving
7. _____ Roving	7. Provides no fiber twist
8. _____ Second-time ginning	8. 40 inches wide and weighs 40 pounds
9. _____ Spun yarn	9. Sliver-lap and ribbon-lap machines
10. _____ Breaker machines in mill	10. May be done two to six times

MULTIPLE-CHOICE QUESTIONS   10 points

Underline your choice from the second column of words that ties in with the statement made in the first column of terms or words:

1. Highest quality cotton — Middling, Uplands, Sea Island, Mississippi

2. Cotton-raising state — Virginia, North Carolina, Ohio, Texas

3. Cotton-manufacturing state — North Carolina, Virginia, Maryland, Illinois

4. Not used to make carded yarn — Roving frame, comber, slubber, opener frame

5. To diminish diameter — Doubling, redoubling, attenuation, twisting

6. Poor-quality cotton — Arizona, Peruvian, Indian, Egyptian

7. High-quality cotton raised in — New Mexico, Virginia, Arkansas, Delaware

8. Greatest in diameter — Roving, slubbing, yarn, sliver

9. Length to be called staple — 1″, 1⅛″, 1⅜″, 2″

10. Seed and foreign matter in cotton is about — 25%, 33%, 40%, 50%, 66%, 75% of total weight

IDENTIFICATION QUESTIONS   30 points

In each of the following questions, *one of the words or terms is out of place.* Place the wrong word or term *number* on the blank line provided to the left of this page. These questions are all on finishing of cotton fabrics.

1. _____ 1. Napping. 2. Shearing. 3. Flannel finish. 4. Mercerizing.

2. _____ 1. Sizing. 2. Starching. 3. Back-filling. 4. Plissé.

3. _____ 1. Seersucker. 2. Dyeing. 3. Printing. 4. Bleaching. 5. Sizing.

4. _____ 1. Tentering. 2. Rigmel. 3. Sanforized. 4. Pre-shrunk. 5. Sized.

5. _____ 1. Mill. 2. Commercial. 3. Natural. 4. Home Laundry.

6. _____ 1. Embossed. 2. Duplex. 3. Calendered. 4. Glazed. 5. Scoured.

7. _____ 1. Sanforized. 2. Controlled shrinkage. 3. Sanforized Plus. 4. French.

8. _____ 1. Beetled. 2. Chased. 3. Calendered. 4. Singed. 5. Mill.

9. _____ 1. Moiré. 2. Singed. 3. Napped. 4. Brushed. 5. Flannel finish.

10. _____ 1. Duvetyne. 2. Suede. 3. Felted. 4. Embossed. 5. Napped.

11. _____ 1. Chlorine retentive. 2. Crease-resistant. 3. Detergent. 4. Heat-set.

12. _____ 1. Impregnated. 2. Drycleaning. 3. Lacquered. 4. Silicone compound.

13. _____ 1. "Zeset." 2. "ZE PEL." 3. Sanitized. 4. "Zelan."

14. _____ 1. Tarnish. 2. Spot and stain. 3. Shower-repellent. 4. Duplex.

15. _____ 1. Soaping. 2. Beetled. 3. Detergent. 4. Syndet. 5. Scouring.

TOPIC: INFORMATION AND DATA FORMS FOR TEXTILE FABRICS

STANDARD TEXTILE FABRICS ANALYSIS

NAME AND SAMPLE	RAW MATERIAL:

FABRIC _____

Warp Fibers _____
Filling Fibers _____

CONSTRUCTION:
Weave Used _____
Warp Yarn Counts & Ply _____ / _____
Filling Yarn Counts & Ply _____ / _____
Texture or Pick Count _____ × _____
Gray Width _____ in. Fin Width _____ in.
Weight in Yds. per Pound _____ · _____
Weight in Ounces per Yard _____ · _____
COLORING, METHOD OF _____

```
    ┌─────────────────┐
    │                 │
    │ Paste sample at top │
    │                 │
    │      only       │
    │                 │
    │ Use photographer's │
    │                 │
    │   paste only    │
    │                 │
    └─────────────────┘
```

Wearing Qualities _____

Characteristics _____   FINISH, TYPE OF _____

Uses _____

STANDARD TEXTILE FABRICS ANALYSIS

NAME AND SAMPLE	RAW MATERIAL:

FABRIC _____

Warp Fibers _____
Filling Fibers _____

CONSTRUCTION:
Weave Used _____
Warp Yarn Counts & Ply _____ / _____
Filling Yarn Counts & Ply _____ / _____
Texture or Pick Count _____ × _____
Gray Width _____ in. Fin Width _____ in.
Weight in Yds. per Pound _____ · _____
Weight in Ounces per Yard _____ · _____
COLORING, METHOD OF _____

```
    ┌─────────────────┐
    │                 │
    │ Paste sample at top │
    │                 │
    │      only       │
    │                 │
    │ Use photographer's │
    │                 │
    │   paste only    │
    │                 │
    └─────────────────┘
```

Wearing Qualities _____

Characteristics _____   FINISH, TYPE OF _____

Uses _____

[64]

FABRIC ANALYSIS WORKSHEET   Fabric Sample # . . . .

Student's Name: _____

Name of Fabric: _____

Fabric Characteristics: _____

Paste

Even Numbered

_____

Major
End Use: _____

Samples

Here

Reason for
Selecting Face as Shown: _____

Reason for
Selecting Warp as Shown: _____

_____

YARN INFORMATION	WARP	FILLING
Filament
1) or Spun:		
Number
2) of Ply:		
Twist
3) Direction:		

Name of Weave	Fabric Count:	
Method of Coloring:		
Special Finishes:		

BURNING TEST	WARP	FILLING
Flame:		
Odor:		
Ash:		
Other Tests for Identification:		
Fiber:		

Paste

Odd Numbered

Samples

Here

_____

_____

_____

_____

_____

_____

CLOTH SAMPLE DATA SHEET FOR TEXTILE AND APPAREL STUDENTS

NAME OF CLOTH _____

RECOGNITION OF CLOTH

1. *Raw Material*
   a. Warp is _____
   b. Filling is _____

2. *Construction*
   a. Weave? _____
   b. Texture-ends and picks per inch _____
      _____ x _____
   c. Is the texture high or low or medium?
      _____
   d. Weight in ounces per yard? _____
   e. Finished width? _____

Paste sample at

top only

Use only

photographer's paste

3. *Methods of Coloring*
   a. Is cloth dyed, printed or in the white?
      _____
   b. If colored, what method was used? _____
      _____

WORKING PROPERTIES OF MATERIAL

6. *Working Properties of Cloth*
   a. Handle or feel? _____
   b. Drapability? _____
   c. Hold crease? _____
   d. Shine with wear? _____
   e. Clinginess? _____
   f. Sagginess? _____

4. *Finish of the Material*
   a. What type of finish has been applied to
      cloth? _____
   b. Is the finish permanent or temporary?
      _____

7. *Manipulation*
   a. In cutting? _____
   b. In fitting? _____
   c. In sewing? _____

5. *Uses of the Material*
   a. May be used for _____
      _____
      _____
      _____

8. *Launderability*
   a. Easy or difficult to launder? _____
   b. Will cloth have tendency to shrink?
      _____
   c. What is the effect of laundering on
      the finish? _____

REMARKS _____
_____
_____
_____
_____
_____
_____
_____

9. *Cleaning*
   a. Will it be necessary to have the cloth
      drycleaned after usage? _____
   b. If so, will the fabric clean well?
      _____

10. *Cost*
    a. What is the estimate of the cost per
       yard of cloth based on a _____ inch
       width? $ _____

SUGGESTED FORM FOR PHYSICAL AND CHEMICAL TESTING OF TEXTILE FABRICS

NAME OF FABRIC: _____ MILL: _____

FIBER CONTENT: ____ % of _____ CONVERTER: _____

____ % of _____ DATE: _____

____ % of _____ % of _____

FINISHED WIDTH: _____ inches _____ FINISHED WEIGHT: _____ oz.,

or _____ YARDS PER POUND

COLOR-RESISTANCE TESTING:

1. Chlorine: _____   2. Crocking: _____

3. Drycleaning: _____   4. Gas Fading: _____

5. Light: _____   6. Perspiration: _____

7. Salt Water: _____   8. Washing: _____

RESIDUAL SHRINKAGE:

1. Drycleaning: _____   2. Washing: _____

MISCELLANEOUS TESTING:

1. Abrasion: _____   2. Crease Resistance: _____

3. Elasticity: _____   4. Non-Flammability: _____

5. Mildew Resistance: _____   6. Moth Resistance: _____

7. Seam Slippage: _____   8. Tensile Strength: _____

9. Water Repellency: _____   a. Warp _____ Pounds

b. Filling _____ Pounds

REMARKS FOR THE FABRIC:

REMARKS AGAINST THE FABRIC:

THIS FABRIC IS SUITED FOR:

Paste sample at

top only

Use only

photographer's paste

[67]

FABRIC DATA SHEET

_____ / ___ / ___
Date

The following fabric— _____ is today being
submitted for your attention:

FABRIC NUMBER IS: _____. STYLE NUMBER IS: _____

DESCRIPTION: _____

_____

WARP YARN COUNTS: _____ / _____. FILLING YARN COUNTS: _____ / _____

WARP CONTENT IS: _____

FILLING CONTENT IS: _____

LOOM OR GRAY GOODS PICK COUNT OR TEXTURE IS: _____ X _____

PICK COUNT OR TEXTURE OF FINISHED FABRIC IS: _____ X _____

LOOM OR GRAY GOODS WIDTH IS: _____ inches. FINISHED WIDTH IS: _____ inches.

SELLING WEIGHT IS: _____ Ounces per yard

_____ Ounces per square yard

_____ Yards per pound

MILL COST IS: ___ $ ____ . _____ Ounces per yard

___ $ ____ . _____ Ounces per square yard

___ $ ____ . _____ Per yard

_____ Yards per pound

POUNDS OF WARP YARN PER PIECE OF GOODS: _____

POUNDS OF FILLING YARN PER PIECE OF GOODS: _____

SUBMITTING DATE WAS: ____ / ___ / ____ RETURN DATE WAS: ____ / ___ / ____

When you have had an opportunity to examine this fabric, we would greatly appreciate your comments. Thank you very much,

Very truly yours,

_____

TOPIC: STANDARD COTTON FABRICS

In the study of any textile fabric there are certain points that should be kept
in mind. First of all, a fabric should be studied for its raw-material content, its
construction as to type of weave used, and the method of coloring, and then the
type of finish given the material. The warp and filling directions in the cloth,
along with the distinction between the face and back of the material, are important items when dealing with any woven fabric. Yarns and yarn twist also should
be noted in every fabric as a possible means of identification. The fabric should
be studied for its end use or terminal use. When a fabric or a garment is pur-

chased, there are certain points, in sequence, that should be considered—season in which it will be worn, occasion, weight of the fabric, color, the weave used, and the finish. Lastly, is the price right? Some fabrics are sold because of their appealing color; others because of the weave effect or the particular finish. In some materials both the weave and the finish are the main selling points. Thought should be given as to whether the fabric is a single-season or an all-year material for wear. Lastly, the fabric may be ideal for men's wear, women's wear, and children's wear, or for only one of these three outlets.

Most fabrics show the greatest stretch or "give" in the diagonal direction. Stretch in the filling may be very little, or at times rather considerable. In the warp direction of the goods there is practically no stretch at all, or only a very little.

An alphabetical list of the major cotton fabrics follows:

AIRPLANE FABRIC: Plain weave, mercerized, water-repellent fabric which comes in widths of 37, 42, and 60 inches. Textures range around 80-square.

Treated with "dope," which is a solution made from a cellulose acetate base and used to cover wings, fuselage, and tail of airplanes. Also used, in bleached condition, for shirting, collars, and cuffs; in dyed state used for boys' suits, ski wear, and uniform fabrics. Has the best of working properties, launders well, excellent wear.

BALLOON CLOTH: A mechanical fabric made in accordance with government specifications. Made of plain weave, fine combed yarns, and the fabric has the same breaking strength in warp and filling, a very strong fabric. Pick count ranges from 92 by 108 to 116 by 128, while yarns range from 60s to 100s.

When vulcanized it is used for air cells in airships and barrage balloons; also as a covering for light planes and gliders. Commercial uses include artificial flowers, cambric; printed glazed chintz, oil-treated tent fabric, fine shirting and shorts, etc. Easy to manipulate, launders well, excellent service.

BATISTE: Soft, sheer cloth, plain weave, textures range about 88 by 80. Mercerized and made of high-quality yarn. Comes in white, printed, or in solid shades; 50s yarn or better used. Dressgoods and underwear material.

Durable; launders very well; limited in use, however, because of its softness. Light in weight, 14 to 16 yards of cloth to the pound.

BOOK CLOTH: Plain or embossed pyroxylin-treated or starched-and-clay-filled cotton cloth used in book binding. This printcloth sheeting comes in a rather wide range of colors; pyroxylin-treated fabric will have washable or waterproof finishes which do not blister, chip or peel. A starch-filled fabric will lose its color when rubbed with a damp white cloth, but pyroxylin-treated fabric will not be affected.

BROADCLOTH: Fine, mercerized cloth with warp and filling usually of the same size. Used much in men's shirting and in striped effects for women's dressgoods. A genuine staple in the cotton trade; comes in white, dyed, or printed.

Very strong, durable; launders well; takes the dyestuff readily, given mercerized, permanent finish. Texture is always good. Shirts made of broadcloth range from three to fifteen dollars in price.

BUCKRAM: Cheap, low-textured cloth, heavily sized. Used for linings in skirtings, in the millinery and suiting trades, and in bookbinding.

Sturdy in feel, stiff, and boardy.

BUNTING: The name derived from the German *bunt*, meaning "bright." Cotton or worsted yarn is used to make this soft, flimsy, plain-woven cloth. Some of the cloth is made from cotton warp and worsted filling. Cotton bunting is made from heavy cheesecloth and comes in the white or is piece-dyed. Ply yarn may be used in this plain-woven, fairly loose-textured cloth which has a texture ranging from 24 by 36 to 24 by 32. All-worsted bunting is used in making flags.

CALICO: Cheap cotton print, of plain weave, low in texture, coarse, made of carded yarns. Small-design effects when printed.

Service will depend on the quality, which is determined by the texture in warp ends and filling picks.

CAMBRIC: Plain weave, bleached or dyed in the piece. The cheaper grades have a smooth, bright finish. Used for handkerchief linen, children's dresses, slips, underwear, and nightgowns.

Light in weight, well-adapted for sewing work; has good body; is well sized and has a neat finish; launders well.

CANTON FLANNEL: First made in Canton, China, and must be described as made of cotton since the word "flannel" would be misleading, because one would believe the fiber content to be wool. A heavy, warm, strong, absorbent, twill-woven cotton cloth which has a long, soft nap on the back of the goods. Soft-spun filling yarn helps to produce the nap when the material is gigged or napped. Some Canton may be made of plain weave. Uses include interlinings and sleeping garments. Slight nap may be seen on the face of goods. Easy to manipulate, launders easily and well, usually gives good service.

CANVAS: Also known as numbered duck, this plain-weave cloth is rugged and heavy. The ply yarns used give much strength and body to the fabric. From 2-ply to 14-ply yarns are used to make the goods. It is manufactured in the gray state or natural condition, but is also dyed olive drab or khaki for the armed services. Duck and canvas are more or less interchangeable terms today. Uses for canvas include tents, wagon covers, many types of army equipage, sails, mail bags, sacks, conveyor belting.

CHAMBRAY: Plain-weave cloth with warp one color and filling another, usually white. Carded or combed yarns are used. Fabric is smooth, rather lustrous, and medium and heavy grades find use in men's work shirts, while lighter qualities are popular in women's and children's wear. Lightweight fabric, in addition to being made plain, may show stripes, checks, or dobby-designs on the chambray background; these are known as fancies.

Chambray is sturdy, easy to manipulate, attractive, wears very well, launders very satisfactorily, and is popular staple.

CHEESECLOTH: Narrow cheesecloths are under 36 inches wide; wide cheesecloths may be finished up to 55 inches wide. The cloth is loosely woven, thin, light in weight, open in construction. Carded yarns are always used. When the cloth is finished at 36 inches, it is called tobacco cloth.

Textures range from 32 by 32 to 48 by 48. Warp yarns are 28s to 30s, while filling yarns range from 39s to 42s. The cloth runs from 6 to 14 yards to the pound.

In the gray the cloth is used for covering tobacco plants and for tea bags and wiping cloths. Applied finishes include buckram, crinoline, and wigan. Uses of finished cloths include curtains, bedspreads, bandages, bunting, dust cloths, sign cloths, label fabrics, hat linings, surgical gauze, fly nets, theatrical gauze.

CHINTZ: Glazed cotton fabric often printed with gay figures and large flower designs. Named from Hindu word meaning "spotted." There are several types of glaze: the wax glaze and the starched glaze are both produced by use of friction or glazing calenders (will wash out in laundering). The only durable glaze is a resin finish, which will withstand washing or drycleaning. Unglazed chintz is called cretonne. Used for draperies, slip covers. Lately it has been used for summer dresses.

CORDUROY: Material widely used for, among other purposes, breeches, trouserings, slacks, coatings, sport suits or jackets, hunting apparel, slip covers, millinery, aviation coats. The material may be made from any of the major textile fibers. It is in the velvet family of fabrics. It is usually made of one warp and two fillings. One filling weaves tightly to form the body of the material, while the other set of yarn will weave with the warp for a short distance, and then float over the next three or four warp ends. All the interlacings of the pile filling are confined to the same group of warp threads, and the floats are over another group of warp ends so that the face of the fabric has the appearance of a filling rib construction. The back will show a plain-weave formation or a small twill-weave repeat.

After weaving, the back of the cloth is given a coating of glue, after which the floats of the filling pile are cut in the center. The glue is used to prevent the filling from drawing out of the goods during the cutting.

Following cutting, the glue is removed and the face of the material is then subjected to a series of brushing, waxing, and singeing operations. Thus, the filling pile is in the form of a velvet-like cord which runs in the warp direction. Some corduroy is now made with the cut-line effects in both the warp and filling directions.

CREPES—BALANCED, BOX, WARP, FILLING, MATELASSÉ: Lightweight dressgoods with crinkled, crepe, granite, or pebble effect. Crepe yarn and crepe weave used. Comes in white or is printed or dyed. Wide range in price, quality, texture, and finish.

This cloth is generally washable without the effect of crepiness being lost. Does not have to be ironed repeatedly.

CRETONNE: Plain weave, although often made on a twill. It has large printed patterns similar to chintz but is not glazed.

Launders well; used for hangings, furniture covering, and beach wear.

DENIM: This staple cotton cloth is rugged and serviceable, and is recognized by a left-hand twill on the face. Coarse single yarns are used most, but some of the cloth used for dress goods may be of better-quality stock. A 2-up and 1-down or a 3-up and 1-down twill may be used in the weave formation.

Standard denim is made with indigo-blue-dyed warp yarn and a gray or mottled-white filling. It is the most important fabric in the workclothes group and is used for overalls, coats, jumpers, caps. Denim is also popular in dressgoods in the women's wear field and has even been used as evening wear. Popular also in the upholstery and furniture trades.

DIMITY: A thin, shear cotton fabric in which corded stripes or checks may or may not be present in the pattern. Dimity resembles lawn in the white state, and may be vat-printed or dyed. This popular staple is easy to manipulate, launders well, and the quality depends on the yarn and the texture used. Made of combed yarn and finished at 36 inches wide, textures range from 76 by 64 to 130 by 94. There are about nine yards of cloth to the pound. Used for aprons and pinafores, art needle-work, bedspreads, curtains, collar-and-cuff sets, carriage covers, children's dresses, infants' wear, summer dressgoods, waists, and underwear.

DOTTED SWISS: A fabric first made by the cottage hand-loom weavers in and around Saint Gall about 1750. The fabric is still made by some of the descendants of these weavers. The hand-woven cloth has a set width of 32 inches.

There are now several types of the cloth, with varying weaves and pattern effects made at present, from the single and multicolored dot motifs placed regularly and irregularly on the material to combinations of dot effects with yarn-dyed patterns and solid grounds and drawn-thread work, and more intricate motifs and effects.

The hand-loomed fabric is made on a loom which has a swivel attachment to tie in the dots or designs on the back of the cloth. Hence, there is a frequent reference to "hand-tied dots" in conjunction with the dotted swiss. A great deal of the present-day fabric is, of course, made on power looms.

DRILL: A durable fabric of medium weight. Usually three-harness warp-faced twills made with carded sheeting yarn used for construction. Weights may vary somewhat and thread count is low. When dyed may be known as khaki, ticking, silesia, herringbone. This fabric usually is made with left-hand twill effect and is rugged, easy to manipulate, and gives good service.

DUCK: The name "duck" covers a wide range of fabrics. It is the most durable fabric made. A closely woven, heavy material. The most important fabrics in this group are known as number duck, army duck, and flat or ounce duck. Number and army ducks are always of plain weave with medium or heavy ply yarns; army ducks are the lighter. Ounce ducks always have single warp yarns woven in pairs and single or ply filling yarns. Other names for variations of these fabrics are sail duck, belt duck, hose duck, tire duck (such as breaker, cord, chafer), wide and narrow duck, biscuit duck, harvester duck, oil press duck, wagon duck, enameling duck, boot duck, canvas, and so on. Generally of ply yarns in warp and yarns of various sizes and weights in filling.

FALL AND WINTER COTTONS: They are of medium to heavy weight and include corduroy, knitted fabric, tweed, and velveteen. The fall group, medium in weight, and consisting chiefly of tweed and knitwear, come in the dark autumnal colors and shades and can be worn for the so-called between-season weather. The winter group, heavier in weight—corduroy, tweed, and velveteen—are developed for warmth and comfort. These fabrics reflect scientific and style advances since many of them have wash-and-wear finishes, practically all of them are wrinkle-resistant, and their colors and motifs are designed particularly to interpret the mood of the season of the year. The filling-pile fabrics, corduroy and velveteen, have made rapid strides in the last few years and are very popular at the present time. Their weight is a decided asset, and new printing techniques which have been developed have enhanced their popularity and increased sales. Wale variation in corduroy has had a particular appeal to the consumer. Tweed fabrics have good weight and excellent textures, and smart color effects have helped establish their use to a considerable degree. These fabrics with their improved styling afford comfort to the wearer and are materials that will stand up very well in wear and in resistance to abrasion and chafing.

Washing is done in any conventional manner, or the garments may be drycleaned. Dark cottons should not be bleached. Starch is not essential. Drying is done in any conventional way unless the hang-tag states otherwise. Ironing should be done in accordance with the information noted on the tag, since these textured surface fabrics must be handled carefully at all times.

FLANNEL, FLANNELETTE: Heavy, soft material that is given a napped finish. There are several types of flannel. Used for pajamas, nightgowns, pocket lining, quilts, clothing, shirting. Flannelette is made in stripes, plaids, prints.

Launders well and is easy to work with. Nap will come off in the cheaper qualities. Soft filling yarn is used so that nap may be insured.

FRIEZETTE: A cotton fabric of lighter weight than standard frieze made of wool and cotton. The rib effect is the same as in frieze, but the texture is not as wiry or harsh in feel. This converted fabric is piece-dyed in solid colors. The rib or repp effect is obtained by weaving alternately, one end of single or ply-yarn under a regular tension, and one end of singles under a slack tension. Used for upholstery fabric, gives good wear, and comes in inviting colors.

FRISÉ: Sometimes known as cotton frieze, the material is used in upholstery trade. It is usually made with uncut loops and is sometimes styled by shearing the loops at varying heights. Some cloth of this name has appeared on the market with a rayon content in fiber construction. Gives excellent service.

GABARDINE: Fabric with diagonal twill effect made by the use of a 45-degree or a 63-degree twill, either right-hand or left-hand. Dyed in the piece, in yarn form, or kept in the white. Fabric is rugged, may be light, medium, or heavy; very durable, launders and tailors well, may be drycleaned, a compact cloth made with good twist yarn. This natty fabric is used in suiting, dressgoods, play clothes, slacks, uniform fabric, etc.

GINGHAM: Plain weave, medium yarns used; comes in stripes, checks, and plaids; is yarn-dyed or printed; averages about six yards to the pound. Texture is varied and averages about 64 by 66.

Strong, rather stout, substantial, gives good wear; launders well; thinner and lower texture ginghams shrink considerably unless they have been pre-shrunk. Cloth varies from very cheap material to really expensive cloth.

HOLLAND: Also known as shade cloth, this plain-woven cotton or linen fabric is heavily sized or starched and is often given an oil treatment to make it opaque. Used for curtains and shades. Gives good service.

HONEYCOMB WAFFLE: A raised effect is seen in this material, which gives the effect of the cellular comb of the honey bee. The high point on the one side of the material is the low point on the reverse side. Care has to be used in manipulation. Used for draperies, jackets, skirts, women's and children's coats and dresses. Belongs in pique family of fabrics.

TESTING

1. Give two uses of airplane fabric; two uses of balloon cloth.
2. Why is batiste rather limited in use?
3. Define a pile fabric and give an example.
4. Why are fabrics such as book cloth, buckram, and cheesecloth rather low in quality and pick count, and have to have sizing applied to them?
5. Why are chambray, crepe, and dimity, as to construction, considered as variations of the plain weave?
6. Name four types of crepe materials.
7. How does a gingham differ from a clan plaid?
8. What are some outstanding characteristics of flannel?
9. Differentiate between a chintz and a cretonne.
10. List five uses for duck.

TOPIC: STANDARD COTTON FABRICS (continued)

Each fabric seems to have its own characteristics and working properties. Many fabrics are closely related to one another. At times there may be only one main difference when one cloth is compared with another. One may read about a material, hear about it, and actually see and feel it. The real test, however, for knowing fabrics well is to give each one a thorough examination and analysis. Optical inspection, handling the fabric, and learning all you can about it are of great help. However, study should be made of the yarns and the twists in these yarns in both warp and filling. Compactness or looseness of texture should be noted. In addition, all phases of the fabric should be noted as to how it is different from any other fabric, with attention given to the weave, the method of coloring, the weight, the type of finish, and lastly, the use that can be made of the particular cloth.

LAWN: Fine, sheer crisp-finish cloth made of plain weave. Lawn is crisper than voile but not as crisp as organdy. High-grade, high counts of yarn used. Comes in white, dyed or printed, and is made of combed or carded yarns.
    Crisp finish is temporary, durable, and must be starched to bring back crispness. Lawn is given a great variety of finishes. It is easy to cut and sew.

LONGCLOTH: A fine, soft cotton woven of softly twisted yarns. It is similar to nainsook but slightly heavier and with a duller surface finish. So called because it was one of the first cloths to be woven in long rolls. Used chiefly in children's wear, longcloth has the same working properties as nainsook.

MADRAS: Fine cotton shirting that has dyed, woven stripes in warp direction. Thin, closely woven, light in weight. Long staple cotton of good quality is used.

Durable, launders well; wear depends on texture. It is a smart-appearing shirting and commands a good price; very popular staple.

MARQUISETTE: Made on leno or doup weave; gauze fabric. It is light in weight. Comes in white, solid colors, and novelty effects; used for curtains and dress fabrics.

Gives good service for a loosely woven material; launders well. Better qualities are made of choice cotton or glass fibers.

MATELASSÉ, MATELLASSÉ: Figured fabric made on dobby or Jacquard looms. The patterns stand out and give a "pouch" or "quilted" effect to the goods. Comes in colors and in novelty effects. Made in cotton, rayon, silk or wool, the cloth will give good wear, drape well, but must be laundered with utmost care. Matelassé garments are very attractive and, when in vogue, are much in demand.

Matelassé means "mattress" in French, and is derived from an Arabian word meaning "bed." As used in textile weaves, matelassé produces a raised effect by interlacings of the yarn which shows the quilted surface on the fabric. Some of the fabric may have metallic threads worked into the pattern.

MIDDY TWILL: Twill-weave cloth: right- or left-hand twill is used. In the white, it is called middy cloth; in colors, it is called jean cloth. Used for uniform cloth, children's wear.

Very durable; easy to manipulate; launders well; gives good service and withstands wear. Cloth is mercerized or plain.

MONK'S CLOTH: Made of very coarse yarn. A 4-and-4 basket or some similar basket construction is used. Hangings, couch covers, and furniture material are uses of the cloth.

Not easy to sew or manipulate; yarns have a tendency to slide. Cloth may sag. It is a rough, substantial, rather bulky fabric.

MUSLIN: A plain-woven, substantial cotton fabric stronger and heavier than longcloth; only the poorer qualities are sized and the calender-finish effect will disappear after washing. Wide muslin is known as sheeting. It can be given a white-goods finish on print cloth and sheeting or may be pure-starched or back-filled to give a dull or "clothy" finish. Gray print cloths and lightweight sheetings are also known as unbleached muslin.

Fine muslin is soft-finished, mercerized, printed, and made of combed cotton yarn. It comes in unbleached, semibleached, and full bleached, dependent on the use to be made of the goods.

Muslin has many finishes applied to it from the sheeting or muslin gray-goods made ready for finishing—batiste, beetled, cambric, chintz, cretonne, lawn, longcloth, mercerized, plain muslin, nainsook, organdy, percaline, Schreinerized.

The material has many uses—bed sheets and pillow cases, aprons, interlining, lining, pajamas, shirts and shorts, summer dressgoods, house dresses, etc. Easy to manipulate, launders very well, and withstands rough rugged wear. (*See* SHEETING.)

NAINSOOK: Soft, fine fabric, similar to batiste but made of coarser yarns. Light in weight; of plain weave and resembles a soft-finished dimity. English nainsook has soft finish; French cloth has calendered finish.

Lacks full body because of the type of finish; wears well; rather durable; launders well and will retain finish if it has been mercerized.

ORGANDY: Sheer, stiff, transparent plain-weave cloth. Textures range from 72 by 64 up to 84 by 80. Combed yarns always used. Arizona or Egyptian cotton used. White, dyed, or printed. Counts of yarn may be 150s in warp, 100s in filling.

Stiffness is permanent or temporary. Very attractive cloth, but difficult to launder and not practical for daily wear. It has more crispness than lawn, cambric, dimity, or other cloths of the same family grouping. May run twenty yards to the pound. Much of the cloth has the well-known permanent Swiss finish applied to it.

OSNABURG: A coarse cotton cloth, often part waste, of plain weave, medium to heavy in weight, and resembles crash. Converted and used for upholstery, slacks, sportswear and, in the unbleached state, for grain and cement bags. Also serves as the base fabric for cretonne. Named for the city in Germany where first made— Osnabrück.

OXFORD: Plain, basket, or twill weaves are used. There are two yarns which travel as one in the warp, and one filling yarn equal in size to the two warp yarns. Better grades of cloth are mercerized.

Rather heavy cloth which launders well. This shirting fabric has a tendency to soil easily.

PERCALE: Closely woven, plain-weave material. Cloth resembles cambric. Cylindrical yarn is used. Comes in white or is printed. Small, geometrical figures are often seen in the designs.

Launders well, colors are very fast; finish gives a good temporary luster. Material stands up well for wear because of its compact texture. (*See* CALICO, page 70.)

PIQUÉ: Medium-weight or heavy cloth with raised cords that run in the warp direction. Combed or carded yarns used; used for women's and children's wear, shirts, vests, neckwear, collar and cuff sets, infants' coats and bonnets, etc. A popular, smart, dressy fabric.

Very durable; launders well; a rather expensive cotton cloth. This substantial cloth is made on dobby, Jacquard, drop-box and other types of looms; it will retain the rugged characteristics irrespective of the type of loom used.

POLISHED COTTONS: They are characterized by either a high or a subdued surface luster. These sheens are made durable by fixing chemicals (resins) into the fibers after the cloth has been woven on the loom. The goods are than buffed mechanically until the surface develops a deep-seated subdued luster or a high glaze as noted in chintz fabrics. If properly applied and cared for, this gloss or sheen will last for the useful life of the fabric. All durably polished cottons have some wrinkle-resistant qualities; many of them will wash and wear. When cotton is given a durable polished luster, the need for ironing is reduced. Pressing becomes easier and can be done very quickly. The chemical finishes for polished cottons are not heat sensitive. Polished cottons can be laundered in hot water with soap or detergents—which is absolutely necessary to get any fabric thoroughly cleaned.

These cottons can be washed in any normal manner, by machine or by hand, but hard twisting and possible washing machine tangle should be avoided. Any bleach may be used on white polished cottons unless the tag warns against chlorine bleaches; in this case, a perborate bleach should be used. The finish on these fabrics makes starching unnecessary. In drying, for the best results, tumble-dry or hang up while wet to drip-dry. A warm iron is all that is needed in ironing.

PONGEE: A soft, plain-weave cloth which is Schreinerized or mercerized in finishing. It has more picks than ends: 72 by 100. Originally a silk cloth.

Launders well and is durable. Used for slips, dresses, summer office coats, shirting.

POPLIN: From the French *popeline*. It is a staple dressgoods material. The original cloth resembles bombazine, and silk warp and woolen filling were used. In the higher-priced cloth, worsted filling is utilized. Filling yarn is particularly cylindrical as it tends to give the rounded form of rib line, noted in the fabric, in the horizontal direction. The cloth is also made from other major textile fibers. In staple and plain colors, the material may be used for office coats and linings.

Cotton poplin has a more pronounced rib-filling effect than broadcloth. The filling is bulkier than the warp and there are more ends than picks per inch in the material. In the carded poplin the textures vary from 88 by 40 to 112 by 46; combed poplin ranges from 88 by 44 to 116 by 56. The cloth is mercerized and usually chased for high luster. May be bleached or dyed with vat colors; printed poplin is also popular. Heavy poplin is given water-repellent finish for outdoor use; some of the fabric is given suede finish.

This rugged fabric is used for blouses, boys' suits, gowns, draperies, robes and shirting; much uniform fabric is made from the cloth as well.

PRINTCLOTH: Carded cotton cloth made with about the same yarns as cheesecloth but with more warp and filling threads per inch. Most printcloths are made in narrow widths up to 40 inches. It is given a wide range of finishes, thus producing cambric, lawn, longcloth, muslin, printed percale, etc.

Narrow widths begin at 27 inches and the constructions vary from 64 by 60 up to 80 by 92. Yards per pound run from 3.50 to about 7.60. Wide printcloths are also on the market, and they come in widths up to 45 inches. Pick count is from 60 by 48 to 64 by 60. Yards per pound range from 4.65 to about 5.35.

RATINÉ: From the French, meaning "frizzy or fuzzy," the cloth is a loose, plain-woven cloth with a rough, nubby surface effect; one heavy and two fine yarns twisted together at various tensions form the curly, knotty ply-yarn. Cheaper qualities use ordinary yarn as the warp while the filling is made of ratiné yarn. Can be bleached, dyed or printed and is usually given a high-luster or other types of finish. A rough-and-ready fabric that gives good service.

RICE CLOTH: Usually made of cotton yarn, this plain-weave fabric comes in a width of about 41 inches with textures ranging from 56 ends and 60 picks to 40 ends and 22 picks per inch.

The filling is always a ply yarn in which a series of loops or nubs provide the rice-grained effect in the cloth. The nub yarn is plied with a smooth, very cylindrical yarn, about which it is wound. Rice-grained effects in the filling are interspersed at set intervals. Comes in piece-dyed and printed effects.

SATEEN: Heavily mercerized cloth made of twill or satin weave. Glossy finish is outstanding characteristic. Cloth is plain or printed. The term "sateen" implies cotton cloth; "satin" implies silk, acetate, or rayon cloth. Used for linings.

SEERSUCKER: Cotton, rayon, or nylon crepe-stripe effect fabric, made on plain-weave variation, crepe weave. Light in weight. Colored stripes are often used. Uses are in summer clothing, boys' suits, slacks, bedspreads, and slip covers.

Launders very well, not necessary to iron; durable and gives good service and wear. Crepe effect is permanent; a popular knockabout cotton cloth. When made of rayon, fiber content must be declared.

SEERSUCKER GINGHAM: Gingham with crinkled or creped-stripe effects comes in a wide variety of patterns.

SHEETING: Plain-weave, carded or combed cloth which comes in light, medium, and heavy weights. Sheeting for converting purposes is usually about 40 inches wide. There are four types at present:

> 64 by 64 (64-square), usually made from 20s or 21s yarn.
> 68 by 76, made from 25s yarn.
> 84 by 92, made from 30s to 40s yarn.
> 96 by 108, made from 40s yarn, upwards.

Laundries buy sheeting in the following sizes:

> 99″ long by 36″ wide
> 99″ by 72″
> 99″ by 81″
> 108″ by 72″
> 108″ by 81″

Industrial sheeting serves as backing for artificial leather, boot and shoe lining, etc. Sizing is an important item in making good sheeting, since strength, flexibility, stretchless backing, body, durability, and firmness are essential. Today's sheeting is made on high-speed automatic looms which require a careful sizing treatment to insure high production. The size must be such that it can be removed easily in bleaching and other finishing operations after weaving.

Sheeting textures are often lower when compared with some printcloths; warp counts may be heavier than the filling yarns used, or they can be of the same yarn count. Because of its great use in industry, sheeting is now woven any width to meet consumer demands. It comes in the following classifications—coarse, ordinary, lightweight, narrow, soft-filled, and wide. It may be unbleached, semi-bleached, fullbleached, or colored.

The texture or the pick count on sheeting ranges from a "112" count up to a "200" or more count, with the most popular textures being 112, 128, 140, 160, 180, 200, etc.

The texture or the pick count in sheeting includes the number of the warp yarns and the filling yarns added together. For example, a 112 sheeting could be 56-square, 60 by 52, 64 by 48, all numbers of which total 112. A 128 sheeting could be 64-square, or 68 ends and 60 picks, or 72 by 56, or 66 by 62, all of which total 128. A 140 sheeting could be 70-square, 72 by 68, 76 by 64, all of which total 140.

SPRING AND SUMMER COTTONS: They are lightweight, cool fabrics that account for the vast majority of textile sales during warm weather. The sales appeal of these cottons has been enhanced through easy care, appealing finishes, and good styling. Batiste, broadcloth, chambray, poplin, piqué, and a host of comparable fabrics and constructions have wash-and-wear finishes. Organdy, for example, can be made durably crisp in finish. The colors and patterns for spring and summer cottons have been styled particularly to satisfy the consumer and to increase sales. Beneath their attractive new faces is the same dependable cotton fiber that has served so well through thousands of springs and summers. These modern interpretations of 100-per-cent cotton are the acme of perfection when it comes to comfort. They are also endowed with the ability of cotton to withstand thorough and frequent launderings, a quality of great importance when choosing practical warm-weather apparel.

Laundering may be done in any conventional way, by machine or hand. Delicate sheer cottons should be hand-washed. Bleaches may be used on white cottons unless the hang-tag advises otherwise. Cottons with these special finishes need no starch. Untreated cottons may be starched for added body and crispness. Drying may be done in any conventional way. Cottons with special finishes need only a warm iron. Untreated cottons need a hot iron.

TAPESTRY: This picture material, woven tightly or loosely and low in construction, has the design as a part of the actual fabric; it is not embroidered onto the cloth. Tapestry is handwoven or power-loomed. The design and color in hand-woven tapestry is very neat and realistic. Some of the larger tapestries took several generations to complete because of the slow task of working the filling over and under the warp threads according to the motif.

The oriental nations—China, Japan, India, Arabia, Persia and Egypt—were noted for their tapestries. In time, Greece and Rome, as their civilizations progressed, also made tapestries. During the third century, the Copts produced some outstanding pieces. During the Middle Ages, tapestries were woven in European monasteries. The weaving of these fabrics was an important contribution to the world during the Gothic era and the fifteenth century. Religious and moral motifs were used.

The sixteenth and seventeenth centuries were marked by the fine work of the Gobelin factory in France. Many tapestries which are still extant from these times are worth thousands of dollars and adorn museums, salons, and wealthy homes.

The past two centuries have witnessed the rise of the power-loom tapestry, which keeps pace with the hand-woven fabrics. The bulk of tapestry today is made of cotton on power looms, and the fabric is now within the reach of the average consumer. It is very popular for upholstery fabric, wall hangings, other decorative purposes, and some dressgoods.

TERRY CLOTH: This cotton fabric has uncut loops on both sides of the cloth. Woven on a dobby loom with terry arrangement, various sizes of yarns are used in the construction. Terry is also made on a Jacquard loom to form interesting motifs. It may be yarn-dyed in different colors to form attractive patterns. It is bleached, piece-dyed, and even printed for beach wear and bathrobes.

A one-sided terry cloth or Turkish toweling has the pile effect on only one side of the fabric, instead of the usual arrangement.

The principle of terry weaving originated in France in 1841; it was first used in silk fabrics. In 1845, John Bright, an English manufacturer, used the weaves in worsteds, at Rochdale. Samuel Holt was the first to apply the principle to cotton cloth. He was the founder of the American Velvet Co., Paterson, N. J., which was organized to make this type of goods in 1864.

Two sets of warp yarn, and one of filling, are used; one of the warps will form the pile, while the other is the ground warp. The warp which forms the pile is slashed on a separate beam, and is kept very slack in the loom. In weaving, a number of picks, apart from each other, are shot through the shed of the loom before they become a component part of the fabric. Terry may be designed as a 3", 4", 5", or 6" pick arrangement cloth. Thus, the action is controlled by a receding reed which takes care of the loose picks and the fast picks. A fast pick will beat the one or more loose picks into their place in the woven goods, in accordance with the designer's plan. The action of the fast pick will cause the pile or accordion effect created in the material by the slack warp.

The picks, as they are beaten into the material, slide over the taut ground warp, but the friction afforded will pull the pile warp threads so that they will be able to give the final pile effect to the cloth.

TERRY TOWELING, TYPES OF:
These are classified according to weave or design:

CAM-WOVEN, *Plain Terry:* Plain border.

DOBBY-WOVEN: Simple patterns in the border, or all over. Border designs include rope and corduroy borders.

JACQUARD-WOVEN: These have rather elaborate allover motifs or names woven into the goods.

MITCHELINE: This border type has a heavy, distinct, raised or embossed border effect, formed by a stout colored filling yarn; the roving is used sometimes instead of a yarn to obtain the effect. Some of this fabric is made on Jacquard looms.

TEXTURE-DESIGNED: This is made on either a dobby or a Jacquard loom. It has an allover, raised, and recessed motif. The athletic-rib towel, which has raised terry stripes with alternating plain ground stripes, is in this classification; also known as corduroy toweling.

These are classified according to type:

ALL-WHITE PLAIN: This has a plain border, white or colors. It also implies fancy-woven, colored border toweling.

PASTEL-COLOR PLAIN: It is made with dyed filling yarns, white pile yarns.

JACQUARD REVERSIBLE ALLOVER: This features colored pile on one side, with white pile effect on the other side. The borders are plain or fancy. The interchanging white and colored loops form a contrasting motif on each side of the material. .

BATH MAT: This is a heavy type of terry made for bath mats. Coarse ply yarns are used to provide bulkiness, strength, and the weight necessary to give the fabric body and substance.

TYPEWRITER RIBBON FABRIC: The highest constructed cotton fabric made today. Combed Egyptian, Pima, or Sea Island cotton is used, and the thread count ranges from 260-square to 350-square. Some imported British fabric has a texture of 400-square. Yarns range from 70s to 120s. Also made of nylon.

VELVETEEN: A filling pile cloth in which the pile is made by cutting an extra set of filling yarns which weave in a float formation and are woven or bound into the back of the material at intervals by weaving over and under one or more warp ends. (American Society for Testing Materials.)

This low-pile fabric is known as a "cotton-velvet." Comes in all colors, is mercerized, and has a durable texture. This strong fabric can be laundered, will provide warmth, and tailors rather well. Used in children's wear, coats, dresses, hangings, suitings, etc.

VOILE: This sheer cotton cloth is light in weight, soft in feel, and is usually made with cylindrical combed yarn. England produces the best voile from gassed yarns which range from 2/100s to 2/200s. High twist is an important factor to obtain a high-class fabric. Voile drapes very well. It is finished from 40 to 45 inches, and the texture will range between 60 by 74 to 56 by 76.

Voile is used for blouses, children's clothes, bedspreads, draperies, doll cloth, dressgoods, lamp shades, scarfs.

There are four types of fancy voiles: seed, shadow stripe, splash, and piqué. Seed voile uses novelty yarn in the filling; shadow stripes are made by weaving the stripes closer together in the reeding plan than in the body of the cloth. Splash voile is made by using slub yarns which give a splashed effect to the finished goods; piqué voile is made by arranging the reeding plan for the warp in such a way that the goods will resemble genuine piqué. (The fabric is sometimes called piqué dimity.) Flock-printing is often applied to voile dressgoods.

Good-quality voile wears well in spite of the limpness of the cloth. It is rather difficult to handle in manipulation. Has clinging effect. One of the most popular cloths on the market. Cylindrical yarn is asset to cloth. Drapes very well.

WASH-AND-WEAR COTTONS: A comparatively new group of chemically treated cottons that require little or no ironing after being washed and dried by normal home-laundering methods. In most instances, these garments look neat enough to wear without pressing; this is, however, determined by the fastidiousness of the consumer and the end use of the product. There are also cottons with wash-and-wear qualities that are labeled "automatic wash-and-wear," "no-iron," "minimum care," "drip-dry," "little or no ironing required," and with other similar terms. Tags which bear these terms assure the user that the cotton cloth from which the item was made received a special chemical treatment (resin or non-resin) and that the fabric will dry smoothly and free from major wrinkles.

An advantage of wash-and-wear cottons is that they require no special washing temperatures. They are not heat-sensitive and can be washed in hot water and soap or detergents, which are absolutely necessary for true cleanliness. They may be washed in any conventional manner; by hand or by machine.

Chlorine bleaches are safe for white wash-and-wear cottons unless the fabric has a chlorine-retentive finish. In such cases the tag on the garment will warn against the use of chlorine bleaches. Bleach is never needed for colored fabrics. Starch is unnecessary. For the best results in drying, tumble-dry or hand-wet to drip-dry. If a touching-up by ironing is desired, a warm iron is all that is necessary. The ease and the speed of pressing wash-and-wear cottons are very important features of these fabrics and garments.

RADUNER WASH-AND-WEAR MECHANICAL PROCESS: Invented by Dr. Alfred Lauchenauer, of Raduner & Co., A. G., Horn, Switzerland, the process can actually stretch cotton fibers. Licensed to the Sanforized Division of Cluett, Peabody & Company, Inc., New York City, the process reduces substantially the tensile- and tear-strength losses which result from resin and cross-linking treatment of cotton for both durable press and wash-and-wear. The treatment can be used even on lightweight, sheer cottons such as batiste, organdy, and voile. Uses of the process include wash-and-wear quality in sheer blouses, sleepwear, light print dresses, curtains, and handkerchiefs.

This micro-stretching machine has a cost of around $20,000, and it is capable of treating cotton cloth already treated by one of the several chemical resins with a minimum of 5 per cent from the original dimensions. Deterioration of fabric that may be caused by the chemicals applied to fabrics is prevented by the treatment. Since wash-and-wear came into vogue a few years ago, the fabrics have been made with a content of cotton and polyester fibers, with the latter acting as a bolster or stimulant to the fabric because of the trouble encountered from resins on the cotton in these materials. Thus it is now possible to eliminate manmade fibers in the fabric content in lighter-weight fabrics, with the heavier cloths using a decreased content of polyester or comparable fibers. The machine used is about the size of an upright piano.

WIGAN: A cotton cloth that is firm, starched, plain-calender finished, and devoid of luster. Usually dyed black, gray, or brown and converted from lightweight sheeting or printcloth. Used chiefly as interlining for men's and boys' clothing to give body and substance to the garments. Named for village of this name in England.

WRINKLE-RESISTANT COTTONS: The term "wrinkle-resistant" on a tag identifies a group of modern cottons which have been treated chemically to maintain a smooth appearance. They wrinkle less than untreated cottons. Wrinkles that might occur hang out overnight. There is only a slight degree of difference between these cottons and those termed "wash-and-wear." Wrinkle-resistant cottons generally need some pressing after laundering, but the amount of ironing needed is so greatly reduced, and can be done so easily and quickly, that these cottons offer major time-saving advantages as well as lasting neatness. Wrinkle resistance is achieved by passing the cotton cloth through a chemical bath which contains a resin. The material is then baked in heat chambers to fix the chemicals into the fibers in the yarn in the fabric. This, in a sense, gives each fiber a "memory," so that when creased or bent it "remembers" to return to its original shape, thus smoothing out the wrinkles.

These cottons are laundered in the conventional manner, by machine or hand. Their finishes are not heat-sensitive and will not be damaged by hot water or detergents. Dryclean if desired or necessary.

The tag on the garment should be read carefully before bleaching. Use a perborate-type bleach on white garments labeled "Do Not Use Chlorine Bleaches." Starch is never needed. In drying, for best results, tumble-dry or hang-up while wet to drip-dry. A warm iron is all that is needed to quickly press the cottons in this group.

TESTING
50 points

1. Name five fabrics that could be called sheer materials.
2. Why may cloths such as lawn, longcloth, dimity, nainsook, organdy, and voile be classed as belonging to the same family of fabrics?
3. Why is marquisette made on a leno or doup weave?
4. Why should it be possible for marquisette and monk's cloth, two vastly different types of fabrics, to have the same uses as curtaining and hangings?
5. What is a characteristic noted in oxford shirting fabric?
6. How is the pick count or fabric texture of sheeting figured?
7. Name two types of terry toweling.
8. Why is velveteen sometimes called a "cotton-velvet"?
9. Name five fabrics made from derivation of the plain weave.
10. In what respects are calico and percale similar to each other?

TRUE-FALSE QUESTIONS
50 points

1. _____ Voile is given a semi-crisp finish.
2. _____ Canton flannel is made of either cotton or wool yarn.
3. _____ Balanced, box, warp, filling, and matelassé should remind you of crepe material.
4. _____ Denim is recognized by its left-hand twill weave on face of cloth.
5. _____ Duck is the most durable cotton fabric made today.
6. _____ Frisé is sometimes called cotton frieze.
7. _____ Gabardine is made only in a 45-degree twill weave.
8. _____ A pouch- or quilted effect is characteristic of matelassé.
9. _____ Piqué is made from only carded cotton yarns.
10. _____ A 140 sheeting always has 70 ends and 70 picks per inch in texture.

TOPIC: Examination on Standard Cotton Fabrics

IDENTIFICATION QUESTIONS   20 points

1. Identify five sheer fabrics in this group: Monk's cloth, piqué, batiste, drill, dimity, seersucker, organdy, voile, sateen, cambric, duck.
2. Name three shirting fabrics in this group: Airplane fabric, ratiné, madras, marquisette, denim, broadcloth, percale, waffle piqué.
3. Identify two fabrics made with a leno or doup weave: Calico, seersucker, curtaining, voile, gingham, marquisette, poplin, repp, broadcloth.
4. Identify five flat-surface materials: Bouclé, ratiné, chintz, dotted swiss, piqué, Bedford cord, chambray, drill, nainsook, cretonne, terry.
5. Identify five uneven-surface effect fabrics: Gabardine, oxford shirting, velveteen, crepe, corduroy, bouclé, osnaburg, ratiné, bird's-eye piqué.

TRUE-FALSE QUESTIONS   25 points

1. _____ All muslin is bleached.
2. _____ Voile has a rather crisp finish.
3. _____ Dotted swiss may have sprigged designs in the fabric.
4. _____ Cambric is made with a plain weave.
5. _____ Carded or combed yarns may be used to make chambray.
6. _____ Calico may be classed as an expensive cotton print.
7. _____ Batiste is a soft, sheer, satin weave fabric with a texture of about 80 by 80.
8. _____ The five types of crepe are balanced, box, warp, filling, and matelassé.
9. _____ Dimity may be made with corded stripes or check effects.
10. _____ Woven dots in dotted swiss may be woven in by means of lappet warp, in the loom.
11. _____ Gabardine is made only on a 45-degree twill weave.
12. _____ Gabardine may be dyed in the yarn form, the piece form, or kept in the white.
13. _____ Gingham is an example of a stock-dyed material.
14. _____ Broadcloth is usually a mercerized fabric.
15. _____ The crispness in lawn is temporary, generally speaking.
16. _____ Middy twill may be made of right-hand or left-hand twill.
17. _____ Monk's cloth is always made with a twill weave.
18. _____ Nainsook is a cotton cloth with much body and substance in it.
19. _____ Carded yarns only are used to make organdy.
20. _____ Oxford shirting is noted for its ability to shed the dirt.
21. _____ Percale is always dyed a solid shade.
22. _____ Pongee usually has more picks than ends in the construction.
23. _____ Voile is used only as underwear fabric.
24. _____ Plissé and seersucker have about the same surface finish.
25. _____ Sateen usually has a dull finish.

COMPLETION-TYPE QUESTIONS   25 points

1. Book cloth is a _____ sized material.
2. _____ is a feature of buckram.
3. Chambray is identified by _____.
4. _____ is important on a flannel.
5. Gabardine is made on a _____ weave.
6. Holland is used as _____ material.

7. The highest-textured cotton material is _____.
8. Organdy is recognized by its _____.
9. Corduroy has the rib or cord effect running in the _____ direction.
10. Chintz is identified by its _____ finish.
11. Osnaburg is the gray-goods cloth for _____.
12. Denim is usually made with _____ twill weave.
13. Marquisette is made on a _____ weave.
14. Monk's cloth is made with a _____ weave.
15. Ratiné is recognized by its _____ effect.
16. Velveteen is often referred to as a _____.
17. Seersucker does not have to be _____ when laundered.
18. Sateen is made with a _____ weave.
19. Another name for Turkish toweling is _____.
20. Percale has a _____ texture than organdy.
21. Poplin is identified by its _____ filling.
22. Cretonne is usually made on _____ weave.
23. Oxford cloth is used as a _____ fabric.
24. Wigan is used in the manufacture of _____.
25. Another name for waffle cloth is _____.

IDENTIFICATION QUESTIONS   30 points

In each of the following questions, *one of the fabric names is out of place.* Place the number before the incorrect fabric on the blank line provided for at left of this page:

1. _____ 1. Drill. 2. Muslin. 3. Chintz. 4. Printcloth. 5. Cheesecloth.
2. _____ 1. Honeycomb waffle. 2. Gingham. 3. Chambray. 4. Plaid. 5. Tartan.
3. _____ 1. Denim. 2. Matelassé. 3. Crepe. 4. Embossed. 5. Seersucker.
4. _____ 1. Calico. 2. Percale. 3. Buckram. 4. Poplin. 5. Oxford.
5. _____ 1. Voile. 2. Terry. 3. Velveteen. 4. Turkish toweling.
6. _____ 1. Damask. 2. Brocade. 3. Broadcloth. 4. Jacquard.
7. _____ 1. Madras shirting. 2. Poplin. 3. Cretonne. 4. Broadcloth. 5. Chambray.
8. _____ 1. Lawn. 2. Longcloth. 3. Organdy. 4. Voile. 5. Sateen fabric.
9. _____ 1. Marquisette. 2. Leno-woven cloth. 3. Piqué. 4. Doup-woven cloth.
10. _____ 1. Flannel. 2. Dotted swiss. 3. Piqué. 4. Lawn. 5. Voile. 6. Crepe.
11. _____ 1. Denim. 2. Duck. 3. Gabardine. 4. Drillcloth. 5. Twillcloth.
12. _____ 1. Chintz. 2. Cretonne. 3. Glazed. 4. Terry. 5. Holland shade cloth.
13. _____ 1. Frieze. 2. Frizette. 3. Ratiné. 4. Organdy. 5. Matelassé.
14. _____ 1. Drillcloth. 2. Canvas. 3. Duck. 4. Wigan. 5. Batiste.
15. _____ 1. Broadcloth. 2. Poplin. 3. Chambray. 4. Oxford. 5. Bunting.

Part 1—Unit 12

TOPIC: THE HISTORY, PROPERTIES, AND CHARACTERISTICS OF FLAX AND LINEN

Linen fiber, obtained from the flax plant, is known as a vegetable bast fiber. The fiber burns like cotton but at a slower rate; it is cellulosic in nature. Linen is the oldest fiber known to mankind, and many references are made to it in the Bible. Over four thousand years ago it was established as a source of industry in Egypt; extant mummies from Egypt are encased in linen fabric. Phoenicians from Sidon and Tyre, sailing westward, are said to have introduced flax raising into Ireland many centuries ago. Today linen and Ireland still have much in common, since the best workmanship is found there, much of it being done in

Courtesy: *Elliott & Nelson, Inc., N. Y. C.; Irish Linen Guild*

Pulling flax
Pool retting
Drying

Courtesy: Elliott & Nelson, Inc., N. Y. C.; Irish Linen Guild

Weaving linen damask
Crofting—sun-bleaching linen

parochial schools and convents. Manipulation of linen is usually a part of the curriculum in the schools of Ireland.

About 1700, Louis Crommelin, a Huguenot weaver from France, came to Ireland by way of England. This genius in flax and linen saw the opportunity there for the development of flax raising and the manipulation of linen. Soil, climatic conditions, and a plentiful supply of workers were the considerations that persuaded him to settle in Ireland, revive the lagging industry, and make the industry a really profitable one. He is considered to be the founder of the linen industry there, as well as instrumental in other European nations' soon taking to raising flax. He developed new techniques in processing flax as well as producing larger acreage yields. His fame and his methods soon spread, and before the end of the century Belgium, which had had a flax-linen industry for centuries, began revitalizing its sources and resources. The best retted flax in the world comes from Belgium along the famous Lys River, which contains chemicals that no other water stream seems to possess. The center of the industry in Belgium is in and around the venerable city of Courtrai. Other flax countries today include Holland, France, China, India, Japan, Asia Minor, and South Africa. Russia produces three-quarters of the world supply, but its flax is the poorest in quality, especially for the better types of fabrics.

Flax is also raised in the United States, not for fabric, but for the linseed oil and meal. The industry centers chiefly in the northwestern area of this country. Oregon is the leading flax state in the Union, with Washington, and areas along the Canadian border to Wisconsin, raising some of the flax. Kentucky is also a flax state.

Much care and attention must be given in planting and raising flax. The seeds are planted close together so that the stems will grow tall and thereby insure long fibers which will be smooth and lintless. Cheap and plentiful labor is a requisite to growing flax.

Linen, known as the "cloth of kings," is still the pride of the future bride in building up her hope chest. Her linens are a mark of distinction in a social way for entertaining guests in the home. She may be judged by her guests from the "type of table she sets," her tablecloth and napkins setting off the dining table.

Linen, because of its absorptive properties, is used for summer wear, "heel-and-toe" in men's socks, toweling, crease-resistant fabrics, dress linen, doilies, and huckaback toweling.

Properties and Characteristics of Linen

1. Plant source; dead fiber.
2. Smoothness and lintlessness keep the finished product, linen, from soiling as easily as many other fabrics.
3. A coarse-pored fiber that takes up moisture rapidly, thereby making the fiber very absorbent.
4. Property of absorbency and its ability to give off moisture rapidly by evaporation make linen a "cool" fiber or fabric.
5. A sanitary fiber, since flax is a poor breeding ground for germs.
6. Boiling water, hot sun, and soap do not affect linen.
7. A hot iron can be used on it.
8. Microscopic view somewhat resembles bamboo.
9. May be difficult to dye evenly.
10. Stronger when wet—like cotton. Linen is stronger than all other vegetable fibers.

11. Has about 20 per cent natural impurities.
12. Chemically, linen consists of cellulose.
13. There are two types of fibers: those over 10 inches long are called "line"; those under 10 inches, "tow."
14. Linens should be dried in the sun, if possible; hot drying makes the fabric rather limp.
15. Yarns may not be even in diameter.
16. Cools by rapid evaporation of water.
17. Odor of burning paper when burned.
18. Bleached with chlorine or peroxide; may be weakened if not carefully bleached.
19. Turns yellowish in caustic soda.
20. Has natural luster, is nonelastic, shrinks unless pre-shrunk.
21. May be finished with a kidskin feel, which is obtained by beetling.
22. Launders well; may be made crease-resistant.
23. Considered an expensive fiber.
24. Excellent tensile strength.
25. Known as the "cloth of kings" and the "fabric of excellence."

Distinction Between Linen and Cotton

These two cellulosic fibers have much in common, and a burning test to distinguish between them is not valid. Both fibers when fully purified and bleached are cellulosic in nature. Chemical tests are not always satisfactory in determining the distinction between them. A microscopic test is the best one to use when working with these fibers. Cotton is a flat ribbon-like fiber, highly twisted; linen will show a bamboo-like structure.

Fiber length may be considered a test, but with limitations. If the fibers are over 2 inches long, chances are the fiber is linen; if less than 2 inches long, they may be either cotton or linen.

FLAX

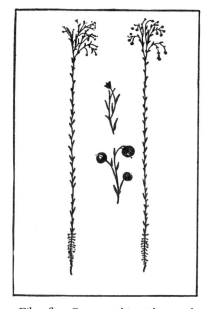

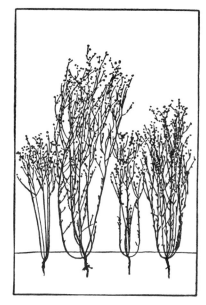

Fiber flax. Compare this with growth of seed flax.

Seed flax

In the fiber-twisting test, a fiber is wetted and held toward the observer. The tip of a cotton fiber turns counter-clockwise; linen turns clockwise. Yarn in a linen fabric is rather irregular.

Cotton Is Unlike Flax or Linen in the Following:

COTTON	LINEN
Absorbs moisture slowly.	Absorbs moisture rapidly.
Less sensitive to chemicals.	Sensitive to chemicals.
Short fiber—½ inch to 2 inches.	Long fiber—few inches to about 36 inches.
Soils rather easily; fuzziness.	No fuzziness; does not soil quickly.
Soft fiber.	Has a natural stiffness.
Dull fiber.	Has a natural luster.
Moisture content of about 7 per cent.	Moisture content will vary; from 8 per cent upward depending on conditions.
Dyes readily.	Care should be exercised in dyeing at all times.
Remains white in caustic soda.	Turns yellowish in caustic-soda bath.

Wet Tests to Distinguish Linen from Cotton

OLIVE OIL TEST: Place a drop of olive oil on a sample of fabric. Blot in and place over a dark background. If the fabric appears translucent, it is linen; if opaque, it is cotton.

MAGENTA TEST: If the sample has been dyed, the color must be removed. Place the sample in a 1-per-cent alcoholic solution of magenta, a red dye. Remove the sample and rinse well with water. If the color washes out, the cloth is cotton; if it remains pink or red, it is linen. It is the pectin in the linen which acts as a mordant for the dye.

ANILINE-RED TEST: A sample of cotton and one of linen are immersed in a light alcoholic solution of aniline red for a short time. The samples are then washed; then a two-hour immersion in a caustic ammonia bath is given. Linen will take on a dark-red shade; the cotton will not be affected.

TESTING   50 points

1. To about what height does flax grow?
2. Name five flax-raising countries.
3. How did Ireland become interested in raising and processing flax?
4. Why do you think linen is called the "cloth of kings"?
5. What does the linen fiber reveal under the microscope?
6. Describe the wet test to distinguish between linen and cotton.
7. Why does Belgium produce the best retted linen fiber?
8. List five differences between linen and cotton.
9. What state is the "linen state" in the United States?
10. Name ten properties of linen fiber or fabric.
11. Why might linen be called the "fabric of excellence"?
12. Which fiber, linen or cotton, absorbs water more quickly?
13. Define line; tow.
14. What is the effect of caustic soda on linen and cotton?

COMPARATIVE EXAMINATION ON LINEN AND COTTON   50 points

The answers to these questions are "cotton" or "linen." Place your answer on the blank line provided to the left of this page:

1. _____ Which fiber is more flexible?
2. _____ Which has a moisture content of about 7 per cent?
3. _____ Which is more absorptive?

4. _____ Which has more natural luster?
5. _____ Which is considered to be the older fiber?
6. _____ Which is easier to spin into yarn?
7. _____ In which is the seed the more important?
8. _____ Belgium and Ireland are closely associated with which fiber?
9. _____ Which fiber is more important to the United States?
10. _____ Which fiber turns yellowish in caustic soda?
11. _____ Which one is opaque on completion of an olive-oil test?
12. _____ In which does the color wash out in a magenta-dye test?
13. _____ Which is not affected in an aniline-red test?
14. _____ Which has a "kidskin feel" from beetling treatment?
15. _____ Which shows convolutions clockwise in a fiber-wet test?

TOPIC: PROCESSING FLAX INTO LINEN

Because of the nature of flax, there is more difficulty in obtaining the flax fibers than cotton fibers. The latter are picked in boll form from the pod either by hand or mechanical picker. To insure long fibers with as little damage done to them as possible, the flax stalks, from 35 inches to about 40 inches in height, are pulled from the ground, roots included.

FLAX RAISING AND LINEN MANUFACTURE

PLANTING, GROWING, AND PULLING: Preparation of the soil, planting, and cultivation are done with care. After the soil has been prepared, planting is done in the spring the same as for corn, wheat, or rye. Seeds are set close together to insure well-grouped stalks, an advantage at pulling time. Late July and August are the harvesting months. Pulling is done when the stalks turn yellow at the base, and the seeds change color from green to light brown. As noted, the stalks are pulled out of the ground by the roots; this conserves fibers.

RIPPLING: The removal of the seeds and leaves from the dried flax, which is in long stalks of flax straw.

BUNDLE TIES: The flax is tied into bundles and is allowed to dry and age in the sun.

RETTING: Rotting of the stalk except the fibers, by various methods:

DEW RETTING: Retting the flax by exposure in fields to the action of dew and sunlight; requires from four·to six weeks' time. This natural method of retting gives uneven results but provides the best wear. Russia uses this method.

POOL RETTING: This is the most rapid natural retting method because of the excess bacteria in stagnant water, which speeds up the fermentation. Requires about one week's time. The flax is placed in crates, and crate-weights are used to insure total immersion of the fibers in the murky water.

STREAM RETTING: Similar to pool retting, except that the flax is placed in a flowing stream, which does not have as many bacteria, so essential in good retting. The Lys River in Belgium gives the best results in the world. The time required is from five to fifteen days. Courtrai, the famous "flax city," is on this river.

TANK RETTING: This is done in Ireland. It is the best and the quickest method of retting, taking only about three days. Finer fiber results from this method. Another feature is that controlled temperature of the plain water used is always possible; the retting may be done at any time of the year.

CHEMICAL RETTING: This method has not yet proved to be a genuinely satisfactory method. Retting is brought about by the action of various chemicals such as soda ash, caustic soda, oxalic acid. Action is violent and uncontrollable. Much effort is being made to perfect and promote chemical retting.

BREAKING: Following retting, the bundles of flax are removed from the water or raked from the ground. Drying follows. The stalks are subjected to a breaking action which breaks the rotted part of the stem from the flax fiber.

SCUTCHING: This machine gives more rigorous treatment to the flax than the breaking rollers. The turbine machines which are used have steel rollers attached to revolving cylinders that beat out more of the woody portions of the fiber straw. The straw is fed automatically from the breaker to the turbine scutcher. The stock then comes from the machine practically clear of shives and other woody waste. A further breaking and separating of the rotted flax stem from the linen fibers follows.

HACKLING, COMBING: This combing action removes any remaining impurities and separates short fiber "tow" from the longer, choicer fiber "line." This hand-manipulated operation consists of throwing a handful of scutched fibers over iron combs. The fibers are pulled through the teeth of the combs, each of which, in succession, has a progressively increasing number of teeth per unit. Several hacklings may be given the fibers. The fibers are now ready for spinning into yarn.

SPINNING: This is the converting of the flax fibers into linen yarn; may be done wet or dry, with the former method providing the better and finer yarn.

Wet spinning is done in a room with a temperature of about 120° F.; this prevents breakages, insures fine, even, flexible yarn. Dry spinning is done under approximately the same conditions as cotton spinning.

MANUFACTURE OF LINEN FABRIC: The weaving of cloth on the loom—hand or power— by interlacing of the warp and the filling threads. Plain goods, or those made with stripes or checks, are made on ordinary plain looms. Material such as tablecloths and napkins are woven on Jacquard looms when motifs, intricate or otherwise, may be desired.

FINISHING LINEN FABRIC: Bleaching, calendering, lustering, and pressing are the major treatments, along with beetling, which is a very popular and vital treatment for the finish of the goods.

BEETLING provides a flattened appearance on fabric by means of a series of beetlers or fallers. The spaces between warp and filling in the fabric are covered up, tending to produce a high sheen or glasslike finish. As the cloth is wound slowly on a roller, the fallers or hammers strike the top layer of the goods with great force and give the material its characteristic thready finish. There is also a sort of moiré effect observed on the goods by the beating of the material in layer form. Linens will show this effect rather well. It is the beetling that gives the fabric its "kidskin feel."

Beetling effects are often simulated on cottons and fabrics made of cotton and linen in the lower price range. Known as a "chased finish," from four to sixteen layers of fabric are "threaded" so that they will pass between the chasing rollers of the machine at the one time. The goods will have a deep-grained luster rather than a top shine, unlike the flat, shiny appearance noted in calender-finished material. This imitation beetled finish is not permanent, and disappears with laundering.

TOPIC: STANDARD LINEN FABRICS

Department stores since their inception have always featured a linen department. They always seem to do a good business. Specialty shops in linen wares also flourish provided they stock good fabrics. Those that do not—and there have been many—soon fall by the wayside. The so-called fly-by-night linen store which is in business for only a short time is peculiar to most large cities. These stores are always cropping up here and there for their short span of life. Stores of this type are always found out and come under the ban of the Federal Trade Commission. The Better Business Bureau, Inc., and, at times, the police, will step in on a report that the shop is selling inferior or counterfeit items. Simulations of genuine linens are rampant and the labeling of the goods is often fraudulent, merely to catch the eye of the unwary consumer.

Uses for linen are many, and include blouses, damasks, dusters, dresses, evening wear, gloves, handbags, handkerchiefs, headgear, jackets, lingerie, playsuits, separate skirts, sheets and pillow cases, shoes, shorts, suits, tablecloths and napkins.

Crease-resistant finishes can now be applied to linen, and the value of using linen that has been pre-shrunk should not be overlooked.

"Over-filled or over-wefted linens" are those fabrics in which there are more filling picks than warp ends per inch in the fabric.

"Shire hems" have one side of the drawn threads hemstitched; "spoke hems" are fabrics in which both sides have been hemstitched. Screen or stencil printing is unexcelled for producing attractive color motifs on linen.

An alphabetical listing of standard linen fabrics follows:

ART LINEN: Plain weave, cylindrical yarn, very soft finish. Bleached or unbleached sheeting may be used for this well-known needlework base fabric from which it is easy "to draw the yarns."

BANDLE: A narrow, coarse, homespun linen made on hand looms in Ireland.

BIRD'S-EYE LINEN: Made of novelty twill and small diamond weaves that resemble the eyes of birds. Cloth is also known as diaper material. Texture is about 66 by 46.
    Used for reversible toweling, has good absorptive properties; durable and launders well. Loosely twisted filling aids properties of absorption. Material must be free from foreign matter.

BUTCHER'S LINEN: Plain-weave, strong, stiff, substantial fabric. Term often used incorrectly in many types of cloths, and unless this material is marked Pure Linen, one may be sure that it does not contain any linen. Genuine fabric is bleached to the white, calendered, and laundered. Sheds the dirt, launders well, is durable, and gives splendid wear. When buying fabrics of this type, be sure to read the label. Linen-textured rayon, a popular dressgoods fabric, does not contain linen fibers.

CAMBRIC: Cloth may be sheer or coarse; of plain weave. Known also as handkerchief linen. Used also for dressgoods.
    If fairly good quality is used, fabric will give excellent wear and service. Material is sized and gives neat appearance after laundering.
    Cotton cambric is made from printcloth or lightweight sheeting construction. It is given special sizing treatment and a calender finish.

CANVAS: There are several fabrics in this category: (1) Open-mesh canvas is used for embroidery; made of hard-twisted yarn, the cloth is very durable, and the most popular type is known as Java canvas. (2) Close-woven canvas is made from hard-twisted yarn in plain-weave construction; comes in various weights, and finishes range from the heavily-sized varieties to soft effects.

CHECKS: The ordinary plain colored checks used for aprons, linen dressgoods, and tablecloths. The checks usually are 8 by 8, 12 by 12, or 16 by 16.

DAMASK: A single damask is made on a five-shaft satin weave; double damask is made on an eight-end satin construction. All damask is made on Jacquard looms.
    This reversible fabric is very durable; the higher the texture, the better will be

the quality. Damask will launder well, retain its luster, and may be all linen, all cotton, or a union material—say cotton warp and linen filling. The smaller motifs give the greater strength to the goods because of shorter float yarns. More luster is possible on the double type because of longer yarn floats, but the single-type damask usually gives longer wear. Used for coverings, doilies, curtains, guest towels, napkins, runners, and tablecloths.

DRESS LINEN: Plain weave; quality depends much on yarn and texture used. Comes in white, or is dyed or printed. Popular for summer wear.
Launders well, wrinkles unless processed, serviceable, durable, gives cool appearance to the wearer.

FISHEYE: Large diamond effect that is similar in shape to the eye of a fish. Comparable with the smaller pattern noted in bird's-eye, and used for the same purposes. Durable, has good absorptive properties, is reversible.

GLASS TOWELING: Plain-weave, highly twisted yarns with red or blue stripes or checks. Other color combinations may be used. Has no fuzziness or protruding fibers, launders well and gives good wear.

HUCKABACK, HUCK: Cloth has a honeycomb effect; the filling yarns are slackly twisted to aid absorption. Material is heavy. This toweling often has the name of a hotel, school, etc., woven through the center for recognition and to establish ownership. In white or colors. Very absorbent, durable, serviceable for towels, and will withstand rough use.

LINEN RUG, FLAX RUG: Reversible, plain-woven, all-flax covering used for narrow areas such as hallways. Ideal for summer.

LINEN-TEXTURED RAYON: A large and important category of rayon fabrics having the distinctive textures of linens. These range from sheer handkerchief-linen texture to heavier, rougher butcher-linen texture. Usually plain-weave. Used in lighter weight for handkerchiefs, women's and children's dresses, tablecloths, towels, sheets, pillowcases; heavier weights for summer coats, suits, sportswear.

LINENS, HOUSEHOLD SIZES OF:
Breakfast cloth is from 45″ x 45″ to 63″ x 80″; napkins, 13″ x 13″.
Luncheon cloth is 54″ x 54″; runners, 18″ x 72″; doilies, 12″ x 18″; napkins, 20″ x 20″.
Bridge cloth is 36″ x 36″; napkins, 13″ x 14″.
Dinner cloth is from 72″ x 90″ to 72″ x 126″; napkins, from 16″ x 16″ to 26″ x 26″.
Buffet runner is 18″ x 72″; center cloth, 16″ x 24″; sides, 12″ x 18″; side cloth, 12″ x 18″.
Tea-wagon cloth is from 14″ x 20″ to 16″ x 24″.
Standard double-bed linen with box mattress is 90″ wide x 108″ long.
Standard double-bed linen is 81″ wide x 108″ long.
Three-quarter-bed linen is 72″ wide x 108″ long.
Single-bed linen is 63″ wide x 108″ long.
Cot linen is 52″ wide x 108″ long.

LINEN STRAW: Any closely braided or woven straw, fine in texture, which is given a finish to simulate finished linen fabric.

LINEN: An unbleached linen lining fabric made in France.

LINON À JOUR: French for a gauze-like linen fabric used as dressgoods.

MESH: Open-mesh fabric that is very strong and durable, and washes easily and well. Ideal for children's clothes, men's shirts, and summerwear garments.

NON-CRUSHABLE LINEN: Plain-weave cloth with highly twisted filling yarn or finished with resin to enhance elasticity. Has about the same uses as dress linen. Serviceable, durable, does not wrinkle, launders well.

OATMEAL CLOTH: Soft, heavy cloth with a crepe or pebbled effect that resembles oatmeal paper. Strong, durable, launders well.

PILLOWCASE LINEN: Plain weave, high count, good texture, bleached. Yarn is very smooth and has high count of turns of twist per inch.

Launders easily and well, sheds dirt, has cool feel and appearance, is strong and durable. Very desirable cloth.

ROUGHS: Lightweight linen canvas used as suit lining in the apparel trades; sold chiefly in brown or natural shades. See WIGAN.

SIMULATED LINEN FINISH: Applied to cotton fabric, it is obtained by beetling to give a soft, full, kidskin type of hand. Mercerizing is also given the cloth, which requires special sizings and pressings so as to flatten out the fabric to produce the effect. Rays of light are reflected by the finish, which is not permanent, and often not durable.

STAMPED LINENS: Usually rather small linen products that have been embroidered or screen-printed to enhance the material.

EXAMINATION ON FLAX AND LINEN

TRUE-FALSE QUESTIONS   30 points

1. _____ Removal of seeds and leaves from stalks is called bundling.
2. _____ Retting of flax is done only in water streams.
3. _____ Scutching is an advanced form of breaking.
4. _____ Hackling and combing may be considered to be the same treatment.
5. _____ Wet spinning of linen into yarn is the same as spinning cotton.
6. _____ All linen fabric is made on plain or ordinary looms.
7. _____ Calendering will add luster to the fabric given this treatment.
8. _____ A chased finish on linen is always permanent.
9. _____ Beetling is a chemical finish on linen.
10. _____ Linens may show a watermarked or moiré effect from beetling.
11. _____ Single damask is made on a five-end satin weave.
12. _____ "Spoke hems" means both sides of the cloth hemstitched.
13. _____ The opposite of a "spoke hem" is "over-wefted."
14. _____ It is not necessary to pre-shrink linen before use.
15. _____ The linen fiber is noted for its even diameter.

DESCRIPTION QUESTIONS   50 points

Give a brief, concise description of any five of the following fabrics:

Art linen	Cambric	Linen-textured rayon
Bird's-eye linen	Canvas	Oatmeal cloth
Butcher's linen	Damask	Pillowcase linen

MATCHING QUESTIONS   20 points

Place your choice from the second column of words on the blank line before the first column of words wherever you believe there is a definite relationship:

1. _____ Tow   1. Center of flax industry in Belgium
2. _____ Oregon   2. Homespun linen from Ireland
3. _____ Russia   3. Butcher's linen fabric
4. _____ Over-filled cloth   4. Men's summer shirting fabric
5. _____ Bandle   5. Under ten inches long
6. _____ Line   6. Flax-raising state
7. _____ Courtrai   7. Greatest producer of flax
8. _____ A misnomer   8. More picks than warp ends
9. _____ Mesh linen   9. A base fabric for embroidery
10. _____ Java canvas   10. Over ten inches long

TOPIC: OTHER VEGETABLE FIBERS USED IN TEXTILES

There are three types of vegetable fibers: seed fiber such as cotton; stalk fiber, as flax; leaf fiber, represented by pineapple fiber. These fibers have many uses: jute for carpet backing abaca and hemp in cordage and twine; henequin and sisal in binder twine; the pineapple fiber in Pina cloth; various straws for hats and mattings. Practically all of them are limited in quantity because of insufficient supply, high costs in raising and processing, scarcity of labor, inaccessibility to markets, etc. These fibers include the following:

Ramie

Also known as Rhea and China Grass, it belongs to the stingless nettle group, and there are two varieties of the plant. The first grows in tropical climates and is called Rhea or China Grass; the second is raised in temperate climates and is known as straight China Grass. Commercially, all are about the same.

The plant has a height of four to six feet in China and Japan, where the cultivation of it is fostered. Great efforts are being put forth in Florida to place the fiber in production. The fiber is strong, white, silken in luster. The cost of production, scarcity of labor, and other difficulties have hindered the raising of the fiber in many sections of the world.

Ramie is a fine fiber and ranks high in tensile strength and elasticity; however, the difficulty encountered in obtaining the fiber from the plant impedes its progress as a leading textile fiber.

Decortication is the name given to the process of obtaining the fiber from the plant. Retting cannot be resorted to, since the mechanical treatments necessary have not reached the stage of perfection. Most treatments and operations necessary to ramie are done by hand, thereby increasing the cost of production. Raw ramie thus obtained consists of fibers that are cemented together and these must be further separated by boiling the stock with soaps and alkalies.

The gum that cements the fibers together consists of pectose, cutose, and vasculose. The latter two are removed in the boiling treatment with caustic alkalies and soap, under pressure. The pectose is then removed by washing. The amount of decorticated fiber is less than 5 per cent and the amount of degummed fiber is about 1 per cent.

In fiber structure, the central canal is constricted and granules are seen here and there in the canal. Knots or nodes may be observed under the microscope. These appear at the joints and they are rough and uneven. Fissures and cracks, as well as swollen areas, may also be observed.

The cells are large and very irregular; they vary from 60 to about 240 millimeters in length and are about 80 millimeters in diameter. Pure ramie, like cotton, is chiefly cellulose.

Ramie is used for dressgoods, tablecloths, fish lines, lining, upholstery, and, in general, has some uses comparable with those of linen.

Jute

This fiber comes from the species known as *Corchorous capsullaris,* and it is also known as Jew's Mallow. One of the cheapest of all fibers, it is raised chiefly in Bengal, India. The root of the plant serves as foodstuff in southern Asia.

The plant attains a height of ten to twelve feet, and the fiber layer is rather thick. The stalk produces from two to five times as much fiber when compared with the flax plant. The leaves are light green and are from four to five inches long and about one-half inch in the base diameter dimension. They have long, saw-tooth edges at the

Courtesy: U. S. Dept. Agriculture

Scutching
Hackling

Courtesy: American Viscose Corp.

Carding
Combing

base. The flowers of the plant are yellowish-white and they grow in clusters opposite the leaves. Seed pods are irregular.

Raw jute fibers are from four to seven feet in length and they are yellowish-brown in color. The root ends of the plant are known as jute cutting, which is used in making paper.

The cells of the jute fiber range from 1½ to 5 millimeters in length and from 20 to 25 millimeters in diameter. Chemically, jute is different from cotton and flax. It consists of bastose or ligno-cellulose, a modified form of cellulose. The woody matter, lignin, belongs to the class of carbohydrates known as pectose. Since jute is ligno-cellulose, it will give a crimson color with phloroglucinol and a bright yellow color with aniline salts. In Schweitzer's Reagent jute becomes blue and will slowly dissolve.

The main difference between ligno-cellulose and cellulose of the ordinary type is that with the use of a mordant, the jute fibers combine directly with basic dyes. This is very likely caused by the presence of tannins in the ligno-cellulose.

The plants are rippled and the fibers retted the same as is done in treating flax. Stream retting is the most popular and this takes from three to five days. Scutching and hackling follow. These consist of giving the stock a rigid, rough combing to untangle and straighten the fibers. Free fibers contain little foreign matter.

Compared with other bast fibers, jute is relatively weak. The chief reasons for its use are its low price and rather good spinning qualities. The fiber is readily affected by moisture, which causes it to weaken and disintegrate. It is a difficult fiber to bleach. good white can be obtained by using hypochlorites.

Jute is very sensitive to oxidizing agents, and the fiber is weakened in the bleaching process. Boiling alkalies also weaken the fibers and cause them to turn yellowish-brown in color. This color may be destroyed by neutralization with acids.

Jute is used in making bags, burlap, and sacks, low-quality satins and sateens, stuffer warps for carpets, furniture webbing for upholstery, and shirtings in some parts of the world. It can also be used in some pile fabrics to advantage, and in outerwear fabrics it may serve as fancy yarn in decoration for novelty effects.

Jute is much used in the manufacture of linoleum, where it is coated with a mixture of ground cork and then is boiled with linseed oil. Jute coverings serve postal employees, coffee packers, and cotton-gin workers. Another use of the fiber is as a "filler-in" fiber for some types of yarn.

Henequin and Sisal

These closely related plants are found in Mexico, chiefly in Yucatan. Fibers are obtained from the leaves, and henequin far outstrips sisal in the Mexican belt with regard to production and use. Sisal, however, is raised in East Africa and in Indonesia. it comes from the same family group as the century plant and belongs to the agave species.

Henequin and sisal are rather easily obtained from the plant, and both are ideal in the manufacture of rope. Salt water, however, will quickly destroy the fiber, thereby impairing its use in maritime circles, a great barrier to greater use of both fibers. Binder twine, small diameter rope, and some hard-fiber twine are other uses of these two fibers. The binder twine is a favorite with workers in the grain fields, since it is ideal for bundling and tying.

Abaca and Hemp

The term "abaca" is the name given the fiber that is raised in the Philippine Islands. It has superseded hemp to considerable degree in the making of rope. It is commonly called Manila hemp, and this is further contracted to the point where abaca and hemp are considered as being more or less synonymous.

The term "hemp" is applied to the product of several fibers of the same or similar appearance. Common hemp comes from the plant *Cannabis sativa*. Hemp will withstand water better than any other natural textile fiber.

Hemp has a very interesting history, and the story of "hemp, twine and rope" can e traced as far back as 2700 B.C. Shen Nung, a Chinese emperor, developed hemp to he point where ropemaking became a great industry. It was called *ma*.

India found use for hemp in the eighth century as a drug. While cotton was known ɔ the Egyptians, Hebrews, Phoenicians, and Persians, there is nothing on record to how that they knew of hemp.

In medieval times hemp found its way into Europe and northern Africa when the Saracens arrived. It was not until the Era of Discovery, however, that hemp began to ake on any importance in European life. The Italian city-states of the Renaissance leveloped hemp for use in maritime circles and it was in great demand. Spanish ex-plorers spread the cultivation and use of the fiber in several world centers and had nuch success. Italy, however, still produces the best hemp raised anywhere in the world, a carryover from the days of the Renaissance.

By 1850, England had a good hemp industry. Cordage makers in this country turned ɔ the Philippines for the abaca fiber and soon were making the best rope in the world in the days of the old whaling ships and schooners so well known in the past istory of this country. Hemp and abaca are still important items in the commercial world here.

Leading centers for these fibers include Italy, India, Iran and Russia, China and apan. Russia is the largest producer of hemp today. Kentucky is the leading hemp tate in this country.

The plant attains a height of fifteen feet and the fiber is obtained from the plant y retting, the most frequently used method.

One hundred parts of raw hemp stalk will give about twenty-five parts of raw hemp ɪ filasse.

One hundred parts of filasse will yield about sixty-five parts of combed fiber and bout thirty-five parts of tow.

One hundred parts of hemp seed will produce about twenty-seven parts of oil.

The seed is about the color of a dried pea but is not so large. This is used for bird eed. The fiber is tan in color, long, coarse, durable, and little affected by moisture and water. The oil is yellowish-green in color and it finds favor in making varnish and rtists' colors.

Uses of hemp include all kinds of twine, rope, and cordage; caulking, webbing, tuffer warps and other yarns in the manufacture of carpets and rugs. Large, heavy ables used in maritime circles are also made of hemp. Tailors use hemp in better-uality suitings for webbing.

Coir

This fiber comes from the outer husk of the coconut and may attain a length of ten nches. It is rough, uneven, and straggly; the strength is variable. The coarsest stock ; used to make brushes, the longer fibers find use in rope and cocoa matting, while the hort, curled fibers are used in the upholstery trade and in packing material. Coir is ot affected by salt water, but it is not as strong when compared with Manila rope.

Cuba Bast Fiber

This fiber is used to wrap cigarettes and packing cigars.

Japan Mulberry Fiber

It is used in the manufacture of ordinary paper.

New Zealand Flax

This comes from a plant of the lily family. It is an ideal fiber in the making of rope. The fiber is classed with Mauritius hemp, aloe, bowstring hemp, pandanus, and yucca.

Pineapple Fiber

The fiber is obtained from pineapple leaves. The coarser fibers are used in making abric and cordage in China, Mexico, and South America. The much sought finer fibers re worked into Pina cloth, which is silken-like in texture and high in quality.

[97]

Straw

This fiber is used to make straw hats, matting, sandals, shoes, and seatings. Th swamp wire grasses of straw are used in grass rugs for the home in summer weather. Thes clean, cool, neat rugs are made in this country in Oshkosh, Racine, and Superior, Wis consin.

Ropemaking

This is an interesting study. In the spinning of yarn for rope, following the hacklin process, it was necessary for the operatives to do considerable walking in the earl days of ropemaking. The walker or spinner had to "back down the walk," and dra out the fibers as they turned on the hooks of a wheel. Some of the walks were covered while others had no shelter at all. The spinner often had a course to walk that covere as much as four hundred yards; he had to keep his backward pace constant with h forward pace in order to insure even rope.

This difficult, irksome, tedious work is now a thing of the past, since today, wit improved methods, the spinner rides a machine which resembles the well-know hand-car used by railroads. The car shuttles back and forth on tracks. The ropemakin industry is constantly making improvements to ease the burdens placed on workers.

TESTING: TRUE-FALSE QUESTIONS

1. _____ Ramie fiber is obtained easily from the plant.
2. _____ Jute is low in tensile strength and easily affected by moisture and wate:
3. _____ Pineapple fiber is an example of a stalk fiber.
4. _____ India produced large amounts of jute.
5. _____ Ramie has little tensile strength.
6. _____ Decortication is the process of obtaining the fiber from the plant.
7. _____ Pectose, cutose, and vasculose are peculiar to ramie.
8. _____ Ramie, like cotton, is composed mainly of cellulose.
9. _____ Jute is a ligno-cellulose type of fiber.
10. _____ Jute is little used in making bags, burlap and sacks.
11. _____ Coir is an ideal fiber in the manufacture of linoleum.
12. _____ Bleaching has little effect on jute fibers.
13. _____ Carpeting is made with jute backing.
14. _____ Jute is rippled and retted similar to flax.
15. _____ Mexico raises considerable amounts of sisal.
16. _____ Salt water has a damaging effect on henequin and sisal.
17. _____ Most abaca fiber comes from the Philippine Islands.
18. _____ Italy is noted for the quality of its hemp.
19. _____ The United States is a major hemp-producing country.
20. _____ Hemp is a comparatively new textile fiber.
21. _____ Much hemp is raised in Russia.
22. _____ Coir is easily affected by salt water.
23. _____ Pina cloth is usually made from abaca fibers.
24. _____ Wisconsin is known for its ropemaking factories.
25. _____ Kentucky is a well-known hemp-raising state.

Part 1—Unit I

TOPIC: THE HISTORY AND CLASSIFICATION OF WOOL

Wool, the animal fiber from the fleece of sheep, is a live fiber; cotton, th vegetable fiber, is a dead fiber. Wool from dead sheep and that obtained fro sheep slaughtered for food purposes is classed as dead fiber. This wool is inferi in all properties and characteristics when compared with live-sheep wool. Shee re the only animals which serve to provide mankind with food and clothing.

The farther away from centers of population the sheep are raised, the greater the production and the lower the price. Consequently, Australia, New Zealand, Tasmania, Argentina, Paraguay, Uruguay, and South Africa are great sheep-raising centers. All these areas are south of the equator. North of the equator the United States, Canada, Russia, and Great Britain are the leading sheep countries. Australia is the leading nation, followed in order by Russia, Argentina, and the United States. Woolen and worsted fabrics and garments are worn by people all over the world, chiefly by those who live in the temperate zone.

Sheep in this country are raised in western states, where the population is sparse compared with other sections of the nation. Texas grows the greatest amount of wool, about 25 per cent of the annual yield of grease wool—the wool with the yolk, suint, and other foreign matter in it when it is shorn from the sheep. The other wool states in order of yield are Wyoming, California, Colorado, Montana, Idaho, New Mexico, Utah, Ohio, Oregon, Michigan, Arizona, Nevada, and Iowa. Londonderry, Vermont, was the original center of the Merino sheep industry in the United States, which began around 1800. Ohio now raises the best wool in this country, a Class One wool which compares favorably with other Merino wool raised elsewhere in the world. The farther away from Ohio, the lower in quality will be the wool. The best Merino strains are still bred there. Wool in the western states is constantly being improved in all respects by crossbreeding.

HISTORY OF WOOL

The Scriptures reveal much about wool and sheep:

Chronicles tell us that the son of Reuben took 250,000 sheep from the Hagarites.
The Arabians honored Jehoshaphat by bringing him 7,700 rams.
The Book of Samuel states that David heard in the wilderness that Nabal did shear his sheep.
In Deuteronomy it is recorded that "It shall be the priest's due; the first of the fleece of thy sheep shalt thou give him."
In Proverbs and Exodus, we learn that "the virtuous woman seeketh wool and flax and worketh willingly with her hands. She layeth her hands to the spindle, and her hands hold the distaff."
Joseph's brethren went to feed their father's flock in Shechem. Being come into Egypt, asked by Pharaoh what was their occupation, they said, "Thy servants are shepherds, both we and our fathers."
In the Book of Samuel, they spoke of Goliath thus: "And the staff of his spear was like a weaver's beam."

Ancient history tells us that the Babylonians of the upper classes were known for their woolen robes. Babylonia means "Land of Wool."

Caesar, with his animal husbandry man, Lucius Junius Columella, fostered the raising of sheep so that the wool could be used for clothing for his armies in cold weather. Columella wrote a noted book, *De re rustica*, which is the best of its sort since antiquity; many of its principles, methods, and suggestions are still used wherever sheep are raised. This famous Roman lived in Cádiz, Spain, with his estates near Córdoba. In D. 50, Columella, during the reign of Claudius, crossed Tarentine rams with native Italian and Spanish ewes. In addition he crossed North African rams with native ewes and laid the foundation for the present breed of Spanish Merino sheep, known all over the world in sheep and wool circles.

Alfred the Great, over a thousand years ago, used wool as a substitute for money, or barter.

In 1190 the famous Calimala Guild was founded in Florence, Italy; its members were the great dyers and finishers of woolen goods in that center. They were the best in the world at the time, and "had no equal in all Europe." All phases of the industry from raising sheep to the finishing of fabric in Europe and the British Isles, were aided by the knowledge and skills of the Humble Fathers of Saint Michael of Alexandria Egypt. These fathers, expert in textiles and particularly in the finishing of fabrics, came to Florence in 1238 and provided the technical processing of goods to the Florentines Their efforts bore fruit for more than four hundred years.

Social, political, and economic changes, combined with the continual warfare among the leading city-states and nations of Europe caused the great woolen industry to decline—in Florence, its capital, as well as in Venice, its great commercial rival. The heirs of the founders of the industry in affluent Florence did not care to follow in their elders' footsteps. In addition to their own indolence and laxity, they became greatly interested in social position and prestige, and strove to join the ranks of the wealthy and socially prominent classes. Social position was the paramount goal.

During the first half of the sixteenth century, Henry VIII of England sequestered and destroyed practically all of the many monasteries in Great Britain and Ireland Thus the days of the famous Monastery Wool were also brought to an end. Henry' action had a great effect on all Europe and Great Britain, which is well known to the student of history. Commerce, agriculture, and trade suffered immeasurably, especially for the Florentines who wanted to become gentlemen of leisure and take a high position in the social world of the time. By the seventeenth century the great, strong, and important Calimala Guild had become but a memory in the Italian city-states.

The sheep of Spain and England were brought to the New World in the sixteenth century. Cortes in 1521 kept flocks of sheep in the valley of Oaxaca in Mexico. He is considered to be the first ranchero and the founder of the sheep industry in the South west. Coronado, in 1540, in his search for "the seven golden cities of Cíbola," made an expedition across the present border of the United States into New Mexico, and he introduced sheep "of the golden fleece" to the Pueblo Indians of Zuñi. For the next two centuries sheep always accompanied Spanish colonists who settled across our southern plains; eventually sheep were grazing on lands from California to Florida.

The English brought sheep to Virginia in 1607, to Massachusetts in 1620, while the Dutch had sheep with them when they settled in what is now New York City in 1609. Soon the entire coast was raising sheep for both food and clothing.

In 1643, the American wool industry was born in Rowley, Massachusetts. In 1664 a second mill was established in Watertown, Massachusetts. By 1693 there was a fulling mill in Connecticut, and by 1700 one began operations in Philadelphia, Pennsylvania By 1794 the first woolen mill to be run by water power was located in Massachusetts preceded only by the Slater Cotton Mill in Pawtucket, Rhode Island, the first successful cotton mill in this country.

George Washington had a flock of 800 sheep at Mount Vernon that he improved constantly by the importation of choice Spanish Merino rams. At least one yard of fabric was woven on the hand looms there daily. The looms and the weave shed incidentally, are still there and in running condition.

Spain had been known for centuries for its Merino sheep. At the time of the defeat of the Spanish Armada in 1588, the Spaniards, by the treaty with England, were supposed to turn over to England a large number of their prized Merino rams. England needed them badly for crossbreeding with their native sheep, which were not considered very good in quality of wool produced. Despite threats and censures, it was not until 1765, almost two hundred years later, that the English finally obtained some of the Merino sheep. This was the first time in the entire history of Merino sheep that Spain had permitted exportation of any of their prized stock. England fostered sheep raising in each of her colonies as they were established; hence, the importance of sheep to England down through the ages.

In what is now the United States, impetus was given to wool and cloth production during the Revolutionary War, when foreign sources of supply were curtailed or cut off After the war, woolen goods of British manufacture again appeared in volume on the

SPACKENKILL SCHOOL LIBRARY
11 CROFT ROAD
POUGHKEEPSIE, N.Y. 12003

Courtesy: U. S. Dept. Agriculture

Romney Marsh Ram
Dorset Ewe
Merino Ram
Southdown Ram

Cheviot Ewe
Border Leicester Ram
Cotswold Ram
Oxford Ewe

Courtesy: Cyril Johnson Woolen Co., and Montrose Worsted M

Sorting	Scouring
Dyeing	Blending, oiling, and mixing
Carding	Combing
Inspecting top	Top dyeing

Courtesy: Cyril Johnson Woolen Co., and Montrose Worsted Mills

Washing after top dyeing	Roving ready for spinning
Yarn conditioning	Beaming warp to specification
Drawing-in warp ends	Reeding-in warp ends
Mill weave shed	Gray cloth

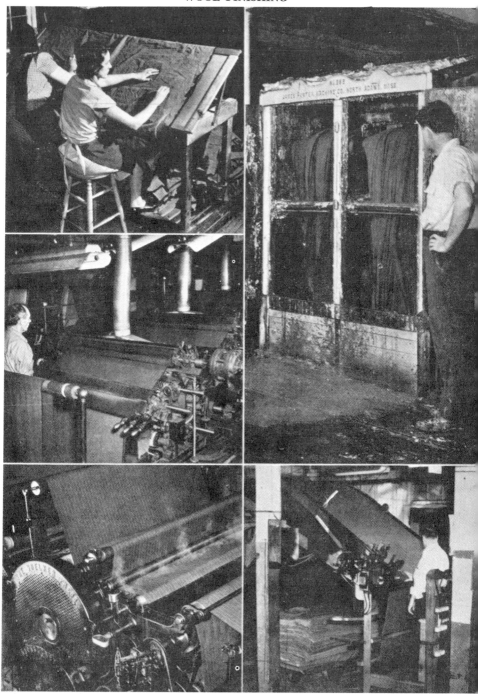

Courtesy: Cyril Johnson Woolen Co., and Montrose Worsted Mills

Burling   Fulling
Shearing   Drying
Pressing

[104]

American market. However, the Embargo Act of 1807 and the Nonintercourse Act of 1809 once more revitalized domestic production, and by 1810 the estimated sheep population rose to seven million head. War again spurred the development of the wool textile industry in 1812, but with the reestablishment of peace in 1815, American markets were flooded with goods of foreign origin. From 1830 to 1837 the improvement of machinery, better transportation, and the growth of cities stimulated the industry and greater emphasis was put on wool growing, which migrated westward.

Following the Civil War, there was a rapid increase in the production of wool fabrics in this country. The growth of the industry after the Civil War was stimulated by the general industrial expansion of the United States and considerably helped by the Tariff Acts of 1867 and the years following. These tariffs provided protection for the domestic wool grower and for the wool-fabric manufacturer as well, and made it possible for the woolen mills in this country to compete successfully with the much-longer-established mills in England and on the Continent. By 1897 more than 90 per cent of our requirements for wool fabrics were being supplied by American mills.

The rise of the manmade fibers (acetate, rayon, and nylon) before World War II and after its close has had a serious impact on the use of woolen and worsted fibers and yarn. While both of these serve as base in blends and mixes, their use has been cut down to a considerable degree since fibers such as "Dacron" polyester fiber, "Orlon" acrylic fiber, Dynel, Acrilan, Verel, Vycron, Creslan, and Zefran came to be used along with acetate, rayon, and nylon in all types and kinds of goods and in varying percentages with the two animal fibers.

The increased use of lighter-weight winter clothing has also cut down on the amount of animal-fiber consumption. The old days of a 30-ounce overcoating are gone; today the heaviest coating fabric used is about 23 or 24 ounces per yard. Suiting fabrics for both men and women are much lighter than formerly. People do not wear heavy fabrics today because they like to dress with lighter clothing, and the mode of living and activity has changed much since 1920, and particularly since 1945. This is the "Age of Blends" in the textile and apparel industries; wool and worsted have been sacrificed because of the inroads of the newer fibers.

New York City, the largest garment center in the world, still clothes over half of America, while other areas are now increasing production in the field. Rochester, New York, is the center for men's-wear apparel, while Boston, Philadelphia, Kansas City, Dallas, Chicago, and several lesser centers are now becoming known for their apparel manufactures. Several of the old textile mill centers of New England which lost out when the mills were either liquidated or moved south, are now apparel cities. For example, Lowell, Lawrence, New Bedford, and Fall River, Massachusetts; Nashua and Manchester in New Hampshire; and Providence, Pawtucket, and Woonsocket in Rhode Island are now considered as apparel centers, with much of the work being done in plants that formerly housed textile mills; other industries also have utilized them.

WOOL-BEARING SHEEP: CLASSIFICATION, GRADES, AND COUNTS OF WOOL

There are about 40 breeds of sheep, and counting the crossbreeds, the total is about 210 distinct grades and types. Sheep are divided into five general groups:

CLASS ONE WOOLS: Merino Sheep, 1″ to 5″ staple length:
Ohio Merino
Silesian: Austria
Saxony: Germany
Rambouillet: France
Australian
South American
South African
New Zealand, plus the small Merino countries of Spain, Sweden, Denmark, Italy.

CLASS TWO WOOLS: 2" to about 8" staple length:
Originated in England, Scotland, Ireland, and Wales, and now grown all over the world.
Bampton, Berkshire, Blackface, Cornish, Cornwall, Devonshire, Dorset, Canadian wools, Hampshire, Hereford, Exmoor, Kent, Norfolk, Shropshire, Southdown, Sussex, Oxford, Welsh Mountain, Wiltshire, Westmoreland, West Riding of England, Irish, and Ryeland.

CLASS THREE WOOLS: 4" to 12" or more in staple length:
The luster wools of the United Kingdom: Lincoln from Lincoln county; Leicester from Leicester county; Cotswold from Gloucester county; Cheviot from the Lowlands and Highlands of Scotland; Romney Marsh from Kent county; Shetland, Hebrides, Harris, and Lewis and other Island sheep.

CLASS FOUR WOOLS:
Those sheep which cannot be classed in one of the first three groups; the results of mixed breeding; the fiber is irregular and ranges from one inch to sixteen or more inches in staple length. The sheep are known as half-breeds and semi-luster or demi-luster sheep. This class, in reality, may be called "mongrel sheep." The wool is used for making carpets and rugs, and low-priced clothing usually for boys and girls.

CLASS FIVE:
This group is not truly a sheep classification but the animals are akin to sheep and are therefore listed: Arabian, Bokharan, Persian lamb and similar fiber stock.

Merino sheep produce the best wool for high-quality clothing; it has the finest diameter, highest number of serrations (from 2,400 to 3,000 per inch), the best of working properties, and resiliency and elasticity are superior as compared to any other types.

Class Two and Class Three wools as well are much used for clothing. Long wools of varying grades are used in carpets and rugs and in boys' clothing. Great Britain is noted for these two classes of stock, since Merino types of wool cannot be raised there because of climate, soil, pasturage, and general conditions. Its Class Two wools go into the better types of men's and women's wear fabrics, while Class Three is ideal for the rugged, long-wearing homespuns, tweeds, cheviots and shetlands. These are made from the long, irregular-diameter fibers characteristic of these fabrics.

Mutton sheep provide fibers much in demand for use in the industry. This dead or pulled wool is obtained from the slaughterhouses, where the fiber is of secondary consideration. It is somewhat inferior in all respects if compared with live wool fiber. There is more pulled wool produced each year than first-clip virgin wool taken from sheep given their first shearing. About one-quarter of the wool used in the United States is of this type.

Many kinds of sheep have given their name to clothes used today: Cheviot Shetland, Merino cloth, Saxony overcoating, Oxford fabric. Scientific methods of improving sheep flocks for better wool are constantly being developed by the United States Bureau of Standards, the Department of Animal Husbandry of the Department of Agriculture, the Department of Commerce, and several other organizations and agencies, national and sectional, throughout the nation. The State Experimental Farms connected with the State Land Grant Universities have done much work in the wool and sheep divisions. Constant experimentation and testing is carried on. For example, many years ago the United States raised carpet wools, the lowest in quality of the four main types (combing, carding, clothing and carpet). Because of the success in breeding, crossbreeding, grazing, soil, and so on, carpet wool is no longer raised; it is now in the status of carding and clothing wools. All our carpet wool is now imported from all over the world—Iran, Iraq, Turkey, North Africa, and other rather isolated areas. Improved fleeces developed by the wool growers of America are considered one of the outstanding accomplishments in animal husbandry.

A full-bred sheep is one in which the ram and the ewe are both full Merino of the same type, e.g., Saxony Merino breed. A crossbreed type could be a Cheviot ram and a Corriedale ewe, for example. The serrations (the unseen waves within waves in a wool fiber) determine the fineness and quality of wool. The highest type fibers will have from 2,400 to 3,000 to the inch; the lowest types will range from 600 to 900 per inch. The sheared or clipped wool from a sheep is known as the fleece. When clipped the wool contains "sheep grease" (this is yolk which may be compared with oil in the human scalp), suint, which is dried perspiration, and there are varying amounts of other foreign matter in the fleece: these may include dried fodder, burs, grass, pebbles, leaves.

The diagram below shows "sorts" or sorting of the wool from a sheep, numbered from 1 to 14.

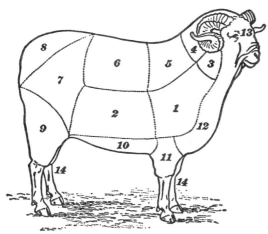

Courtesy: National Association of Wool Manufacturers

WOOL SORTS

Shoulder wool (Number 1) is usually the best fiber in the sheep fleece. Next comes side, neck and back wool. The numbers show order of preference.

EXPLANATION OF AREA NUMBERS:

1. Shoulders, best in the fleece
2. Full side area
3. Front top shoulder area
4. Top back area
5. Front back area
6. Back area
7. Loin area
8. Top rump area
9. Hind quarter, rump area
10. Britch and belly area
11. Top leg area
12. Chest and throat area
13. Head area
14. Shank or leg area

ABB: Edgings or skirtings obtained by the wool sorter when trimming a fleece; low in quality.

BRITCH: Wool from the hindquarters, usually coarsest on the body and often approaches hair; very low in quality.

BROKES: Short staple wool from the belly of the sheep; poor in grade.

CHOICE: The so-called third quality obtained from a fleece; comes from middle of the sides of the fleece.

COMMON: Uneven fibers obtained from top rump and hind side; slightly better than brokes.

COW-TAIL: Very coarse britch wool taken from tail end of a low-luster fleece. May be spun to low worsted counts of about 28s. Wool cow-tail is more like hair than wool.

DOWN-RIGHTS: Wool from the lower parts of the sides of the fleece; low quality.

MIDDLE: Wool obtained from the center of the back and middle sides. May be spun to about 36s worsted count of yarn; average quality.

PICKLOCK: The second best sort from the fleece; formerly a grade above XX wool, little of the wool is now seen in the American market. The term implies "the pick of the lock of fleece." Excellent quality.

PIECES: Small batches of wool obtained from fleeces and which, when gathered up in the sorting room of the mill, are sold as irregular or mixed lots. Vary considerably in quality.

PRIME: Choice fiber taken from the sides of a very fine fleece or from the shoulders of a good fleece. May be classed with picklock and sometimes considered as the first quality of the fleece.

SECONDS: The best Merino clothing wool from the edge of the throat and breast of the sheep. Also obtained along the top of the fleece in areas other than choice, prime or super.

Another meaning of the term is that it is wool taken from the skirt of the Merino fleece. This stock is coarse in nature.

SUPER: British Empire term for superior wool from a fleece, the best in the fleece. However, in this country, the term is applied to pulled wool such as "B Super" and "C Super."

DIAGRAMS OF WOOL FLEECES AND GLOSSARY OF WOOL SORTING TERMS

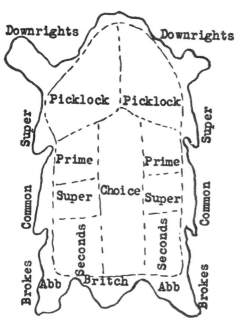

Diagram of wool sorts

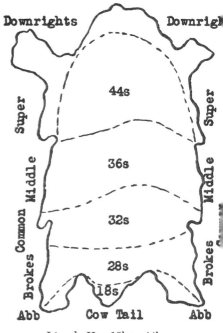

Lincoln Hog 18's to 44's

Courtesy: John Wiley & Sons, Inc., from Textile Fibers *by J. M. Matthews, fourth edition*

Designating Grades of Sorted Wool

There are two methods used, one of which, "the blood system," is peculiar to the United States. The other, the count system, is more universally used and is increasing in use in this country. Both, however, relate to the average fineness of diameter of the fibers. Originally, in the "blood system" of grading wool, the fine wool of the Merino sheep was the criterion or standard, and the coarser grades were considered as the result of crossing choice Merino sheep with the English breeds. While still used to indicate wool fineness, it does not give any indication of the true strain of breeding.

In the "blood system" used in this country, the fineness standard would be that a one-half-blood wool, for example, would be finer than a three-eighth-wool and coarser in diameter when compared with a three-quarter-blood wool.

The count system has as its basis the theoretical limit of the "spin of wools" of certain fineness—e.g., the finer the wool, the finer will be the yarn spun from it. The table below compares the three major systems of grading wool, and gives an idea of the approximate percentage of the various clips in the United States:

GREAT BRITAIN COUNT SYSTEM	CANADIAN GRADE	UNITED STATES GRADE TERMS	APPROXIMATE PERCENTAGES OF UNITED STATES CLIP
72s to 80s	Fine	Fine, full-blood, XX type, X and ¾ blood	49
66s to 72s	Fine medium	½ blood	15
56s to 66s	Medium	⅜ blood	21
44s to 56s	Low medium	¼ blood	13
24s to 44s	Coarse	Common	2
below 24s	Luster	Braid and britch	nil

Under the British system shown above, the following explains the numbers used in designations: A number is given each type of wool; it means that the wool when scoured can be spun to the count of worsted yarn designated by the number. If the number is, say, 40, the wool can be spun to a 40s worsted yarn, unless the number is very low when it is applied to woolen counts of yarn.

There are 560 yards in one pound of a 1s worsted yarn. Thus, 40 times 560 gives 22,400 yards of yarn that can be spun from one pound of the scoured worsted stock, English grading system. In a 60s, there would be 33,600 yards in the pound of yarn (60×560 equals 33,600). English mills are known the world over for their very fine high-textured, high-grade worsteds.

Four Types of Wool

COMBING WOOL: The highest, finest and best wool obtained from sheep. The fibers are always carded and combed, since they have the properties and characteristics necessary for the best grades of worsted yarn and fabric. Worsted fibers that have been combed are of the same approximate length; they are even, parallel, smooth, devoid of foreign matter. Wool to be used for combing purposes has a high percentage of yolk and suint in the grease condition. Merino wool is always combed and usually is manipulated into high-grade fabric.

CARDING WOOL: Of good quality, but not always satisfactory for combing purposes. Some stock, however, can be combed for use in medium to high quality fabric for men's wear and women's wear. Most carding wool, however, is of varying staple length and is used chiefly in woolens.

CLOTHING WOOL: A term used in wool grading to designate staple length. There is no standard length implied by the term, since it varies with the fineness of the wool in question.

Fine wools, 64s and over, are called clothing wool, and are below 1¼ inches in staple length. As the wools become coarser when being sorted, there is an increase of about

¼ inch per grade. Like carding wool, this wool shows much irregular fiber and there are, at times, goodly amounts of foreign matter, chiefly in the grease condition, such as burs, dried grass, fodder, motes, pebbles.

Clothing wool, in a broad sense, differs from carding wool in that the former may have varying amounts of other fibers worked with it in manipulation.

CARPET WOOL: Any wool not classed in the above grades; the lowest in quality of the four types. It cannot be counted and often gives trouble in carding. Practically all carpet wool used here comes from abroad, since our flocks have been improved by scientific methods to the point where they grade in the classifications given above. Used in floor-covering trade and in low-quality boys' apparel, ski cloth, mackinac fabric, etc.

Other Wool Types

There are several other types and varieties of wool used today, and they are classified according to fineness, color, staple length, etc. Some few of these distinctive types are:

ALPACA WOOL: Fine long-staple woolly hair of the alpaca, a South American goatlike animal.

ANGORA WOOLS: Long, soft, hairlike wool from the Angora goat, native to Anatolia, the homeland of the Turks; now raised extensively in Texas, with Kerrville as the center. Used in combination with wool, mohair, and mixture fabrics.

BOTANY WOOL: Very fine Merino wool from Botany Bay area in Australia. Used only in the finest of woolen and worsted fabrics.

CASHMERE WOOL: Very fine, soft wool found underneath the outer or harsh hair on goats raised chiefly in the Himalaya Mountains area.

KEMPY WOOL: Harsh, irregular, rough wool used chiefly in carpets. Sick or diseased sheep will often produce a type of wool that is known as kempy.

LAMB'S WOOL: Elastic, soft, resilient wool fibers obtained from lambs when they are seven to eight months old—the first or virgin clipping from the animal. This lofty stock is used in better grades of fabrics.

SHETLAND WOOL: Rugged wool, ideal for cheviots, shetlands, homespuns and tweeds, raised chiefly in Scotland and the adjacent islands. Cheviot wool is comparable with shetland wool.

TOP WOOL: Worsted slubbing or sliver wound into a top form which resembles a cheese in size. Noil has been removed from these fibers in combing, and top stock contains fibers of the same staple length throughout. Used in making worsted yarn and fabric.

Pulled Wool

This is obtained from the pelts or hides of dead sheep. It is inferior in all respects to fleece wool, which is taken from live sheep. The stockyard centers produce pulled wool. However, the packing houses are interested mainly in the carcass; the wool is of secondary consideration. They dispose of all this stock to textile plants.

There is more pulled wool produced per year than first-clip wool. Pulled wool is used with better grades of fleece wool to make woolens and worsteds.

Methods to Obtain Pulled Wool

There are three ways to obtain pulled wool:

SWEATING PROCESS: The hides are sweated until the wool is loosened so that it may be taken from the pelts with ease. However, the hides may be affected if the work is not properly done.

LIME METHOD: The flesh sides of the pelts are painted with lime. This allows the wool to be removed easily after a short aging. Hides are subject to injury, and dyeing is sometimes irregular.

DEPILATORY METHOD: This is the best method to use. A solution of sodium sulfate will loosen the fibers. In the solution there is also sulfuric acid and an alkali made of oyster shells. The flesh side of the pelt is treated just as soon as it comes from the slaughtered animal. Aging will last from eight to twenty-four hours. The action is such, that when aging is consummated, the fibers will leave the pelt in the same way lather may be taken from a man's face in shaving. The largest wool pullery in the world is in Mazamet, France.

TESTING

1. For what two reasons are sheep raised?
2. Who is considered as the founder of the Merino breed of sheep?
3. Give a brief account of the sheep and wool industry in the United States.
4. Name three types of sheep in Class One; in Class Two; in Class Three.
5. What breeds of sheep are found in Class Four?
6. Why does not England raise Merino sheep?
7. Define serration; grease wool.
8. Explain the "blood system" used to grade wool in the United States.
9. Discuss the "count system" in grading wool.
10. If a wool were rated in the 56s, how many yards of worsted yarn could be expected in one pound of this wool count?
11. What is a ewe?
12. Why is it necessary to use a microscope to count serrations in a wool fiber?
13. Name five points to look for when grading or judging wool.
14. About how many varying grades or types of fiber may be obtained from a wool fleece?

Part 1—Unit 17

TOPIC: SOME GENERAL CHARACTERISTICS OF WOOL AND WORSTED FIBERS AND FABRICS

Short wool is 1 to 6 inches in staple length; long wool runs from 6 to 14 or more inches; while worsted fibers range from 1½ inches up to 6 inches in staple.

Wool burns with the odor of burning feathers, and leaves a brittle, black, globular bead which is easily crushed.

Classed as a semi-lustrous fiber, wool will felt with heat, moisture, and friction. The fiber has an interlocking formation which because of its minute scale structure and crimp causes felting, the only textile fiber which possesses this property. These serrations allow the wool fiber to absorb moisture quickly and to retain it for a considerable time.

Normally wool is water-repellent, but vapor will penetrate the fiber.

It is pliable and flexes easily in bending and stretching, thereby making wool ideal for garments, since clothing must yield, bend, and twist with the motions and movements of the body. It does not break, and is wrinkle-resistant because of its resiliency.

The fiber is tough, and garments of wool or worsted do not become shabby or threadbare in a short space of time; it has good resistance to abrasion and chafing.

It dyes easily and well, and comes in a very wide range of colors, tones, and shades. It has very good affinity for the dyes used, which penetrate into the actual fiber. Fastness to sunlight is an important factor in woolens and worsteds, thereby preventing fading of the garment.

Moisture vapor from the body is trapped in non-absorbent clothing. In clothing of fibers absorbing body moisture, there is an insulated air space. Baseball players wear woolen uniforms throughout the season because the wool in the uniform holds in suspension the heat given off by the body, thereby preventing chilling after strenuous exertion.

Wool is weaker when wet; strength returns on drying.

Wool fibers are carded only, except in rare instances, when they are combed for use in very lightweight fabrics which command a good price. Worsted fibers are carded and always combed, and may be run more than once through a combing machine. In addition, they are run through gilling and drawing operations further to make the fibers, which are all of the same length, parallel. Woolen yarn is composed of a more or less conglomerate mass of fibers, varying in fiber length, and often having other fibers mixed in. Worsted yarn is even and uniform at all times. Wool is spun on the mule or the ring spinning frames; worsted is spun on any one of four frames—ring, cap, flyer, or mule.

Wool is a generator of heat but a poor conductor.

Both fibers, when used in garments, withstand hard, rugged wear and are ideal for cold climates. Good yarn twist will lengthen the life of either type of fabric. Worsteds will outlast woolens in wear and service.

Garments made from these fibers will catch and hold grime and dirt and other foreign particles.

Mothproofing agents will prevent destruction by moths. Attention should be given to the storage of these garments at all times.

Woolen fabrics are lower in texture or pick count when compared with worsteds. Both retain their shape well, particularly worsteds.

Both will shrink, and in the case of woolens will felt if cleaning is not done with care; may be pre-shrunk.

May be bleached with a peroxide bleach, if carefully used. Can be stripped of color by the use of potassium permanganate.

Are weakened in a chlorine bleach and will take on a yellowish cast.

While worsted garments will retain a very good crease, this may be offset by shine, sheen, or undesirable luster which cannot be removed permanently. Most woolen fabrics are given some napping treatment which prevents their acquiring a sheen or luster through wear, abrasion, or chafing. Unfinished worsted is the only worsted fabric to have a nap applied to it.

Garments made from either fiber will not feel cool, cold, or clammy when damp because of the hygroscopic property.

Woolens and worsteds will tailor well because of their resiliency and their ability to shape well. Woolens are more difficult to tailor than worsteds because the apparent softness and bulkiness of woolens hinder the tailor in setting the fabric for the cut-fit-trim operations. Worsteds provide a more form-fitting garment and tailor well not only in men's wear but in mannish-type worsted suitings for women.

Lightweight worsteds, such as tropicals, will not shrink; good pre-shrinking is provided prior to their being made up into garments.

Woolens seem "to spot quicker" than worsteds, and it is more difficult to remove a stain from the former because of the nap on the goods.

Steam pressing revives the fibers, making the garment look like new.

Occasional drycleaning should be given these garments, since they will not only clean easily, but added life will be given to them.

Comparison of Woolen and Worsted Yarns and Fabrics

WOOLEN YARN	WORSTED YARN
1. Carded only	1. Carded and combed
2. Soft, slubby	2. Substantial, harder than wool
3. Fuzzy, uneven fibers	3. Smooth, even, uniform fibers
4. Weaker	4. Stronger
5. Fibers in conglomerate mass	5. Fibers are parallel
6. Uneven twisting	6. Even twisting and greater twist
7. Bulky type of yarn, uneven	7. Uniform in diameter

WOOLEN CLOTH	WORSTED CLOTH
1. Lower texture—ends and picks	1. Higher texture, more compact
2. Less shine	2. More shine or sheen
3. Tendency to sag and not to hold crease	3. Does not sag, holds crease very well
4. Less tensile strength	4. Greater tensile strength
5. Poorer yarn in fabric, generally speaking	5. Better, more expensive yarn used in materials
6. Heavier, bulkier cloth	6. Lighter, less bulky fabric
7. Does not tailor as well	7. Tailors well and easily
8. Gives good wear	8. Will last longer and usually gives better wear
9. Less expensive fabric	9. More expensive fabric

Data on Wool from the Greasy Fleece to Finished Fabric

The following figures of the National Association of Wool Manufacturers, 386 Park Avenue South, New York City, are revealing and informative:

Three-fourths of one fleece of wool furnishes the following:

    6 pounds of grease wool or equivalent.
    4.4 pounds of scoured wool and noil.
    4.1 pounds of carded roving stock.
    4.0 pounds of spun woolen yarn.
    3 yards and 1 inch of gray goods, ready for dyeing.
    3 yards of finished fabric after sponging.
    This yardage will make one woman's woolen coat.
    Women also wear worsted materials in outer apparel.

One and one-fifth fleeces of wool furnish the following:

    8.68 pounds of grease wool.
    3.34 pounds of scoured wool.
    4.17 pounds of carded sliver stock.
    3.62 pounds of worsted top, combed fibers; plus .55 pounds of noil, a by-product of the combing operation.
    3.44 pounds of roving stock ready for spinning.
    3.20 pounds of spun worsted yarn.
    3 yards and 27 inches of gray goods, ready for dyeing.
    3 yards and 18 inches of dyed goods, piece- or yarn-dyed; the fibers could have been stock-dyed if desired. This operation would follow scouring and precede carding.
    3 yards and 13½ inches of finished fabric after sponging. This yardage will make one man's worsted suiting.

TESTING

IDENTIFICATION QUESTIONS   50 points

The following questions on woolen and worsted fibers and fabrics are to be answered by either the word "wool," or the word "worsted." Answers are to be placed on the blank line provided to the left of this page:

1. _____ Fibers are carded and combed.
2. _____ Yarn shows fuzzy, uneven, and protruding fibers.
3. _____ More uneven in fiber diameter and twist.
4. _____ Lower quality yarn, generally speaking.
5. _____ Provides the stronger yarn.
6. _____ Rarely napped fabrics.
7. _____ Finer yarn and higher texture in the cloth.
8. _____ Tendency to sag, and may not hold the crease very well.
9. _____ Smooth, even, uniform fibers of same length in the yarn.
10. _____ Will not develop a shine through wear very readily.

GENERAL QUESTIONS   50 points

1. Discuss briefly five physical properties of wool fibers. Five chemical properties.
2. Why must care be exercised when storing woolen or worsted garments?
3. Discuss the burning test for wool fibers.
4. Why does a worsted suiting take on a shine more quickly than a woolen garment?
5. Why is it usually more difficult to remove spots and stains from woolen garments than from worsteds?
6. Why is wool a poor conductor but a good generator of heat?
7. Define resiliency as applied to wool fibers.
8. Why do woolens and worsteds catch dirt and similar particles?
9. What does a wool fiber possess that makes it the only textile fiber that will felt in a natural manner?

Part 1—Unit 18

TOPIC: THE WOOL PRODUCTS LABELING ACT OF 1939—UNITED STATES GOVERNMENT REGULATIONS

The four major types of wool are combing, carding, clothing, and carpet. The staple or fiber length of wool fibers may be long, medium, or short. Wool in a single fleece may vary considerably as to fiber length, serrations per inch, fineness, resiliency, elasticity, in the amount of foreign matter in the stock, shrinking properties, tensile strength, pliability, softness, and the amount of moisture present. Some grades of the much cheaper fiber, cotton, may cost more per pound than the lowest grades of wool—the type obtained from the shanks, legs, and rump.

The quality of any textile fabric depends upon two things: (1) the grade or quality of the raw material used; (2) the techniques and the skills of every worker who takes part in the manufacture of the fabric during construction, coloring, and finishing of the goods. For example, a flannel, sharkskin, unfinished worsted, tweed, or any other staple fabric used in a suiting, depending on the raw material and on worker techniques, may range in price from $35 up to $350 per garment. Ready-to-wear suiting is made on a mass-production, assembly-line, standard-size basis. Job specialization is necessary for higher-quality garments or custom-made garments; hence, the wide price range in, say, the flannel suit. Comparison of the various qualities of flannel fabric will soon reveal wide differences in the materials as to hand or feel, drape, crease-retention, possible sagginess, or resiliency.

In 1923 the late Senator Capper of Kansas introduced a "Truth-in-Fabrics" bill in the United States Senate. For several years no action was taken toward its passage. The Senator introduced the bill year after year, but to little avail. In due course of time, the wool growers of the western states, The Wool Bureau, Inc., of New York City, and other interested agencies began to see the value of the bill. In the early 1930's a coordinated effort was made to have the bill passed by the Senate. Strong opposition was encountered all along the line. Gradually, however, Senator Capper's efforts began to bear fruit. Great efforts were made to enlist the aid of all organizations that might be of help. Finally, after a rather bitter fight in the House and in the Senate, the Wool Products Labeling Act was passed in 1939. To the present day there are still some groups who are not at all

[114]

pleased with the law, and there have been many exchanges of thoughts and words as to its value. The law is still seriously questioned in many quarters, as it has not satisfied all concerned; it seemed to aid the textile plants which made the better-quality fabrics while the mills which made lower-quality fabrics apparently did not gain anything by passage of the bill. Similarly, the higher-price apparel houses liked the bill, while the lower-price-line houses did not. The Textile Fibers Products Identification Act of 1959 has made few changes in wool labeling. (*See* page 354.)

The demand for wool throughout the world each year is generally greater than the amount of new wool produced. As a result, during the past fifty years there has been an increasing demand for reused wool, whch is used in combination with the stronger new wool. In addition, the wool textile industry in recent years has been using larger quantities of manmade fibers as adulterants. During the past decade this practice has become so general that today reused wool, acetate, rayon, cotton, and the newer manmade fibers constitute well over 50 per cent of the fibers used by the entire American wool textile industry.

TERMS OF THE WOOL PRODUCTS LABELING ACT OF 1939— UNITED STATES GOVERNMENT REGULATIONS

In order to protect the consuming public against the unrevealed use of these substitutes and adulterants, Congress in 1939 enacted the Wool Products Labeling Act which requires that all products containing wool shall bear a tag or a label stating in terms of percentages the fiber or fibers present. The enforcement of the law is under the direction of the Federal Trade Commission. Three definitions for wool were established by the law. They are:

WOOL: The legal definition of the word "wool" in the United States means the fleece of the sheep or lamb or the hairs of the Angora or Cashmere goat, and may include also the fibers from the camel, alpaca, llama or vicuña, being used for the first time in the complete manufacture of a wool product. It includes new wool which has been partially processed up to, but not including, either weaving or felting. These partially processed wastes are included under the term "wool" on the basis that the damage resulting from the semi-manufacturing is not sufficient to seriously diminish their original qualities.

VIRGIN WOOL: The Federal Trade Commission considers this term synonymous with "new wool." It states that "the term virgin or new wool as descriptive of a wool product or any fiber or part thereof shall not be used when the product or part so described is not composed wholly of new or virgin wool which has never been used, or reclaimed, reworked, reprocessed or reused from any spun, woven, knitted, felted, or manufactured or used product. Products composed of or made from fiber reworked or reclaimed from yarn or clips shall not be described as virgin or new wool, or by terms of similar import, regardless of whether such yarns or clips are now used or were made of new or reprocessed or reused material."

Another meaning of the term is that of the first clipping from a sheep that has never heretofore been sheared, a shearling or yearling sheep. The first clip from the animal will be the best to be obtained; each successive clip becomes inferior in quality, for the older the sheep, the poorer will be the grade of fiber.

Another concise and brief meaning of the term is that of wool, irrespective of the clip, that has not been manipulated into yarn and cloth.

In some respects, the term may be somewhat of a misnomer. Care should be exercised to give the correct impression as to what is meant in speaking of virgin wool. Advertising has done much to add to the confusion in interpreting the correct or implied meaning. Some will say that some grades of virgin wool may cost less per pound than certain good-quality cottons; thus, to the buying public the term may be somewhat misleading.

There is also some apparent misunderstanding concerning the term "100-per-cent wool." Some will say that when it is considered that wool from the belly, rump, and shanks of the animals is used in the manufacture of woolen goods, it can be gleaned that while the resultant garment may be advertised as all-wool or 100-per-cent wool, the quality may be deficient despite the fact that the cloth may have been made entirely of virgin wool.

WOOL PRODUCT: The term "wool product" means any product, or any portion of a product, which contains, purports to contain, or in any way is represented as containing wool, reprocessed wool, or reused wool.

Reprocessed Wool

The term "reprocessed wool" describes wool which has been completely manufactured into a woven or felted state for the first time and which has then been reduced to fiber for reuse without ever having been worn or used in any manner prior to reprocessing. Reprocessed wool includes mill ends accumulated during manufacturing, and clothing manufacturers' clippings of unused new materials.

Reused Wool

This definition covers by far the largest proportion of reclaimed wool used. It represents the ordinary used rags, old clothing, blankets, etc., collected by dealers who sort them according to the type of goods, their color, and their weight. These rags are shredded into fiber either by reused-wool manufacturers or by textile manufacturers themselves. Reused wool fibers are broken and weakened in service and in garnetting them back into fiber. They are generally blended with stronger new wool and are utilized by manufacturers as an economy in cost of raw materials. Reused wool, used legitimately in the production of utility fabrics, has definite values. It may be better in some respects than manmade fibers as an "adulterant" since it retains, in some degree, varying according to the damage suffered through use and reprocessing, the intrinsic qualities which are the exclusive properties of wool. The usage values of the fibers depend greatly on the source from which they are recovered and the skill used in manufacturing them into fabrics.

All Wool or 100-Per-Cent Wool

Where the product or the fabric to which the stamp, tag, label, or mark of identification applies is composed wholly of one kind of fiber, either the word "All" or the term "Hundred Per Cent" may be used with the correct fiber name; as for example, "Hundred-Per-Cent Wool," "All Wool," "100% Reprocessed Wool," "All Reprocessed Wool," "100% Reused Wool," "All Reused Wool." If any such product is composed wholly of one fiber, with the exception of the fiber ornamentation not exceeding 5 per cent, such term "All" or "100%" as qualifying the name of fiber may be used, provided it is immediately followed by the phrase "exclusive of ornamentation," or by a phrase of like meaning; such as, for example:

"All Wool   or   "100% Wool
Exclusive of Ornamentation."   Exclusive of Ornamentation."

TESTING

1. Who is considered the "Father of the Wool Labeling Law"?
2. What are the two factors which control the quality of any fabric?
3. Define the term "wool," in accordance with the Wool Labeling Law.
4. Discuss the possible meanings that the term "virgin wool" may imply.
5. What is reprocessed wool? Reused wool?
6. Discuss the term "all-wool" or "100-per-cent" wool.
7. Why should wool be the most important fiber for men's suiting fabric?
8. State how a cloth or garment may be 100-per-cent wool and still be of low quality.
9. Explain how a cloth made of virgin wool might not be high in quality.
10. Show how an advertisement which states that a cloth or suiting is "all wool" may be misleading.

Part 1—Unit 19

TOPIC: WOOLEN AND WORSTED MANUFACTURE FROM RAW STOCK TO FABRIC

Before considering the manufacture of woolen and worsted yarn from the raw stock to the finished fabric, it is deemed advisable to give an overall view of the differences between woolens and worsteds, with special attention to the fabrics made from both fibers. There are three types of fabrics made from the wool of sheep—woolens, worsteds, and unfinished worsteds. Woolen cloth may be distinguished from worsted fabric by its softer feel and a rather uneven, napped or fuzzy surface effect.

Unfinished worsteds may be made of: (1) worsted warp and woolen filling; (2) soft-spun French-system worsted yarn; (3) warp and filling with certain amounts of the so-called waste or substitute fibers mixed in.

French spun yarn is softer than the English or Bradford spun yarn. The cloths seem to have a softer, loftier feel. It is, however, sometimes next to impossible to determine whether a fabric is spun on the French or the Bradford system.

Worsted fabric should show a clear outline of the weave construction and pattern. If the weave is a twill, the diagonal lines should be symmetrically balanced; if made of a plain weave, the fabric should show the construction clearly. When held to the light, worsteds reveal a luster without sheen.

Clear-finish worsteds should have a clean, smooth surface effect, in all respects even; that is, the material should be well and evenly sheared in the dry finishing, the texture should be uniform and even and show no blemishes. A clear-finish worsted will shine, in time, because of friction, chafing, and wear. It is virtually impossible to remove the shine from the fabrics of this type. The cloth holds the crease very well and the wear is good to excellent.

Unfinished worsted will not shine but does not hold the crease as well as clear-finished fabric. Shearing must be done with utmost care if it is resorted to, and the nap or protruding fibers must be finished so that these fibers add to the appearance of the goods. Cropping requires a high degree of skill. Knots and other possible blemishes must be removed prior to shearing since a knot or slub falling under the shear blade may do irreparable damage. Shearers must watch the cloth constantly during shearing to guard against flaws that might spoil the fabric should the shear blade scrape or catch the blemish.

Worsteds and woolens may be woven in double- or triple-cloth construction.

Double and triple constructions attain their effect by the use of two or more warps and fillings woven together in distinctive patterns or designs.

Some staple woolens and worsteds include single-construction fabrics such as cassimere, cavalry twill, Cheviot, crepe, flannel, gabardine, homespun, serge, tweed. Double and triple constructions may include, when deemed necessary, some of the foregoing cloths, as well as beaver, broadcloth, chinchilla, covert, kersey, melton, ski cloth, Whitney, and plaid-back coatings.

THE MANUFACTURE OF WOOLENS AND WORSTEDS

SHEARING OF SHEEP: The fleeces are obtained by hand or power shearing or clipping in April, May, and June. Operation is similar to getting a haircut. All wools, except Texas and California wools, are shorn once a year. These two wools are shorn twice a year because of climate and burs.

SORTING: Dividing the fleece into qualities and grades. From 4 to 20 grades may be obtained from the same fleece, depending on care in sorting. Wool is divided into XX, ¾, ½, ⅜, etc.

BLENDING: Grease wool stocks; an initial stock combination.

DUSTING, WILLOWING, PICKERING: Mechanical operation that knocks out considerable portions of loose matter absorbed by the fleece in the year's growth that is allowed. Leaf, chaff, dried grass, pebbles, burs, etc., are removed to considerable degree.

SCOURING: Washing and removing as much yolk, suint, grime, and dirt as possible. Compared to washing the hair of the human head. Leaves wool clean.

HYDRO-EXTRACTING, WHIZZING: Taking out excess scouring liquor and water from the wool that has been scoured. Leaves wool in damp condition.

DRYING: Actual drying of wool at right temperature to make it suitable for further manipulation.

CARBONIZING—optional operation: Treating wool with hydrochloric or sulfuric-acid bath of the proper strength to reduce any remaining vegetable matter to carbon.

BLENDING, OILING, MIXING: Making up, layer upon layer, the stocks that are to be used to make up the wool lot. Wastes—shoddy, mungo, extract wool, cotton, etc.—are placed in the blend at this stage, if the mix is not to be an all-wool yarn or cloth. Oleic oil is put down on each layer so that the wool will "work" better in the

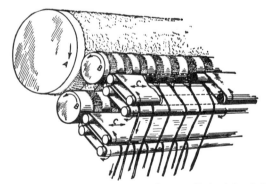

Courtesy: National Association of Wool Manufacturers

**CARD DELIVERY OF ROVING FROM SLIVER FORM
FOR WOOLEN YARN**

The wool fibers lie on the large roller (A) in web-like form. The two smaller rollers (B) lift these fibers in ribbon-like sections by their alternate strips of wire clothing and pass them on to the rub aprons (C). These aprons, by a sidewise motion, impart a mock twist and condense the "ribbons" into round strands of roping.

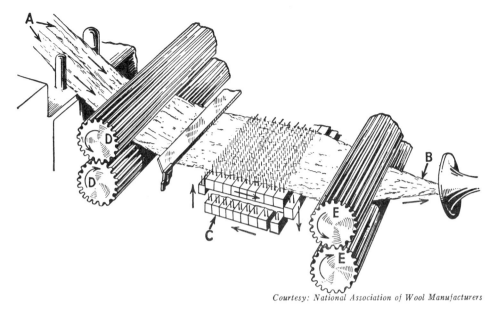

Courtesy: National Association of Wool Manufacturers

DRAWING OR GILLING

Two slivers (A) are drawn and combined to make one smaller sliver (B). The fallers (C), looking like metal combs, move forward through the wool fibers faster than the slivers are fed by the feed rolls (D) but slower than the combined fibers are drawn off by the delivery rolls (E). The fallers parallel the wool fibers and the greater speed of the delivery rolls over the feed rolls stretches or "reduces" the strands of sliver.

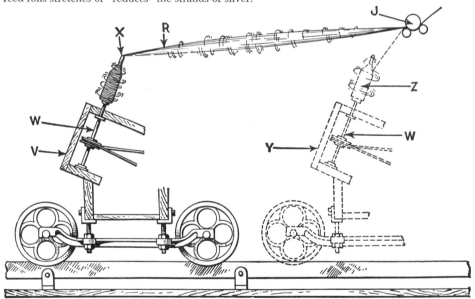

Courtesy: National Association of Wool Manufacturers

MULE SPINNING

In mule spinning the carriage (V) on which the spindles are mounted moves to and from the main spinning frame that holds the feed rollers (J). On its outward trip with the spindles idle, it draws out the roving (R). At the end of this motion, the feed rollers (J) stop; the spindles (W) revolve, allowing the roving (R) to slip over the spindle top (X) thus twisting it into yarn. On the inward trip (indicated by (Y) dotted lines), the yarn is wound onto the bobbin (Z) by the continued revolving of the spindle (W).

[119]

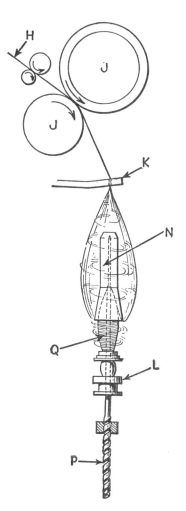

Courtesy: National Association of Wool Manufacturers

DETAIL OF FRAME (CAP METHOD) SPINNING

Illustrated is its difference from mule spinning. Actions are continuous. Spindles revolve on stationary frames. Roving (H) fed continuously from feed rollers (J) through fixed center eyelets (K) is whirled into yarn by revolving spindles (L) which whip it around the cap (N), producing the required twist. Caps (N) on innershafts (P), moving up and down, control winding of yarn on bobbins (Q).

machine operations to follow. Mixing is tearing down the blend in a motion from side to side and from top to bottom to make the stock ready for carding. Original colors here begin to lose their individuality and to merge.

CARDING: Opening up of the matted wool by passing the stock through a series of rollers on the carding machine: cylinders, workers, and strippers. Carding lays the fibers parallel to some degree, gets out some of the foreign matter, and puts the wool in sliver form. The sliver is about the size of a man's thumb. Wool is now in a manageable condition. The last card in the set condenses sliver into a roving form.

COMBING: Done only on wool that is to be made into worsted yarn. An advanced carding that takes out all the short, immature, undesirable fibers which are under a certain specified length. These short fibers are called "noil." Choice fibers are made parallel and the combed stock is all the same in fiber length. Stock is still in sliver, top, or slub form, all these forms signifying at this stage one and the same condition.

DRAWING: On worsted only. Advanced combing which doubles and redoubles the fibers and does the drawing, drafting, twisting, and winding of the stock. Stock is condensed from sliver to slubbing, to roving, which is one step removed from being finished, spun yarn. Also called gilling.

SPINNING: Final operation to make wool or worsted yarn. Final drawing, drafting, twisting, and winding. Spinning is the result of all the foregoing operations. The finished product, yarn, is the result. Spun yarn is a more or less compact, solid, cohesive group of fibers which have enough strength to withstand friction and to give good commercial value in wear. Woolen yarn is spun on mule or ring-spinning frames. Worsted yarn may be spun on one of four machines: mule frame, ring frame, cap-spinning frame, flyer-spinning frame.

MANUFACTURE OF FABRIC

1. WOVEN CLOTH: Woolen and worsted yarns are used in many standard, well-known fabrics. Fabric is made in the loom by the interlacing of the warp ends and filling picks according to the pattern made by the stylist or designer.
2. KNITTED CLOTH: This is made by an interlooping of the yarn, a loop within a loop. Many knit fabrics and garments of woolen or worsted yarn are on the market.
3. PLAITED, BRAIDED, OR LACE FABRICS: While these could be made of woolen or worsted yarns, there is very little call for them. Made by an interlacing of yarn at any angle.

TESTING

1. Name the three types of fabrics made from the wool of sheep.
2. Describe a clear-finish worsted fabric.
3. What is the importance of blending, oiling, and mixing in yarn manufacture?
4. What is the purpose of carding wool fibers?
5. Describe worsted combing.
6. Discuss the operation of drawing in worsted yarn manufacture.
7. Name the three functions of spinning roving into yarn.
8. What are the two machines used to spin woolen yarn?
9. Name the four machines on which worsted yarn may be spun into yarn.
10. Define sliver, slubbing, roving.

Part 1—Unit 20

TOPIC: WOOLEN AND WORSTED FINISHING

Woolens and worsteds receive a great many different finishes because of the wide range of fabrics the market demands and the many uses the fabrics are put to by the consumer. Meltons, kerseys, and beavers have similar finishes; but they may be entirely different from the finishes given to flannel, cassimere, covert, or crepe fabrics. Some materials may have a dull finish, others a rather lustrous effect or sheen. Cloth is converted from the loom or gray-goods condition into a fair, medium, good, or excellent fabric ready for use. Cloth "is made in the finishing," and the finished material after receiving a number of treatments or processes is a commercially salable piece of goods. It should be kept in mind, however, that merely because a fabric has an appealing finish, this is no guarantee that the cloth is of high quality. Many fabrics may have an appealing surface effect, but the wearing qualities may not be of the best. The term "loom goods" is used to imply that the cut of cloth has been woven, taken from the loom, and is now ready for the finishing treatments, wet and dry, that it is to be given. A general plan of finishing follows:

[121]

DRY-FINISHING OPERATIONS WHICH PRECEDE
WET-FINISHING OPERATIONS

PERCHING: Examining cloth for all kinds of defects and blemishes while it is being run over a roller. All imperfections are marked with chalk. The perch resembles the uprights on a football field.

MEASURING: Checking the actual yardage of the cut as it has come from the loom. The weaver is paid on this basis for his work—often at the rate of "so many mills per woven pick of filling."

BURLING: Removal of loose threads and knots by means of burling irons, a type of tweezer. Many knots are pulled to the back of the cloth if cutting of them would make a slight hole in the goods.

SPECKING: The removal of specks, burs, and other detrimental objects that might impair the final appearance of the cloth. This is usually done with tweezers or burling irons.

MENDING: The darning of flaws or defects if mending is the best way to remove them.

SEWING: This involves the experienced sewers in the dry-finishing department of the mill. Ends that are out, picks that are missing, and other similar defects are actually sewed to perfection by weaving-in a new end or a new pick in order to make the fabric conform to the pattern design.

When the cloth has been made perfect as to construction, it is then ready for a number of wet-finishing operations, which may be considered more or less optional, depending on the type of fabric and the finish desired.

WET-FINISHING OPERATIONS

DYEING: The caring for the application of color to the goods. Stock-dyed fabric is colored after scouring and before blending, oiling, and mixing of the stock to be used in the material. Yarn- or skein-dyed fabric: *the coloring* follows spinning of the yarn and precedes the weaving of the cloth in the loom. Piece-dyed fabric is colored after the experienced sewers in the dry-finishing department of the mill have completed their work. Piece-dyeing precedes other wet treatments that the material may receive in finishing.

SCOURING, WASHING: Giving the goods a thorough washing and scouring to remove dirt and clean up soiled areas so that the cloth will be as clean as possible. The treatment is usually rather rigid on the goods, and the time element will vary with the construction of the cloth—loosely woven, medium or average structure, or compact and tightly woven, with high number of ends and picks per inch in the material. The treatment may be compared with the washing of one's hair.

FULLING: Also known as milling or felting, the material is placed in warm, soapy water in the fulling mill. The goods are "pounded and twisted" to make them felt and cause the fibers in the yarns to interlock. This application of heat, moisture, and pressure, followed by a cold rinse, does much to whip the cloth into shape for future treatments.

Sometimes chemicals are used to help moisten, soften, and lubricate the minute fibers so that desirable matting will result.

SHRINKAGE: Fulling does this to considerable degree and gives the material additional thickness and a firmer, fuller texture. Shrinkage, while it may be done by a fulling bath, can also be achieved by ordinary water baths. The longer the shrinkage treatment, the greater will be the shrinkage of the goods, with consequent increase in the strength of the material.

DECATING, DECATIZING: This may be done wet or dry; a shrinking operation in conjunction with cylinder shrinking. In decating, the cloth is shrunk by winding it under tension on a perforated cylinder through which steam is passed. The treatment sometimes replaces London Shrinking.

CRABBING: A treatment given to set the cloth and the yarn twist permanently. The material is passed over several cylinders that rotate in hot water and then is immersed quickly in a cold-water bath. The goods are held firmly and tightly to prevent wrinkling. Repetition of the treatment with increased pressure results in setting the cloth and the finish.

SPONGING: A pre-shrinkage by dampening with a sponge, by rolling in moist muslin, or by steaming, given to woolens and worsteds by the clothing maker before cutting to insure against a contraction of the material in the garment. A very popular sponging treatment is "London shrunk," which is a cold-water treatment originating abroad, and which is frequently applied and guaranteed by the cloth manufacturers themselves. (See LONDON SHRUNK.)

LONDON SHRUNK: Hot- and cold-water treatment, given to worsted fabrics especially, to obtain definite shrinkage percentages; all worsteds should be given this treatment. It relaxes stresses and strains left in the fabric after manufacture; provides a soft and supple hand, and improves the appearance of the material. The shrunken fabric is refinished after the treatment in accordance with the wishes of the purchaser. A trademark name, over 250 years old, owned by Perrott & Perrott (Holdings) Ltd., England.

TENTERING: Its purpose is to bring the cloth to the desired width and to "straighten and level the material." A moistening or wetting of the goods occurs in order to make the cloth supple so that a uniform stretching will be possible. Tentering is done on a long machine; both edges of the fabric are held by clamps from the time it enters the frame until delivered at the front of the machine. The clamping action may be compared with the caterpillar wheels on an army tank—an endless chain that picks up the cloth, carries it along the frame, and then releases it at the front of the machine.

CRAVENETTING: A finishing process which makes fabrics waterproof, rainproof, and spot-proof. The name is a registered trademark of Bradford Dyers' Association, Ltd. The Cravenette Company, U.S.A., is a division of Crown Chemical Corporation, Providence, Rhode Island. The term is now applied to waterproof or water-resistant fabrics in the United States regardless of their nature; the proper name of the cloth, however, is not changed by the application of the process, in accordance with a decision of the United States Customs Service. The process has been used for more than one hundred years. Known all over the world, the treatment uses a solution which destroys the absorbent nature of the fiber and makes it water-repellent; the pores in the yarns or threads and the interstices in the fabric, however, do not become filled, so that the cloth remains porous.

WATERPROOFING: Making material repellent to water. There are many processes on the market today; waxing or liquid treatments are used in waterproofing.

MOTH-REPELLENT: Chemical treatment of wool to make it impervious to moth attack. There are several processes used and they seem to differ in resistance to dry-cleaning and laundering treatments.

DRY-FINISHING OPERATIONS WHICH FOLLOW WET-FINISHING OPERATIONS

NAPPING: The raising of the fibers on the face of the goods by means of teasels or rollers covered with card clothing (steel wires) that are about one inch in height. Action by either method raises the protruding fibers and causes the finished fabric to give more warmth to the wearer, makes the cloth more compact, causes the fabric to become softer or smoother in feel, increases durability, covers up the minute areas between the interlacings of the warp and the filling, and adds to the selling points of the articles made from these napped fabrics. Napped fabrics include blankets, flannel, unfinished worsteds, and some dressgoods and costing fabrics.

A napped fabric can be sheared to an even-height napped effect, and when this sheared cloth is very closely sheared, it is then known as a cropped-finish cloth. Other names for napping are gigging, genapping, teaseled, and raised.

SHEARED: The operation of leveling the napped effect on cloth to give an even, "same height" to the fibers on the face of the goods. Done on woolens and worsteds, as well as on some cottons. The shearing regulates the height of the nap or protruding fibers by a machine which has two or more shearing blades, comparable with the blades on a lawn mower, and the nap can be regulated to one thirty-second of an inch.

CROPPED: A staple finish given to woolen fabrics such as melton, kersey, beaver, and some broadcloth. Actually it is a closely sheared fabric in which the nap effect is quite subdued. Often given to good quality fabrics for use in rather expensive men's coatings. Cropping gives the appearance of a crew cut on a person.

SINGEING: The passing of cloth over a series of gas jets to singe off any protruding or straggly fibers. It gives the goods a smoother, cleaner appearance. Singeing aids to give the characteristic hard finish noted in many worsted fabrics. Both sides of a fabric may be singed, and the treatment may be compared with a person having his hair singed in the barber shop.

UNFINISHED: This term usually applies to "unfinished worsteds." This type of finish applied to worsted is the only one in which the cloth is given a napping or raising treatment on the face of the goods. The weave construction is obscured to considerable degree. The term, however, seems to be a misrepresentation, because this nap is actually a finish on the goods which are ordinarily left with a smooth surface after the cloth is woven in the loom.

PRESSING: A machine that presses or calenders the material to make it presentable. It gives a smart appearance to the goods and is applied to practically all materials. Pressing is done by heated rollers or drums under controlled temperature.

FINAL INSPECTION: As the name implies, it is the final inspection in the mill or in the sponging and examining house in the apparel areas. Final inspection may reveal narrow goods, poor fabric, rejects, faulty selvages, etc. Following this the goods are measured, tags attached, data on the piece or bolt are given a final check, and the goods are then wrapped and ready for shipment to the consignee.

TESTING: TRUE-FALSE QUESTIONS

1. _____ Cloth, as it comes from the loom, is always gray in color.
2. _____ Cloth is usually in the finished condition as it comes from the loom.
3. _____ All woolens and worsteds are given a napped finish.
4. _____ Finishing operations are considered optional, depending on the type of finish to be applied to the cloth.
5. _____ Perching is a wet-finishing operation.
6. _____ Burling and specking precede scouring of the goods.
7. _____ Mending and sewing are wet-finishing operations.
8. _____ Another name for washing is milling.
9. _____ Fulling is a type of felting treatment.
10. _____ Crabbing gives a permanent setting to the material.
11. _____ Decating is a treatment given to bring cloth to proper width.
12. _____ All worsteds are waterproof.
13. _____ London shrinking is a hot-water method to prevent spotting.
14. _____ Singeing is another name for napping.
15. _____ Gigging and raising are considered to be synonymous.
16. _____ Protruding or straggly fibers are removed by shearing.
17. _____ The leveling-off of the nap is done by singeing.
18. _____ Pressing of cloth in the mill is done by hand.
19. _____ Singeing may be applied to both sides of fabric.
20. _____ Teasels may be used in napping woolens.

TOPIC: STANDARD WOOLEN AND WORSTED FABRICS

It has often been said that "fabric is made in the finishing." This statement is very true concerning woolens and worsteds because of the wide variety of the many fabrics in this category with their various types of applied finishes and their many face finishes given for surface effect—usually a particular characteristic that identifies the material.

The following points should be kept in mind regarding woolens and worsteds:

1. Many fabrics are made on a small-repeat twill weave; some few are made with a plain weave, or a small basket weave as in the case of hopsacking.

2. Many cloths may use a two-ply warp to add strength to the warp in the weaving and thus afford better wear to the consumer.

3. Fabrics in the group should be drycleaned rather than washed or laundered.

4. Colors should be fast: fading will impair the life of the garment.

5. Labels should always be read for fiber content and other information.

6. Some cloths remain staples and have a continuous sale; others have waves of popularity and then seem to have little demand.

7. Keep in mind that "the fancy fabric of today may become the staple cloth of tomorrow."

8. Keep in mind the felting qualities of woolen fabrics. Some fabrics which have been felted and thereby had the weave construction covered up include melton, kersey, beaver, broadcloth, fabric used by the Service Academies, uniform fabrics for policemen and firemen.

9. Some fabrics are very closely related, such as crepe and crepon; tricotine, cavalry twill, and elastique; duvetyne and doeskin; covert and whipcord.

10. In the face-finished group of materials there are beaver, broadcloth, bouclé, chinchilla, frieze, melton, kersey, Saxony, tree-bark cloth, ulster, Whitney, poodle cloth, zibeline, etc.

11. The twill-weave group includes cavalry twill, covert, elastique, gabardine, tricotine, whipcord, serge, cassimere, etc.

12. The homespun-tweed fabrics include Cheviot, Donegal, Harris, English, Irish, Jersey, Linton, Manx, Scotch, etc.

13. The serge group includes cassimere, double serge, filling-back serge, French serge, Frenchback serge, storm serge, etc.

14. The check-plaid group includes color-effect, Glen, Glen Urquhart, gun-club check, overplaid, shepherd's check, plaid, tartan, district checks, etc.

15. The women's wear group refers to fabrics such as bolivia, lightweight broadcloth, cashmere, crepes of several types, duvetyne, hopsacking, Poiret twill, silvertone and goldtone, woven tricot, velour, velour checks, chinchilla, zibeline, and a considerable number of other winter-wear fabrics made from basic weaves and staple and novelty yarns combined in the same cloth.

ALBATROSS: Lightweight cloth of wool or worsted with crepe surface. Plain weave; material is soft and has good texture. Washes well, gives good wear. Catches dust and lint and is difficult to handle in tailoring.

ALL-WOOL: A material of any description whose yarns are all wool, understood to be the wool of the sheep. The term is rather deceptive at times, since it includes, in addition to the pure, new fibers, other stocks, such as reused, remanufactured, and low-grade fibers. All-wool is often misunderstood in the trade in buying fabrics and the public is the loser. Very often an all-wool fabric does not mean very much where quality is concerned. All-wool, 100-per-cent wool, and some virgin wool suitings for men's wear have been advertised from $25 to $125 per garment or suiting.

ALPACA: Cloth of fine, silken nature, soft in feel, light in weight. The fiber is obtained from the animal of that name. The yarn is often used as filling in some cotton warp cloths. Alpaca resembles mohair and is imitated in cheaper cloths or those in combination with the genuine. The cloth has much luster and is boardy in some instances. Much alpaca is now made from wool-and-rayon blends. It is used for women's spring or fall coats, suits, sportswear.

ANGORA: Plain-weave dressgoods made of cotton warp and mohair or worsted filling. There is also a twill-woven angora fabric which shows a shaggy, fuzzy face. The name of the animal that gives the mohair fiber used as filling yarn is the angora goat.

ASTRAKHAN: Heavy pile cloth made to imitate the fleece of a sheep. Made of wool, cotton, mohair, waste materials, etc. Curly face. Durable, warm, rather bulky, has to be manipulated carefully. Used to imitate fur. Is woven or knitted.

BACKED CLOTH: Single-texture material with addition of an extra warp or filling that is added for weight and warmth. The extra warp or filling may be of wool, worsted, or cotton. This type of construction is found in Frenchbacks, vestings, worsteds, dressgoods, suitings, and skirtings. Satin weave construction, as well as twill weaves, may be used in the designing of the cloth.

BANNOCKBURN: Name is derived from village of that name, which is about twenty-five miles from Glasgow, Scotland. Obviously, this is a tweed center. Cloth should be made with alternating single and two-ply yarn, the latter being of contrasting colors. Used for suitings and topcoatings, and always in demand. One of the best tweeds on the market, a typically British fabric. The famous battle of Bannockburn was fought in 1314.

BEACH CLOTH: A very broad term with several interpretations. Most beach cloth is strong, coarse, made of heavy yarn and low textures. Plain weave is invariably used. Stripes, checks, prints, and solid colors are used in this rough-and-ready material. Any of the major fibers may be used in making the fabric; blends often feature some of the goods. Beach Cloth is a registered trade mark of the Palm Beach Co., Inc.

BEAVER: Has softer body and longer nap when compared with kersey. Somewhat resembles the animal of that name. Fulled the least when compared with kersey and melton. Solid colors and shades. Heavy in weight. This glossy-face-finish cloth has to be well handled for good results. Gives good wear, warmth, is a neat cloth, and holds up well.

BEDFORD CORD: The practice of adopting English localities for the names of many cloths, not necessarily of local make, is again resorted to in naming this material. Cloth has longitudinal cords that run in the warp direction. Used for coatings, suitings, riding-habit cloth, and uniform material. The color of the cloth resembles that of covert cloth. Bedford Cord is the "sister-cloth" of piqué. The corded effect is secured by having two successive ends weave in plain weave order, thereby actually holding the fabric in place and showing the cord plainly. Cotton and silk Bedford Cord are also made today for the trade.

The material is easy to manipulate if care is exercised since skill and specialized techniques must be used in making garments. Rugged, excellent wear; tailors well.

BLANKET: This cloth is named in honor of the man who first used it as a covering for warmth and sleeping purposes, Thomas Blanket (Blanquette). He was a Flemish weaver who lived in Bristol, England, in the fourteenth century. The cloth is made of wool, worsted or cotton, or by combining these fibers in varying percentages in the construction. Material is heavily napped and fulled. Used for bed covering, robes, steamer rugs. An essential cloth to people in the temperate zone.

BOLIVIA: Light, medium, or rather heavy-weight cloth. Has napped face and is usually piece-dyed. A three-up and three-down twill or similar weave is used in making the cloth. This cloth "is made in the finishing." There are several types of finish available. Weight ranges from nine to sixteen or more ounces per yard.

Cloth is a cut pile, with lines or ribs cut in the warp or in the diagonal direction. The height of the pile varies much. Bolivia is used for cloakings, coatings, and has appeared in suiting cloth. Weave color and finish are salient selling features.

BOUCLÉ: From the French and means "buckle" or "ringlet." Staple suiting fabric on the order of a worsted cheviot with drawn-out, looped yarn construction. These yarns give a "ring appearance" to the face of the cloth. Also made in cottons. Bouclé yarn is very popular in the knitting trade. There are many types of this yarn to be found in this end of the textile business.

BROADCLOTH: Originally the opposite of so-called narrow cloth. Considered as inferior material. Modern broadcloth is a term used that has no particular significance and covers a host of materials. The cloth in woolen and worsted trade is a splendid material, made in staple colors, has compact weave and is given high, lustrous finish.

In men's wear, black broadcloth has a limited use as it has been superseded by dress worsteds for evening and full-dress purposes. The cloth is still popular in legislators', diplomats', and other formal apparel.

Popular broadcloth runs from ten to fourteen ounces per yard in weight. Plain weave is used. Cloth has to be set very wide in the reed of the loom to allow for the great shrinkage to get the proper width. Higher qualities of the material are form-fitting and ideal for women's wear tailored suitings, where drapiness and clingingness are essential.

Crowfoot weaves may be used to advantage in making the fabric; it now belongs to the family group of melton, kersey, and beaver and is the lightest in weight of the group.

BUNTING: Plain-weave, loosely constructed cloth made of wool yarn. Finds use in flags and bunting. Its open texture is suggested because of the fact that the material was originally used for meal sifting or bolting. The term "bolting" is a corruption of this cloth. Not used as apparel. Piece-dyed. Made in cotton cloth now. Boardy in feel.

CASHMERE: The cloth was first made from the downy hair of goats of the Vale of Cashmere (Kashmir). Commercial cashmere cloths are found in overcoatings, suitings, and vestings. Cloth is made of fine wool that may be mixed with hair fibers. Soft finish is noted in the fabric. In an all-hair fiber cloth, the material is made into the famous, well-known, highly desirable shawl cloths.

CASSIMERE: Often confused with and sometimes sold as cashmere. Little resemblance between the two. Cassimere is a two-up and two-down right-hand twill-weave worsted suiting of ordinary stock. Holds crease well. Harsh feeling in either material, worsted or wool. Worsted is far more popular. Easy to tailor, will shine with wear. Finish is somewhat lustrous. Average-quality cloth.

CAVALRY TWILL: A strong, rugged cloth made with a pronounced raised cord on a 63-degree twill weave; woolen or worsted yarn is used. The weaves used for cavalry twill and elastique are the same, and there is no set weave for either fabric. The weave may vary according to the size of the yarn used and the fabric weight per yard. Cavalry twill is the original name; elastique is a United States Government term used very likely because of the different texture of the alternating picks which give the fabric more elasticity and the properties and characteristics of knitted fabric. Cavalry twill has the coarser rib effect when compared with elastique, which has a smoother effect and feel. It also appears in blended fabric constructions.

CHALLIS: Lightweight woolen or worsted cloth of medium texture, made of plain weave. Comes in solid colors and is one of the very few printed wool fiber cloths. Wears and launders well. Too light for good tailoring. Drapes well. Natty cloth. Often is a union cloth. Softness hinders manipulation.

CHECKS, HOMESPUNS AND TWEEDS, STANDARD SCOTCH: The National Association of Scottish Woolen Manufacturers, Edinburgh, Scotland, gives the following list of standard checks, homespuns, and tweeds:

Ardtornish	Erchless	Lochmore
Arndilly	Fannich	Mar
Ballindalloch	Glengarry	Minmore
Balmoral	Glenfeshie	Minto
Brooke	Glen Urquhart	Pitgaveny
Bateson	Glenmorriston	Poltalloch
Black Watch	Gordon Highlanders	Seaforth
Benmore	Hay or Dupplin	Strathspey
Corgach	Invercauld	Strathmashin
Carnegie	Invermark	The Kintail
Carnousie	Kinlochewe	Wyvis
Dacre	King's Own	Welsh Guards
Dalhousie		

CHEVIOT: A rough-surfaced woolen fabric characterized by a hairy nap that distinguishes it from homespun and tweed. Similar in some respects to cassimere, it can also be a worsted material. Usually made on twill weave, the fabric is often stock-dyed, but some piece-dyed cheviot appears from time to time. The yarns may be finer than those used in homespun and tweed and there is much variation in the quality of the goods. Careful attention to the material in manipulation has to be exercised.

The name is derived from the sturdy sheep of the Cheviot Hills of Scotland, whose hardy wool is used to make the cloth. Many other fabrics use cheviot wool as well, but they are not necessarily in the cheviot group of fabrics—homespun, tweed, and shetland.

So-called true cheviot, whether made from plain or twill weaves, is very rugged, harsh, uneven in yarn, does not hold a crease, and has a tendency to sag with wear. It is a good "knock-about" fabric and ideal for sports wear. Made on hand or power looms, it is a genuine British fabric.

Cheviot, tweed, and homespun may be compared in the following manner: Strictly speaking, the original tweed cloth showed warp and filling stock dyed and of the same color. There is now a wide range of color used in all three cloths. While a homespun should be made with a plain weave and a cheviot with a twill weave, there is much confusion in the trade today as to just what is a homespun and what is a tweed. Homespuns are sold for cheviots and vice versa. In the mill, however, a plain-weave cloth of the usual characteristics is called a homespun, and a twill-weave cloth, a cheviot.

Homespun, as a tweed, is the heaviest tweed in weight per yard. It has the salient features noted in genuine tweed. In the trade today, the belief seems to be that homespun is very coarse, rather irregular, and of low texture. The lighter cloths in this group are called tweeds.

The center of this cloth industry, in the olden days, was along the banks of the Tweed River, which separates Scotland from England. Prior to the Industrial Revolution, the material, from raw stock to finished cloth, was made in the home—

shearing of the sheep, sorting, mixing, carding, spinning of yarn, dyeing, and weaving. From about 1750, the factory system began to replace the home system. The result was that most of the cloth was now made on power looms that were coming into use.

Despite the great rise of power-loomed cloths, hand-woven cheviots, tweeds, and homespuns are still in good demand. They bring a good price. Incidentally, there is a good psychology in advertising homemade materials and articles. The better-type store features this end of the trade very much. This is the reason as to why the old home industry still carries on and is flourishing in some of the more remote sections of the world.

CHINCHILLA: The name of a rodent whose fur is mixed with other textile fibers in making cloth of high quality. The cloth of today does not resemble the pelt of the animal. The knotted-face, modern overcoating takes its name from the town of Chinchilla, Spain. The present-day type of chinchilla cloth was first made here. The product is made into coatings, uniform cloth, and livery wear.

Chinchilla is made in double and triple construction. Cotton warp yarn is often used because of its property of twist. This is essential because of the construction of the material. The cotton warp does not show on the face or back of the cloth, and adds to the wearing quality. The nubs found on the face of the material are made by the Chinchilla machine. It attacks the face of the cloth, and causes the long floats used in the construction to be worked into nubs or minute balls. The length of the floats is usually five or seven. Chinchilla is a pile cloth and may be piece, "stock," or skein-dyed. Weaves, other than the filling to be floated, are usually satins. Nubs aid in bringing about the best possible appearance of the cloth. The fabric is one of the "cycle group" and comes into prominence about every seven or eleven years and for a year or so is a genuine leader in the trade.

COTTON-WARP UNION: Staple or fancy cloths made with cotton warp and animal fiber filling. Cotton warps can stand more friction, chafing, and tension than animal fibers. Hence, their use for some particular purpose. The use of cotton warps is an economic measure and some woolens and worsteds do not call for any type of yarn better than these warps.

COVERT: Medium-weight suiting or topcoating. Yarn- or piece-dyed, substantial in feel, natty in appearance. Made of 3-up and 2-down steep twill weave. In plain or window-pane effects. High texture and compact. One of the most durable cloths on market, cuts and tailors very well. Often waterproofed. Good all-around properties.

CRAVENETTE: Registered name given to a celebrated rainproofing process for woolen and worsted apparel cloth by a Bradford, England, manufacturer named Wiley. For want of a better name he gave it the name of the street in which he lived, Craven Street in London. The process was invented about sixty years ago, is now patented, and, while permanent in its application, is understood not to be a chemical saturation treatment. Cravenetting is particularly effective on cloths of well-balanced weave construction.

CREPE: Anglicized from the French word crêpe. Originally a mourning cloth that showed a crimped appearance in fine silken material which got its derivation from the Latin term crispus, meaning "curled." The cloth, when black, is much used in clerical circles. Light in weight, strong, and well-constructed woolen or worsted, it is of superior quality and made with a minutely wrinkled surface in imitation of the silken tissue of crinkled appearance. Crepe will wear and wash well, but there is the danger of shrinkage; care must be used in processing.

CREPON: Of the crepe group of cloths, but stouter and more rugged than the average crepe. The effect is obtained by the types of yarn used in making the cloth. One way is to use yarn of right- and left-hand twist according to some plan or motif; another method is to use yarns with varying twists so that the looser-twisted yarns used will give the crepe effect. Taken from the idea of silk yarns used in making Georgettes and crepe de chines.

CROSS-DYED CLOTH: Textile fabrics that have two or more different fibers in them are cross-dyed. A cloth might have a cotton warp and a worsted filling. The cotton yarn is dyed prior to weaving, and the animal fiber yarn, worsted, requires a dyestuff of different chemical composition than the cotton. The cloth as it comes from the loom would show a dyed cotton warp and an undyed worsted filling. The cloth is then dyed in a vat and the worsted stock is colored—cross-dyed. While this is the accepted definition of cross-dyeing, the process need not be confined to the fibers of the order of their arrangement as here noted. The piece goods do not have to be one color. Expediency is one of the reasons for cross-dyeing. Much used in obtaining blacks and solid shades.

It is claimed that goods taken care of in this manner have a softer and more appealing feel than they would otherwise have, if dyed entirely from the "gray-goods stage" or original condition of the constituent stock.

DOESKIN: Used for trousering, broadcloth coating, waistcoat cloth, and riding-habit fabric. The material is of fine quality, medium weight, smooth-face finished, compact, and is made of wool. There are some points of similarity between this cloth and a buckskin. A five- or eight-harness satin weave is used and the yarn employed is of high count and twist. A dress finish and slight nap are features of the finished garment.

DRAP D'ÉTÉ: French meaning is "cloth of summer." Used for evening wear and very popular with the clergy. Material is a thin staple woolen that has a fine twill weave with high counts of yarn used. It is rather expensive.

DUVETYNE: Suede-like material with fine, soft, silky nap. Kindly feel. Made on a satin weave with cotton warp and spun-silk filling. Ten to twenty ounces in weight. Stock-, skein-, or piece-dyed. For dressy wear, gives good service, warmth; fine draping material and easy to manipulate. Other yarns also used.

ELASTIQUE: A 63-degree, right-hand twill weave is used to make this narrow-and-wide-wale, diagonal-line fabric. It is made of woolen or worsted yarn, tailors exceptionally well and gives the best of wear. (*See* CAVALRY TWILL, page 127–8; TRICO-TINE, page 138.)

ÉPONGE: The name means "spongy." A dressgoods cloth that is very soft and sponge-like. Texture is low, about 20 by 20. A plain-warp and novelty-yarn filling are used, or the reverse can be used to advantage. Cloth is bleached or dyed.

FACE-FINISHED FABRIC: Cloth finished only on the face. Much resorted to in case of meltons, kerseys, and other overcoatings. The weaves used are such that they will permit the type of finish, notwithstanding the fact that the texture is high and the interlacings tight. Plain, twill, and satin weaves are all used jointly in proper construction of the various face-finish cloths.

Other face-finish cloths are bolivia, bouclé, chinchilla, montagnac, tree-bark cloths, Saxony overcoating, and Whitney finishes.

FELT: From the Anglo-Saxon meaning to filt or filter, a defecating device. The cloth is a matted, compact woolen material, of which melton might be cited as an example. There are two types of felt cloth—woven and unwoven. Woven felt is what we are concerned with here. The term may be misconstrued easily and not understood. Felting is another form of the word when speaking of cloth being "felted." Felting of woven cloth is perfected by an interlocking of the natural, scaly serrations on the surface of the contiguous wool fibers through the agencies of heat, moisture, steam, pressure, and hammering. Some felted cloths have admixtures of hair fibers by agglutination. Many types of overcoatings are correctly and incorrectly alluded to as being "felt."

FLANNEL: Lightweight, soft woolen cloth with napped surface. Dull finish conceals weave. In colors and fancy effects. Weight and texture vary somewhat. Kindly feel and hand. Shrinks much if care is not taken in laundering. Sags with wear, does not shine, nor hold crease. Works well.

FLEECE: Heavy, compact, long-napped overcoating much in use. Interlacings well covered up by nap. Range from cheap to expensive cloths. Stock-, skein-, or piece-dyed. From 15 to 25 ounces per yard. Good-quality cloth, gives good wear. Material is often cumbersome and bulky, therefore it may be difficult to manipulate. Nap wears out in time.

FRENCH SERGE: Men's and women's wear cloth of high quality. Cloth is fine in feel and texture, has liveliness and loftiness. High-grade stock is used. Weight runs from six to ten ounces per yard. Weave is often a two-up and two-down, right-hand twill. Yarn is particularly cylindrical in both systems. Piece-dyed and given excellent finish.

·FRENCHBACK: A cloth with a corded twill backing of different weave than the face of the cloth, which is clear finish in appearance. It is a staple worsted cloth. Back weave is of inferior yarn, often cotton, when compared with the face stock. The backing gives added weight, warmth, more texture and stability to the cloth. The interlacings are covered up better than in the average single cloth. Frenchbacks can be made with little extra cost to the cloth. Cloth is usually made of two warps and one filling. It is piece- or skein-dyed, weight ranges from fifteen to twenty ounces per yard. Cloth has good feel and clingingness and may be used for formal or informal wear.

FRIEZE: Heavy woolen overcoating with a rough, fuzzy, frizzy face. Cloth is said to have originated in Friesland, Holland. Irish frieze has an established reputation. Cloth ranges from 22 to 30 or more ounces per yard. Much used in times of war, as overcoating for soldiers. The grade and quality varies considerably. The average army frieze is made of cheap stock, is stock-dyed, harsh and boardy in feel, has much flock in it and is not too serviceable. A composition of frieze could be 67 per cent of three-eighths wool and 33 per cent of shoddy and reworks. Much adulteration is given the cloth, hence the wide variance as to the quality.

GABARDINE: Construction is the same as for cotton gabardine; a 45- or 63-degree twill. These weaves give the characteristic single-diagonal lines noted on the face of the cloth. Material is piece-dyed and used in men's and women's wear. Combination of yarn as to color and cast may be used, as in the case of covert cloth. In this event, the yarn should be skein-dyed. It is also possible to use the stock-dyed method. Because of the twist in the yarn and texture, the cloth wears very well and outlasts similar materials used for the same purposes. Weight ranges from 8 to 14 ounces per yard, clear finish is given. Cotton yarn is often found as the warp structure in the cloth.

GLENGARRY: An English tweed cloth of the homespun and tweed group. Made from woolen yarns of the "hit-and-miss" type. This cloth may have varying grades of fiber content.

GUN CLUB CHECKS: Men's and women's wear dressgoods used for street and sports wear. Three colors of yarn are used in making the cloth. The warp and filling make a natty combination in the cloth. Men's wear cloth may have a smaller check than women's wear cloth. Men's wear cloth could be laid out in warp and filling, as 6 blue, 6 brown, 6 green in warp and filling arrangement. Women's wear cloth could be constructed as follows: 12 light brown, 12 dark brown, 12 green in warp and filling.

HERRINGBONE: Used for suitings, topcoatings, overcoatings, sport coats, dressgoods in men's and women's wear. The cloth gives a weave effect in fabrics that resembles the vertical structure of the fish known as herring. The cloths are staples and always in demand. All herringbones are broken-twill weaves, but not all broken-twill weaves are herringbones. The latter should balance perfectly to be called herringbones and not broken twills. Many types of stock, color, and weaves are used in making the cloth.

HOMESPUN: Originally an undyed woolen cloth spun into yarn and woven in the home with the rather crude machinery used by the peasants and country folk the world over. The industry came to the fore in the British Isles and then spread to the Continent. Because of its substantial appearance and serviceable qualities, homespun is to a great extent woven on power looms today. Genuine homespun cloth supply is very limited, and much power-loom cloth is sold as genuine homespun. The term is much abused, and the gullible buying public may often be confused when buying the cloth as some particular quality. The cloth should be made on a plain weave. Coarse, irregular yarn is used, and quality varies much. The material is coarse and rugged, an ideal rough-and-ready type of cloth. All types and kinds of stock from the highest to lower grades may go into the cloth in its wide range.

HOMESPUNS AND TWEEDS: Tweed is the Scottish word for "twill." Tweeds are closely allied to homespuns. They should be made from a two-up and two-down twill weave of 45 degrees. Homespuns and tweeds can be used to show readily the difference between the plain weave and the twill weave. In tweeds, several variations of twill weaves are often used—broken twills, straight-twill weave, color effects, pointed twills, twilled baskets, fancy entwining twills, braided twills, diamond weaves, ice-cream effects, and combinations of these weaves taken in a group. Much variation of design and color is noted in the cloth. Some of the more prominent tweeds in the trade include English, Irish, Scotch, Cheviot, Donegal, Harris, Jersey, Manx, and Linton.

There are certain cloths sold as homespuns which in reality are tweeds, and vice versa. Consequently, in the trade, it can be seen that either cloth may be made with either weave, plain or some twill, and be accepted by the public under the name given to it. Homespuns, when used in tweeds, usually have the heaviest weight of the cloths in question. It has the average characteristics—yarn, feel, finish, twist, body. From this it may be gleaned that in the trade today the heavy homespun is classed as a tweed. Disregarding the trade and looking at the problem from the mill and manufacturing angles, the following may prove of interest: the homespun should be made from plain weave, the tweed from a twill weave. After the cloth leaves the mill it may be called tweed or homespun to suit the buying public.

In many of the districts of the world today both cloths are hand-loomed and the industry is on a firm footing. Some of our southern states make a substantial amount of the fabric. Asheville homespuns from the Carolinas and other nearby sections are sold in the best stores in the large cities and bring high prices here and abroad. They have color background, tradition, sentiment, history, a psychological appeal, and, best of all, are correctly advertised to catch the eye of the person who can afford to pay the rather high prices asked. (*See* CHEVIOT, page 128.)

HOPSACKING: While the real hopsacking is a coarse, plainly woven, undyed stuff made of jute or hemp fiber, otherwise known commercially as burlap, and serving among the hop growers as well as general merchandise shippers as bagging, the name has been applied to a class of staple and fancy rough woolen cheviot apparel cloths in basket weaves which resemble the original in effect. Most fabric is made on a 2-and-2 basket.

JERSEY CLOTH: Woven or knitted and popular at times and always a staple material. Woven jersey, made of silk, is made into men's shirtings. Much of the cloth is made in woven trade for dressgoods and very often for want of a better name is called jersey cloth.

KERSEY: Originated in Kersey, near Hadleigh, Suffolk County, England. The present kersey cloth is heavily fulled or milled and made of woolen yarn, has a high lustrous nap and a "grain" face. In southern districts of this country there is a cheap type of cloth that is a "Union" but is sold as kersey. Kersey when compared with beaver is fulled more, has a shorter nap, and a higher luster. The weight of the cloth runs from 14 to 25 ounces per yard. Face-finish weaves have to be used so that the ultimate finish will be acceptable to the trade. Cloth gives good wear and is of the dressy, conventional type. Found in blues, browns, blacks, and all popular shades.

KERSEYMERE: A fancy woolen fabric. A cassimere. The name seems to indicate that the cloth is a product of the mills along the waterways of Kersey, England, but since there are no meres or lakes in the vicinity of this town, it is more probable that the term is simply a variation of "cassimere."

KHAKI: From Hindu, meaning dusty. Cloth is made in cotton, wool, worsted, and linen, and with combinations of these fibers. Cloth first gained prominence when it was taken as the standard color for uniform cloths of the Britsh army in all parts of the Empire. Since then, other nations have adopted the color. It is an ideal shade for field service. Fabric has limited use in civilian dress. Some trousering and riding breeches are made with that color.

LINTON TWEED: A distinctive range of tweed fabrics used in summer and winter coatings and ensembles for women's wear. Fabric weight runs from 8 to 18 ounces, with most of the material averaging 12 to 14 ounces per yard. Australian Merino wool, 66s to 72s (medium to fine in quality) is used to make the materials, well known for their extreme softness, wide variance in motif and design, and an appealing hand.

The yarn used is figured on the Galashiels system of 300 yards, where the number of cuts in 24 ounces is the count of the yarn. All Linton tweed is woven on power looms in 60-yard cut lengths, and the finished width is 54 inches. Product of Linton Tweeds, Ltd., Carlisle, England.

MACKINAC, SKI CLOTH, SNOW CLOTH, WINDBREAKER FABRIC: These cloths are in the same group. Heavy coating material, usually low in price and fair in quality. Plaid effects are feature of material, 15 to 25 ounces in weight. Nap and face often different from back. Double cloth in construction. Strong and durable, difficult to tailor. Used much for everyday wear. Keeps shape quite well and does not shine. Good warmth.

MANIPULATED CLOTH: While manipulated woolen and worsted cloths are not literally a hand process of preparing and combining, as the term implies, they are cloths in which the yarns are part wool and part cotton. The yarn is usually made from homogeneous combinations of fibers in the carding and spinning operations. Cloths that contain a small percentage of cotton are often spoken of, in the trade, as "commercial all-wool fabrics."

TESTING

1. Discuss the term "all-wool suiting" in detail.
2. How would you identify a backed fabric, or a double cloth?
3. How does a cashmere fabric differ from a cassimere material?
4. Why are cotton warps used in making some woolen and worsted fabrics?
5. Name one feature or characteristic of each of the following fabrics: (*a*) doeskin; (*b*) drap d'été; (*c*) duvetyne; (*d*) éponge; (*e*) cotton-warp union cloth; (*f*) crepe.
6. Give three reasons why herringbone suiting and coating are popular.
7. Name five types of tweed on the market today.
8. Why are manipulated fabrics much used in children's wear?
9. Give three characteristics of mackinac fabric.
10. Give some reasons why gabardine is always a popular staple material.

TOPIC: STANDARD WOOLEN AND WORSTED FABRICS (continued)

Before purchasing any fabric or garment, certain points should be present in he mind of the purchaser. These include the hand or feel of the cloth, and ts other properties and characteristics, which might include drapability, sagginess, rease-resistance or crease-retention, possible shine through wear, clinginess, compactness or looseness of the weave, texture and surface effect, and whether or not the fabric will stand up under friction, chafing, and wear.

Some fabrics in this group may have hair fibers mixed in to improve the hand and give a more appealing surface effect. Such materials are always somewhat more expensive because of the use of these specialty fibers. Always check the label for the fabric content.

Worsteds will take a much better crease than woolens, but the former may in time shine with wear, and this shine cannot be permanently removed. Some garments are form-revealing while others are form-concealing; some are rather loose-fitting, others are of tighter fit. The occasion, the season of the year, and the weight of the fabric or garment should, therefore, always determine your final choice. Attention should also be given to the color, or combinations of color, along with the weave and the finish of the goods.

The popularity of the ever-present homespuns, tweeds, cheviots, and shetlands shows that these give good service and take much punishment in wear. These and some other fabrics are good for the so-called "town-and-country" wear. Other fabrics are suited to school wear, business wear, formal wear, travel, and knock-about wear. Ease of packing garments is also an important consideration when buying a casual item or a new wardrobe.

Fabrics in the women's and children's wear group include woolens such as bolivia, challis (woolen or worsted), cheviot, crepe, gabardine, duvetyne, éponge, flannel, herringbone, homespun, hopsacking, flannel, some woven jersey, manipulated fabrics, tweed, velour, plaid effects, chinchilla, polo cloth, sharkskin, and Worumbo fabrics.

Mannish-type worsteds in women's wear are ideal for some women who work in offices and are mingling with the public every day. Garments of this type are always in good taste and considered to be smart.

Woolens and worsteds for winter wear are usually on the dark side. During this "gloom period" of the year, grays and browns seem to be predominate—the so-called "dirt-shedding colors," because of their neutral shade or color cast. These colors show spots and stains from travel in bad weather less than other colors that might be used.

Some fabrics are rather expensive, such as Montagnac, cashmere, camel hair, guanaco, and the very expensive vicuña material, which is limited to about 250 coatings a year, since only 10,000 animals can be slaughtered in the one year in Peru and it takes 40 fleeces to make a coat.

Plaids, large and small, are always in demand for both men's and women's wear, as well as the usual run of flannels. The increase of the manmade fibers in blends with wool and worsted has opened up a great vista for "combination materials" that serve well in suitings and coatings.

MELTON: A popular staple in the overcoating group of fabrics which include, in addition to melton, beaver, broadcloth, and kersey. Melton is a heavily felted, hard, plain face-finished fabric. It is used for riding habit, hunting cloth, and in overcoatings. One of the most serviceable cloths for outerwear. In garment making, Melton in lighter construction is used as "under collar cloth." The name of the cloth is said to be that of the originator of the material, but very likely the name comes from the famous Melton Mowbray fox-hunting area of Leicestershire, England. In the group of cloths, Melton is fulled the most, has the shortest nap. It is not a laid nap and cloth is dull in appearance and non-lustrous. Double shearing is given in finishing so as to give the cropped appearance that is one of the distinguishing marks of the fabric. There are many grades of Melton, depending on the type of trade for which it is intended. (*See* BEAVER, page 126; KERSEY, page 132.)

MELTONETTE: Women's wear cloth of very lightweight Melton.

MONTAGNAC: The registered trade mark of E. de Montagnac et Fils, Sedan, France. The fabric is classed as a soft material, and the warp is entirely hidden by the filling. Montagnac is heavily fulled and given great care in further finishing in order to produce the characteristic hand-beaten tufts for the curled effect on the surface of the material.

The material has a fabric weight of 36 ounces per yard. Twill weaves are used in the cloth construction. Montagnac is made with wool and cashmere stock. The cashmere adds much to the appearance, feel, and beauty of the cloth. This silken-like feel is one of the main assets of the fabric, which is made into smart, dressy overcoating.

MOSCOW: Overcoating of the shaggy, napped type, heavy in weight. Cloth gives warmth and somewhat resembles Shetland cloth. Name is given because of the fact that the cloth is in favor in Soviet Russia as well as in other cold sections of the world, where it is used for winter wear. There are many types and grades of the cloth, ranging from very cheap quality to high, expensive materials.

NUN'S VEILING: Plain-weave, soft, lightweight cloth in black or white. Rather flimsy but of good quality. Somewhat harsh in feel but substantial. Resembles worsted challis. Washes and launders well. Gives good wear and fine draping effects. Care must be exercised in manipulating. Also made of nylon, and "Dacron."

OVERPLAID: In reality a double plaid. This is a cloth in which the weave, or, more often, the color effect is arranged in blocks of the same or different sizes, one over the other. Again, the cloth may show a plaid design on a checked ground construction. This effect is noted in English mufti and in golf togs, neat business woolens, and worsteds for morning, lounge, and semiformal wear. This cloth goes under the name, sometimes, of "Glen Urquhart," the name of the Scottish clan that is given credit for bringing this type cloth to the fore. Urqhuarts are usually light or medium in weight, running from 9 to 13 ounces. Two, three, or more colors are used in designing the patterns. Overplaids are ideal for travel, as they do not show the dirt as readily as other cloths, generally speaking. Use of the cloth as overcoating and topcoating is considerable. Overplaids are cycle cloths that come in vogue about every seven or eleven years, and, when in demand, they seem to overshadow other fabrics. There are many grades and qualities found on the market.

OXFORD MIXTURE: Usually a color effect in dark gray noted in woolens and worsteds. The degree of shade is governed by the mixed percentages of black and white stocks used. Mixing takes place prior to the carding and spinning of the yarn. Its reference to Oxford, England, has suggested calling the lighter-weight mixture cloths by the name of Cambridge, the rival university of Oxford. Oxford and Cambridge are the two oldest universities in England and are known all over the world. The colors of the schools are dark blue and light blue, respectively. Hence, the use of dark and light oxfords or grays under those two names. In this country much gray cloth is given the name of Oxford, irrespective of the shade of gray.

PALM BEACH: Registered trademark and name of the Palm Beach Co., Inc., associated with a summer suiting material ranging in weight from 7 to 10 ounces. Plain weave, cotton warp and mohair filling, or other combinations. Cloth is piece- or skein-dyed and is given a clear finish.

PIN CHECK: Worsted suiting that has a small, figured effect about the size of a pin head. Color effects are used in making the design, and the finished fabric shows a cloth studded with the minute pin checks.

PLAID BACK: A light, medium, or heavy overcoating made on the double-cloth principle—two systems of warp and filling, with a binder warp or filling arrangement. The underside of the cloth is a plaid—a series of cross stripes that form a dull or vivid effect. Weight, warmth, and the covering up of the interlacings are features of the material. Plaid backs take the place of linings in some of the cloths used for coating material.

PLUSH: Woolen or worsted pile cloth, the pile being one-eighth of an inch or more in height. Plush has many well-known uses and is an exaggerated form of velvet. The term is from the French *peluche*. This, in turn, is taken from the Latin *pilus*, which means "hair." The cloth is compact and bristly. Made in silk, cotton, mohair, and combinations of fibers, as well as in wool or worsted.

POIRET TWILL: Women's wear dressgoods made of worsted yarn and one of the pronounced diagonal twill cloths. Named for the late Paul Poiret, famous Parisian designer. Cloth is made on a 45-degree twill and there are twice as many ends as picks per inch in texture. A three-up and three-down, right-hand twill weave may be used and some of the cloth has been made from a steep twill of 63 degrees. High twist counts of yarn are used and the material has a soft feel and excellent draping and clinging qualities, which make it ideal in tailoring. Weight of cloth ranges from 8 to 14 ounces per yard. Material is well balanced, has excellent finish, and comes in all shades and colors. This is a piece-dyed cloth, genuine staple, and very popular at intermittent times.

POLO CLOTH: Polo Cloth is the camel-hair fabric manufactured by J. P. Stevens & Co., Inc., of the finest camel hair available. It comes in several weights and the finish is lofty and dense. The most popular color is the natural camel's hair; however, it is also dyed to many other shades.

PRIESTLEY: A well-known English worsted that is found in the better types of clothing stores. Made by the English manufacturer Priestley.

PRUNELLA: A dressgoods material and cloth used in children's apparel made from a two-up and two-down right-hand twill weave. Worsted yarn is used in the cloth. Light in weight, usually piece-dyed and not in vogue at the present time.

RABBIT HAIR: This hair is used in combination with other fibers. It is soft and lustrous and in the better-quality fabrics enough hair may be present to justify the use of the term. Much used in varying percentages in wool and blend fabrics.

RIB CLOTH: Woolens and worsteds that show rib lines in warp or filling because of the fact that cylindrical yarn or rib weaves were used in making the material. Cloths in this group could be poplin, repp, Bedford cord, piqué, corduroy, Tweeduroy, certain fancy dressgoods materials.

SERGE: Popular staple, diagonal effect cloth, dyed in piece and may be made in mixture or fancy effect. It is possible to stock-dye or yarn-dye the materials, but piece-dyeing is preferred. The name is derived from the Latin *serica*. This would imply that the cloth was originally made of silk. The weight of serge runs from 10 ounces upward, and it is one of the most staple of cloths. Made of wool, worsted, cotton-worsted, and in other combinations. The material is usually given a clear finish, although unfinished and semi-finished serge is on the market. Mohair serge is used as a garment lining. A two-up and two-down right-hand twill is used in constructing the cloth, 45-degree angle. The quality and price range is from the lowest to the highest because of the call for all types of serges. It is a formal dressy type of cloth and is conventional at all times. Serge holds the crease very well but will shine with wear. This shine cannot be removed permanently. It is a good cloth in tailoring, as it drapes and clings very well.

Storm Serge: Heavier in weight, lower in texture, and made from poorer stock than the average serge. Three-up and three-down twill weave used, as well as the customary two-up and two-down twill. The cloth has luster, is harsh and wiry in feel. A good imitation of straight serge. It is usually piece-dyed.

French Serge: Very high-type dressgoods with a fine, lofty, springy feel. Superior to the average run of serge and one of the best cloths on the market. Warp may be singles or doubles and filling is usually single-ply-worsted. Weight runs from 6 to 10 ounces per yard. Fabric is piece- or yarn-dyed. An ideal cloth for women's wear of the better sort. The yarn is cylindrical and fabric has excellent tailoring qualities. The best of this cloth is imported from the noted textile centers of France: Amiens, Arras, Lille, Roubaix, Rouen, Tourcoing, and Fontainebleau.

Frenchback Serge: Men's wear serge of two warps and one filling. Runs from 16 to 18 ounces per yard in weight, is piece-dyed, given clear or semi-finish. Used much in winter suitings. Quality and price vary considerably.

Filling Back Serge: Serge of one warp and two fillings. Has same characteristics as Frenchback serge.

Double Serge: Made of two warps and two fillings. Heavier than other worsted serges. Cloth is clear-finished, dyed in the piece, and runs from 12 to 20 ounces in weight. The cloth is not as much in demand as formerly. This is because people do not dress as warmly as they used to years ago.

SHARKSKIN: Fine quality cloth made from small color effects and fancy designs, wherein the effect noted in the finished cloth resembles the skin of the shark. Cloth receives a substantial finish and wears very well. High-texture material with high twist in the yarn. Most of the cloth comes in gray, either from gray yarn or by combinations of black and white yarn. An ideal suiting cloth for the businessman, it is dressy and conventional and does not show the dirt readily. A popular staple material.

SHEPHERD'S CHECK, OR PLAID: Used for suitings, cap cloth, coatings, dressgoods, sports wear. Made of cotton, woolen, worsted, or rayon. The cloth shows black and white checks or plaids. Other color combinations are used as well. The design resembles the Scotch shepherd plaid or check. Some of the fabrics, because of the color combinations used, have the tendency to cause the eyes to "jump," and some people soon tire of the cloth. Conservative designs, however, are much in demand by the trade. There is a wide range of quality and price. In producing the check, the warp and filling arrangement is four black and four white, ends and picks. The weave should begin with the "raisers" up in the lower left-hand corner of the weave. If this is not adhered to, a straight check will result, which is not, strictly speaking, known as shepherd's plaid.

SHETLAND: Overcoating cloth used for storm coats, ulsters, reefers. The cloth is rough and shaggy and has a tufted face. Made of harsh rugged wools of the sheep that come from the Shetland Islands. Other wools are now used in making the popular shetland suiting fabric which is in the small family with homespun, tweed, and cheviot.

SILVERTONE AND GOLDTONE: A coating cloth made from woolen or worsted warp with woolen filling. Fabric is stock-dyed, and weight varies from 16 to 24 ounces per yard. Material is heavily napped. Construction may be single or double. The cloth gets its name from the fact that strands of gold- and silver-colored threads are worked into the face of the material. This produces a gold or silver sheen to the fabric, which is usually attractive. Varies much in quality and price. Popular only at times.

TARTAN PLAID: A conventionalized, multicolored fabric, the outstanding material of which is kiltie cloth. Plaids are used for blankets, robes, many types of dressgoods, neckwear, ribbon, silks, etc. This cloth was given to the world by the well-known Scottish clans of Campbell, Cameron, MacPhee, Stewart, Douglas, MacDonald, MacPherson, MacTavish, etc. In woolens and worsteds, in subdued effects it has use in suiting cloth. The word, formerly spelled "tartanem," was borrowed from the English, who took it from the Spanish term *tiritana*. The Spaniards gave this name to colored cloths as far back as the thirteenth century. The Scots have capitalized on tartans more than any other nation, and the general belief is that these plaids were Scottish in origin. The Gaelic term is *breacan*. It takes about seventeen yards of material to make a complete kiltie outfit for an adult. The cloth is most interesting, and a study may be made of the symbols and meanings of the plaids by enterprising students interested in the subject. Two-up and two-down twill weaves are used in construction.

TRICOT: High-grade woolen or worsted cloth used in ladies' wear. The term in French means "knitting." The woven cloth usually repeats on four or eight picks, and there are horizontal rib lines in the finished fabric. Cloth is made from a double cloth weave on the principle of the double plain weave. Tailors very well and is conventional.

TRICOTINE: Of the family of whipcords, coverts, and gabardines. Made from a 63-degree twill that gives the characteristic double twill line on the face of the cloth. A good weave to use in making the material is $\dfrac{3\ 3\ 1\ 1}{1\ 1\ 2\ 1}$. Other weaves of similar nature may be used as well. This thirteen-harness fabric is dyed in all staple colors. The cloth drapes well, is easy to tailor, and is a smart conventional fabric. A staple cloth. Skein-dyed tricotine is on the market. Cloth is usually of medium and best quality.

TROPICAL: Fancy suiting material of plain and rather open weaves. It is a lightweight worsted of the semi-staple group. Fabric is ideal for summer and tropical wear, and somewhat resembles Palm Beach cloth. Weight goes from 6 to 12 ounces per yard. Warp and filling are of high counts, usually 2/60s or better. Material is skein- or piece-dyed, and clear finish is given. Tropical mixtures and heathers are popular cloths in the tropical range, and these cloths are stock-dyed to give the desired pattern effect.

TROUSERING: Use is obvious. The material is woven firmer and tighter than suiting cloth. It is also heavier in weight. Stripings are the main feature of the fabric. Used for dress occasions and in ordinary everyday wear. Made from combinations of basic weaves. The garment has a dark or black background to better enhance the striping effect. The cloth is often of double construction in warp and filling or may be made of two warps and one filling.

TWEED: SOME MAJOR TYPES

Cheviot Tweed: Differs from other tweeds in that warp and filling are stock-dyed the same color. Wide range of colors are observed, and quality varies much. A very popular fabric.

Donegal Tweed: Uses about the same stock as that used in Irish tweed, but the weave used is herringbone. Irish tweed is a two-up and two-down twill weave. White nubs are seen in the warp, while filling has nubs of blue and green wool fibers introduced in carding of wool.

Harris Tweed: Sixty miles northwest of Scotland lie the Outer Hebrides, the home of Harris Tweed. Harris and Lewis, Barra, Benbecula, North Uist, and South Uist comprise the compact islands, with Harris and Lewis known locally as the Long Island. The islands are wide stretches of peat bogs and rocky moorland unsuitable for cultivation and of little grazing value. Except for the modern port city of Stornaway, the islands seem to have stood still; there are no towns, and the villages are called townships. The common grazing ground for the sheep is around the villages. The crofters' cottages stand out in isolation against the somber background of the hills and moors. Dwellings are very primitive, made of double dry walls of undressed stone, thatch-roofed, with the floors made of beaten earth with a stone hearth in the middle for the peat fire. Furniture is very simple. The Harris Tweed industry has become the mainstay of the islanders, who are kept busy with the ever-increasing demand for Harris Tweed all over the world.

Because of the paucity of grazing ground for sheep sufficient to provide for the increasing demands for the fabrics, it has become necessary to import wool from the Scottish mainland. All the wool used in making the tweed must be virgin

Scottish wool. After the fleeces are sorted for grade, the grease and other waste matters are washed out in the soft peaty water of the lochs or burns. Much vegetable matter is removed by hand. After washing or scouring comes drying, which is done on the stone walls or on lines under the influence of the sun and the ocean breezes.

At the present time only synthetic dyes are used for coloring. The old-time hand method of carding, tedious, time-consuming, and laborious, has been superseded by the use of machine carding frames. The womenfolk spin and ply the yarns, and it is one of the few places in the Western world where this practice is still in vogue. Every piece of Harris Tweed is still hand-woven on looms in the homes of the islanders. This is a laborious process, but when a hand-woven tweed is compared with power-loom fabric, it will be noted at once that the results justify the labor expended.

Concerning finishing or waulking, the old-time hand methods have been pretty well superseded by mechanical means. This converts the loom fabric from a harsh hand to one that is appealing in touch and in surface effect.

According to the Federal Trade Commission, Washington, D.C., "Harris Tweed" is limited to fabric made from virgin Scottish wool and woven on hand looms on the islands of the Outer Hebrides. This eliminates the question of imitations, inasmuch as Harris Tweed is definitely a distinctive fabric. There are two types—fabric made from hand-spun yarn and that made from machine-spun yarn.

The Harris Tweed Certification mark is owned and administered by The Harris Tweed Association, Ltd., London, England. Its exclusive trademark is the long familiar (since 1912) "orb mark," a ball-shaped figure surmounted by a cross. All of its wools are processed into yarn in the spinning plants in the Outer Hebrides and then the yarn is sent to the many crofters in the islands to be hand-woven into fabric and then returned to the spinning plants in Stornaway to be finished. The certification is then stamped onto the fabric, which is the guarantee that the tweed complies with the definition of Harris Tweed.

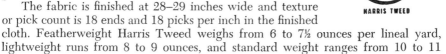

HARRIS TWEED

The fabric is finished at 28–29 inches wide and texture or pick count is 18 ends and 18 picks per inch in the finished cloth. Featherweight Harris Tweed weighs from 6 to 7½ ounces per lineal yard, lightweight runs from 8 to 9 ounces, and standard weight ranges from 10 to 11 ounces per yard.

Irish Tweed: Made of white warp with filling of dark shades of blue, brown, black, or gray.

Jersey Tweed: A soft-feeling tweed that comes in plain colors; much used in women's wear ensembles which feature a tweed skirt of regulation or fancy twill effect and a jacket of plain jersey.

Manx Tweed: Made on the Isle of Man, the fabric ranges between 15 and 16 ounces per yard. The warp is dove-gray in color, while the filling is one pick of solid brown and one of brown and bright-green twisted together. Popular in men's wear coating and suiting.

Monotone Tweed: Tweed of mixed effect made by weaving together yarns of different shades of the same color. Must be made of all wool.

Scotch Tweed: Cloth with a white warp and stock-dyed filling or vice versa. The colors used are often vivid, and much contrast is noted in the garment. This tweed often may have fibers other than the usual type used in construction since there is a rather wide range of fabric under this name. The yarn is quite irregular and there is a great range in fiber lengths used in the yarn.

ULSTER: Heavy overcoating fabric, rather loosely woven with warp of right-hand twist yarn and filling of left-hand twist yarn. All types and kinds of fibers are used in the material, depending on the type of cloth wanted. May be piece-dyed or stock-dyed for mixed effects. The long nap given the fabric in finishing is pressed down. Material is good for cold, stormy winter weather. Fabric weight is from 24 ounces to about 30 ounces.

UNIFORM CLOTH: A family of serviceable woolen cloth on the general order of kerseys and flannels as the most important. Colors are blue, gray, khaki, brown, and mixed effects. The cloth is used as uniform material for military, naval, police, fire, postal, railway, bus, public service, chauffeurs, regal livery, and other public and private groups. As most of these cloths are furnished under certain approved and decreed specifications, according to contract, a very exact demand is made on the goods to meet requirements.

UNION CLOTH: Woolens and worsteds which have textile fibers from other fiber kingdoms in them. For example, a cloth that has a cotton warp and worsted filling is classed as a union.

VELOUR: From the Latin *villosus*, meaning "hairy." Cloth is used as overcoating material and in velour check form is used for dressgoods and coating cloth. The material is a thick-bodied, close-napped, soft type of cloth. The name is used rather indiscriminately and is applied to suiting fabric as well. Generally speaking, a velour is a lightweight cloth that runs from ten to twenty ounces per yard, and is given a face finish. Various kinds of yarn are used in making the several types of velour on the market. Twills or broken constructions are used in laying out the pattern. There are several fabrics of the same construction, but of slightly different finish, to be found in the trade—suedyne, suedette, lustora, duvedelaine, valora, etc. The cloth is made in the finishing and much of the best-grade velour is really beautiful cloth.

WEST OF ENGLAND: Woolen fabrics of high repute made in the West of England, notably in Stroud and Trowbridge. The quality and finish of the fabric are known throughout the world, and they are distinctly associated with this part of England and should not be confused with "West Riding" materials produced in the Yorkshire area.

WHIPCORD: Dress woolen or worsted of fine, high texture. The twilled yarn is sharply defined with some fancy suggestions to whip lashes or cords. There are several cloths, some major and some minor in this group—coverts, tricotines, Poirets, twillcords, chicotines, piquetines. The yarn in a whipcord is bulkier than the yarn of the tricotine or gabardine. The cloth is lower in texture and heavier in weight than these two materials. Weight ranges from 12 to 20 ounces per yard. Whipcord finds use in livery cloth, topcoats, uniform cloth, suitings, and in public utility materials. The cloth may be made of cotton warp and worsted filling, and steep twill weaves are used in construction. The fabric is exceedingly durable and rugged and stands hard usage and wear. Shines in time with wear.

WHITNEY: A soft-bodied, tufted-face overcoating fabric not unlike chinchilla. The effect, however, in finishing the goods is that of a transverse wavelike series of lines rather than the nub or knot effect seen on chinchilla. Whitney is fulled, napped, and sheared, and it is the passing of the fabric through a set of brushes with an oscillating movement which brings out the desired pattern finish. These brushes, by abrasion, wear down the nap for the final effect. The machine moves at the rate of about one inch per minute, and it takes considerable time to finish the belt of cloth. Whitney-finish comes only in high-grade, rather expensive coating.

WOOLENS: Cloth made from woolen yarn but not always 100-per-cent wool in content. The average woolen has a rather fuzzy surface, does not shine with wear, may not hold the crease, has nap, and in the majority of cases is dyed. Woolen finish is easily recognized on cloths to determine the difference between this cloth and a worsted material.

WORSTEDS: Popular class of cloths made of choice woolen stock using fibers of approximately the same length in staple. The process of making worsted cloth originated in the little village of that name in Norfolk County, England.

The Paris Exposition of 1889 "made" worsteds; it was also at this event that Count Hilaire de Chardonnet showed his first fabric made of what was then known as "artificial silk." Now known as rayon and acetate, the Philadelphia Sesquicentennial Exposition of 1926 had much to do with fostering the advent of these two manmade fibers.

WORUMBO: The construction of the fabric is such that there are long floats on the face of the goods. Following preliminary finishing operations, the fabric is passed through a machine somewhat on the order of the Whitney finishing machine. Named for Worumbo Mills, Lisbon Falls, Maine, the fabric is ideal for heavy-weight winter overcoating of the better type. It is now owned by J. P. Stevens & Co., Inc.

ZIBELINE: Used for cloakings, coats, and capes in women's wear. The cloth is made from cross-bred yarns and the fabric is strongly colored. Stripings, sometimes noted in the cloth, work in very well with the construction and appearance of the finished garment. The finish is a highly raised type, lustrous, and the nap is long and lies in one direction. The cloth may or may not be given a soft finish and feel.

TESTING

1. Define a blended fabric. Name three possible fiber combinations that could be used for winter wear.
2. What is meant by the term "staple fabric"; "fancy or novelty fabric"?
3. Name three types of serge.
4. What is the difference between a check and a plaid?
5. Define overplaid.
6. Name three fabrics that might be used in a mannish-type women's wear worsted suiting.
7. Explain the rise of the use of manmade fibers in tropical suitings.
8. Define a union fabric. Give three possible fiber combinations that could be used in a cloth of this type.
9. How does a union fabric differ from a blended fabric?
10. Define uniform fabric. Name three cloths that could be classed as uniform material.

Part 1—Unit 23

TOPIC: EXAMINATION ON STANDARD WOOLEN AND WORSTED FABRICS

TRUE-FALSE QUESTIONS   40 points

1. _____ An all-wool suiting is always of good quality.
2. _____ A 100-per-cent woolen suiting assures the purchaser of the garment that the quality is of the best.
3. _____ A virgin wool suiting is always high in quality.
4. _____ Worsteds will hold the crease better than woolens.
5. _____ Woolens have the tendency to shine more than worsteds with wear.
6. _____ Tropical worsted suiting is noted for the high twist in the yarn.
7. _____ Jersey fabric may be woven or knitted.
8. _____ Cheviot should be made on a twill weave.
9. _____ Homespun is always yarn- or skein-dyed.
10. _____ Nun's veiling, in colors or prints, is called challis.
11. _____ Tweed should always be made with a plain weave.
12. _____ Gabardine is constructed by the use of a satin weave.
13. _____ Serge is usually piece-dyed.
14. _____ The cord-effect in Bedford cord suiting fabric runs in the warp direction.
15. _____ Gray goods are always gray in color.
16. _____ Woolen fabric usually has a higher texture than worsted cloth.
17. _____ Astrakhan is an example of a heavy pile fabric.
18. _____ Albatross is characterized by its crepe effect.

19. _____ Cashmere fabric is made from wool and hair fibers.
20. _____ Cassimere is an example of a clear-finish worsted fabric.
21. _____ Cashmere is a softer feeling fabric when compared with cassimere.
22. _____ Reused wool or remanufactured wool may be used in melton fabric.
23. _____ Melton is an example of a heavily fulled woolen cloth.
24. _____ Kersey cloth may be considered as a formal, conventional type of fabric for dress wear.
25. _____ Kersey usually has a softer hand or body when compared with beaver.
26. _____ When compared with kersey, melton, and beaver, broadcloth is the lightest-weight fabric in the group.
27. _____ Bolivia coating is a woolen or worsted filling pile fabric.
28. _____ Chinchilla is made only in a double-cloth construction.
29. _____ Velour is characterized by its short, soft, thick nap.
30. _____ Chinchilla coating is always made from chinchilla fur.
31. _____ Fleece coating is known by its short nap on the surface.
32. _____ Another name for mackinac cloth is ski fabric.
33. _____ Wool crepe is usually considered heavyweight dressgoods.
34. _____ Flannel comes only in solid colors.
35. _____ Windowpane effects may appear in covert coating.
36. _____ Elastique, in surface effect, closely resembles worsted serge.
37. _____ Serge appears on the market only in hard finish.
38. _____ Elastique, tricotine, cavalry twill, and whipcord may be classed as belonging to the same group of twill fabrics.
39. _____ Whipcord is usually made of finer yarns when compared with gabardine.
40. _____ Zibeline is a fabric with a closely cropped nap.

MULTIPLE-CHOICE QUESTIONS   10 points

Underline your choice in second column of words.

1. Has a nubby face effect.   Melton, Frenchback, bouclé, bunting.
2. Made from a steep twill weave.   Duvetyne, éponge, flannel, elastique.
3. Has a mottled surface effect.   Serge, challis, Bannockburn, drap d'été.
4. Face-finished cloth.   Frenchback, gabardine, beaver, overplaid.
5. Made with right-hand and left-hand   Plush, tropical, herringbone, Bedford cord.
   twill combined.
6. Ideal for use as raincoating.   Wool crepe, cravenette, flannel, cheviot.
7. A very heavy overcoating.   Tweed, ulster, doeskin, crepon.
8. Very soft in hand or feel.   Cassimere, serge, cashmere, frieze.
9. Made from basket weave.   Shetland, velour, hopsacking, bolivia.
10. Usually rather low in quality.   Whipcord, zibeline, Whitney, manipulated fabric.

MATCHING QUESTIONS   10 points

Place the number of your choice from the second column of words on the correct blank space before the words in column one:

1. ____ Kersey   1. Should be made of plain weave.
2. ____ Plush   2. Should be made of twill weave.
3. ____ Montagnac   3. Popular fabric with the clergy.
4. ____ Herringbone   4. Popular fabric used in uniforms.
5. ____ Tropical suiting   5. Double diagonal line seen in weave.
6. ____ Homespun   6. Has cotton warp and woolen filling.
7. ____ Drap d'Été   7. Always made with satin weave.
8. ____ Tricotine   8. Contains varying amounts of cashmere fiber.
9. ____ Union fabric   9. Popular upholstery fabric.
10. ____ Tweed   10. Lightweight summer suiting.
                               11. Characterized by its rather long nap.
                               12. Made from broken-twill weave.

COMPLETION-TYPE QUESTIONS   20 points

1. Melton, kersey, broadcloth and _____ belong to the same family group of fabrics.
2. Homespun, cheviot, shetland and _____ belong to the same family group.
3. Cavalry twill, tricotine, whipcord and _____ belong to the same family group.
4. Flannel, in order to possess a good nap, should have a _____ filling.
5. Shoddy, mungo, reused and _____ fibers may be classed as substitute or waste fibers used in woolen and worsted manufacture.
6. Gun club check, shepherd's check and _____ are usually yarn- or skein-dyed fabrics.
7. Woolen or worsted bunting is usually made on a _____ weave.
8. Poiret twill fabric is made on a _____ twill weave.
9. Monk's cloth and hopsacking are made on a _____ weave.
10. Covert is always made on a _____ weave.

IDENTIFICATION QUESTIONS   20 points

One of the fabrics contained in each question below does not belong with the other cloths listed. Underline the name of the material which does not belong in the respective groupings.

1. Ulster, zibeline, plush flannel, nun's veiling.
2. Bunting, homespun, crepe, blanket.
3. Tricotine, elastique, cavalry twill, bouclé.
4. Gabardine, serge, whipcord, covert, challis.
5. Melton, kersey, pin check, beaver, broadcloth.
6. Homespun, tweed, duvetyne, shetland, cheviot.
7. Overplaid, gun club check, Glen Urquhart, velour, Scotch tartan.
8. Frenchback, backed fabric, fleece coating, union fabric.
9. Chinchilla, Whitney, zibeline, chalk stripe, Montagnac.
10. Herringbone, covert, melton, tropical, mackinac fabric.

Part 1—Unit 24

TOPIC: HAIR FIBERS OR SPECIALTY FIBERS

COMPARISONS AND CONTRASTS BETWEEN HAIR AND WOOL FIBERS

An animal fiber consists of a root situated in the depression of the skin (hair follicle) and a shaft of the hair proper. A typical hair has three definite tissues:

1. Epidermis or the outer layer.
2. Cortex or the cuticular layer.
3. Medulla or the pith.

The long, stiff, elastic hair of the hog is known as a bristle.

Bristle hair is short, straight and stiff, with a medulla such as the body hair of a horse.

Beard hair is long, straight, or slightly wavy, and the hair is regularly distributed, generally with a medulla, which give the pelts of various animals their value.

Human hair and hair from the manes and tails of horses also belong in this class.

[143]

Wool fibers are soft and flexible, and the pronounced serrations peculiar to wool cause wool fibers to felt or mat easily, a decided advantage of wool fibers over other animal fibers.

It is difficult to determine the point where an animal fiber ceases to be a hair, since the one by imperceptible gradations merges into the other, so that a continuous series may be formed; from the finest Merino wool fiber to the rigid bristles of the wild boar. Thus, the fine, soft wool of the Australian Merino sheep merges into the cross-bred sheep of New Zealand. This merges into the long English and luster wool fibers, which in turn merge into alpaca and mohair materials with clearly marked but undeveloped scale structure. Again, such animals as the camel and the Cashmere or Kashmir goat yield fibers which it would perhaps be difficult to classify rigidly as either wool or hair.

Wool fibers seem to make the most desirable fiber in the animal-fiber kingdom. Sufficient length, strength, and elasticity, together with certain surface cohesion to enable many fibers to be drawn and twisted in the spinning operation in order to form a coherent and continuous yarn or thread, prove to be valuable properties.

The power of absorbing coloring matter from solution and becoming dyed thereby, and the property of becoming bleached or decolorized when treated with suitable chemical agents, seem to give wool some advantage over the other animal fibers.

Wool fibers felt or mat easily, thereby causing them to have uses for which other animal fibers are unsuited.

The unmodified term "wool" has special reference to the product obtained from the many varieties of sheep.

There are several animal fibers other than wool and silk used in textile manufacturing. The limited use of these fibers is due to their limited supply. The so-called rare specialty fibers include alpaca, camel hair, cashmere, guanaco, llama, mohair, and vicuña. The common animal fibers include hair from the cat, cow, goat, horse, and rabbit.

Dehairing of hair or specialty fibers is a process which separates the soft down hair in camel hair, cashmere, etc. There are several methods used, and basically it is a carding process done after the hair fibers have been scoured. Each processor has his own secret method of dehairing fibers. Depending upon the origin, of, say, cashmere fiber, the yield after scouring and dehairing ranges from 25 per cent to about 45 per cent.

INFORMATION ON HAIR FIBERS

ALPACA: Raised in the Andes Mountains, the fleeces of the alpaca are usually obtained after a two-year growth. The fiber diameter is about 1/800 inch. The fiber is lustrous, soft to touch, strong, rather wavy; the fleece will weigh about ten pounds.

Fine alpaca is from 4½ inches to 8 inches in length; medium alpaca is 5½ inches to 9 inches long; coarse alpaca is from 7 to 11 inches in staple length.

In color, alpaca fibers range from white to brown or black. The two types of fibers obtained from the 180-pound animal are:

1. Soft wool-like hair.
2. Stiff beard hair.

Alpaca is coarser than either camel or vicuña.

CAMEL: There are two types of camel: the dromedary or one-hump type, and the Bactrian, or two-hump type. Dromedaries, whose fibers are never used in fine fabrics, are found in Arabia, Egypt, Iran, Senegal, and Syria. Bactrians are native to all parts of Asia from the Arabian Sea to Siberia, and from Turkestan to the steppes of Tartary, Tibet, Mongolia, and Manchuria, and parts of China.

Three types of hair are obtained from camels:

Quality One: The "down-type" of fiber, also known as noil and next to the hide, is short, soft, and silken-like in feel. The fibers are beautiful light-tan shades; they have good tensile strength and may be used in the natural condition or dyed dark colors. Quality one is used in high-grade fabric which comes in tannish colors. The fibers of this quality are from 2½ to 3 inches long.

Quality Two: Beneath the outer hair of the animal there is a growth which combines the outer hair and the shorter, less coarse portion of the fleece. This grade is used in apparel fabric.

Quality Three: The outer hair—coarse, tough, and wiry—possesses cactus-tipped ends and ranges in color from brownish-black to reddish-brown.

The fibers, which range from 4 inches to 10 inches in length, are used by natives in making blankets, tents, cord, and rope.

The camel sheds its hair in clumps and therefore is not shorn or plucked, as in the case of other fleece-bearing animals.

CASHMERE: The finest cashmere is raised in Tibet, Cashmere or Kashmir in northern India, Iran, Iraq, and southwest China. Cashmere is more like wool than any other fiber. The hair of the Kashmir goat is very cylindrical, soft, strong, and silken-like. True cashmere, which is brownish in color, ranges from 1¼ to 3½ inches in length. The long, coarse outer fibers are from 3½ to 4½ inches long. The fiber diameter is about 1/1600 inch. The hair is used chiefly for cashmere and paisley shawls.

CAT HAIR: It comes in many colors and has good luster; it is from 0.4 to 0.8 inch in length. The hair is used as "filler-in" fibers in some dressgoods.

COW HAIR: The fiber is used in coarse carpet yarns, blankets and chief felted goods. The industry centers in Siberia. The hair which is from 0.6 to 2 inches in length, is classed in the following manner:

1. Thick, stiff beard hair.
2. Soft, fine beard hair.
3. Very fine, soft "wool hair."

GOAT HAIR: In addition to mohair and cashmere, which are obtained from goats, there are two common types known as ordinary goat hair and meadow goat hair. The hair ranges in color from white to yellow to brown or black. The fibers have some use in lower-quality fabrics.

GUANACO: The guanaco, found chiefly in Argentina, is the wild member of the llama family. The fleeces of the animals are seldom seen in world markets and do not seem to have much commercial value.

HORSE HAIR: Russia sponsors the industry. The body hair of the horse is more lustrous than cow hair. The length is from 0.4 to 0.8 inch, while mane and tail stock ranges from a few inches to several feet. It is used for stuffing in upholstery and summer horsehair hats, as a shape retainer in lapels of coats, and as "filler-in" stock.

LLAMA: The members of the llama family include four distinct types and two hybrid types. The distinct types are llama, alpaca, guanaco or huanaco, and vicuña; the hybrids are huarizo, the offspring from a llama father and an alpaca mother, and paco-llama or misti, the offspring from an alpaca father and a llama mother.

Llamas are raised in Bolivia, Peru, southern Ecuador, and northwestern Argentina. Lake Titicaca, 110 miles long and 35 miles wide, which forms a part of the boundary between Bolivia and Peru, is the center of llamaland.

The animal, which weighs about 250 pounds and is about one-third the size of a camel, will not thrive under a 12,000 foot elevation; hence, llamas are found

Courtesy: S. Stroock & Co., Inc.

Kashmir goats

Vicuña
Misti

Huarizo
Guanaco

Courtesy: S. Stroock & Co., Inc.

Suri   Llama
Camel   Alpaca

in the Andes Mountains of the aforementioned countries. The life span of the animal is ten to fourteen years. The animal is not found north of the equator.

Full-fleece bearing capacity of the llama is not obtained until the animal is more than four years old. The fleece, obtained every two years, weighs about five pounds; the staple ranges from ten to twelve inches.

The outer coat of the animal is thick and coarse; the hair next to the body is very fine and closely resembles the hair of the alpaca. The color ranges from brown to black or from white to a mixture of colors. Underbelly hair is usually white.

MOHAIR: The angora goat, which furnishes mohair, is one of the oldest animals known to man. Mohair is 2½ times as strong as wool and will outwear it. The goats are raised in South Africa, western Asia, Turkey, and neighboring countries, and in Texas, California, and Oregon. Kerrville is the great center of the mohair industry in Texas.

Foreign mohair, 9 to 12 inches in staple length, is allowed a full year's growth prior to shearing; domestic fleeces are obtained biannually in California and Texas, annually in Oregon. The hair of the animals found in Texas and California will fall out if allowed a full year's growth. Texas fleeces weigh about 2½ pounds; Oregon fleeces about 4 pounds.

Angora goat fleeces show fibers which average about 9 inches. The fibers, which are very strong, high in luster, whitish in shade, fairly soft in handle, and straight in staple appearance, possess good uniformity. The diameter is about 1/700 inch. The length and luster of mohair fiber is more desirable than staple fineness. Mohair is used for braid, fancy dress materials, felt hats, linings, and plushes.

RABBIT HAIR: It is spun with major textile fibers in making yarn for women's wear dressgoods, since it will give smoothness and good handle to lower-quality fabric. Ranges from 0.4 to 0.8 inch in length.

VICUÑA: The animal is found at elevations approximating 12,000 feet in the almost inaccessible regions of the high plateau area in Peru, northern Bolivia, and southern Ecuador. Vicuñas, which live above the clouds, are about three feet high and weigh from 75 pounds to 100 pounds. The animal has a life span of about twelve years. The fiber varies from golden chestnut to deep, rich fawn shades, to a pallid white beneath the body and on the surface of the extremities, with light markings on the face and jaws.

Vicuña fibers, which are strong and resilient, have a marked degree of elasticity and surface cohesion. These fibers are the finest of all known animal fibers, being less than 1/2000 of an inch in diameter, with a count of about 2500 to the inch, which is about one-half the diameter of the finest sheep's wool. The respective diameters of the two fibers are vicuña, .00043; fine sheep wool, .00080 inch. The outer beard of the animal serves as a coat and is not used in making good-quality fabrics. The inner hair, which grows close to the skin of the neck, under shoulders and on the sides and underportions of the body, is very soft and silken-like.

Vicuña, the aristocrat of fibers, may be used to best advantage in the natural state; if dyed, it is necessary, because of the tendency of the fibers to resist absorption of dyes, to remove at least half of the natural grease and oil.

Forty fleeces are required to make enough fabric for a single coat. Since only 10,000 fleeces may be obtained during any one year, the total number of vicuña coats produced is limited to about 250 annually.

TESTING

1. Give some of the outstanding facts concerning camel hair: where found, the types of hair, and fiber length.
2. Do the same with any three of the following: Alpaca, llama, mohair, angora goat, and vicuña.
3. List five differences between wool and hair.
4. Why is vicuña such an expensive fiber?

TOPIC: APPAREL USES FOR THE HAIR FIBERS

The rarer types of hair fibers are used in fabrics and garments of quality and are rather high priced. The fibers may be used alone or else blended with other fibers of like nature, or with wool in varying percentages. A coating may have 60 per cent wool, 30 per cent camel hair, and 10 per cent cashmere in its fiber content. Fabrics and garments using hair fibers have added smoothness and a more appealing hand and surface texture compared with similar cloths not containing such fibers.

With the exception of the very expensive fibers such as vicuña, cashmere, and guanaco, which are beyond the purchasing power of the average consumer, hair fibers are mixed with wool, or at times, in some special fabrics, with worsted, to give added support to these specialty fibers when spun into yarn—the wool acts as a base and support for the fibers. The wool fiber is the only animal fiber that will felt in a natural manner; hair fibers are devoid of any felting property.

Fabrics used in the manufacturing of coatings in this group must carry the content label of each fiber used with its exact percentage in the material. This is in accordance with the Wool Labeling Act of 1939.

Garments made from the specialty fibers follow:

ALPACA: Alpaca cloth, alpacuna, lining materials for coatings. Also used with other hair fibers and wool in "hair-fiber coatings."

ANGORA GOAT: Very popular for the best types of knitting yarns for hand and power work. The fiber is much imitated in this field in textiles. It is also used in making capes, plushes, crepon, mantle cloth, astrakhan, zibeline, brilliantine, cashmeres, and novelty materials for fancy-design work.

CAMEL HAIR: Suiting fabric for men's wear and women's wear, topcoats, overcoats for men, windbreakers, sweaters, sport jackets, hats, caps, dresses. Fabric weights are about 6 ounces for women's wear dresses to about 30 ounces in men's wear ulsters.

CASHMERE: The famous luxury shawls known as cashmere and Indian cashmere; the fiber is widely used in varying amounts mixed with other fibers. The name "cashmere" is much used in the woolen and worsted trade to mean material that has some of this fiber in the finished cloth. Seventeen variations of the spelling have been noted as trade names: Kashmir, Kashmiri, Cashmeer, Kasha, etc.

LLAMA: Llama fabrics are used in sportswear, women's coatings, suits, dresses, etc., and in men's lightweight suitings, year-round suits, slip-on topcoats, year-round coatings, and heavy overcoatings.

MOHAIR: This fiber is used in many staple and fancy materials: plushes, coat linings, tropical worsteds, lap robes, curtainings, furniture covering, bathing suits, Henrietta cloth, zibeline, astrakhan, coatings, car seats in railroad coaches and Pullmans, in braids and portieres.

VICUÑA: The fabric is made from this finest and most expensive natural fiber in the world. It is used chiefly as men's wear coating. Vicuña fabric was introduced in the United States in 1938 by S. Stroock & Company, Inc., of Newburgh, New York. At that time the fabric sold for $100 a yard and a coat sold for $900. In recent times the price per yard has been as high as $150, with the coating selling for $1,000.

[149]

TESTING   50 points

1. Name the most expensive textile fabric to be found anywhere in the world.
2. Are 100-per-cent-hair-fiber materials or garments what might be called good wearing fabrics? Give specific reasons.
3. Why is mohair usually in good demand?
4. What is the main difference between wool and hair fibers?
5. Why would wool, when mixed with hair fibers, aid in the durability of a garment made with a content of hair fiber and wool?

TRUE-FALSE QUESTIONS   50 points

1. _____ Llama, alpaca, guanaco, and vicuña belong to the same family grouping of hair-bearing animals.
2. _____ Bolivia is noted for raising Kashmir goats.
3. _____ Vicuña fiber is finer in diameter when compared with the fiber from the alpaca.
4. _____ The llama may be used as a burden-carrying animal.
5. _____ A huarizo is the offspring of a llama father and an alpaca mother.
6. _____ Alpaca fibers range from 4½ inches to about 11 inches.
7. _____ Sheep fibers of high quality are finer than vicuña fibers.
8. _____ Vicuña may be raised at elevations of about 5,000 feet.
9. _____ A Bactrian camel is the name given to a camel which has one hump.
10. _____ Camels usually shed their hair.
11. _____ Mohair fiber comes from angora goats.
12. _____ Much mohair is now obtained from the state of Texas.
13. _____ It is possible to obtain cloth for vicuña coating by combining the fleeces of ten to twelve animals for the raw material.
14. _____ Camel hair cloth comes only in natural shades.
15. _____ Hair fibers are usually spun without the aid of any supporting fiber.
16. _____ Most coating advertised as camel hair cloth may not have 100 per cent hair fiber in the garment.
17. _____ Angora yarn is much used for trimming in knitted fabric.
18. _____ Rabbit hair will give a rough feel to a fabric made of 80 per cent wool and 20 per cent hair.
19. _____ Vicuña fibers are used in making tweeds.
20. _____ Much rabbit hair is sold as angora.

Part 1—Unit 26

TOPIC: SUBSTITUTE AND WASTE FIBERS USED IN WOOLENS AND WORSTEDS

The Wool Products Labeling Act of 1939 defined the term "wool" to mean the fiber from the fleece of the sheep or lamb or the hair of the angora or cashmere goat (and possibly to include the so-called specialty fibers from the hair of the alpaca, camel, llama, and vicuña) which has never been reclaimed from any woven or felted product. It also defined "wool product" as any product, or any portion of a product, which contains, purports to contain, or in any way is represented as containing, wool, reprocessed wool, or reused wool.

Because of the wide range in quality and price of woolen and worsted fabrics to meet all types and kinds of consumer spending from the lowest to the highest, some of these cloths use additional fiber content in them to lower the cost per yard. Obviously this is a substitute ingredient. The principle of substitute ingredients is also used in other commodities: oleomargarine for butter, egg powder instead of eggs for baking, cottonseed oil as the base for many salad dressings, artificial leather for the genuine product.

If the world population had to rely on the annual clippage of true virgin wool from sheep (the first clip), only one person in eight would be clothed in woolen or worsted garments. And it is a known fact that some woolens and worsteds do not give very good wear. This is usually because the better base fibers have been blended with lower-grade fibers of the so-called waste variety. It should be kept in mind, however, that these fibers—despite the fact that they are known as waste fibers—are not always low in quality or actually "waste fibers." The quality of any fabric depends upon the quality of the raw material and the techniques of every worker connected with the making of the cloth.

Usually, small percentages of waste fibers are used in fabrics. Their color, individuality, and other properties will more or less lose their identity when worked with basic straight-run wool or worsted stocks. The statement that "nothing goes to waste in a mill" is true when it is known that all fibers, machine wastes, fly, lint, card wastes, flocks, and other wastes are collected when the mill is given its cleaning. These bags of fibers find their way to jobbers, or the mill may use its own waste for further manipulation. Many of these fibers are used as 'filler-in fibers" in certain fabrics. These wastes, however, when used in correct ratios in the cloth content, help to clothe the people who wear woolens and worsteds. In addition, about 20 per cent of our annual wool clip is pulled wool obtained from the pelts of dead sheep and slaughterhouse sheep, and this product finds its way into certain types of cloths, usually heavy fabrics such as overcoatings, windbreakers, mackinacs, and jackets.

TYPES OF WASTE FIBERS USED

CARBONIZED NOIL: Obtained from cloths which contain cotton or other vegetable matter. Staple is from ½ inch to 2½ inches and may be white or colored. Handle is fairly good but does not cope with that of combed noil. The fibers have a shredded appearance and are used in certain types of woolens and lower-quality worsteds.

COMBED NOIL FROM WORSTED MANUFACTURE: From ½ inch to 2½ inches in fiber length. Comes white or in colors. Combed noil is usually good to excellent in quality, since choice wool fibers are utilized in the manufacture of worsteds. Appearance is good, since the fibers naturally possess good hand, elasticity, and felting properties.

Noil is much used as "filler-in" fiber in many fabrics, and it mixes well with base fibers used to make cloth. Noil is usually an asset to a fabric, since the quality is highly desirable.

COTTON: Sources are obvious, and Peruvian cotton has certain properties that make it ideal for use in some woolen cloths. Fiber length is from ½ inch to about 2 inches; it is smooth and even, and at times rather silken-like in handle. In appearance, these cotton fibers are white or tinged.

In some fabrics the use of cotton up to 10 per cent or 12 per cent may be an asset rather than a liability since the natural twist properties of the fibers may be used to advantage with the other stock used to make the cloth. Cotton is ideal, in many instances, for use in warp yarns, since it will have the tendency to add increased tensile strength, which is so necessary in weaving cloth in the loom.

EXTRACT WOOL: Obtained from cloths that have been carbonized or from scoured stocks. Fiber length is from ¼ inch to about 1½ inches. Comes in white or colors, while the fiber has a shreddy or boardy handle. Appearance is thready and somewhat lifeless. It has the same uses as shoddy and mungo.

[151]

FLOCKS: Fibers obtained from finishing operations in woolen and worsted mills. Ranges from ⅛ inch to ¾ inch in length and may be white or colored. Handle depends on grade of cloth from which obtained and may be used in blending raw stocks and as a filler fiber in the fulling of some overcoating fabric.

HARD WASTES: These include yarn, thread, and hard ends obtained from sources such as spinning, spooling, winding, dressing, and weaving. Length depends on source from which obtained. Comes in white and colors, and the handle will vary with quality of basic stock. Appearance of hard wastes will vary with that of the original stock used.

These wastes are garnetted and then mixed-in, in varying percentages with basic wool or worsted stocks to be used for dressgoods and coatings.

MUNGO: Obtained from all kinds of felted cloths, tailor's clippings, overcoatings, etc. Felted clippings are used to considerable degree. Fiber length ranges from ¼ inch to about ¾ inch. Color, hand, appearance and uses are similar to those for shoddy. It should be borne in mind that shoddy and mungo may be of excellent, good, fair, or poor quality, all dependent on the stock from which they were obtained.

PULLED WOOL: Obtained from sheep that have been fattened for their carcass, "slaughter-house sheep." Fiber length is the same as that for live or clipped fiber, from 1 inch to about 6 inches, with some fiber 12 inches or more in staple. Color is that of grease wool before scouring, at which time the fiber becomes white. Handle is rather lifeless, boardy, harsh, flat. Appearance is dull.

Used with fleece wool fiber in varying percentages in woolen and worsted fabrics. Pulled wool is a valuable asset in the industry, since virgin wool does not always meet the requirements for cloth yardage demanded by the public.

REPROCESSED WOOL: The fiber resulting when wool which has been woven or felted into a wool product, without ever having been utilized in any way by the ultimate consumer, subsequently has been turned back again into a fibrous state (by the garnetting process).

REUSED WOOL: The fiber resulting when wool or reprocessed wool which has been spun, woven, knitted, or felted into a wool product, used in any way by the ultimate consumer, subsequently has been made into a fibrous state (by the garnetting process).

SHODDY: Obtained from all kinds of unfelted cloths, tailor's clippings, discarded cloths of many types, etc. Fiber length is from ½ inch to 2½ inches. Comes in varying colors depending on the cloth run through the shoddy picker or garnetting machine.

The handle will vary from rough or coarse to smooth or good, depending on original quality. Appearance depends on original stock. Used in dressgoods, over-coating, suiting, etc. May be used as a "filler-in" fiber to reduce fabric cost. Shoddy is used in varying percentages based upon fabric price.

SOFT WASTES: These come from the carding, combing, gilling, and drawing departments of the mill. Sliver, slubbing, top, and roving furnish the wastes, which may be white or colored. Staple length, handle and appearance will be the same as those of the original source.

These wastes have much call in woolens and are used to some degree in worsteds because of the good-to-excellent quality of fiber. They are reworked from the initial operations in the mill and are run through the regulation blending, oiling, mixing, and subsequent treatments.

TESTING

1. What is carbonized noil?
2. Why would combed noil obtained in worsted manufacture be an asset in a cloth?
3. Discuss the use of cotton in fabrics, either used alone or blended with woolen or worsted fibers as warp yarn.

4. Define extract wool.
5. Why would flocks in a fabric be considered detrimental?
6. Differentiate between mungo and shoddy.
7. Name three characteristics of pulled wool.
8. Why would tailor's clippings be considered as reprocessed wool?
9. Why would the fiber obtained by shredding or garnetting from old discarded clothing of almost any type be considered as reused wool?
10. When are soft wastes considered to be high or low in quality?
11. Why is it necessary to use so many wastes in making woolen and worsted fabrics?
12. Have you ever bought a low-quality or low-priced garment and soon found that there was very likely too much substitute stock in it? Explain in detail what you observed. Why was the article not to your liking after you had worn it for a time?

TOPIC: History of Silk

Silk is the fibrous substance produced by several kinds of insects, chiefly in the form of a cocoon or covering. Spiders and worms produce silk by emitting the fiber from within and gradually encasing themselves while doing so: this is the spinning of the cocoon. Silk fiber or filament used in industry, of the cultivated type, is produced exclusively by the mulberry moth of China and Japan, the *Bombyx mori,* and a few other kinds of moths allied closely to it. The Chinese call silk Si; the Koreans call it Soi; the Latin term is *Sericum;* the French is *Soie;* the German is *Seide,* and the English-speaking nations know it as silk.

Korea and China both lay claim to the origin of silk. China bases its claim on native records bringing out the fact that Empress Se-Ling-She, consort of the emperor Hwang-Te (2640 B.C.), encouraged the cultivation of the mulberry tree, the rearing of worms, and the reeling of silk filament from cocoons. The Empress is regarded as the patron saint of the silk industry, since she fostered silk, and in addition she is given credit for the invention of the hand loom for the weaving of silk cloth. The Koreans claim that they taught the Chinese the intricacies of sericulture and the manufacture of silk fabric. In the third century A.D., the Koreans gave the story of silk to the Japanese. Of course, whether silk originated in Korea or China is relatively unimportant today.

The *Nihongi,* one of the ancient books of Japanese history and folklore, stated that some Koreans were sent to China from Japan to obtain competent workers who could teach the art and culture of raising and manipulating silk. Tradition has it that the Koreans brought back to Japan four Chinese girls adept in sericulture and in the making of fabric. A temple was erected in the province of Setsu in their honor and memory.

A Chinese princess is supposed to have taught the knowledge of silkmaking to the people of India. She is said to have carried the eggs of the silkworm to them in her headdress, as well as some mulberry seeds for the forthcoming worms to feed upon. Silkworms were first reared in Japan in A.D. 195. For the first five centuries of the Christian era, the only regions that knew about silk were China, Korea, Khotan, Japan, Persia, India, and a few small states in central Asia. Japan

From the textile archives of the author

Introductory pages of the letter from James I, King of England (1603–25), King of Scotland as James VI (1567–1625), to the Virginia colonists, printed in London in 1620. This is the famous letter in which the King urged his colonists to grow silk in place of tobacco, and told them how they should do it. The complete letter covers twenty-three pages in the book.

another, from the East to the West, or from the North to the South, to the end that the fresh ayre and breefes, hauing free passage thorow and thorow the chambers, may refresh the Wormes in their great heapes: for when they come neere to the end of their workes, what through the silke wherewith they are then filled and clogged; and what through the great heat of the season at that time, they are then ready to stifle, if they haue not some fresh ayre let in, to coole them, at conuenient times. Neuerthelesse you must take heed, that the windowes to open and shut, bee well glazed or papered, and made to shut so close in a cold season, that no cold ayre get in at them; for coldes are as hurtfull to the Silk-wormes in the beginning of their worke, as heates are in the ending of it.

These creatures also desire to bee in a light place, as not willingly abiding the darke, from which they creepe away, seeking the light; therefore their roomes must be lightsome, parguetted also, and smoothly whited on the inside, so as Rats may not be able to creepe vpon the walls being slippery: All chinkes, creuises, and holes, must be close stopped, that there be no place of retrayt left, for Mice, Rats, Lizards, Crickets, or other vermine, enemies to our Silk-wormes.

The windowes also would haue nets hung before them, to keepe out poultry, and birds, which

windowes to open and shut close.

Nets before the windowes.

which may fly in and eate the Wormes, at such time as it is needfull to set open the windowes.

The second and next principall preparation after the lodging, is the foode of the Silke-wormes; which is the Mulbery leafe well qualified, not of euery Mulbery tree, nor of all ages, nor planted in euery soyle, nor set without regard of due distance; but it must be in all these respects select and choyce, for the well-prospering of this delicate creature.

Concerning the Mulbery tree, you must obserue these foure things, for to haue the best leafe for the food of your Wormes.

First, the diuers kindes of Mulbery trees, and which is the best for silke.

Secondly, the best foyle wherein the Mulbery is to be planted for this purpose.

Thirdly, the best time and order to plant and renoue them, and at what age the leafe is good.

Fourthly, in what distance to set them, that they may be well qualified by the Sunne.

First then you must know, that there be two races of Mulbery trees; the blacke Mulbery tree, and the white Mulbery tree, which differ in wood, leafe, and fruit: of the blacke Mulbery tree there is but one fort; the flocke whereof is thicker, the wood more solid and strong, the leafe more large, hard, and rough in the handling, than that of the white, the fruit also being

The food of the Silk-wormes, the Mulbery tree.

Foure things considerable in the Mulbery tree.

The blacke Mulbery tree.

From the textile archives of the author

Showing two pages from the twenty-one-page book, published in London in 1620, which contains the letter of King James I on OBSERVATIONS TO BE FOLLOWED IN THE RAISING OF SILKWORMS BY THE COLONISTS OF VIRGINIA.

by the end of the third century had developed a full-fledged silk industry and has been the leader since that time. Silk culture was not known in the Western world until the thirteenth century as a result of the famous travels of Marco Polo to the Far East.

In A.D. 552, two Nestorian monks on their way to Greece hid the secrets of silk in the hollows of their canes and gave information on sericulture to the Greeks and the Turks. From there silk-raising and fabric-weaving spread to what is now Italy and Spain, and in time other European nations became much interested in silk. This was particularly true of France, which today is the leading silk-fabric design center in the world, with the city of Lyons as the center of weaving. To the present day Lyons has held this position, and Paris has been the center of fashion since the days of Francis I, king of France (1515–1547). Francis, considered the "Father of the Silk Industry" in France, had learned a great deal about silk during his boyhood days spent in Savoy, and from the writings of Marco Polo more than two hundred years earlier.

The leading silk nations today include Japan and China, which supply more than two-thirds of the production, France, Austria, Spain, Italy, and India, along with a few minor countries in the area of the old Ottoman States. The best-quality silk in the world comes from the valley of the Po River in northern Italy.

Silk became very popular in the modern world, and especially so in the United States. Up to World War II, we imported 90 per cent of the world production, and 90 per cent of this amount was consumed in this country. After the war, valiant efforts have been made to bring silk back to the high status it had previously enjoyed, but to little avail. Silk, of course, will always be with us, and it is and always will be the "fabric of milady."

Just before the war and following it, the rise of the manmade fibers, especially nylon, made serious inroads on silk. In this country the decline in silk use has been very great, and silk is no longer classed as a major textile fiber. The same is true in several other countries which were large consumers of the fiber.

SERICULTURE

The United States has never successfully raised silkworms because of economic conditions—high standards of living, high wages and working conditions. Chinese girls receive from five to ten cents a day for reeling silk; Japanese girls about twenty-five cents, and Italian girls from twenty-five to about forty cents. These wages are not commensurate with those paid to working girls here. Thus, silk raising and reeling have not taken hold in this country.

The silk industry throughout the world was in a very bad condition in the 1860's. Disease was rampant among silkworms, and there was danger of this great industry passing into oblivion. Louis Pasteur, the "Savior of the Silk Industry," took great interest in the industry. He used scientific methods in selective choosing of the eggs. An examination of each moth was made after it had produced the eggs. If the moth was diseased, the eggs were destroyed; only healthy moths were allowed to hatch.

Testing stations in silk areas were established, and all farmers had to take their moths to some station for rigid examination. Pasteur, better known in history for his work in bacteria and a host of other scientific problems, initiated, therefore,

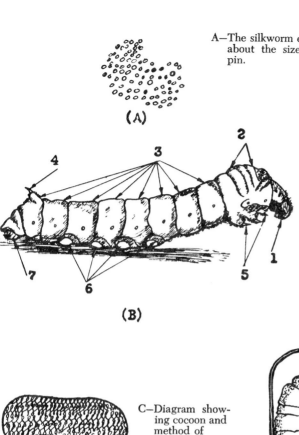

A—The silkworm eggs. These eggs are about the size of the head of a pin.

(A)

(B)

B—The full grown silkworm:

1.—Head
2.—Rings on head
3.—Rings on body
4.—Horn
5.—Articulated legs
6.—Abdominal legs
7.—False legs

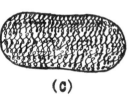

C—Diagram showing cocoon and method of winding.

(C)

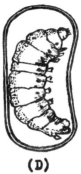

D—Silkworm in cocoon.

(D)

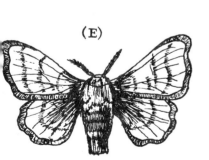

(E)

E—Silk moth.

(F)

F—Silkworm eggs on mulberry leaf.

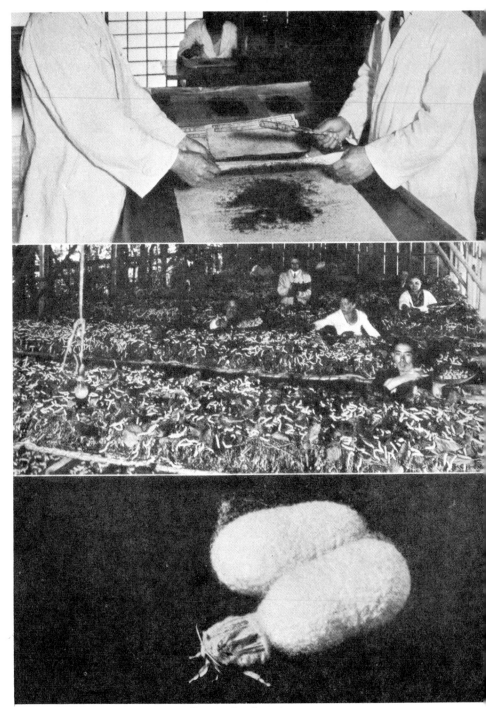

Silkworms hatching from eggs
Raising silkworms
Silk moths coming out of cocoons

Picking cocoons
Storing cocoons
Reeling

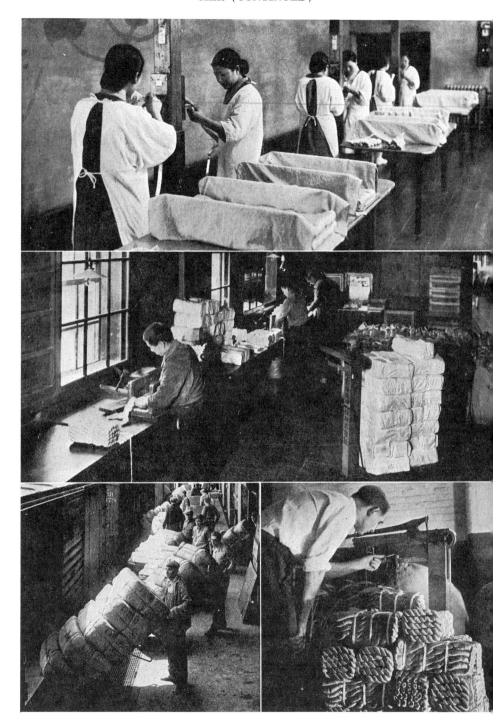

Skeining reeled silk
Booking

Bales of raw silk   Weighing books of raw silk

he scientific raising of silkworms for the production of high-quality raw silk—ericulture. He has well merited the title of "Father of Modern Sericulture."

The female moth of the *Bombyx mori* lays the eggs. When the worms hatch from the eggs, they feed on the leaves of the mulberry tree and become full grown in about thirty days. In the last stages of growth, a worm will eat its own weight daily. This full-grown "worm" is, in reality, a caterpillar.

As soon as the caterpillar is ready to spin its cocoon, it ceases to eat. Spinning of the cocoon takes about three days of continuous work. The worm encases itself with filament that is emitted from two openings underneath its mouth; two minute sacks supply the silk gum or sericin which "cements" the filament. The silk is spun in the form of a figure "8." Emitting of the filament and the gum will continue until the glands can no longer function.

When the cocoon is completed, the worm changes its form to a chrysalis, and in this condition lies in its cozy nest for about two weeks. By the end of this time, the formation of the moth has developed to the point where a secretion is emitted, alkaline in nature. This liquid attacks the shell of the cocoon at the "head-of-the-moth" end. There is a softening of the shell so that the moth comes forth into the world and is soon ready to lay its eggs. Thus the cycle is completed.

CONDENSED LIFE CYCLE OF THE MOTH, THE *BOMBYX MORI*

MOTHS produce the eggs, about 350 to 500 per moth.

LARVAE hatch the eggs, which, when grown, become silkworms.

SILKWORM spins its cocoon for three days without stopping, until all glandular fluid has been used. The residue inside the spent cocoon is known as the chrysalides.

COCOON produces the moth in about 15 days; the full-grown moth is the result. Hatching of the eggs takes from 20 to 30 days. The caterpillar stage lasts for about 30 days, and the chrysalis stage only a few days. The moths die as soon as they have mated and laid a new generation of eggs. Thus, the cycle: moth, eggs, silkworm, chrysalis, back to the moth stage.

FACTS ABOUT THE COCOON

There are two glands along the underside of the body, from head to tail, known as silk ducts. These glands terminate in a tiny hole at the mouth, known as a spinneret, from which the silk thread is spun.

In the last segment of the caterpillar there are two minute bags which contain the gummy fluid called sericin.

When the silkworm begins its spinning task, two fibers are emitted from the silk ducts and are covered by the silk gum or sericin from the sacks before they come from the mouth.

As the liquid is emitted by the silkworm, it solidifies on contact with the air.

A separate filament is called brins.

The two filaments are cemented together by silk gum or sericin.

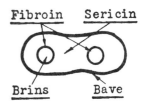

The solidified filament is called silk or fibroin.

The two filaments joined together produce what is known as the cocoon thread or bave.

The moth dies within two days after the eggs are produced. Each moth and tray of eggs are numbered and indexed. Only a portion of the total number of cocoons is used for breeding purposes. The great majority of cocoons are placed in a hot, dry room, and this heat causes the chrysalis in the cocoon to be stifled or stoved.

TESTING

1. How did sericulture find its way to Japan, India, and finally to Europe?
2. Give some reasons why silk fabrics appeal to you.
3. Why is Louis Pasteur known as the "Savior of the Silk Industry"?
4. Discuss the life cycle of the silkworm.
5. Define: brins, silk gum or sericin, fibroin, bave.

TOPIC: THE GRADES AND PROPERTIES OF SILK

Silk cocoons, after stifling, are carefully assorted for size, shape (oval, round, peanut-shape), and color. The next step is to remove the silk from these stifled cocoons. This process is called reeling. Each cocoon has two filaments, and reeling is the winding off of these filaments from the cocoon onto a reel or swift. The cocoons are placed in a basin of hot water to be softened, so that the beginning of the filament may be obtained for winding off. The filaments are brought upward and run onto the swift or reel; this is not a spinning operation. Silk from only one cocoon is too fine to work commercially; consequently the filaments from three to twelve cocoons are reeled together in order to obtain a workable thickness.

Some cocoons are known as pierced cocoons. Breeding stock is allowed to pierce the cocoons so that continuous breeding may be possible. Some other cocoons may also become pierced by handling or damage, and by other causes. Damaged cocoons can be used for the product spun silk, since they are short in length and can be spun into yarn on conventional spinning frames.

Several grades of silk are obtained during reeling operations. The grade is determined by a series of tests which determine the rating to be given the silk.

Desirable Qualities of Silk

1. Evenness
2. Elasticity
3. Strength
4. Brilliancy
5. Crossings
6. Freedom from imperfections
7. Cleanliness
8. Proper size
9. Cohesion
10. Elongation

Imperfections in Silk

1. Poor crossings
2. Hairiness
3. Nibs
4. Slugs
5. Loops
6. Lousy silk
7. Double knots

(In conditioning, silk is allowed a moisture content of 11 per cent.)

TESTING GRADES OF SILK

Special AAA, AAA, AA, A, B, C, D, E, F, and G.
Silk is also graded for quality on a percentage basis: 100, 95, 90, 85, 80, 75, etc.
Grades of raw silk in the buying markets of the world:

Triple Extra.
Grand Double Extra.
Double Extra.
Best Number One Extra.
Best Number One.
Number One.

In the matter of the handling, testing, and grading of silk that comes into the United States, the United States Testing Company, Inc., Hoboken, New Jersey, is the company that handles all questions relative to silk. It acts as a board of arbitration and has done so for many years.

PROPERTIES AND CHARACTERISTICS OF SILK

1. Filament length 300 to about 1600 yards.
2. About one-third of cocoon filament is easily reelable and of desirable quality for good work.
3. Silk burns similar to wool.
4. Caustic soda dissolves true silk.
5. Silk may turn yellowish in time.
6. Weakened by saliva.
7. Has about 11 per cent moisture content.
8. Spun by nature into a cocoon.
9. Finest natural fiber or filament known to man.
10. Is not made into actual yarn by any machine process or method; is spun by the silkworm.
11. Silk filaments are twisted together by machine operations to make the silk yarn of commerce.
12. Has good tensile strength and elasticity; exceptionally strong.
13. High textures easily obtained.
14. Before World War II, silk was our greatest dollar-value import.
15. Silk may be weighted with tin or other metallic salts: 15% on blacks, 10% on other colors.
16. Does not wrinkle easily.
17. Perspiration will destroy silk.
18. Dyes easily and well.
19. Launders easily and gives good service.
20. Pure silk dyed fabrics will last for centuries.
21. Sheds dirt, has good absorption properties, and does not deteriorate.
22. Silk is soft, smooth, warm, and has kindly feel.
23. Known as the "fiber of romance" and the "fabric of milady."
24. Silk has an interesting background in art, history, literature, and textiles.
25. Made into beautiful and elegant fabrics.

TESTING

1. How many cocoons are reeled at one time?
2. Differentiate between reeling and spinning.
3. How is silk actually spun?
4. What is a pierced cocoon? Of what value is a cocoon of this type?
5. Name five desirable qualities of silk; five imperfections in silk.
6. How is silk graded?
7. What company in the United States acts as the board of arbitration in all silk matters, foreign and domestic?
8. List ten properties and characteristics of silk.

Part 1—Unit 29

TOPIC: SILK MANUFACTURE AND TWIST IN SILK AND OTHER YARNS

Raw silk is silk that still contains silk gum or sericin. The first treatment given this silk is to remove the gum: the process is known as silk boil-off, boiling-off, silk washing, or silk degumming. Hot water and soap are used to remove the gum. The amounts of boiled-off liquor may vary with the several grades of silk; the higher the boil-off, the better will be the quality of the silk, the less the yield and the more expensive the resultant yarn or thread.

Boiled-off liquor is used later on in the dyeing operations, since it makes for better affinity and penetration of the dyestuff in the material and the color evenness. The following tabulation will show the approximate boil-off of the major silk stocks:

1. Tussah Silk 10–11%
2. White China 17–19%
3. White Japan 18–19%
4. Tsatlee 19–20%
5. Yellow Japan 21–22%
6. Canton 22–23%
7. Italian 23–25%

DETAILED PROCEDURE IN SILK MANUFACTURE

Reeling

In the same manner that the silk from one cocoon is too fine for commercial value, it is also too fine to be woven into fabric or knitted into cloth. Consequently, the silk must be prepared for use in the filature and the textile mill. This preparation is called reeling; it is the actual combining of the filaments from several cocoons to produce what is known as the raw silk thread of commerce.

The filaments from the several cocoons are reeled into a skein form. These filaments are unwound from the cocoons in reeling basins and are then led to the swift or reel for skeining.

The silk skeins are made into silk bundles or silk books which may weigh from five to ten pounds. There are as many skeins in a book as there are books in a silk bale. Silk bales weigh about 133.33 pounds.

Throwing

This is the transforming of reeled silk into silk yarn or thread. The term "throwing" comes from the Anglo-Saxon word *thrawn*, which means to twist. Those engaged in this work are known as throwsters.

Silk throwing, mistakenly referred to as silk-spinning, is comparable with the spinning of cotton, linen, wool, and worsted. Unlike these fibers, the throwing of silk does not include blending, mixing, carding, combing, drawing, roving.

Raw silk skeins are sorted for color, length, quality, quantity, and size.

Soaking

The raw silk skeins are soaked in a warm water bath that contains desirable soap or oil content. The action causes the silk to become supple and therefore makes the skeins easier to handle. After mechanical drying, the skeins are placed on light reels; from these reels the silk is wound on bobbins.

Winding

During this operation, single strands may be given any desired amount of twist within reason. If two or more yarns are to be doubled, they are twisted again in the same direction or in the reverse direction, depending on the type of thread desired. To equalize the diameter, the thread is run between rollers, inspected, and then packaged for shipment to fabric manufacturers. Proper winding of the yarn or thread onto bobbins or spools is important so that they may be easily handled in the mill by the operatives, and even shipped long distances.

Types of Thrown Silk Yarns

The following chart shows the major types of thrown silk threads:

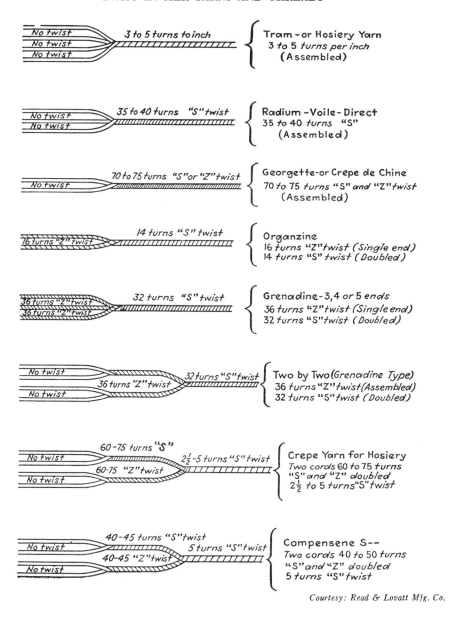

Courtesy: Read & Lovatt Mfg. Co.

TYPE	TURNS OF TWIST PER INCH	USE OF THE YARN
Tram	From 2 to 12	Filling yarn and hosiery
Organzine	From 12 to 20	Warp yarn
Crepe	No twist in singles, 65 to 85 in doubles, which are then doubled with 2½ to 5 turns per inch, opposite direction.	In all kinds of crepe fabrics—in warp or filling, or both.
Grenadine	20/18 to 60/60; a very hard-twisted organzine thread.	In all kinds of sheer cloths such as voile, organdy, grenadine.

TWIST IN YARNS

"s" TWIST: A yarn or cord has "S" twist if, when held in a vertical position, th spirals conform in slope to the central portion of the letter S. Formerly called left hand or clockwise twist.

"z" TWIST: If the spirals conform in slope to the central portion of the letter Z the twist is then classed a "Z" twist. Formerly known as right-hand or counter clockwise twist.

ZERO TWIST: Sometimes referred to as "no twist." The thrower may request tha cuprammonium (Bemberg) yarns be supplied with no twist. This is rarely done however; usually one to five turns of twist are given the yarn. Viscose rayon an acetate yarns with from three to five or six turns per inch are normally supplie to the thrower; this twist is known as "tram twist." Used for filling yarn in fabric

CABLE TWIST: A cord, rope, or twine construction in which each successive twis runs in the opposite direction from the preceding twist. This type is called "S-Z-S or "Z-S-Z" twist.

DIRECTIONS OF TWIST

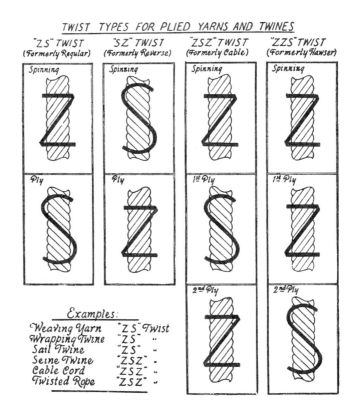

Officials of the Mt. Vernon Mills, Inc., Baltimore, Md., circulated the above chart among their employees to educate them on the new designations for direction of twist.

[166]

Define and explain the terms "filature," "silk throwing," "organzine silk," "tram silk."
What is the purpose of boiling-off silk?
Explain silk reeling.
Is silk actually spun on a machine in the textile plant? Explain.
Discuss the purpose of soaking silk skeins.
How do you account for the fact that crepe twist is ideal for sheers?
Why is crepe yarn able to resist such a high degree of resistance when pulled or stretched?
Explain in detail the following terms used in twist in yarn: "right-hand twist"; "left-hand twist"; " 'S' twist"; " 'Z' twist"; "zero-twist"; "cable twist"; " 'S-Z-S' twist."

Part 1—Unit 30

OPIC: Silk Finishing

Silk fabrics are "made in the finishing," just as other commercial textile mate-
als. Many of the finishes are supposed to be "of a secret nature," and the plant
)ecializing in some particular finish will hold "the secret" of obtaining the de-
red finished effect. Silk goes through a complete transformation from the greige
oods condition to the finished product. As the name "finishing" implies, the fin-
hing of any particular textile fabric is the actual treatment given the goods to
lake them acceptable on the market. Because of the relatively high cost of the
iw material, silk cloths must be finished with utmost care. The major finishing
perations follow:

OILING-OFF: Known also as boiling-out or degumming, it is the removing of the silk
gum or sericin from the raw silk. Tussah silk will have a boil-off of about 10
per cent; true silks may lose 25 per cent or more.

LEACHING: This will produce a white material devoid of any coloring matter.

YEING: To impregnate material with color by thorough penetration.

RINTING: The actual printing of designs, motifs, or patterns onto material by any of the
printing methods in use today. Printing does not, in all instances, give a thorough
penetration of dyestuff, but the face of the material is always colored in a uniform
manner.

ALENDERING: Passing the goods between a series of rollers, some or all of which may
be heated, in order to press or iron the fabric and to increase luster and improve
surface effect.

RICTION CALENDERING: Passing material between heated rollers, one of which has a
slightly excessive speed over the other one, thereby creating a friction-calender
treatment which adds considerable luster, sheen, or gloss to the material.

EIGHTING, LOADING: Prior to World War II, silk fabrics were often heavily weighted
by the use of tin (stannic)) chloride or lead plumbate. The chloride treatment
accounted for about 95 per cent of the weighting. Iron salts were also used, but
they never became popular for weighting in the United States. In November 1938,
the Federal Trade Commission established trade practice rules for the silk industry
which curbed silk weighting. Prior to that time, when weighting ran rampant, it
was not uncommon to find silk materials that had been weighted 200 per cent or
more. For example, in the early part of the present century, stockings supposed
to be all silk might have from 40 per cent up to 60 per cent or more of weighting
applied. The Commission decreed that all fabrics which had been weighted should
have labels attached informing the consumer of the actual amount of weighting
given the material. The percentage or proportion of such metallic weighting to be
disclosed under the ruling was the percentage or proportion of the total weight

of the metallic substance to the total weight of the silk in the finished condition with a tolerance of 5 per cent because of unavoidable variations in processing Thus, hang-tags bore labels such as the following:

Silk weighted not over 50 per cent.
Silk weighted over 50 per cent.

Since the announcement of these rulings, a further change has been made by the Commission and it is still used today. A silk fabric dyed black may have up to 15 per cent weighting if it is to be sold as a "pure-dye silk." Silks dyed all other colors are allowed a 10 per cent weighting, and these may be sold as "pure-dye silks." These allowances were granted when logwood dyes were used.

Advantages and Disadvantages of Weighting: The knotty problem of silk weighting is controlled by the countries in which the goods are made; hence the wide diversity in many staple fabrics which bear the same name.

ADVANTAGES

Gives crispness to fabric.
Heavier than pure-dye silk.
Not as expensive as pure dyes.
Pleats well and gives firmness to fabrics.
Ideal for taffeta, moiré taffeta, and other crisp stiff-finished cloths.
Use the burning test to distinguish between pure dye and weighted silk.

DISADVANTAGES

Fabric has less elasticity.
Less compactness to the goods.
May be weakened over a span of time.
Loss of strength possible.
Will deteriorate in time to point of cracking or can be easily torn or split.
Weighted silks are likely to shrink when laundered or drycleaned, but not as much as pure dyes.

SIZING: The use of starches, sizes, or waxes to aid in obtaining a desirable finish on the goods.

NAPPING: Producing a nap or "fuzzy"-face finish on cloth by raising the short, loose or protruding fibers to the surface of the goods. Napping is done by means of rollers which are clothed with fine, pressed steel wire or card clothing, or by teaseled roller. The teasel method is used altogether on spun silk fabrics.

SHEARING: The shearing machine cuts and levels off the nap on cloth to give it a uniform evenness on the face. The shearing machine is based on the principle of a lawn mower.

CERÉ, CIRÉ: A wax pressure treatment used to impart a smooth luster to the cloth which is finished with some stiffness. Difficult to dryclean or launder.

STIFFENING: A term which means that cheaper grades of fabrics have been starched or sized to some degree.

STEAMING: Steam is applied to pile fabrics in order to set the material.

WRINGING AND STRETCHING: Some fabrics are wrung and then stretched to soften up the fibers so that increased luster in finishing may be attained.

PRESSING: Treatment given to some silk fabrics to remove wrinkles from the finished goods by passing them between heated rollers. The cloth is soaked in a dilute acid to develop the luster.

MOIRÉ, WATERMARKING: This is a watered or bright-and-dim effect given to silk, cotton, rayon, and acetate fabrics. The effect is achieved by means of engraved rollers that exert very heavy pressure on the material in order to enhance its beauty. May deteriorate in due course of time.

SINGEING: Passing the cloth rapidly over a series of gas jets or white-hot electric plates in order to take off the fuzzy, straggly, or protruding fibers. Singed fabric is very smooth in appearance and to the touch.

EMBOSSING: This gives an effective appearance to material by causing the rays of light to reflect and give a sort of bright-and-dim effect to the cloth. Embossed finish may more or less resemble or simulate a moiré finish. Likely to wear off in time

WATERPROOFING: Treatment to make cloth water-repellent.

SCROOPING: This treatment is given silk yarn to provide a crunchy, rustled hand by the addition of acetic acid to the bath. The treatment tends to stiffen the yarn and is particularly advantageous for yarn to be used for knitting. An oil treatment may be used if softening up the yarn is desired.

TESTING

1. What is meant by the boiling-off of silk?
2. Differentiate between calendering and friction calendering.
3. Define a pure-dye silk fabric.
4. Distinguish between a moiré or watermarked silk fabric and one that has been embossed.
5. What is the ceré finish given to some silk fabrics?
6. Describe silk weighting.
7. Name three advantages of weighting; three disadvantages.
8. What is meant by scrooping of silk?

Part 1—Unit 31

TOPIC: THE STORY OF THE DENIER IN DETAIL

For the Lay Person

Each trade or industry has set up certain standards of measurement for its own guidance, as that of horsepower for engines, candlepower for light, volts and amperes for volume and quality of electricity. The manmade fiber industries have likewise established their unit-length standard for the size of yarn and their method for figuring the yards per pound in any size or count of yarn made from the manmade (cellulosic and noncellulosic) fibers. Acetate and rayon are the cellulosic manmade fibers while the noncellulosic fibers include nylon, Dynel, "Orlon" acrylic fiber, "Dacron" polyester fiber, Creslan, Fortrel, Acrilan, Verel, Zefran, Caprolan, Kodel, Avisco Vinyon, Saran, Velon, etc. Some schools of thought formerly referred to the noncellulosic fibers as specially manmade, true synthetics, or test-tube filaments.

The textile industry has adopted the old silk-filament yarn standard which was established in France in the sixteenth century—the standard known as "denier."

A filament of a 1-denier size would measure about four and a half million yards in length. The exact figure, 4,464,528 yards, is obtained from the following equation:

$$\frac{492.13, \text{ standard length in yards, } \times 7,000, \text{ grains in one pound}}{.771618, \text{ standard grain weight on one denier}}$$

Thus 1 pound of a 1-denier filament or indefinite-length strand would average about 2,530 miles, or the distance from New York City to Phoenix, Arizona. As the size or the number of the denier increases, the yardage per pound will decrease. To find the number of yards of yarn in 1 pound of a 15-denier yarn, merely divide 15 into 4,464,528. This will reveal that there are 297,635.2 (300,000) yards of the yarn in 1 pound. For calculative purposes, as in the foregoing, the 300,000-yard number would be used instead of the exact number, or 297,635.2 yards.

Women as lay persons have a great interest in the term "denier," since stockings are bought and sold according to a particular denier size. All women know for example, that a 20-denier stocking is finer and sheerer than a 30-denier stocking, and that a 15-denier type is finer than a 20-denier stocking. They do not however, have any idea as to what the term actually implies or means. They are interested merely in buying stockings of a particular denier size to suit their needs. Therefore, in the relation of denier to stocking, the layman should keep in mind certain features of the particular denier size and the pertinent serviceability and sheerness of the stocking.

In 1964, about nine hundred million pairs of nylon stockings were bought in the United States, an average of about twelve pairs per consumer. The vast majority of these stockings were 15-denier or finer, including the popular 12 denier, 10-denier, and even as fine as the 7.5-denier type first made in Arwa, Germany, and first sold here in 1956. The service sheer or walking stocking is made from 30-denier yarn. Introduced in 1939, it was the sheerest type on the market until some time after the close of World War II. Daytime dress sheer stockings sold today are made from a 20-denier or a 15-denier yarn. Along with the 7.5 denier stockings, they are used almost exclusively for formal and evening wear For rugged service and good wear one should buy a 20-denier or a 30-denier stocking. Every pair should be given careful attention at all times in washing hanging to dry, putting on for wear, taking off after wear. Snag hazards from fingernails, chairs, and gloves should and can be avoided or cut to a minimum if proper care is afforded the stockings.

For the Technologist

The denarius, or denier as it is known today, was originally a coin used before and during the time of Julius Caesar. Of small value, it was first made of silver but copper and gold were used to mint the coins later on. Incidentally, the English coin, the penny (d.; plural, pence), and the American penny are descendant of the original denarii. (See DENIER COIN, page 183.) The coin was first used outside Rome during Caesar's Gallic wars in what is now France. The value of the coin was small, and it is supposed to have been worth about one-twelfth of the old-time French sou, although some numismatists believe that it was worth between 16 and 24 cents according to monetary standards of today. Its size is about that of the middle fingernail of a man. While of little monetary value today, it is a genuine collector's item among numismatists. One in superb condition, face and obverse, may cost up to $50 or more. Used and worn coins may run as high as $20

Caesar, of course, lived for posterity, but his denier lapsed into oblivion soon after his death in 44 B.C. Little was heard of the coin again until the time of Francis I (king of France 1515–1547), the "Father of the Silk Industry." Francis who was to become known as a deep thinker, received much of his education in the Duchy of Savoy, later part of Italy. He had ample opportunity to observe the lavishness of the life there, and became keenly interested in the beautiful silk fabrics made by the intricate techniques of Italian weavers. Becoming obsessed with the idea of aiding his native land, Francis was to realize his dream in due course of time of making France the center of the great silk industry.

When Francis became king of France, one of his first acts was to establish the silk industry in Lyons, Paris, St. Etienne, and other centers. Textile workers were brought in from Italy.

Up to this time the old method for measurement was the ell or aune, taken originally as the length measurement for the human arm. This length was 45 inches in England, 46.69 inches in France, and 37.2 inches in Scotland. Tradition has it that Henry I or Beauclerc (1068–1135), king of England, who was the son of William the Conqueror and who reigned from the year 1100 after conquering Normandy until his death, corrected what he termed the false ell used by a merchant and decreed that as a standard for the future the ell be the length of his arm.

Francis abolished the old method of measuring silk. This old system used 80 skeins of 120 aunes for a total length of 9,600 aunes. Francis established a system of weight in terms of the denier—i.e., the number of denier coins or weights necessary to balance the silk in question. The denier weight standard was 0.0531 grams. The procedure used today to figure denier in terms of grams is to find the weight in grams of 9,000 meters or 9,846 yards of yarn. For example, if 9,000 meters of filament weigh 100 grams, the filament is known as a 100-denier yarn. A gram is approximately 1/28th of one ounce or 1/450th of one pound. Since there are 492.13 yards used as a standard length and there are 7,000 grains in one pound, the length of 1 denier is found by multiplying these two numbers together and then dividing by .771618, the standard grain weight of 1 denier. This result would give 4,464,528 yards in 1-denier filament yarn—and this figure has been used as the standard for well over four hundred years.

Toward the end of the eighteenth century, Matley, a silk scientist, observed that the grain weight was 1/24th of the denier and he conceived the idea of taking skeins of 400 aunes (1/24th of 9,600) and weighing these in grains, thereby preserving the ratio. He made a machine for measuring these 400-aune skeins and the trade seemed to accept the change but only to a limited degree. It was difficult to get away from the time-worn, deep-rooted meaning and use of the denier. Thus the denier of today is really one grain Poid de Marc, and is 1/24th of its original value. The standard denier weight was at that time set at 0.0531 grams or 3.33 grains. The 400-aune skein was now equal to 476 meters, or 520 yards and 20 inches.

The International Yarn Numbering Congress at its meeting in Vienna, Austria, in 1873 spent a great deal of time on the subject of denier. It was decreed finally that the denier should now be defined as the weight in grams of 10,000 meters of filament silk. The basis used today, however, in England and in the United States for the sizing of thrown silk filament is the weight in grams of 1,000 yards of the filament. To convert this weight into deniers it is necessary to multiply by the factor used, 33.36.

Thus, if 1,000 yards of filament weigh three grams, it would be the equivalent of 33.36 times 3, or a 100.8-denier yarn.

The Congress decreed the following denier table:

TYPE	WEIGHT IN GRAMS	LENGTH IN METERS
1. Italian, legal	0.05	450 or 492.13 yards
2. Milan	0.051	476
3. Turin	0.0534	476
4. Lyons, Old Denier	0.531	476
5. Lyons, New Denier	0.531	500
6. International Denier	0.05	500

With the legal denier in use today of 0.05 grams for the length of 450 meters or 492.13 yards (often used in calculations as 492.2 yards) it is possible to convert to ounces by multiplying the grams by 0.0353.

SUMMARY FOR STUDENT AND TECHNOLOGIST OF THREE METHODS USED TO FIGURE DENIER

1. Standard Yardage Method

As previously noted in this Unit, there are 4,464,528 yards of filament in one pound of a 1-denier size yarn. Thus, to find the number of yards in one pound of any size denier, silk filament included, divide the yarn size into the standard. Hence, in a 150-denier filament or yarn there would be the following computation:

$150\overline{)4,464,528}$, standard (27.763.33 yards to the pound or, roughly, for ease in figuring, 30,000 yards of yarn to the pound. The figure, "4,464,528 yards," is sometimes referred to as "The Rule of the Seven Fours."

SILK SIZES

These are expressed with the aid of a diagonal line . . . . / . . . . such as a 24/26 silk filament denier size yarn. In figuring silk, the mean number is taken, which in this instance would be 25. Thus,

$25\overline{)4,464,528}$, standard (178,581.1 yards, or 180,000 yards in one pound of yarn.

2. Gram Method

It originated during World War II in France and is now very popular in practically all major textile areas throughout the world, especially where the metric system is used. As previously noted, one denier weighs .05 grams, a standard weight. Multiplying .05 grams by 20 will give one gram in weight. The standard length used in this procedure is 450 meters, or 492.13 yards in the standard-length yardage in the skeins used for weighing. Thus, using the 20 once more in the computation, 20 times 450 in meters gives 9,000 meters. Therefore, all that has to be done is to weigh a reeled skein of 9,000 meters, and its weight gives the size of the denier filament, yarn or thread.

Thus, if a skein of 9,000 meters of a filament yarn skein weighed 200 grams, the denier size of the yarn will be a 200-denier.

3. Thousand Meter-Units Per Kilogram Method

This is based on the weight of 1,000 meter-units per kilogram. Thus, there would be 60,000 meters of yarn in a 60-denier, since 1,000 times 60 gives 60,000 meters of yarn per kilogram, the English equivalent of which is 2.2 pounds.

APPROXIMATE SIZE DENIER YARNS OR THREADS COMMONLY USED IN SOME BASIC APPAREL ITEMS

These sizes in denier, generally speaking, seem to be the most popular in these products. Other sizes, finer or greater in diameter and lighter or heavier in weight, may be used as the occasion arises.

ITEM	FINE	MEDIUM	COARSE OR HEAVY
Blouses	15–30	30–70	70–150
Dresses	30–70	70–150	150–300
Home decorations	15–100	100–300	over 300
Hosiery	7½–15	20–30	30–60
Lingerie	15–30	30–70	70–150
Outerwear	50–100	100–210	210–300 or higher

TESTING

1. Name two cellulosic fibers; four noncellulosic fibers.
2. Write the line equation which gives 4,464,528 yards, the standard for a 1-denier yarn.
3. How many yards in 1 pound of a 30-denier yarn? A 600-denier yarn?
4. Give a brief account of the work done by Francis I, king of France, in the establishment of the silk industry in France in the sixteenth century.
5. How many inches in the English ell or aune?
6. What would be the denier size of a yarn if 9,000 meters of yarn weighed 75 grams?
7. What is the weight in grams, and the length in meters used, with regard to the standards decreed by the International Yarn Numbering Congress at its meeting in Vienna, Austria, in 1873?
8. If 1,000 yards of filament yarn weighed four grams, what would be the denier size of the yarn? For solution, see The International Yarn Numbering Congress, Vienna, Austria, 1873. (*See* page 171.)
9. If 1,000 yards of filament yarn weighed six grams, what would be the denier size of the yarn?
10. How many yards in one pound of a 22/24-denier silk yarn?
11. If 75,000 meters of filament yarn weighed one kilogram, what would be the size of the yarn in terms of denier?

Part 1—Unit 32

TOPIC: Standard Silk Fabrics

Silk fabrics vary considerably in hand or feel, appearance, weave and construction, finish, drapability or clinginess. Dependent on the basic fabric used, when cut into a garment it may become a form-fitting or a form-hiding dress, frock, or gown. Other factors to keep in mind when handling silks include softness or stiffness, washability, drycleaning, durability, and color. The following list of fabrics will show the wide range apparent in silk materials:

BARATHEA: A plain twill or fancy-weave fabric of English origin used as mourning fabric, cravat cloth, and dressgoods. The fine texture of this silk or rayon warp, wool filling fabric is of broken character, to give a granulated or pebbled effect. Barathea is usually dyed black. One of the popular types today is made with rayon warp and cotton filling.

BEADED OR CUT VELVET: Velvet with a cut-out pattern or velvet pile effect. Often done on chiffon velvet. Brilliant designs and effects noted. Made on Jacquard loom. Principal use is for evening wear. Other uses are for hangings, decorative material, salon furnishings.
  Most difficult to handle and manipulate. Drapes well, will dryclean, crushes. Wear depends on quality and type of design.

BENGALINE: A popular material made from the more important textile fibers. This heavy poplin or rib-effect fabric was first made of silk in Bengal, India. The texture is high and the use of coarse filling gives the pronounced corded effect. Bengaline appeals to the public, particularly when made of silk warp. This cycle cloth give good wear, is very durable, and finds much use as mourning material, coating ensembles, suiting, and for women's headgear. Piece-dyed or yarn-dyed, the fabric is finished at about 40 inches. Grosgrain, incidentally, is classed as bengaline "cut to ribbon width."

BROADCLOTH: A very fine, high-texture, smooth, flat silk fabric ideal for shirting, sports wear, pajamas, and dressgoods. Made of plain weave, it comes in white, color and stripe effects. Launders well and gives the best of wear; an expensive material

BROCADE: Jacquard construction with an embossed or raised effect. Face easily distinguished from the back. Wide range in quality and price.

Material wears well; evening dresses made from brocade are durable and dry clean. Reflects the light's rays. Made of silk, acetate, rayon, and nylon.

BROCATELLE: In the group of fabrics such as damask and brocade, it differs from the former in that the woven figure, design or motif is satin in texture relieved by a dull-effect ground construction which forms a pleasing contrast in the material Made on a Jacquard loom, the motif is usually a raised or blistered effect. Used for hanging, interior decoration, upholstery, etc. (See DAMASK.)

CHIFFON: A plain-weave, lightweight, sheer, transparent cotton, rayon, or silk fabric made with fine highly twisted strong yarn. Chiffon is often used as a "drape" over silk or rayon. The fabric is difficult to handle but drapes and wears well. This stately or conventional fabric is very durable despite its light weight. It is not a material for everyday wear, and must be laundered with great care.

CHIFFON VELVET, TRANSPARENT VELVET: A clear cut pile fabric which comes in several grades and types; good qualities are expensive. Fabric drapes well, is durable drycleans neatly, but has tendency to crush. Crush resistants, however, are now applied to the material. Ideal for evening wear.

CREPE: A very broad term applied to a large family of fabrics with crinkled, pebbly or puckered surface, obtained by varying combinations of twisted yarns and slight variations of the plain weave. A plain weave has a float of one. Crepe effects may be enhanced by leaving out certain raisers in the construction, thereby giving a float of three in some parts of the fabric and increasing the crinkled effect. Crepe are made from practically all the major textile fibers, alone or in combination. The Federal Trade Commission decreed that "crepe" indicates a silk material unless the term is otherwise qualified with a fiber appellation. Some of the more important crepe fabrics follow: (See FLAT CREPE.)

CANTON CREPE: This filling crepe has a pebbly surface and is made with 6 threads of right-hand twist followed by 6 threads of left-hand twist in the construction. The filling is silk of 14/16 to 20/22 denier in size. Canton is heavier than crepe de chine. It is made today chiefly from acetate or rayon and finds use in coat linings dressgoods, dressing gowns, negligees, pajamas, scarfs, lounging robes, and accessories.

CREPE-BACK SATIN, SATIN CREPE: Satin weave with a crepe-twist filling used in this silk or rayon cloth. As the fabric is reversible, interesting effects can be obtained by contrasting the surfaces. Used for dresses, blouses, linings.

CREPE DE CHINE: A raw silk cloth reeded in the loom at about 4/50/2, which means that there are 4 ends in each of the 50 reed splits, and that each of the 4 ends is a double thread, a total of 400 ends per inch in the texture.

Filling texture ranges from 60 to 80 picks of 2 or 3 threads, 20/22 denier with 60 to 65 turns of twist per inch. A plain weave is used to make the fabric, which is soft and more or less lustrous. Used for blouses, dressgoods, evening wear, skirting, underwear. The material is form-fitting since it is a line-revealing fabric. This fair-to-excellent-quality staple is dyed or printed. It is easy to manipulate, launders well, and gives good wear.

Differs from Georgette crepe in the following manner: In crepe de chine, the filling is woven with 2 picks of left-hand twist yarn; in Georgette this so-called "two-and-two" arrangement is in both the warp and the filling, thereby giving the material a harsher, crinklier feeling and appearance. In crepe de chine, ordinary raw silk warp is used, with the result that the material is softer and more lustrous when compared with Georgette.

CREPE MAROCAIN: This heavy Canton crepe of dressgoods weight is made of rayon or silk warp and rayon or cotton filling. Proper crepe twist is an important factor in production of the fabric. Filling yarn is much coarser when compared with the warp yarn used, and it gives a cross-rib effect in the goods.

CREPE METEOR: A satin-weave construction is used on the face of this fabric while the back is made of a 2-up and 2-down twill weave. Light in weight, the filling arrangement is the same as that used in Georgette crepe. The cloth is soft to the touch, drapes very well, and gives good wear. Comes in light shades and colors, launders well, and is easy to manipulate. Made with silk or rayon yarn.

CREPON: Crepe weave in one direction; very often a union cloth—wool and silk, worsted and silk, etc. May be all silk.
    Durable, drapes and launders well. Crepe yarns, however, may shrink.

DAMASK: Named in honor of the ancient city of Damascus, the gateway to the Far East in the days of Marco Polo (1254–1324). The fabric is a reversible and does not have the raised effect noted in brocade and brocatelle. Bright and dim effects are seen on either side, with the bright effect on the one side becoming dim on the reverse. Made on Jacquard looms and used for hangings, upholstery, decorative purposes.

DUVETYNE: Smooth, short-napped cloth with substantial feel and body. Satin weave used for this silk or spun silk cloth. Resembles compact velvet.
    Wears very well, good draping effect, soft to the feel, and spots easily.

FACONNÉ: French for a fancy type of weave. Small designs appear in the cloth, which is made on a Jacquard loom, although some of the goods can be made on dobbies. This rather broad term used in fabrics is popular at times; materials wear and drape well, as a rule.

FAILLE: A ribbed silk or rayon cloth with crosswise rib effect. It is soft in feel and belongs to the grosgrain family of cross-rib materials. Used for coats, dressgoods, handbags. Faille is rather difficult to launder well, has good draping effects, and will give good service if handled carefully. Finished at 36 to 40 inches wide.

FAILLE CREPE: Has a smooth, dull, and richer face effect than crepe de chine. Fiber content must be declared if not made of all silk.

FAILLE TAFFETA: Made on plain-weave, occasionally on twill construction, it is crisp and stiff; and has a very fine cross-rib filling effect. Made in silk, rayon, or acetate, it is used for coats and dresses.

FLAT CREPE: A major type of crepe in which the warp with flat yarn and the filling with "S" twist and "Z" twist yarn are used to make this fabric, finished at about 41 inches. Denier of the warp may be 150, 100, or 75; filling is of 100-denier or 75-denier yarn. Textures range from 80 by 40 to 48 up to 150 by 76, which is a print-cloth texture.
    The word "crepe" originates in the Latin crispus, which means "crimped." As the name indicates, the material is comparatively flat and reveals only a slight pebble or crepe effect. The use of crepe filling imparts a soft, pliable hand that enhances drapability despite the light weight of the goods. Reed widths are from three to five inches wider than the finished width. The print-goods texture is extremely popular in the apparel trade and is used in garments such as accessories, blouses, dressgoods, negligees, and pajamas. Any of the flat crepe textures may be used in the above-mentioned garments, as well as in the lining trade.

GAUZE: A leno or doup-woven fabric in which the ends cross each other according to the design to give a gauzy or lace effect. Much curtain fabric is made with this construction, such as marquisette.

GEORGETTE CREPE: A staple silk fabric, plain or crepe weave, usually woven with a 40-reed or a 45-reed with 2 ends per dent. The warp is usually 2-thread or 3-thread, 13/15 up to 20/22 crepe yarn twisted about 60 turns per inch. The filling is generally the same as the warp. Textures range around 80 by 70.

The warp and the filling arrangement is 2 ends of right-hand twist, followed by 2 ends of left-hand twist. This produces a pebble-like feel and crepe effect. Incidentally, crepe de chine may have the same warp as Georgette, but the filling is softer and receives fewer turns of twist per inch. Georgette is harsher than Canton crepe.

Georgette may be white, dyed, or printed. This rugged lightweight fabric has stiffness and body, and gives excellent wear because of its construction.

HABUTAI: Made in Japan, China, and in this country, this plain-weave fabric is noted for its smoothness, light weight, and even texture when made of silk. Used in blouses, draperies, lamp shades, office coats, shirts, undergarments. Gives good, rugged wear and launders very well. Also made with other fibers.

JACQUARD: A more or less elaborate design or motif woven into fabric by the use of a special head motion. A loom equipped to make these patterns is known as the Jacquard loom. Many weaves can be utilized to make the motifs and there is no restriction as to their possible combinations. Jacquard materials include brocade, brocatelle, damask, tapestry, novelty effects in shirting and dressgoods, decorative cloths, evening-wear fabrics, lining for the better grade of cloth and fur coats.

JERSEY: A plain stitch knitted cloth in contrast to rib-knitted fabric. Material may be made circular, flat or warp knitted; the latter type jersey is sometimes known as tricot. Used in dressgoods, sportswear, underwear. Gives good service and launders very well. A very popular staple.

Woven jersey is not popular at present and little of it is seen on the market; a type of lightweight silk broadcloth in which some porosity in the weave prevailed. Used as shirting in the white or in colors and stripes.

LINGERIE CREPE: Practically a French crepe; it is not now being embossed to produce a rippled effect. In textile technology, it is not considered as a full-fledged crepe texture today. Now being made of silk, acetate, rayon, or nylon.

MATELASSÉ, MATELLASSÉ: Figured fabric made on dobby or Jacquard looms. The patterns stand out and give a "pouch" or "quilted" effect to the goods. Comes in colors and in novelty effects. Made in cotton, rayon, silk, or wool, the cloth will give good wear, drape well, but must be laundered with utmost care. Matelassé garments are very attractive and, when in vogue, are much in demand. Some cotton fabric is used for bedspreads.

Matelas is French for "mattress," from the Arabian *matrah*, meaning bed. As used in textile weaves, matelassé or matellassé means a raised effect produced by interlacings of the yarn to show a quilted surface on the fabric. Some of the fabric may have metallic threads worked into the pattern.

MESSALINE: A five-end satin-weave fabric made in rayon or silk and noted for its softness and pliability. Messaline should be manipulated with care; it launders well, is lustrous, and is a very dressy women's wear cloth.

METALLIC CLOTH: Any cloth, usually silk, that has gold, silver, tinsel, or other metal threads woven into design in the cloth. Lamé is metallic material. Usually gives cross-wise rib or repp effect in the cloth.

Rather stiff, harsh, stately, formal, prone to tarnish, quite durable. Ideal for formal evening wear. Of many grades and qualities.

MOIRÉ, WATERMARKED: A watered, or a bright-and-dim effect, given to acetate, rayon, silk, and cotton fabrics. Produced by means of engraved rollers which exert very heavy pressure on the goods in order to enhance its beauty. Much taffeta, voile, and organdy receives the finish. Acetate fabrics will retain this wavy effect permanently, rayons will not.

MOSSY OR SAND CREPE: A fabric with a fine moss or sand effect on the face.

MOURNING CREPE: A dull black material which may or may not be given a moiré effect. A pronounced crepe weave enhances the final lusterless effect.

MOUSSELINE DE SOIE: Silk muslin on the order of chiffon with a crisp, firm finish. While cool, and popular in evening wear, the material does not launder satisfactorily. Its service to the wearer is comparatively short.

NANKEEN, SHANTUNG: A plain woven, rough fabric made from Tussah or wild silk. It is a rugged type of cloth on the order of pongee but is always a light coffee or ecru color in the finished state. Uses include dressgoods, handkerchiefs, office coats, shirting. Withstands rigors of washing and wearing and gives good service.

PANNE: A satin-faced, velvet, or silk material, named from the French for "plush," which has a high luster made possible by the tremendous roller-pressure treatment given the material in finishing. Panne velvet is often referred to as panne and is a staple silk fabric.

    The term was originally spelled "penne," and implied a pile cloth which had a longer or higher pile effect than velvet but a shorter one than plush.

PANNE SATIN: Silk or rayon satin with an unsually high luster from a special finish. If made of rayon or acetate, fiber content must be declared.

PANNE VELVET: Silk or rayon velvet with a finish in which the pile is flattened and laid in one direction. Lustrous and lightweight. If made of rayon, fiber content must be declared. From the French word for plush. (*See* PANNE.)

RIB VELVET: Cloth of the velvet group with a lengthwise rib effect. In cotton, material is called corduroy.

    Good draping quality, though rather difficult to handle and manipulate. Durable, must be drycleaned, crushable.

ROMAINE CREPE: A sheer or semi-sheer crepe, somewhat on the heavy side. Made with hard-twisted yarns about 13/15 denier. A 2–2 basket weave is used in the construction, and warp and filling are woven with 2 "S" twist and 2 "Z" twist. Textures range from 100 by 90 to 120 by 110. The fabric is set at about a 50-inch reed width, and is finished at 40 inches.

ROUGH CREPE: Broad term for any heavily textured crepe fabric made on a 2 "Z" and 2 "S" plan for twist in both warp and filling. This fabric comes in a variety of textures and crepe effects. Made from silk, acetate, rayon, nylon, wool, and worsted yarns.

SATIN: The name originated in Zaytun or Zaitun (Tzu-t'ing), China. Satin weaves are used in making satin fabrics, thereby insuring the full-face color of the warp or the filling on the material.

    For example, in an 8-shaft satin-weave filling effect the warp ends show on the face of the cloth only one interlacing in every 8; the filling would show on the face of the goods every 7 out of 8 interlacings. Seven-eighths of the face of the cloth would show the filling effect. It would appear to the casual naked eye as a "solid effect." This effect makes satin ideal for evening gowns and dresses. Satins are smooth, have clinginess, are form-revealing, and smart in appearance.

    When satins first came into prominence, the spelling of the term in Europe was "aceytuin" and then Italian spelling became "zetain." From the original Chinese spelling the term was contracted to "zetin" and finally became "satin."

    Satins were known in the European world at the time of the first rumblings of the Renaissance in Italy in the twelfth and thirteenth centuries. The cloth was known in England by the fourteenth century. In court life, satin soon became a reigning favorite because of its exquisite qualities and feel.

    All of the many satin weaves, both warp and filling, are used in making satin fabric; the different weaves used readily gave rise to the many fancy names applied to cloths made of the weave. Each satin has its peculiar or particular characteristics which set it more or less apart from the other satins.

In cheaper satins, cotton warp or cotton filling is often used. A low-grade silk is often used in the cheaper cloths. Rayon and acetate materials are popular in the market when made of satin construction. The price range in satins is varied. There is probably more variance, with wider extremes, in the price per yard of satin than of any other fabric; this is certainly true of the staple cloths produced today.

In cotton-back sateen, the underside of the cloth is made of cotton, the face of the goods is silk or rayon. This arrangement allows the material to be worn to better advantage.

Satin is often woven face down in the loom because of the great lift of the harnesses when 8 or more shafts are used. By weaving it face down, only one or two harnesses at a time need be raised when the shed of the loom is formed for the actual weaving. The wear and tear on the loom is therefore greatly reduced.

Satin gray goods must be handled and treated with the utmost care. The cloth as it comes from the loom, of course, is not in presentable form. Cloth is made in the finishing, and since satin woven from silk is expensive as compared with other major fibers, every operative who comes in contact with the goods must give his or her undivided attention to the handling and work at hand. Some procedures in finishing this type of silk are secrets.

The uses of satin are many—for slips, gowns, and dresses, both classic and haute coutures, in the apparel field; lining fabric, for use in the millinery trade; drapes, hangings, covers, pillows; and many other uses.

Some satin fabrics developed today differ, no matter how slightly, in order to warrant a new name: Satin de Chine, de Lyons, double-faced satin, satin Duchesse, Turc, satin taffeta, Serrano, panne, messaline, merveilleux, Luxor, Canton, Empresse, de Bruges, crepe, Grec, etc.

TAFFETA: A cloth supposed to have originated in Iran (Persia). The term means "twisted-woven." Always a staple fabric, it is in the same class and demand as satin made of silk. The cloth is made of a plain or tabby weave and the textures vary considerably. The pickage for taffeta ranges from 70 to 130 or thereabouts.

The cloth is sometimes made in changeable effects. Solid shades and fancy prints are popular in the trade as well. Taffeta is made in corded effect, plaid designs, rib effects, and in plain textures.

Taffeta is often given a moiré effect, which it takes very neatly. The silk that should be used for a good taffeta must be of the best quality and it must be "worked" and inspected constantly. In the "watering" of taffeta, care must be exercised to have the fluid just right so that the correct tone of luster will be apparent in the goods. Calendering must be done carefully since it is an easy matter to apply too much heat to the goods. Excessive heat will tender the goods.

Taffeta will not wear as long as other silk fabrics of high quality since weighting is given the material. Excessive weighting will cause the goods to crack or split. However, the weighting gives the material its characteristic property of stiffness and scroop. Much taffeta is made at present with manmade yarns, alone or in blends.

Uses of this ever-popular fabric are for slips, dresses, ribbons, shirtwaists, umbrella fabrics, and evening wear.

Some popular taffetas include the following:

Faille taffeta is made with a plain or a twill weave in order to give a pronounced cross-rib effect. Paper taffeta is light in weight and treated to give a crisp, paperlike finish. Pigment taffeta is woven with pigment-dye yarns which give the goods a dull surface effect. Tissue taffeta is a very lightweight transparent taffeta.

TULLE: A sheer silk or rayon fabric with hexagonal mesh; stiff, used much in ballet materials. The cloth comes in white and in colors and is cool, dressy, delicate, and difficult to launder. In dressgoods, it is a stately type of material. It may be used with other fabrics, for overdraping; and is also known as rayon net or silk net. Nylon tulle is now very popular.

VELVET: From Latin *villus,* shaggy hair; related to *vellus,* fleece. Most of the cloth is made of silk or rayon and cotton, but there is some wool and worsted velvet on the market. Nylon is also used a great deal.

Velvet made of silk or rayon comes in many types and qualities. The back of the cloth is plain, the pile is rayon, silk, spun silk, Tussah silk, etc.

Better-grade velvet is washable, may be crush-resistant, water-resistant, and has stately draping qualities; but the finish does not stand up well and seems to take on a worn appearance in a short time. Laundering must be done with utmost care. Tussah silk is ideal as filling yarn in velvet, since it will dye easily and well, and does add some wearing qualities with regard to time.

Some suggestions for the care of velvet: a brush with soft bristles is suggested for picking up dust and lint. Padded hangers should be used to hang coats and suits. Water spots may be rubbed lightly with a small piece of damp velvet and then brushed with a soft brush when dry.

Velvet may be restored to pile effect and enlivened by hanging the garment over a tub of hot water in a sealed room. The garment should be left hanging for about one hour and allowed to dry before wearing. Restoration may be done at the time of taking a hot bath since the doors and windows are closed. The heat and steam in the room will bring the garment back to normal appearance if it has been carefully hung on a padded hanger.

Some of the commoner velvets include:

Bagheera: Fine uncut-pile velvet with a roughish surface that makes it crush-resistant.

Chiffon Velvet: Lightweight soft velvet with the pile pressed flat. Used for dresses, suits, evening clothes.

Ciselé Velvet: A velvet with a pattern formed by contrast of cut and uncut loops.

Faconné Velvet: Patterned velvet made by the burnt-out print method.

Lyons Velvet: A stiff thick-pile velvet. Used for hats and dresses when thick velvets are fashionable.

Nacré Velvet: Velvet with the back one color and the pile another, giving a changeable, pearly appearance (nacré).

Transparent Velvet: Lightweight soft draping velvet made with a silk or rayon back and a rayon pile.

Strictly speaking, the main difference between velvet and velveteen is that the former always has a warp-pile weave construction, while the latter is made with a filling-pile weave formation.

TESTING

1. Distinguish between a brocade and a brocatelle.
2. How would you identify bengaline?
3. Name three sheer silk fabrics.
4. Differentiate between crepe de chine and Georgette crepe.
5. What are some differences between faille and taffeta?
6. What are some features of matelassé fabric?
7. Explain watermarking or moiré effect on some fabrics.
8. Why is satin classed as a form-fitting fabric when used in a gown?
9. List five properties of velvet.
10. Name four types of velvet and identify each one.

TOPIC: TUSSAH OR WILD SILK

Tussah is as old as the raw true silk coming from cocoons of cultivated silk-worms fed on mulberry leaves. It is obtained from worms that have been raised on uncultivated mulberry leaves, or on leaves of the cherry tree, oak tree, castor oil paint, etc. Tussah is spelled in a variety of ways—Tussa, Tassui, Talar. The silk comes chiefly from China and India and a few remote areas in Japan. Real cultivation cannot take place, hence the term "wild"; boys climb trees to gather the cocoons. Reeling is done by native farmers. Usually 18 cocoons are reeled together, the resultant thread averaging about 32/34 denier in size; tussah by the pound costs about one-half as much as true silk yarn. The amount of the silk production is limited because of the primitive conditions of its natural growth and weaving.

Wild silk is strong, irregular, uneven, and difficult to bleach. The natural color is tan, ecru, or brownish, determined by the mineral matter in the soil, which has an effect on it. It is less lustrous than true silk. The fiber length of Antherea Mylitta, a leading native Indian tussah silk, is even longer than that of true silk: 600 up to about 1,800 yards or more. Boil-off is about 11 per cent, and the filament is difficult to dye except in solid shades. The Canton area of China, chiefly in the more or less isolated inland areas, produces the greatest amount of tussah.

Spun tussah is spun mechanically from the staple fiber; filament tussah is spun naturally by the cocoons which furnish the long filament. All-tussah fabrics are made; but the silk is ideal for blending with other fibers, and the fabrics made with such stocks are much more in demand than the all-tussah cloths. The uneven yarns lend unusual texture to cloth; the materials may be lustrous, soft, smooth in hand, or with shot-about effects having an uneven, irregular surface. At times the materials seem to be many ends and picks of waste yarn. Much of the cloth is made in natural color, and the durability of tussah fabrics is good to excellent. Easy launderability and good service are two features of the fabrics.

One of the great uses of the fiber is as filling in pile fabrics, since toughness of fiber is an essential in such cloths, some of which have to withstand much wear and abrasion. Suiting fabrics are made using tussah; although these cloths are light in weight, the yarn can withstand much punishment during wearing. Nankeen, rajah, shantung, and douppioni are in the same group of fabrics. Douppioni, however, is not usually classed as tussah or wild silk. It is the result of two cocoons nesting together; the quality, if one disregards evenness of fiber, may be very high, since for the most part the fiber comes from cultivated silkworms. (See below.)

STANDARD TUSSAH SILK FABRICS

DRAPERY FABRICS: Many of these use tussah filling because of its toughness and durability. These union cloths provide excellent service.

DOUPPIONI OR DOUPION: This silk thread is reeled from two cocoons that have nested together. In spinning, the double thread is not separated. The yarn is uneven, irregular, and the diameter is large. It is used in cloth of this name as well as in nankeen, pongee, shantung, and for fabrics for local consumption where the silk is obtained. The fabrics are very irregular in surface effect. Douppioni is popular in suitings, used either alone or in combination with wool, worsted, tussah, and manmade fibers in fabric blends. Not a true tussah.

NANKEEN, NANKIN, RAJAH, SHANTUNG, TUSSAH: These closely related cloths come in white, natural color, or in colors. The yarns are more uneven than true pongee fabric. Trade names are given to many of the varying grades and qualities on the market today. These lightweight fabrics are popular for summer wear; they launder well, and give good to excellent wear. These cloths are also printed for women's wear dressgoods.

SHANTUNG SUITING: This fabric is worn by men and women in the summer, and it comes in the natural tan or ecru color, or may be dyed various shades. Some of the fabrics of this name contain other fibers as well, in blended fabrics. Weight and texture will vary in quality for this plain-weave or twill-woven material. Durable, cool; withstands chafing, friction, and wear; tailors very well, and does not wrinkle to any marked degree. Douppioni often a part of content.

TUSSAH IN LINEN-LIKE FABRICS: These materials simulate linen cloths. Tussah is used for the filling, and its effect is appealing. These goods launder easily and well, are fresh looking even after repeated launderings, and give good wear.

VELVET: Many fabrics in the velvet family, along with some other pile fabrics, use tussah for filling yarn. The coarse uneven yarn, when properly used in pile construction, is an added asset to the fabric, particularly in durability. The material drapes well, will dryclean, but will probably crush, as in the case of velvets which do not use this type of yarn. If the tussah has been well dyed, it takes the place of the more expensive true silk used in pile-fabric weaving.

TESTING

1. What are the features of shantung suiting fabric?
2. Why is tussah silk ideal for use in pile fabrics as filling?
3. Discuss douppioni silk as to how it is produced and how it is used in men's and women's suitings.
4. Name four fabrics in which tussah silk is used.
5. Why might tussah be an asset in a drapery material?

Part 1—Unit 34

TOPIC: Spun Silk

Spun Silk is obtained from the following sources:

PIERCED COCOONS: Caused by the moth emerging and cutting the entire length of filament into short lengths, an inch or so long. Pierced cocoons come from breeding worms, and from damaged stock.

FRISONS: Coarse, uneven silk at the beginning and at the end of the silk filament length that is spun by the cocoon. The length of filament may range from about 300 yards to about 1,600 yards. The first third and the last third of the entire reelable length may be classed as frison stock.

FLOSS: Silk brushed from cocoons prior to reeling. Also comes from waste in manipulating spun silk stock.

SILK WASTES: Scraps, short ends and pieces.

The silk gum is removed before processing or manipulating. Its properties show that it is less lustrous than, not as strong as, and has less elasticity than reeled silk. It is a rough-and-ready type of yarn that has considerable call in the pile-fabric trade. It has little value as warp yarn. Spun silk works in well with wool, worsted, or cotton when used in dressgoods. It is a washable silk that gives good service to the wearer.

The fibers are processed into yarn on the principles used in the spinning of cotton yarn: picking, combing, dressing, separation into a lap form, drawing out into sliver form, condensing, drawing, drafting, attenuating, doubling, redoubling, roving, and, finally, spinning into yarn. Spun silk yarn is classed as a rather inexpensive type of yarn.

Because of its rugged properties, it is much used for braids of all types, flag trimming, fringes, lace, duvetyne, and pile fabrics.

Schappe Silk

A much discussed term; considered the same as spun silk in this country. Technically, however, there is a difference because of the manner of removal of the gum from the waste silk, which is often done by a rotting process of fermentation in manure.

Formerly all Continental European systems differed from the English and the United States methods. At present, all European silk of this type is classed as schappe silk. Since the Europeans have adopted our method of caring for this stock, the product is known by the name of schappe silk. In some of the more remote areas of Europe, manufacturers still cling to the old methods of classification.

The word "schappe" comes from the French verb *hacher*, which means to chop.

TESTING

1. Define "pierced cocoon," "frison," "floss silk," "schappe silk."
2. Name three uses for spun silk.
3. On what principle is spun-silk fiber spun into yarn?
4. Compare true silk with spun silk as to working properties.

Part 1—Unit 35

TOPIC: EXAMINATION ON SILK, TUSSAH SILK, AND SPUN SILK

TRUE-FALSE QUESTIONS   75 points

1. _____ Sericulture checks disease among silkworms.
2. _____ Silk is not grown here because it is impossible to raise mulberry trees successfully.
3. _____ There is more silk fabric used here than manmade fiber goods.
4. _____ The United States uses more silk than any other country.
5. _____ China, Japan, and Canada are the leading silk-raising nations.
6. _____ Italy produces the best type of silk in the world.
7. _____ Weighted silk is a special type of raw silk.
8. _____ Perspiration does not affect silk.
9. _____ Silk may be attacked by moths.
10. _____ Mildew will affect silk cloth.
11. _____ Douppioni silk is produced when two cocoons spin their silk together.
12. _____ Tram silk has less twist than organzine.
13. _____ Throwing is preparing raw silk for weaving.
14. _____ Silk is one of the strongest of all textile fibers.

15. _____ Stoving permits the silk moth to emerge from the cocoon.
16. _____ Brins is an individual silk filament.
17. _____ The bave is made up of brins, sericin, fibroin, and moiré.
18. _____ It is possible to reel the silk from a single cocoon.
19. _____ Pierced cocoons are not reeled.
20. _____ The moth spins the cocoon.
21. _____ Spun silk is more lustrous than true silk yarn.
22. _____ Frison is coarse, uneven silk wherein the cocoon is attached to the straw bed upon which cocoons have been placed.
23. _____ The moisture content of silk is 6 per cent.
24. _____ Denier is a term that is used in expressing the size of the silk yarn or thread.
25. _____ Eggs hatch out the larvae, which when grown are the silkworms of commerce.

MULTIPLE-CHOICE QUESTIONS   25 points

1. Faconné   silk gum, type of finish, cloth, dull effect on silk.
2. Brocade   made on plain, worsted, Jacquard, or swivel loom.
3. Dynamiting   reeling, spooling, weighting, boiling-off, stoving.
4. Lustrous cloth   taffeta, duvetyne, crepe, satin, Canton crepe.
5. Filature   faille, crepon, throwing plant, cocoons, tram.
6. Spun silk   satin Canton, taffeta, Georgette crepe, tub silk.
7. Waxed cloth   moiré, waterproofed, ciré, weighted, embossed.
8. Raises silk   Germany, Mexico, China, Peru, Switzerland, Siam.
9. Loosely twisted   organzine, singles, tram, crepe.
10. Watermarking   ciré, weighted, pressed, moiré, embossed, sized.

ROMAN DENIER MADE OF SILVER

This coin is from the collection of the author. A book about coins written by Babylon gives the date of this coin as about 250 B.C. British Museum Catalog: "Coins of the Roman Republic," written in 1910, ascribes this coin to from 217–197 B.C. See British Museum Catalog II, page 213, where it is pictured.

Head of Roma, in profile, wearing winged helmet with visor in three separate pieces of unequal length, not peaked; earring of single drop, and necklace; hair tied and falling in three symmetrical locks.

Obverse—horses are Castor and Pollux, mythological protectors of Rome.

PART TWO

TABLE OF CONTENTS

Part 2—Unit 1

TOPIC: BASIC DIFFERENCES BETWEEN NATURAL AND MANMADE TEXTILE FIBERS

The greatest single difference between the natural and the manmade textile fibers is that the natural fibers have been gathered or harvested by man since they were first known in recorded history. Man has had comparatively little control over them, generally speaking, in their use, and even in production and manipulation. Man has had to do the best he could with these fibers provided by nature, and had to overcome to the best of his ability the questions and problems of staple length, weight, strength, cross-section, elongation, modulus, toughness, resiliency, and other characteristics and properties.

Definite uniformity of the fibers has been one of the most irksome problems that man had to overcome. Cotton, wool, flax, and silk presented these problems since their inception. Cotton, for example, despite the fact that it is classed as a short fiber, shows considerable variation in staple fiber length and in its uni-

[184]

formity, like so many fingerprints or oak leaves. Classing and sorting these fibers always had to be done with utmost care by experts with years of training to gain the necessary experience in handling the fibers. Down through the ages, man has done remarkably well in controlling these fibers and has really done an outstanding piece of work for all mankind.

The four major natural fibers, of course, are made from long-chain polymers which lend themselves in an ideal way for spinning into yarn and weaving into cloth. Each of them has the difficult to define but altogether necessary quality of being pleasing to the touch, known as the "hand." All of them do have certain shortcomings, since, being natural, organic substances, they are subject to attack from bacteria and/or mildew. Wool and silk, for example, provide nutriment for certain insects. All of them are vulnerable to fluctuation relative to supply, and must depend upon the prevailing conditions for this supply. The elements affect production very often through drought, blight, disease, poor cultivation or raising, mineral matter in the soil, insects, etc.

All four fibers do not retain a crease readily and well, and may have a less than desirable resistance to wear and service. Ordinary cotton and linen have rather poor wrinkle resistance and do require careful ironing. Wool has poor stability to laundering and in fabric often presents a rather sagging or baggy effect, especially in men's suitings. Worsted will hold an excellent crease but will shine with constant wear. Silk is affected by sunlight. While these fibers have served man for better than 99 per cent of recorded history, there is, nevertheless, room for improvement. The manmade fibers seem to have provided this improvement.

In the manmade, chemical fiber kingdoms, it should be noted that man actually writes the formula for the molecule, the basic element contained in them. He can diagnose and specify what kind or type of fiber will be produced within the broad limits of its chemistry. He can, as well, alter or modify his specifications at will, thereby "chemically tailoring" the fiber to its end—or terminal—use in the home, in apparel, and in industry. He predetermines the size of denier-count of the filament or fiber, its weight, etc., and when he spins his manmade fiber it is always endlessly uniform with regard to his specifications. Manmade fibers are not "seasonal," as is the case with the natural fibers; they can be produced every working hour throughout the day, week, or year, and pinpointed as to exact annual production almost to the pound. Thus man can build discreetly differences or modifications into his chemical fibers, and obtain them unfailingly. This is why nylon, for example, varies in its properties when used in tire cord, hosiery, a shroud rope, a sheer dress fabric, or in a bulletproof vest, yet all these are unmistakably still nylon. And this is the reason why manmade filaments and fibers can be "tailormade" to achieve this or that objective. Except for acetate, rayon, and nylon, the host of manmade fibers has been developed since the close of World War II, a wonderful achievement by man in his mastery and ever-increasing knowledge of all things chemical.

TOPIC: Introduction to and Facts about Manmade Textile Fibers

The term "manmade" is used at present to describe all fibers other than those which have a natural origin, such as:

ANIMAL FIBERS: wool, worsted, hair fibers, and silk (a filament).
VEGETABLE FIBERS: cotton, flax, ramie, jute, hemp, and other bast fibers.
MINERAL FIBERS: asbestos, glass fibers, slag wool, etc.

MANMADE FIBERS

There are seventeen categories in the group of Manmade Fibers as decreed by the Federal Trade Commission. Generally speaking, the following breakdown is used in the textile industries:

Group One

1. Regenerated Type—Rayon (Viscose and Cuprammonium [Bemberg]).
2. Cellulose Derivative—Acetate, Arnel.
3. Acrylic—A-Acrilan, Creslan, "Orlon," Zefran.
4. Modacrylic—Dynel, Verel.
5. Olefin—Polyethylene, Polythene, Polypropylene, Polyurethane.
6. Polyamide—Nylon.
7. Polyester—"Dacron," Kodel, Fortrel, Vycron, Vectra, Blue "C."
8. Nytril—Darvan-Travis.
9. Vinal—Vinal.
10. Vinyon—Vinyon HH.

Group Two

The products in this group are usually set apart from those in Group One. They may or may not be classified singly or as a complete group; data, production, statistics, etc., are usually given separately in bulletins and reports issued to the trade:

1. Azlon—Fibrolane, Lanital, Merinova; no longer made in the United States.
2. Glass Fibers—Fiberglas, Garan, Unifab, Pittsburgh, PPG, Modiglass.
3. Lastrile.
4. Metallic—Alistran, Chromeflex, Fairtex, Lamé, Metlon, Malora.
5. Rubber—Laton, Lastex, Revere, Contro, Darleen, Filatex.
6. Saran—Dawbarn, Velon, Boltaflex, Saranspun, Lus-Trus, Rovana, Saran.
7. Spandex—"Lycra," Spandelle, Vyrene, Interspan, Numa.

Manmade fibers are manufactured wholly by chemical treatments and processes of certain raw materials such as wood pulp, cotton linters, petroleum extracts, by-products of coal, casein, air, water, salt, et al.

These fibers are used in a wide variety of textile articles in apparel, clothing, decorative fabrics, domestics, household items, and industrial fabrics. They are much used today despite the fact that the natural fibers, known for centuries, have certain basic properties and characteristics all their own. However, they do have certain limitations due to which they cannot cope in many instances with the performance noted in manmade fibers. Through research, development, experimentation, pilot-plant operation, and performance that has earned consumer acceptance, the development of manmade fibers has widened the field of textile fibers from which textile manufacturers may choose, resulting in a much greater choice of textile fabrics for the consuming public.

Manmade fibers are not an imitation of, or a substitute for, the natural fibers. They have made a very decided impact in the textile fiber kingdoms. They can resemble each other in surface appearance or texture effect in many ways, but each manmade fiber does possess its particular merits and properties and can be adapted in many ways for a great many fabrics and purposes.

A manmade fiber can be controlled accurately during manufacture so that there is a constant high quality to meet particular end uses. The chemist is also able to modify unlimited variations of these fibers for some particular use, such as strength, crimp, luster, color, stretch, elasticity, extensibility, shape, size, modulus, etc. Versatility of these fibers is easily possible and almost endless in scope. The textile stylist is thus aided in engineering better, more interesting, different, and more eye-appealing and attractive materials. Fabric quality has also been enhanced, which arouses more consumer interest in practically all types of fabrics, and at reasonable prices.

This versatility observed in present-day fabrics is easily apparent to the public with the rise of blends and mixture fabrics wherein natural and manmade fibers are combined in the same cloth. Manmade fibers can also be blended with each other to produce outstanding fabrics. The following short history of some of the fibers should prove of interest to the reader.

NYLON was introduced in 1939 and was soon a household word. At first people thought of hosiery as nylon and vice versa. Now nylon has hundreds of uses. It is outstanding in its tear resistance, a very high breaking or tensile strength, and its ability to withstand chafing, wear, and abrasion.

"ORLON" became available in 1951 following ten years of research and an expenditure of sixty million dollars to place it on the market. This versatile fiber, while its strength is not too high, does have about twice the strength of the wool fiber with which it competes. It has sturdiness, body and substance, and in garments provides bulkiness without added weight.

"DACRON" first appeared in 1951 and was soon making its presence felt. There is the true story of the famous man's suit that was worn for sixty-seven successive days, immersed twice in a swimming pool, washed once in a washing machine, and then it was ready for pressing. The suiting showed the great crease resistance and crease retention peculiar to "Dacron" fabrics and garments. Very rapid drying is another asset of "Dacron."

VINYL UPHOLSTERY was introduced at the World's Fairs in New York City and San Francisco in 1939. It is actually a coated fabric in which a cotton-knit fabric serves as the base which is coated with vinyl compounds. The knit backing supports the vinyl coating and provides an elasticity that resists tearing.

FABRILITE VINYL UPHOLSTERY made its debut shortly after the close of World War II. There are at present over two hundred variations of texture, surface, embossing, and comparable effects available. Durability and ease of care, water and soil resistance feature this vinyl product. A damp cloth will wipe unsightly surface effects from the material.

URETHANE FOAM: One of the bases for this foam is the well-known DuPont "Hylene" organic isocyanate group which furnishes the basic ingredients for the foam. This foam is much used in laminated interlinings to provide warmth and give lasting shape retention to garments. The product is used in bulky but featherweight topcoats, raincoats, jackets for all-weather purposes, sports jackets, etc., and there is a lasting well-tailored effect noted on garments in which it has been used.

KODEL is the lightest in weight of the polyester fibers and is the whitest in cast as well. Its specific gravity is very low, 1.22 to 1.38. Its pilling tendency is extremely low, thereby making it ideal for blending with woolen or worsted fibers in woven or knitted fabrics. Its resistance to outdoor wear and exposure surpasses wool and rayon and is about the same as cotton and rayon in these respects.

DYNEL and VEREL are the two modacrylic fibers made in the United States. One of their great uses is in combination for the manufacture of pile fabrics such as bulky coatings, blankets, trimmings, pile shoe trim, filters, etc. Their shrinking properties vary so that they can be made into fabrics of the type that have a wavy or undulating effect in the finished goods to give an interesting surface effect.

There is, of course, no universal fiber that can meet all requirements for public consumption. Cotton is often known as "the universal textile fiber," but like all other natural fibers, its supremacy has felt the great impacts and inroads from the manmade fibers. Each fiber, it may be said, is a spoke in the great wheel of fibers. These manmade fibers have survived the tests of time and usage; they have demonstrated their satisfactory performance to the consumer, and have contributed something of importance and note to the great textile industry. The modification of the properties of these fibers does not imply that they can be altered or changed completely, so there is now a genuine need for a selection of fibers with its own group of particular or special properties. There are today in the United States about two hundred trademark names and brand names, which cover all these manmade fibers. There are about eight hundred other names for the various types of manmade fibers outside the United States. Many of the fibers are short lived, and new ones are continually entering the market in an effort to withstand the test of time, usage, and acceptance. Manmade fibers have achieved, as previously noted, great success since the close of World War II. Prior to the war, only three manmade fibers were being used here—rayon, acetate, and nylon.

Generally speaking, it is now possible to select the best fiber for a particular purpose. Most of these fibers may be used alone or in combination with other fibers, either natural or manmade. These fibers cannot be identified by appearance, hand or texture. The adaptability of the fibers admits of their being used in literally hundreds of different fabrics for the trade. Many fabrics made from these fibers closely resemble those made from the natural fibers. The wide use of blended fabrics on the market today further complicates identification of fiber content. Thus buyers should always insist on full details as supplied on labels or hang-tags as decreed by the Federal Trade Commission in its Textile Fiber Products Identification Act of March 3rd, 1960. All necessary instructions as to content of the fabric or garment, as well as to the care of the article, must be stated on the labels attached to the item. All reliable suppliers will always furnish any necessary information for their products.

Identifying particular fibers in fabrics, either in a fabric made from only one fiber or in blended fabrics where two, three, or more fibers have been used, is done by chemical testing, which can easily become rather complex. The textile technologist, the textile technician, textile testing companies, and the textile companies themselves are most interested in giving adequate information about their products to the buying public. Pamphlets, bulletins, magazines, television and radio, public relations and advertising, etc., are all mediums through which the public becomes aware of every textile fiber produced. All manufacturing agencies, large and small, are interested in the ultimate consumer—from fiber to fabric to fashion and the future for their wares.

The names of several of the manmade fibers and their products are now household words. The leader in popularity and use is rayon, followed by acetate and nylon. Next in order come "Orlon," "Dacron," Acrilan, Arnel, Vycron, Kodel, Creslan, Estron, Avisco, Fortrel, and Antron.

TESTING

1. Name one fiber from each of the ten fibers listed in Group One.
2. Name one fiber from each of the six fibers or products listed in Group Two.
3. Name three basic elements or ingredients used to serve as a base in the manufacture of manmade fibers or products.
4. Give an outstanding property of each of the following: (1) Nylon. (2) "Orlon." (3) "Dacron." (4) Kodel. (5) Dynel and Verel.
5. What fiber is sometimes known as "the universal textile fiber"?
6. What is the correct name of the Act decreed by the Federal Trade Commission, effective March 3, 1960?
7. Discuss some experience, positive or negative, that you have had with some manmade fiber product such as a suiting, skirt, shirting, sweater, sportswear, coating, etc.

Part 2—Unit 3

TOPIC: DEFINITIONS AND TRADE CUSTOMS FOR THE RAYON-, NYLON-, AND SILK-CONVERTING INDUSTRY

Approved and Promulgated by the Committee on Standards of the Textile Distributors Association, Inc., 1040 Sixth Avenue, New York City

ON GRAY (GREY, GREIGE, GRIEGE) GOODS

DELIVERY ABOUT: The word "about," when used with respect to a calendar day, means "within five days before or after such date."

DELIVERY CALENDAR: A delivery specified as during a calendar week shall be shipped during that calendar week. A delivery specified over a month or more shall be shipped in equal weekly installments, unless otherwise specified.

PROMPT DELIVERY: If described as for "prompt delivery," shipment must be made not later than eight calendar days after acceptance of the order by the home office.

SPOT DELIVERY: If sold as "spots," or for "spot delivery," it is understood that subject goods are on hand and shipment must be made not later than the first business day following that on which the order is accepted.

RUN OF THE MILL: Technically, this expression may be applied to cloth as it comes from normal manufacturing operations and before it has been classified as "first quality," "second quality," and other inferior gradings.

It is customary for the mill to eliminate from goods so described any merchandise which may not be fairly classified as first or second quality.

GRAY GOODS FOR PRINTING: The contract should be marked as to the type or method of printing. It should be described as either
   a) "For all-over printing," *or*
   b) "For printing," which would be suitable for any type of pattern.

SHORT LENGTHS: First-quality goods in 20–40 yard lengths or cuts.

PERCENTAGE OF DARKS: This is an individual contract condition.

PATENT DEFECT: A defect that is visible upon examination—upon optical inspection.

LATENT DEFECT: A defect that is present but is not visible upon immediate examination of the goods in the gray condition.

FINISHED GOODS

PROPER PROCEDURE FOR ISSUING CONTRACTS:

a) Prepare all contracts in triplicate.

b) Send two unsigned copies to your customer for his signature with the request that both copies be returned to you as soon as possible.

c) Upon receipt of both copies, you will complete one copy and then return it to your customer for his files.

PROCEDURE RELATIVE TO COLOR ASSORTMENT: The following letter and invoice to cover such transactions are recommended:

Letter: Gentlemen: Re: Contract No.: _____:

We have not as yet received your color assortment against the above contract.

Unless we receive the assortment by return mail, we shall have no alternative but to set aside the gray goods for your account and invoice them to you at finished goods prices, in accordance with paragraph 7 of our contract,

Very truly yours,

. . . .

Invoice: 10,000 yards Quality: _____ at Finished Goods Price of $_____.

These goods are being held for your account and at your risk.

NOTE: The important thing to do is to earmark the gray goods in your records.

FINISHED GOODS WIDTH: Where a single width is specified, there should be a tolerance of ¼ inch either way—plus or minus.

Where a tolerance is specified in the contract—e.g. 44½–45 inches—there should not be any tolerance at all. In other words, the finished goods are to be delivered with a tolerance of ¼ inch plus or minus, except on contracts where a tolerance has already been specified.

AS ARE: If goods are purchased "as are," the buyer waives all right to any claim because of defective quality, either patent or latent.

SECONDS: The word "seconds" is applied to cloth inferior in grading according to industry standards. It is commonly used to describe cloth containing greater or more weaving imperfections than the industry standard and it may also contain more than the ordinary dyeing imperfections. It also may be applied to cloth made of irregular yarn.

REMNANTS: First- or second-quality goods from two to twenty yards in length. Remnants are purchased at the risk of the buyer.

COLOR CHANGES IN PLEATED FABRICS: Tests must be made before subjecting the fabric to pleating.

GAS FADING: Fabrics which contain acetate fibers are subject to gas fading caused by gaseous exposure. Each case is to be decided upon its own merits, or by arbitration.

NOTE: The foregoing definitions and trade customs are also applicable to acetate, triacetate, acrylic, modacrylic, olefin, and polyester fibers and fabrics, etc.

STANDARDS FOR THE EXAMINATION OF FINISHED GOODS

As jointly approved and adopted by the Textile Distributors Association, Inc., and The National Federation of Textiles, Inc., November, 1955.

Explanatory Note

1. The Standards for the Examination of Finished Goods cover market-wide fabrics of manmade and/or natural fibers alone or in combination, whether in the gray or finished state. These Standards were drawn to provide, as a practical matter, for visual examinations as a basis for settling disputes over the quality of fabrics. The Standards apply to all fabrics regardless of width or construction.

    The Standards are intended primarily for the examination of finished goods, but they can also be used for the examination of gray goods. Naturally, finished goods will not show all the imperfections which will be noted in gray goods.

2. These Standards explain the penalties to be assigned for imperfections for warp defects and conditions, and filling defects and conditions. They explain generally what constitutes defects and the penalties in points to be applied against each. The grading is designed to apply to every imperfection according to size, regardless of type, but in the case of goods over 50 inches in finished width, an increase of not more than 10% in penalty points will be allowed in "first" quality.

    The total penalty points for each piece is to be recorded, and if the number of such points is less than the number of yards in the piece, the piece is graded a "first." If the number of penalty points exceeds the yardage, the piece is graded a "second." Some pieces frequently hover on the borderline between "firsts" and "seconds." For example, a 100-yard piece might be penalized to the extent of 99 to 100 points. Although pieces of this type pass the test for "firsts," it is considered highly inadvisable from the standpoint of market policy and customer relations to permit too many of this type to be shipped in any one delivery.

    In the case of print cloth any piece of gray goods which contains less than 50% more penalty points than yardage may be passed for printing purposes, since print patterns usually conceal approximately 50% of gray imperfections. If the imperfection should show through the print in the finished fabric, penalty points would, of course, be assessed in accordance with the Standards.

3. Use of these Standards by qualified examiners has proved and will prove that Standards are satisfactory for all examination purposes and are sufficiently flexible and simple for continuous use. It is important, of course, that examiners using the Standards should be fully qualified to examine the goods in question.

    The examiners should also be made aware of the end use to which the goods will be put. Such end use should always be stated in the request for examination.

    It will be noted that the Standards are set up for the same point score for all types of yarn and fiber. Qualified examiners are sufficiently aware of normal irregularities peculiar to any particular quality or construction. To set up individual Standards for every construction, type, or quality of goods would result in a volume of Standards far too technical to be practicable, and the entire object of standardizing the examination of finished goods in a feasible manner would be defeated.

General Considerations

Both the manufacturer and his customer, and the converter and his customer, have been considered in formulating the plan for examination of finished goods, which follows herewith.

The customer is not interested in the cause of a defect. He is interested in how much loss in cutting will be necessitated and how seriously his customer in turn will complain.

The manufacturer, on the other hand, contends that finished goods go through various complicated processes, and that besides normal irregularities natural to the fibers used, a reasonable number of manufacturing defects must be expected.

The object of the following plan is to establish a standard for examination of finished goods that will result in conclusions which may be approximately duplicated by a number of examiners trained in this method, working independently of each other, and who qualify to examine the goods in question.

EXAMINATION TECHNIQUE

a) Finished goods should be examined in units of one complete piece. They may be examined by machine or over a perch and the face side of the material shall be examined full width.

b) When the examination is made manually, the penalty points (if any) are determined and noted. Thus upon the completion of inspection, there is available an accurate record of the total penalties. From this the grading may be computed as hereinafter described. No goods are to be examined by the manufacturer unless 33⅓% of the pieces in question are examined by the complainant and penalty points noted.

c) Inspection shall be made using north daylight free from reflections and shadows, or approved type of lighting system.

d) The machine or perch shall be placed perpendicular to the rays of light and the material shall run at an angle of 45 degrees to the vertical.

Imperfections and Irregularities Defined

a) Imperfections are defects which can be prevented under normal conditions or with reasonable care.

b) Normal irregularities are defects beyond the reasonable control of the manufacturer or natural to any particular quality or construction.

NOTE: For the purpose of grading merchandise, such irregularities should at no time be considered as imperfections.

Classification of Imperfections

a) Vertical imperfections or those running parallel to the warp thread.

b) Horizontal imperfections or those running parallel to the filling thread.

PENALTIES FOR IMPERFECTIONS

WARP DEFECTS		FILLING DEFECTS	
10 to 36 inches	10 points	Full width	10 points
5 to 10 inches	5 points	5 inches to half width	5 points
1 to 5 inches	3 points	1 to 5 inches	3 points
Up to one inch	1 point	Up to one inch	1 point

NOTE: 1. No one yard should be penalized more than 10 points.
2. Any warp or filling defects occurring repeatedly throughout the entire piece makes it a "second."
3. A combination of both warp and filling defects when occurring in one yard should not be penalized more than 10 points in any one yard.

METHOD OF GRADING

The grading of a piece of material should be determined from the penalty points charged for imperfections by the method hereinafter described.

Grading

"First" Quality: A piece is graded a "first" if the total penalty points do not exceed the total yardage of the piece.

"Second" Quality: A piece is graded a "second" if the total penalty points exceed the total yardage of the piece.

An increase of not more than 10% in penalty points will be allowed on "first" quality goods over 50 inches wide.

Inspection Guide

a) Imperfections appearing within one-half inch of either edge should be disregarded.

b) When not otherwise specified, it shall be understood that the material is to be examined on one side only, the face.

Construction

All goods that are considered not to be of a commercial standard construction shall be considered as manufactured at the customer's risk. Decisions involving such quality disputes shall be made by arbitration.

Converting Imperfections

Manufacturers shall not be held responsible for converting imperfections due to the insufficient removal of gum, tint, or fugitive stain.

The following dyeing and/or printing conditions, if prevalent in a piece, grade it a "second":

> calendar marks; chafe; clip marks if further than ½ of an inch from the selvage; dye streaks; embossing roller damage; finishing dirt; misprints; rope marks; side-to-side shading or poor penetration; stains; tears along the selvage; weak or tender merchandise when proved that gray goods were normal strength, etc.

Courtesy: Hilda A. Wiedenfeld, Managing Director of Textile Distributors Association, Inc., 1040 Sixth Avenue, New York City.

Part 2—Unit 4

TOPIC: History of Rayon and Acetate

While acetate and rayon are cellulosic in nature, as are the two of the oldest natural fibers, cotton and flax, they are of comparatively recent origin, although the first rumblings of what we today call rayon and acetate occurred in the seventeenth century. Experimental fibers were made during 1885–89, and the first American production was in 1910. In 1924 the name "rayon" was coined. Up to this time rayon was known as art silk, artificial silk, fiber silk, milkweed silk, luster silk, and Glos. Its history and development follow:

1664: Robert Hooke, the English naturalist and research scientist, was born in 1635, the son of a minister. He studied at Oxford and Cambridge universities. Living in the time of Cromwell and Charles II, he was a close friend of Samuel Pepys, the diarist of the era, and knew many persons of prominence. Hooke built a microscope which, up to his time, was the best one yet developed. In 1664, when he was 29 years old, his chief interests included the development of filaments by synthesis. *Micrographia,* the book he brought out, stressed the fact that it was possible to produce yarn by mechanical means. Dr. Hooke wrote as follows:

And I have often thought, that probably there might be a way, found out, to make an artificial glutinous composition, much resembling, if not full as good, nay better, than the Excrement, or whatever other substances it be out of which, the Silk-worm wire-draws his clew. If such a composition were found, it were certainly an easier matter to find very quick ways of drawing it into small wires for use. I need not mention the use of such an Invention, nor the benefit that is likely to accrue to the finder, they being sufficiently obvious. This hint, therefore, may, I hope, give some ingenious inquisitive Person an occasion of making some trials, which if successfull, I have my aim, and I suppose he will have no occasion to be displeased.

1734–1742: During these years, René de Réaumur (1683–1757) wrote his greatest work, *Mémoirs Pour Servir a l'Histoire des Insectes*, which contained suggestions for the manufacture of artificial silk. In 1710 this French scientist, who discovered white opaque glass, had written a paper on the possibility of using silk from spiders; it became so celebrated that the Chinese emperor Kang-he had it translated into the Chinese language.

In this span of eight years, Réaumur tried to imitate the method of the silkworm and the spider by drawing out a continuous strand of waterproofed varnish. His efforts were not successful, and since he was more interested in the making of tin, he allowed his work to pass into oblivion. He did, however, give food for thought to later scientists. There is a thermometer named in honor of this great scientist. (*See also* under 1885–1889.)

1840: F. Gottlob Keller, of Hainichen, Germany, was a textile weaver. He was a man of amazing talents but is practically forgotten today. Keller, who knew the papermaking trade very well, devised a technique for making pulp for paper by squeezing powdered wood given off by wood coming in contact with a grindstone. His pulp took the place of that made from rags, which at this time were scarce and expensive. He sold his rights for $700; but Keller, unknown to himself, had made possible the future production of rayon, newspapers, and other similar items cellulosic in nature.

In this same year, Louis Schwabe, silk manufacturer of Manchester, England, who made silk fabrics for Queen Victoria and the French court, developed the first spinnerettes through which a spinning solution could be extruded. Made of glass, these spinnerettes were easily broken.

1846: The German chemist, C. F. Schönbein, discovered guncotton or nitrocellulose by using alcohol as a solvent. He made collodion or "new skin," an item of interest for future scientists in the field.

1855: George Audemars, in Lausanne, Switzerland, gave much thought to work done by Réaumur and Schönbein. He used the extract of mulberry bast and the extract obtained from alcohol and ether in an attempt to bring about a combination of collodion and rubber. While he was not successful with his mixing of the bast and the alcohol-ether extracts, he did make it apparent that it would be possible to make a filament by this principle of coagulation.

1857: A patent was taken out in London, England, for production of a glass-like fiber. In this same year, Schweitzer, a German chemist, used a copper-ammonium solution to dissolve cellulose, thus producing a forerunner of present-day cuprammonium (Bemberg) rayon—the second method of rayon manufacture to be perfected in the course of time. Schweitzer's work resulted in his still well-known and much used Schweitzer's reagent, his ammoniacal solution of copper oxide which will dissolve cotton and silk but not wool. Cellulose, the base for rayon, is precipitated by sugar and acids, but silk by acids alone.

1860: Sir Joseph W. Swan, English electrician and physicist, made filaments from paper (cellulose) and was actually the first person to produce an artificial fiber or filament. His chief interest, however, was in the making of carbon filaments for use in lamps. By 1863, Swan had laid the groundwork for producing a nitrocellulose filament. Thomas Alva Edison, in 1879, used the principles of Swan in the perfection of his incandescent lamp in the United States. (See 1880.)

1862: Ozanum, an Englishman, designed a spinnerette with which he thought he could make artificial silk that could compete with true silk. A plant was established by a German concern in Eilfeld, Germany, to make the spinnerettes. Ozanum used glass for his spinnerettes, but because of the easy breakage of glass, his venture using this material did not last long.

1869: Naudin and Schutzenberger, German scientists, introduced what was in time to become known as acetate filament and fiber. They used acetic acid to dissolve cellulose and form cellulose acetate, a chemical compound. Their methods, however, were not applied to the making of artificial silk, as it was then known, until the close of the century.

1880: Swan obtained a fiber-filament by treating a cotton thread with sulfuric acid and then collodion, producing thread by forcing the resultant solution through the minute holes (orifices) of a spinnerette into a coagulating bath to form the filaments. It was Swan who developed the spinnerette as it is known today, a most important item in the manufacture of manmade filaments.

1882: Edward Weston, English-American electrical scientist, from his studies of the work done by Schweitzer around 1857, developed a fiber to be used for carbon filaments in electric lamps. He obtained a patent for making the filaments by his method.

1885–1889: Count Hilaire Bernigaud de Chardonnet (1839–1924), the "Father of the Rayon Industry," was a native of Besançon, France, and did all his work in the field of science there. He studied chemistry under Pasteur's brother-in-law, Professor Loir of the Faculty of Sciences in Besançon. Chardonnet began his studies at the age of fifteen. In 1859, he entered École Polytechnique, Paris, and studied under the great Louis Pasteur. They became firm friends and this friendship lasted until the death of Pasteur. On May 12, 1884, he received a patent (Number 165,349) for *"une matière textile artificielle resemblant à la soie."*
Pasteur sent Chardonnet to southern France to make an exhaustive study of the then rampant diseases among silkworms which were wreaking havoc in sericulture and seriously threatened the silk industry on the Continent. He found that silkworms fed on mulberry leaves, which are cellulosic (vegetable) matter, to produce the silk filament, a protein (animal) matter or substance. He recalled the writings on the possibilities of artificial silk done by the noted physicist and naturalist, René de Réaumur, especially the statement that "silk is only a liquid gum which has become dried; could we not make a silk ourselves with gums and resins?" Thus began the work on developing artificial silk, which was brought to a successful climax by Chardonnet. Funds for his research were underwritten by the government of France.
Chardonnet used an extract from the twigs and leaves of the mulberry plant

in gradually building up to his artificial silk, now called rayon. His findings, after many years of research, resulted in producing a filament or thread made of the cellulose contained in guncotton dissolved in alcohol and ether, and then transformed into a solid filament by the evaporation of the solvent—the first commercial rayon to be made by the nitrocellulose method. He built a plant in his home town, and his fabrics were shown at the Paris Exposition in 1889. The materials received great acclaim, and Chardonnet's fame became worldwide. A member of a wealthy family of France, he was a scientist of the first order, a philanthropist, and a great benefactor to mankind.

In 1910, the great British scientist Henry G. Tetley, one of the founders of the Samuel Courtauld Company, Ltd., made the following statement at a meeting in Bradford, England, to honor Chardonnet on his seventy-fifth birthday:

"His discovery is more than an invention. It is an absolute creation. Nothing like it existed before, and exactly what it may mean to the future no one can tell."

1890: L. H. Despaissis, French chemist, a pioneer in the field of artificial silk, was the first person actually to produce cuprammonium filament for commercial purposes. Try as he did, however, he could not operate his venture on a going basis. But several German scientists, using the ideas of Despaissis, later made modifications of his method, and commercial production began in 1898. Further improvements were made by Elsaesser, who developed the Thiele stretch method of making the filament which is still in use today. By 1899 the filament was being made commercially.

1891: Two Englishmen, Wardle and Davenport, organized the Chardonnet Silk Mill of Tubize, Belgium. The reason for the plant's being built in Belgium was that the English duty on alcohol was much too high, and much lower rates were available in Belgium, since great amounts of alcohol were necessary to dissolve the nitrocellulose used in the process.

1892: Two English chemists, Charles F. Cross and E. J. Bevan, discovered the viscose method of making artificial silk. They were fellow students in the research laboratories at Owens College, Manchester, England. Both had great interest in cellulose. They discovered that cellulose treated with caustic soda, and then with carbon disulfide, was converted into an entirely new compound which would dissolve in water or in a dilute caustic soda solution to give a thick, straw-colored solution resembling honey in color and consistency—the viscose solution. They obtained patent rights during that year, in order to manufacture carbon filaments for electric lamps.

1894: The American Viscose Company was established in Waltham, Massachusetts, by Dr. Arthur D. Little and his associates to acquire the American rights to the Cross and Bevan (British) patents for viscose. The company made solutions, sheets, and molded forms of viscose, but did not attempt to make filament yarns. This company should not be confused with the present American Viscose Div. FMC Corp. Cross, Bevan, and Beadle formed The Viscose Syndicate, Ltd., Erith, Kent County, England, to develop viscose that could be molded. A precipitating bath was used to harden the filaments, and the idea of "aging" was given close attention.

1895: Dr. Little of Boston, Massachusetts, was now making progress with acetate, as a result of his findings based on the work done on viscose. Cross and Bevan made arrangements with Dr. Little whereby research and experimentation were commenced by Cross and Bevan in Kew Gardens, London, and by Dr. Little in Boston. With their combined knowledge of viscose, it was believed that an acetate fiber could be made commercially valuable. Working with reactive cellulose recovered from viscose, they were able to produce cellulose acetate in films of considerable thickness and two to three feet square. Dr. Little made the film in his Waltham plant. He formed a partnership with Dr. William H. Walker of the Department of Chemistry at Massachusetts Institute of Technology, Cambridge, Massachusetts. Further research, deeper in scope, was begun on cellulose acetate and its possibilities in the manufacture of fine electric-wire insulation.

1897: Dr. Max Fremery and Johann Urban, who had used cuprammonium for carbon filaments, succeeded in making artificial silk. Their patent was obtained in the name of Herman Pauly.

1898: The manufacturers by the cuprammonium method were known as the Vereinigte Glantzstoff-Fabriken company and a plant was erected to make this type of filament in Aachen (Aix-la-Chapelle), Germany.

1898–1905: C. F. Topham and C. H. Stearn made rapid progress in the spinning phases of artificial silk manufacture. In 1900 Topham invented his famous spinning box, still used in the manufacture of manmade filaments. Instead of winding the yarn on a spool, as had been done up to this time, the Topham invention consisted of dropping the end of the yarn into a revolving cylinder where centrifugal force laid it against the sides and wound the yarn in a cake formation from the outside to the center. His first spinning box was an ordinary tin can mounted on a spindle. When fully perfected, Stearn adopted the principle; and most viscose is still made in this manner.

1899–1900: Dr. Emile Bronnert modified the cuprammonium system and made the method commercially successful. A plant was built in Oberbruck, Germany, to produce the filament. The method is still used and amounts to about 3 per cent of present world production. Beaunit Mills, Inc., Fibers Division, is the producer in this country.

1900–1901: Cellulose Products Company, South Boston, Massachusetts, was formed by Dr. Little, Dr. Walker, Willard Saulsbury, W. C. Spruance, and W. C. Spruance, Jr. This group took over the American rights to the Cross and Bevan patents from the American Viscose Company formed in 1894 in Waltham, Massachusetts. This company, however, exhausted its funds within one year. It is worthy of note, however, that Mr. Spruance, Jr., afterwards became a vice president with E. I. du Pont de Nemours & Co., Inc., and was the person who interested the du Pont Company in textile fibers and their possibilities. Nitrocellulose filament was selling for three dollars a pound at that time.

1900–1919: The Chemical Products Company was formed in 1900 by Dr. Little, Dr. Walker, and Harry S. Mork for the production of fine wire insulation from cellulose acetate. The company was granted a patent to spin artificial silk from cellulose acetate, the first patent awarded in the United States for a man-made filament. It was not until 1914 that some success was achieved when the Lustron Company began to operate the patents. By 1916 there was a production of 300 pounds a day of 150-denier filament. Lustron purchased the company in 1919. (*See also* under 1914–1927.)

1901–1905: The General Artificial Silk Company was formed in Philadelphia, Pennsylvania. The president was Mr. T. S. Harrison, President of Harrison Brothers, a century-old chemical and paint company. This concern later became a unit in the du Pont Company and laid the foundation for this company to go into the heavy chemical and paint business. The Stearn method of spinning was installed. A second plant was founded in Lansdowne, near Philadelphia. The company, however, was not able to pay royalties to Stearn and it failed in 1905.

1903: Platinum was first used to make spinnerettes. At present they are made of platinum and iridium, platinum and gold alloys, and stainless steel.

1904: The Cellulose Products Company, which had closed its doors in 1901, had taken over the American rights to the Cross and Bevan patents from The American Viscose Company, which failed in 1900. General Artificial Silk Company then obtained these rights in 1901 on a royalty basis and also bought the Topham and Stearn rights directly from the inventors. When this company failed in 1905, the purchaser of these rights was a Philadelphia lawyer, Silas W. Pettit, at the time the largest stockholder in the General Artificial Silk Company. He paid $25,000 for these rights. Pettit also purchased the viscose spinning rights and some of the machinery in the Lansdowne plant for another $25,000.

Meanwhile, Samuel Courtaulds & Co., Ltd., a silk-weaving company in Bocking, England, became interested in the manufacture of artificial silk because of the interest evinced by two members of the concern, H. G. Tetley and T. P. Latham. During this year, the company took over the laboratory in Kew Gardens, near London, and the British rights for the manufacture of viscose rayon.

1905: Courtaulds built a second plant in Coventry, England, for the manufacture of artificial silk. By 1909 it was considered to be a successful venture; it was producing viscose rayon at the rate of 150,000 pounds a year. By 1910, production was two million pounds annually.

1908: Artificial silk was being imported into the United States for use in stockings. Several mills in the Philadelphia area were knitting the stockings.

1909: In 1905, Silas Pettit formed Genasco Silk Works. He had bought the Cross and Bevan patent rights from the General Artificial Silk Company, which had failed in 1905. Pettit had then formed the Genasco Silk Works in the same year and still owned the patents. This company failed in 1909 and the patent rights were now in the hands of Pettit's son.

It so happened that at this time the representative for Courtaulds in the United States was Samuel A. Salvage. In due time, he became known as the "Father of the Rayon Industry in the United States," and also as Sir Samuel Salvage. He saw the great possibilities for artificial silk here and believed that the future held much for his company. He persuaded Courtaulds to purchase the American rights for the manufacture of viscose rayon from the son of Silas Pettit. The way was now open for this country to become a major factor in the industry. Courtaulds also bought the rights and patents of Cross, Bevan, Topham, and Stearn.

1910: The American Viscose Company was organized and began operations under the patents that Courtaulds had acquired from the Pettit estate. This name was kept until 1915, when it was changed to The Viscose Company. The plant was erected in Marcus Hook, Pennsylvania, between Philadelphia, Pennsylvania, and Wilmington, Delaware. By 1911, the production of viscose rayon was about 350,000 pounds per year. By 1937 the company was operating five spinning plants to make the fiber.

1911: American knitting mills were now using domestic viscose rayon in the manufacture of hosiery.

World War I (1914–1918): A new great use for cellulose acetate was as a coat for the wings of airplanes; it was also known as "dope."

The famous Dreyfus brothers, Camille and Henri, entered the picture at this time. They had been graduated from the University of Basle, Switzerland, in 1910. In 1916 these two chemists developed their famous airplane "dope": they dissolved their cellulose in acetone, and this nonflammable lacquer was of great use in forming a very firm, tough coating on plane wings. They built a plant in Spondon, England, and it produced ten tons of the "dope" a day until the end of the war in November 1918.

In 1916, Newton D. Baker, Secretary of War for President Woodrow Wilson, contacted the Dreyfus brothers in order to obtain some of their "dope." Not being able to come to Washington themselves, they sent Major E. E. Boreham of the British Army to see Secretary Baker. As a result of the visit, the War Industries Board began to build a plant in Cumberland, Maryland. This plant is still a unit of the Celanese Corporation of America, located in Amcelle, about three miles from Cumberland. Eastman Kodak was also able to make the "dope," and because of extenuating circumstances the Amcelle plant was only about half completed by the end of the war and never turned out a pound of the "dope." The point at issue was what to do with the idle plant.

Enormous stockpiles of cellulose acetate had been set up in all warring nations, and with the end of the war, uses had to be found for these stockpiles. The United States had several mammoth stocks throughout the nation. The plastic industry at this time had not come into its own, although cellulose acetate was being used to some degree in Europe by this industry. The supply far outdistanced the demand.

The Dreyfus brothers set out to find a use for it, and to discover a method to produce cellulose acetate yarn. It took about a year before progress was reported, and two more years of intensive research followed. One of the associates in Spondon, Mr. Pool, found a way to make the denier filament even and uniform. Up to this time it had been rather irregular and uneven, a hindrance to any success the product might have had. Henri Dreyfus developed weaving and knitting techniques and built his own machines; Camille took up the problems of dyestuffs, since none of the methods in use at the time would dye acetate in a satisfactory way. Thirty chemists and dyers from the Swiss textile finishing firm of Clavels and Lindenmeyer developed a set of successful dyes, an entirely new group never used before. These were the famous S.R.A. dyes (sulfo-resinic-alcohol).

1914–1927: The Lustron Corporation was formed to operate under the Little-Walker-Mork patents for the spinning of acetate yarns. The first commercial production of acetate yarn in the United States is credited to this company as beginning in 1919, following pilot-plant production which began in 1916. Celanese Corporation of America acquired certain assets of Lustron when the company was liquidated in 1927.

The process of making acetate when the company was formed in 1914 differed from that in use today chiefly in that it used fibrous cellulose and a liquid setting bath. The product was used for twisting with cotton and with wool warp yarns for various types of stripes in men's suiting fabrics. The effect was brought about by cross-dyeing the goods in the piece, since acetate takes a different dyed effect from either wool or cotton. Dr. Little, Dr. Walker, and Mr. Mork furthered the cause of cross-dyeing because they could obtain varied color effects, and they laid the foundation for the popularity that this method of dyeing enjoys today. During World War I, Lustron turned out great quantities of cellulose acetate.

1918: Courtaulds, Ltd., began the manufacture of Fibro, a new staple fiber made of viscose rayon. It is still a popular favorite.

1920: The Tubize Company, Tubize, Belgium, began operations in the United States. The company made its yarn on the nitrocellulose method, Chardonnet's invention. Originally the yarn was called Chardonnet-Tubize, and the company, Tubize-Chatillon. Tubize up to 1934 accounted for about 10 per cent of the artificial silk made here. Their plants were in Rome, Georgia, and Hopewell, Virginia. Tubize became embroiled with the late President Franklin D. Roosevelt over certain regulations and restrictions of the ill-fated N.R.A. After some bitter arguments and hearings in Washington, the company refused to comply with what they considered unfair requests of the government, and decided to sell the plant and its equipment. The Hopewell plant was sold quickly in 1934, the machinery going to a plant in the province of São Paulo, Brazil. At present, however, because of the inroads from other rayons and acetate, the nitrocellulose method is not used anywhere. The plant in Rome is now a unit, by purchase and merger, of the Celanese Corporation of America.

Another pioneer in the field was Dr. C. A. Ernst. He had been with The Viscose Company, then went to Genasco, then to Courtaulds, and back to The Viscose Company. Sir Samuel Salvage succeeded him as president. From this time on, the company made rapid strides in all its endeavors. Its affiliation with Courtaulds lasted until World War II, when they parted company, and American Viscose Corporation no longer remained allied with foreign interests. Up to the year 1920, The Viscose Company was alone in the field in the United States. By 1925, however, as an aftermath of the war, there were eight manufacturers of rayon here, and by 1936 the number had risen to sixteen. The Viscose Company was turning out more than one-third of the actual production here.

1924: The Dreyfus plant in Spondon, England, became very active under the name of the British Cellulose and Chemical Manufacturing Company. The manufacture of acetate was now on firm ground. In this year the British company took over the abandoned plant in Amcelle, Maryland, for the purpose of making acetate in this country (the present Celanese Corporation of America). Three million dollars were spent to put the plant in order. The company bought some of the assets of the Lustron Corporation in 1927 when the latter concern liquidated. These, along with the patents and processes of Drs. Camille and Henri Dreyfus, gave the company the necessary knowledge and foundation to progress very rapidly.

Rayon received its name at this time. The late Mr. Kenneth Lord of the fabric firm of Galey & Lord, Inc., now a unit of Burlington Industries, Inc., suggested the word "rayon" to replace the rather negative and misleading terms "artificial silk" and "Glos." It should be remembered that rayon at this time referred only to yarn made by the viscose method. A ruling of the Federal Trade Commission, October 26, 1937, decreed that rayon refers to filaments or yarns consisting of regenerated cellulose, while acetate refers to filaments and yarns from cellulose acetate. Until February 11, 1952, acetate was known as acetate rayon. Since that time it has been referred to as acetate without the word "rayon" added to it. Acetate, therefore, is not a regenerated fiber like viscose and cuprammonium rayons; it is classed as a cellulose-derivative fiber or filament, although it is made from the same base as these two rayons—the method of manufacture, of course, is different. The great fiber "rayon" had by this time been recognized on its merits and was no longer considered as an imitation of or a substitute for any other textile fiber.

1925–1929: Several companies were now engaged in the manufacture of rayon and acetate rayon. Celanese Corporation of America was the first to produce acetate, in 1925. Companies in the field, in addition to The Viscose Company, included:

American Enka Corporation, affiliated with Dutch interests.
American Viscose Corporation.
E. I. du Pont de Nemours & Co., Inc.
North American Rayon Corporation (Bemberg)—rayon but not acetate.
Eastman Kodak Company, in conjunction with Tennessee Eastman Company, now a unit of Eastman Chemical Products Corporation.

The Rayon Institute (now defunct) was founded to inform the public of rayon, which, of course, at that time included acetate.

1926: Dull rayon made its debut; up to now it had been bright and shiny. Titanium dioxide was used, and still is, to dull these fibers, although acetate was not to appear in dull cast until 1931, when The Viscose Company perfected the method.

1927: It was now possible to crepe rayon. The principle of twisting it into a crepe yarn had been mastered. Rayon crepe and pebble effects were even more pronounced on rayon than on silk.

1928: Rayon was being made in plain and serviceable fabrics for apparel; luxury fabrics were on the market, and in the range of quality of cotton, linen, silk, and wool. Fabric development was beginning to do much for and with rayon. Parisian couturiers took notice of rayon around this time, and this was a great boon to this future giant in the textile industry.

1935: Rayon which had sold for about $6.00 a pound in 1920 was now being sold around $.55 a pound; demand and supply were equalizing.

1936–1937: The Viscose Company, Marcus Hook, Pennsylvania, profiting from its alliance with Courtaulds, Ltd., England, produced Fibro rayon staple at the rate of about 270,000,000 pounds a year. In 1937, the present American Viscose Corporation received its new name.

World War II (1939–1945): Rayon and acetate did their share of work during these six years. The United States in 1940 produced 390,000,000 pounds of filament and 81,000,000 pounds of staple fiber, for a total of 471,000,000 pounds. At the present time, production in this country is about 700,000,000 pounds of filament yarn and about 425,000,000 pounds of staple, for a total of 1,125,000,000 pounds.

Following World War II: Both fibers are still prime favorites among the manmade fibers. The rise of rayon is still phenomenal and production increases each year. Many other new fibers have come over the textile horizon, such as nylon, Dynel, Saran, "Orlon," Arnel, Verel, Acrilan, Creslan, Zefran, etc., all of which have more than kept pace with acetate and rayon. Cellulosic and non-cellulosic fibers are about even in total annual production. Rayon and acetate are about the same in yearly production.

Rayon and acetate have come a long way since the time of Swan and Chardonnet in the last decades of the nineteenth century. Following World War I, textile mills were very skeptical about these fibers. They did not know enough about Glos, as it was then known, and the price was high, $5.00 to $6.00 a pound. In fact, several of the old-time established leaders in the silk industry were outspoken about rayon, saying that these fibers "would not and could not last, since they were only passing fancies." The manufacturers, however, who had faith in their products, performed a great deal of research, experimentation, and pilot-plant work, along with much advertising and promotion. Up to the late 1920's, production was very small, and there was little demand for either fiber in the textile and apparel trades. In 1924, the first knitted fabric to be made from rayon appeared. It was tricolette, and it met with some favor in women's wear. Mignonette soon followed, a medium-to-fine-gauge knit fabric. Compared with present-day tricot knit, the materials would seem very coarse and heavy. However, this was the beginning of knit fabrics made from rayon and acetate, and their rise in the knitwear field has been very great. Thus the old-time artificial silk filament has made its way in the textile world, so much so that rayon is surpassed only by cotton, often referred to as "the universal textile fiber."

1954: Because of the rise of other manmade fibers and filaments, and other interests, American Viscose Corporation, Marcus Hook, Pennsylvania, ceased the manufacture of rayon in its plant there. Since 1910, a span of forty-four years, this was the home base for the company. Cellophane is now being made in this plant. The company was formed in 1910, and on December 19, 1910, the first rayon filament to be extruded from a spinnerette became an actuality. In 1911 rayon production was 362,544 pounds of viscose rayon. The company, now known as AVC, is a division of FMC Corporation. (*See also* under 1909.)

1955–1959: General highlights of these years included much increased research and development in the manmade-fiber industries. Some of the fruits of this work included the following: solution-dyed carpet staple fiber, the impact of tufted floor covering, the rise of textured yarns, the debut of high-tenacity rayon yarn, cross-linked rayon staple, slubbed filament yarn, hollow filament yarn, and flat "straw" fiber.

Avisco unveiled its new fiber, Avron (formerly Avisco XL), now much used in blends with cotton, making it compatible with acrylic, modacrylic, and polyester fibers in blends. It is a much stronger rayon fiber when compared with ordinary rayon.

Zantrel, now a product of American Enka Corporation, was introduced. It is a high wet-modulus fiber in staple form. Outside of this country it is called a polynosic rayon fiber (*poly* meaning "many," and *nosi* meaning "fiber" or "single strand.")

1960: New fibers on the textile scene during the year included Avlin (Fiber 40 and RD 100), and Avril of Avisco; Fiber 500 of American Enka Corporation. In the field of acetate fibers, Celanese Corporation of America brought out its tri-acetate fiber, Arnel, which has been very popular in the dressgoods trade. Other Celanese products which came out around this time include Celaloft, bulked acetate; Celacloud, a springy acetate fiber used in bedding; Celafil, used for stuffing in comforters and pillows; Celaire, used in carpeting, and Celaperm, which is made with a sealed-in color. The "50" and "75" acetate fibers of Eastman Chemical Products, Inc., were also announced.

1961: The golden anniversary of rayon was celebrated during the year. Much acclaim was accorded rayon in advertising, magazine articles, radio, and television. Its history and progress were very well covered. Rayon is still the leading manmade fiber in production and use despite the inroads that have been made to a marked degree by other manmade fibers. Its excellent price position has been of great help to rayon.

The new definition of rayon, in accordance with the decree of the Federal Trade Commission, March 3, 1959, follows: "Rayon is a manufactured fiber composed of regenerated cellulose, as well as manufactured fibers composed of regenerated cellulose in which the substituents have replaced not more than 15 per cent of the hydrogens of the hydroxyl groups."

Coverage for manmade (manufactured) fibers is ably cared for by the following:

Man-Made Fiber Producers Association, 350 Fifth Ave., New York 1, New York. This association disseminates information about the cellulosics, acrylics, modacrylics, polyesters, saran, Azlon, polyamides, nytrils, vinyls, Spandex, Olefins, and Vinyons. It does not cover the natural fibers, glass or metallic fibers, or rubber yarns.

The Textile Economics Bureau, Inc., 10 East 40th St., New York 16, New York, through its publication, *Textile Organon,* provides information. This monthly journal in the interests of good business gives an arrangement of authentic market data, and a digest of current business conditions in the United States manmade fiber industry. Its worldwide statistical information is of great value to its readers.

Sources: Man-Made Fiber Producers Association, 350 Fifth Ave., New York 1, New York; Textile Economics Bureau, Inc., 10 East Fortieth St., New York 16, New York.

TESTING

1. Name the two German scientists who discovered what in time was to be known as acetate filament.
2. Discuss the work done by Charles F. Cross and E. J. Bevan in England.
3. Give some details of the work done by Dr. Arthur D. Little in this country.
4. What use was made of cellulose acetate during World War I?
5. Discuss the rise of the Celanese Corporation of America through the work done by Camille and Henri Dreyfus.

The following statistics and figures show estimates for the future as to population, civilian fiber consumption, and civilian per-capita consumption in terms of pounds:

ESTIMATED POPULATION IN 1965

	1955	1965	% CHANGE
Under 10 years	35,062,000	37,616,000	+ 7.3
10 to 19 years	24,532,000	35,959,000	+46.6
20 to 34 years	34,855,000	35,732,000	+ 2.5
35 to 50 years	32,972,000	35,447,000	+ 7.5
50 to 65 years	23,388,000	27,826,000	+19.0
65 and over	13,973,000	17,336,000	+24.1
Total	164,782,000	189,916,000	+15.3

Combining these estimates, the one for per-capita consumption and the other for population, implies a general level of total fiber use as follows:

CIVILIAN FIBER CONSUMPTION
(in millions of pounds)

	1939	1953	1965	% CHANGE 1939–53	1953–65
Total	4,021	5,621	7,533	+ 40	+34
Cotton	3,159	3,779	4,636	+ 20	+23
Wool	405	515	654	+ 27	+27
Manmade	457	1,327	2,243	+190	+69

AVERAGE ANNUAL CIVILIAN FIBER CONSUMPTION IN THE UNITED STATES
(Under War, Peace, Prosperity, Depression)

PER CAPITA, IN POUNDS

PERIOD	CIVILIAN POPULATION	MANMADE FIBER	COTTON	WOOL	TOTAL
	(39)	(40)	(41)	(42)	(43)
1920–1924	110.2	0.2	23.8	3.7	27.7
1925–1929	118.9	0.7	26.0	3.3	30.0
1930–1934	124.8	1.3	20.6	2.3	24.2
1935–1939	129.0	2.7	24.9	3.1	30.7
1940–1944	129.8	4.3	27.5	2.9	34.7
1945–1949	141.8	6.4	26.7	4.2	37.3
1950–1954	156.2	8.9	26.5	3.2	38.6
1955–1959	171.9	10.3	23.7	2.8	36.8
1960–1964	186.5	12.6	22.5	2.9	38.0
1950	152.3	9.5	29.3	4.5	43.3
1951	151.6	8.6	27.6	2.5	38.7
1952	153.9	8.6	25.3	3.1	37.0
1953	160.2	9.0	26.3	3.4	38.7
1954	163.0	8.7	23.8	2.7	35.2
1955	165.9	11.0	25.3	3.0	39.3
1956	168.9	9.7	25.0	3.1	37.8
1957	172.0	9.9	22.6	2.6	35.1
1958	174.9	9.6	21.3	2.4	33.3
1959	177.8	11.3	24.0	3.1	38.4
1960	180.7	9.9	23.3	3.0	36.2
1961	183.7	10.7	22.0	2.9	35.6
1962	186.6	12.4	22.9	3.1	38.4
1963	189.4	14.2	21.8	3.0	39.0
1964	192.1	15.8	22.6	2.5	40.9
1965	194.6	18.3	24.0	2.7	45.0

PER-CAPITA CONSUMPTION: Civilian per-capita consumption of cotton, wool, and the manmade fibers is shown in the table above. The 1965 total was 45 pounds, as compared with 40.9 pounds in 1964 and a Korean War high of 43.3 pounds in 1950.

The use of manmade fibers increased to a new record level of 18.3 pounds per capita in 1965, up 2.5 pounds over 1964. Cotton increased by 1.4 pounds to 24 pounds, while wool was up .2 to 2.7 pounds.

Per-capita consumption is obtained by dividing domestic consumption by the population each year; the population figure includes military personnel, wherever located. During World War II (1939–1945) and the Korean War (1950–1953), however, the extraordinary military use was separated from the civilian data.

The overall level of per-capita fiber consumption is affected by numerous, diverse, and often contradictory forces. Among the major factors tending to raise the level are improved living standards, which may foster an earlier replacement of textile products with new or improved items; increased leisure time, with a

[205]

corresponding requirement for more variety in, and greater quantity of, leisure-time apparel; an increased demand for home furnishings, automobiles, new homes, etc.

New developments in the field of textiles in the last five years have caused increased demands for items such as "wash-and-wear" articles, durable press garments, tufted floorcovering, nonwoven fabrics, spunbonded fabrics, bonded fabrics, fiberwoven fabrics, stretch fabrics, laminated and molded fabrics, flocked materials, et al. Manmade fibers have contributed a great deal in serving as the raw material in all the foregoing developments.

WORLD MANMADE FIBER PRODUCTION
(Millions of Pounds)

YEAR	RAYON + ACETATE			NON-CELLULOSIC		
	YARN	STAPLE	TOTAL	YARN	STAPLE	TOTAL
1950	1,920	1,626	3,546	120	33	153
1951	2,122	1,886	4,008	168	60	228
1952	1,831	1,704	3,535	202	83	285
1953	2,088	2,051	4,139	250	100	350
1954	2,041	2,449	4,490	310	120	430
1955	2,298	2,725	5,023	405	182	587
1956	2,251	3,001	5,252	441	238	679
1957	2,320	3,128	5,448	560	342	902
1958	2,115	2,899	5,014	592	332	924
1959	2,409	3,128	5,537	774	496	1,270
1960	2,493	3,238	5,731	919	629	1,548
1961	2,503	3,411	5,914	1,095	735	1,830
1962	2,649	3,649	6,298	1,407	973	2,380
1963	2,714	4,014	6,728	1,716	1,220	2,936
1964	2,933	4,353	7,286	2,154	1,568	3,722
1965	3,020	4,357	7,377	2,431	2,019	4,450

UNITED STATES MILL CONSUMPTION OF FOUR FIBERS

YEAR	MANMADE FIBER		COTTON		WOOL		SILK		TOTAL	
	LB.	%	LB.	%	LB.	%	LB.	%	LB.	%
	(24)		(25)		(26)		(27)		(28)	
1950	1,518.4	22.2	4,682.7	68.4	634.8	9.3	10.5	0.1	6,846.4	100
1951	1,478.6	21.6	4,868.6	71.2	484.2	7.1	7.2	0.1	6,838.6	100
1952	1,490.2	23.1	4,470.9	69.4	466.4	7.3	12.6	0.2	6,440.1	100
1953	1,523.7	23.5	4,456.1	68.8	494.0	7.6	7.8	0.1	6,481.6	100
1954	1,508.3	25.0	4,127.3	68.5	384.1	6.4	8.5	0.1	6,028.2	100
1955	1,902.5	28.3	4,382.4	65.3	413.8	6.2	11.0	0.2	6,709.7	100
1956	1,727.4	26.4	4,362.6	66.7	440.8	6.7	12.7	0.2	6,543.5	100
1957	1,792.6	28.8	4,060.4	65.2	368.8	5.9	8.3	0.1	6,230.1	100
1958	1,764.2	29.6	3,866.9	64.8	331.1	5.5	5.3	0.1	5,967.5	100
1959	2,064.8	30.2	4,334.5	63.3	435.3	6.4	8.0	0.1	6,842.6	100
1960	1,878.0	29.0	4,190.9	64.6	411.0	6.3	6.9	0.1	6,486.8	100
1961	2,060.9	31.4	4,081.5	62.2	412.1	6.3	6.7	0.1	6,561.2	100
1962	2,419.2	34.3	4,188.0	50.5	429.1	6.1	6.5	0.1	7,042.8	100
1963	2,788.0	38.5	4,040.2	55.7	411.7	5.7	6.4	0.1	7,246.3	100
1964	3,175.5	40.8	4,245.2	54.5	355.4	4.6	6.7	0.1	7,782.8	100
1965	3,624.5	42.7	4,476.3	52.7	386.9	4.5	5.8	0.1	8,493.5	100

NON-CELLULOSIC

STATE & AREA	RAYON & ACET.	ACRYL.[a]	NYLON	OLEFIN	POLY-ESTER	OTHER [b]	TOTAL	TEXTILE GLASS	GRAND TOTAL
New England									
Massachusetts	1			4			4		5
New Hampshire		1					1		1
Rhode Island			1			4	5	1	6
Vermont	1								1
Total N.E.	2	1	5			4	10	1	13
Mid-Atlantic									
Delaware			1	1			2		2
Maryland	1		1	1	1	1	4		5
New Jersey			1	4		2	7		7
New York	1		1	5	1	1	8	2	11
Pennsylvania	2		4	2	1	1	8	1	11
Total Mid-Atl.	4		8	13	3	5	29	3	36
Piedmont									
North Carolina	1		2		5	1	8	2	11
South Carolina	1	1	7	3		1	12	2	15
Virginia	3	2	4	2		4	12		15
West Virginia	2	1	1		1		3		5
Total Piedmont	7	4	14	5	6	6	35	4	46
South									
Alabama	2	1	1		1		3		5
Florida	2	1	1	1		1	4		4
Georgia				2			2		4
Kentucky								1	1
Tennessee	4	1	4	1	4		10	1	15
Total South	8	3	6	4	5	1	19	2	29
Midwest & West									
Arkansas								1	1
California								1	1
Indiana								2	2
Iowa			1	1			2		2
Kansas								1	1
Michigan						1	1		1
Missouri				1			1		1
Ohio	1				1		1	2	4
Total West	1		1	2	1	1	5	7	13
Total No. of Plants	22	7	30	29	15	17	98	17	137
Total No. of States	13	6	14	14	8	10	20	12	26

This table shows the number of *product-plants* located in each state, not necessarily the number of *plant* locations. Thus some producers manufacture two or more fibers at the same plant and it is this data (the number of fibers) that is shown, not the number of individual plants.

Acetate and triacetate made at one plant, as well as polyethylene and polypropylene (olefin) made at one plant, are counted as one fiber. The yarn+monofilaments vs. the staple+tow types of fiber are not counted separately.

a *Acryl.* means acrylic+modacrylic.

b *Other* includes 1 fluorocarbon, 4 saran, 9 Spandex and 3 Vinyon.

Courtesy: Textile Economics Bureau, Inc., Stanley B. Hunt, Editor, 10 East 40th Street, New York City.

TOPIC: Viscose Rayon and Its Manufacture

Viscose rayon came into its own under the aegis of Sir Samuel Salvage when he served as the president of The American Viscose Corporation. Today there are thirteen manufacturers of the product in the United States. American and world production accounts for about 97 per cent of the annual rayon output. Since the time of F. G. Keller in Saxony, Germany, who in 1840 discovered the chemical process of dissolving wood pulp, viscose has come a long way with much success. Swan, Chardonnet, Cross and Bevan, Little, Despaissis, Elsaesser, and other scientists in their respective fields laid the foundation for the present-day viscose rayon. Salvage organized the work that had to be done, and since his time viscose has progressed to the point where it is the second fiber in production in the United States, surpassed only by cotton.

The basic needs of a plant for manufacturing manmade fibers are the following:

1. Proper location, and plentiful and suitable labor.
2. Limitless use of water.
3. Accessibility of fuel.
4. Adequate waste disposal facilities.
5. Accessibility to all raw materials and markets.

One of the most impressive things about the rayon industry, along with the other industries in the manmade fiber field, has been the sound judgment used in educational programs and other forms of promotion. Advertising media such as newspapers, magazines, radio, television, plus seminars, public relations, information services, fashion shows, and thorough cooperation with department stores and apparel manufacturers, have been used in a truly cooperative manner to make the consumer public aware of the products of the manufacturers of fabrics and apparel and accessories. A new set of household terms has been born in the last twenty years, made up of words such as acetate, rayon, nylon, "Dacron," "Orlon," Dynel, Acrilan, Kodel, Arnel, Verel, Creslan, Zefran, etc.

Briefly, in the manufacture of viscose rayon purified cellulose is made into a solution and then regenerated (solid-liquid-solid) into yarn by chemical procedures. Stretching produces high-tenacity types of rayon. The filaments can be cut into a suitable length to give the staple fiber.

THE MANUFACTURE OF VISCOSE RAYON—CROSS AND BEVAN METHOD

1. The product from which all rayon is made is called cellulose. This is obtained by the reduction of cotton linters, spruce, or other high Alpha-cellulose woods to a pulp, the same as in the manufacture of paper.
2. The pulp is bleached and pressed into sheets which resemble blotting paper. This is done in the pulp mill.
3. In the rayon plant, the sheets are soaked in alkali, caustic soda, and then shredded. The machine which actually does the shredding into a flake form is called a "pfleiderer."

The feasibility of manmade fiber occurred to dreamers such as Dr. Robert Hooke (1635–1703), an English naturalist and scientist who recorded his ideas in 1665—more than two hundred years before science was ready with the necessary techniques and tools. Another visionary, René de Réaumur (1683–1757), the famous French scientist, proposed in 1742 that artificial fibers might be formed from gums and resins. Most of his ideas came from observing the natural phenomena of producing filament in the life cycle of the silkworm.

The first commercially successful method for producing synthetic filaments was invented by Sir Joseph Swan in 1880. Searching for a cellulose fiber that could be carbonized into filaments for electric light bulbs, Swan forced Audemars' solution through tiny holes, denitrated the fibers with ammonium sulfide.

In 1884, Count Hilaire de Chardonnet combined the work done by Audemars and Swan and eventually built the world's first rayon production plant in his beloved home city of Besançon, France.

In 1855, George Audemars, the Swiss scientist of Lausanne, produced the world's first manmade fiber by dissolving cellulose nitrate in alcohol and ether, then adding gum to the mixture. He formed filaments by dipping a needle into the sticky or viscous fluid and drawing it out.

In 1889 at the Paris Exposition, the first dresses made of the newly developed material were exhibited and aroused great interest. A protégé of the great Louis Pasteur, who had saved the silk industry from extinction by his marvelous findings, Chardonnet is considered the "Father of the Rayon Industry."

Forty-one machines from France and England were shipped to American Viscose Company, Marcus Hook, Pennsylvania. Only one machine was shipped complete; the other forty were stripped down to their essential metal parts to save import duties. The machines spun crude yarns of 150 denier, more or less, with

the greatest thickness variation at the beginning of each "cake," or production unit. By redesigning the pumping system, engineers overcame this problem and made an important contribution to improving the quality of the yarn.

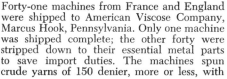

Marcus Hook was chosen as the site for the first plant of the American Viscose Company to produce what is now known as rayon. Marcus Hook was close to Philadelphia, then the manufacturing center for ribbon, tapestry, embroidery, and other textiles that could be made of rayon. The first rayon was made in this country in 1911.

This picture shows the company plant as it appeared in 1948.

As deliveries and quality of rayon yarns became more dependable, knitters tried the new yarn tentatively, then started a trend. It was an overnight success in hosiery, later in lingerie and tricolette—a pioneer knit dress fabric. The knitting industry was also attracted by rayon's relative price stability. Between 1911 and the highest-price period during World War I, rayon moved slowly from $1.80 to $7.75 a pound; in the same period silk fluctuated between $3.00 and $16.00 a pound.

Courtesy: American Viscose Division of FMC Corporation, Marcus Hook, Pennsylvania, and 350 Fifth Avenue, New York, New York

Viscose process of making rayon is based on a fundamental principle—cellulose, a solid, is dissolved to a liquid, then hardened back into a solid, in the form of filaments, which are textile fibers, a highly complex process involving intricate technical and chemical steps.

Cellulose, the solid part of the cell walls of plant life, is the raw material from which rayon is made. Cellulose for rayon comes from wood pulp . . .

. . . or from cotton linters, the short fibers left on the seeds after they have been separated from the cotton.

Raw stock, in the form of spruce, pine, and hemlock chips or cotton linters, is cooked by chemical action and live steam into pulp, which is run over screens and through heavy rollers to squeeze out water and press the pulp into sheets the thickness of blotting paper.

The cellulose sheets are steeped in a solution of caustic soda to extract certain impurities and to change the sheets chemically into "alkali cellulose." After steeping, the sheets are squeezed by hydraulic ram to remove excess liquid.

The sheets are dropped into crumbling machines, called "pfleiderers." These contain revolving blades that tear the sheets into small, fluffy particles,

Courtesy: American Viscose Division of FMC Corporation, New York

After aging, the alkali cellulose crumb is placed in revolving churns and liquid carbon disulfide added. When this process is finished, the crumb, now orange and known as "cellulose xanthate," can be readily dissolved. This shows the crumb coming from a churn.

To be sure it is the correct consistency a steel ball is dropped through the solution. The length of time it takes to fall a given distance is measured, and this determines the viscosity of the solution.

The viscose solution is then aged in large tanks at controlled temperatures. A vacuum on each tank removes air bubbles, which might cause breaks in the chemical spinning process.

The cellulose xanthate crumb is now mixed in a weak solution of caustic soda in a machine with revolving blades that beat and mix the substance, converting it into a liquid known as "viscose solution." Viscose, derived from viscous, means sticky or gluelike. The viscose solution looks like clear molasses or golden honey.

Bright   Semi-Dull   Dull

The addition of dulling agents controls luster

At this stage, the luster of the rayon is controlled. The addition of dulling agents, which become a part of the rayon itself, makes possible varying degrees of luster. If nothing is added to the viscose solution, the rayon has a brilliant luster.

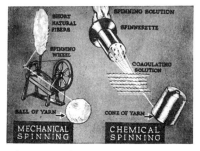

The process by which the viscose solution is changed into rayon yarn is called spinning, but it is not like mechanical spinning. It is primarily a chemical process in which a liquid is extruded through minute holes into an acid bath and then solidified into yarn.

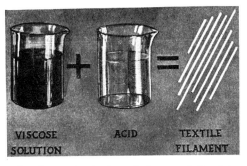

VISCOSE
SOLUTION
ACID
TEXTILE
FILAMENT

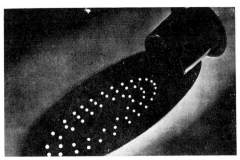

The chemical spinning of viscose solution into yarn is a highly complex process. Stated simply, the alkaline viscose solution hardens into filaments upon coming in contact with acid.

The heart of the process is the tiny spinnerette, about the size of a thimble, made of platinum. It has a number of fine holes from two to five one-thousandths of an inch in diameter.

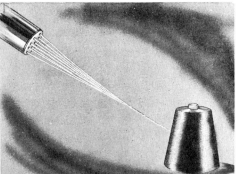

Each hole in the spinnerette forms one filament or strand, which is hardened in the acid.

The combined filaments from one spinnerette twisted together form yarn. Filaments produced in long unbroken strands make yarn known as continuous filament rayon.

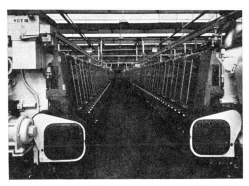

Here is a view of a spinning room, where the chemical spinning of rayon takes place.

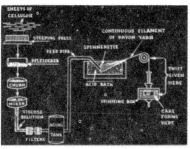

This diagram summarizes the various steps in the production of rayon. The cellulose is now back in the original pure state, but instead of being in the form of pulp it is in the form of yarn. Thus rayon is often referred to as "regenerated cellulose."

When yarn has been spun into the box, the spindle is stopped, and the rayon yarn wound in the form of a hollow cylinder called a "cake" is removed.

Repeated washings with soft, filtered water and other treatments remove all acid and thoroughly clean the yarn. It is placed on continuous carriers that move slowly through automatic tunnel dryers.

Machines wind the rayon yarn into bobbins, skeins, cones, beams, and other forms required by the textile manufacturer. Winding rooms have humidity control to maintain standard moisture in the yarn.

Rayon yarn has high tensile strength and thus is widely used for tire cord fabrics for heavy-duty vehicles. Its high-strength properties make it adaptable for sturdy fabrics and for spinning into very fine yarns for sheer fabrics.

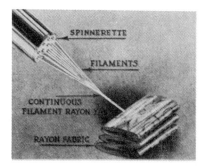

Continuous filament rayon yarn imparts definite characteristics and textures to fabrics woven or knit from it.

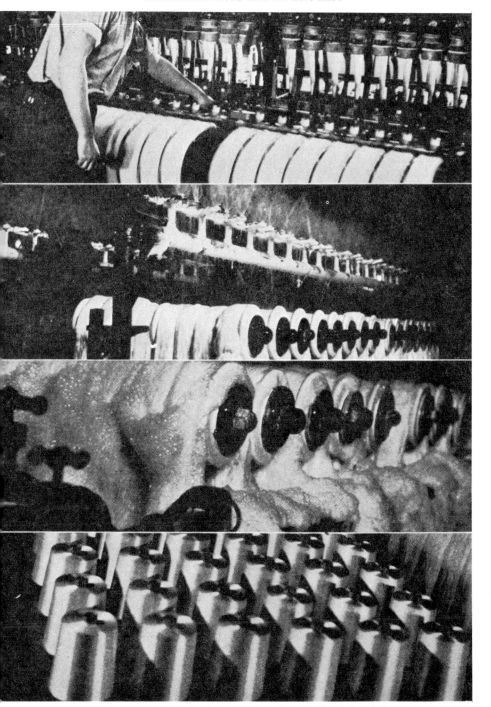

Courtesy: *American Bemberg Corporation, Fibers Division of Beaunit Corporation, New York*

Stretch spinning
Removing acid and copper sulfate
Washing
Finished yarn

4. Aging of the flake or alkali crumb form follows—a great secret in the making of rayon.
5. Carbon bisulfide (disulfide) is added to the crumbs to produce the orange crumb, cellulose viscose *xanthate*—the latter word is from the Greek, meaning "orange."
6. Further treatment with a dilute solution of caustic soda follows, and the mass is again aged. It is during this procedure that the mass slowly turns into the liquid called viscose, which has the color and consistency of honey.
7. The viscous or viscose solution is then forced through spinnerettes which are submerged in a dilute acid bath. The alkaline viscous solution reacts with the acidic bath which neutralizes the alkalinity. The action causes the cellulose content of the viscose solution to harden into filament.

A spinnerette may be called a type of nozzle, usually about the diameter of a dime, through the face of which are bored a number of beveled holes or orifices which average from two one-thousandths of an inch to five one-thousandths of an inch. Through these minute holes the viscose solution is forced to form the filaments that comprise one strand of yarn. Spinnerettes are made from a combination of iridium and platinum; they are rather expensive.
8. After the filament is finally formed in the atmosphere, it is passed around a feed wheel, twisted, and then passed into a revolving feed box, where it winds itself into what is known as a rayon "cake." This form resembles an angel-food cake and is made possible by the revolving motion of the feed box.
9. On completion, the "cake" is removed from the container.

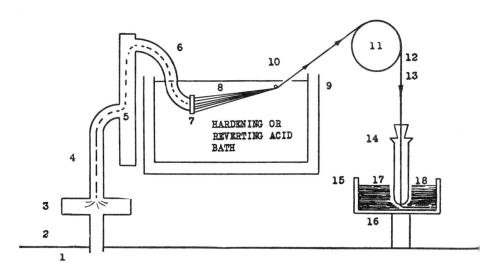

THE VISCOSE BOX METHOD OF MAKING RAYON—SPINNING BOX

FROM THE AGING CELLAR TO THE SPINNERETTE

1. Pipe from aging cellar to conduct the viscous solution.
2. Area and box above the aging cellar.
3. Pump to draw the viscous solution from aging cellar. This pump forces the solution through the filter which removes foreign particles.
4. Filter pipe to filter.
5. Filter.
6. Pipe to conduct the filtered solution to the spinnerette.
7. The spinnerette. This is a thimble-like device that has many minute holes or orifices through which the solution is forced. The minute portions of the spinning solution are strongly alkaline. They harden as they come in contact with the hardening or acid reverting bath to form the filaments of rayon.

8. Filaments as they leave the spinnerette. They are gathered together in the hardening bath and are led around a small guide roller that is in the acid bath. From this small roller, the filaments are led into natural atmospheric conditions. By this time, they are hardened or coagulated. No mechanical twist has, as yet, been given the filaments.
9. Tank.
10. Yarn.
11. Revolving feed wheel around which the yarn is passed.
12. Twist is applied to the filaments from the feed wheel to the outlet at the bottom tip of the glass funnel (No. 18).
13. Thread taking the twist turns that are necessary—mechanical action.
14. Glass funnel or tube that raises and lowers in the revolving feed box (No. 15).
15. Revolving feed box.
16. Shaft to revolve the feed box.
17. Rayon "cake" being made by the revolving motion of the feed box.
18. Yarn coming from the outlet of the glass funnel and led to the cake form. On completion of the cake, the yarn is removed from the container.

RAYON STAPLE AND SPUN YARNS

Filaments of manmade origin, as they emerge from the spinnerettes, can easily be cut or chopped in fiber staple length, which is controlled by the speed of the cutting device and the number of blades used for cutting. The denier of the filament is controlled by the amount of the solution pumped through the spinnerette orifice, the spinning stretch in use, and other local factors minor in nature.

Spinning of rayon staple can be done on the cotton, woolen, worsted, jute, linen, and spun-silk systems of spinning. The staple may be run alone to make yarn, or blended with other major fibers for blended or mixture yarns. Rayon staple is ideal in blends for fabrics such as challis, crepe, shantung, and comparable materials.

The characteristics of staple rayon are similar to those of filament rayon. The cost of spun-rayon fabrics, and of those fabrics in which rayon is used with other fibers, is within the reach of all consumers. Because of their good wearing qualities, these materials have great appeal for a large buying public.

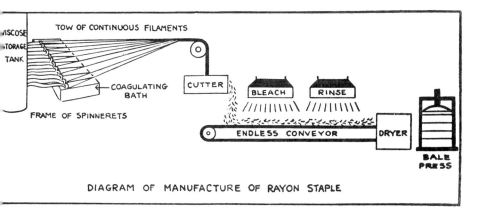

DIAGRAM OF MANUFACTURE OF RAYON STAPLE

Some General Properties and Characteristics of Viscose Rayon

There are three types—regular, medium-tenacity, and high-tenacity.

All the types burn like cotton, quickly; do not melt; have odor of burning paper; and form a small, fine grayish-black residue without a beaded edge.

Strong alkalies cause swelling and reduce the strength in all instances.

Acids affect viscose about the same as cotton. Hot dilute or cold concentrated solutions will disintegrate the fiber.

None of the types is damaged by weak hypochlorite or peroxide bleaches. Good rinsing after bleaching should be done. All types are generally insoluble except in cuprammonium and comparable compounds.

May be attacked by mildew; there is loss in tensile strength following long exposure; very little discoloration.

Specific gravity is uniform, 1.50–1.54.

Water absorbency, in all three, 27 per cent at 95 per cent relative humidity.

Moisture content may vary from about 3 per cent to about 11 per cent. Moisture regain is 11 per cent commercial standard, and 13 per cent standard condition.

Viscose rayon is never weighted. Its draping qualities are good, and crepe effects are easily obtained.

Resistant to moths.

Will remain white permanently; not affected by age.

Comes in smooth filament and may be made bright, dull, or pigmented in luster.

Sheds dirt easily and well.

Rayon staple costs about as much as a pound of cotton, around 35 cents a pound, with little fluctuation in price.

Not affected by perspiration.

Comes within the price range of all consumers.

The term "spun rayon" should be used as an adjective only. Rayon staple should not be called spun rayon, rayon staple fiber, cut rayon, or cut staple.

Viscose rayon fabrics, made of filament or staple, alone or in blends with other fibers, can be made to have good, appealing hand, good drape, creasability, luster or lack of it; and particular finishes may be applied to specific fabrics to improve the woven texture and surface effect.

Suggestions in Handling Viscose Rayons

1. Handle fabrics carefully so that there will be no tendency for the cloth to slip or shift in manipulation.
2. Guard against possible seam slippage in garments.
3. Keep in mind the end use of the fabric and be guided accordingly.
4. Check the quality of knit goods made of viscose rayon. The quality of the material will determine the productability of runs in the goods.
5. Color matching should be done with great care.
6. Always read garment labels carefully and follow the directions. Might be well to keep sales slips.
7. Check possible stretch in handling and laundering of the garments.
8. Use the proper setting when ironing the fabrics or garments.

Staining Test for Identification of Viscose Rayon

Texchrome and Testfabrics Identification Stain are excellent agents to use. The directions and final stain are noted on a chart which comes with each agent.

Viscose will stain lavender in Texchrome and blackish-blue in Testfabrics Identification Stain.

In chemical testing, the most commonly accepted test is the 60-per-cent sulfuric acid (by weight) method. Viscose is soluble in the 60-per-cent solution. Viscose rayon is not affected by acetone, nor is cuprammonium or Bemberg rayon; acetate is destroyed by acetone.

Uses of Viscose Rayon

In filament or in staple form, the uses include many types of apparel, house furnishings such as carpets, rugs, blankets, and upholstery. Viscose finds much use in the dressgoods field with fabrics such as crepe, faille, lining, taffeta, and velvet. The fiber is much used in blending with other fibers, natural or manmade, in a host of so-called everyday-wear materials.

TESTING

1. Define regenerated fiber. Name two regenerated fibers.
2. What is cellulose? Cotton linters?
3. Why does viscose burn like cotton in a burning test?
4. List five basic essentials for a successful rayon plant.
5. What is the moisture content of viscose rayon?
6. Define "pfleiderer," "orange crumb" or "cellulose viscose xanthate."
7. What is the function of the spinnerette in the spinning of viscose rayon?
8. What is a rayon cake?
9. List five suggestions in the handling of viscose rayons.
10. For what is Sir Samuel Salvage noted in the history of viscose rayon?
11. Who discovered the process of dissolving wood pulp to obtain cellulose?
12. Name five fabrics made of viscose rayon.

Part 2—Unit 6

TOPIC: CUPRAMMONIUM (BEMBERG) RAYON AND ITS MANUFACTURE

Cuprammonium is a regenerated manmade textile fiber, the same as viscose rayon. Briefly, in its manufacture purified cellulose is dissolved in ammoniacal copper hydroxide and through chemical processing is then regenerated into yarn. It is a stretch yarn as compared with regular viscose rayon yarn. Also known as Bemberg, a product of Beaunit Corporation.

MANUFACTURE—DESPAISSIS AND ELSAESSER METHOD

1. Cotton linters are boiled with caustic soda and soda ash.
2. Bleaching with chlorine follows.
3. Washing and drying are next in sequence.
4. The dried pulp is dissolved in copper oxide and ammonia—ammoniacal copper oxide—which forms a solution, blue in color, and ready for spinning.
5. The solution is forced through large holes or orifices in the spinnerette, which are intentionally larger than the diameter of the finished filament, because the filament is to be stretched and twisted into a finer diameter known as stretch spinning, the Elsaesser development.
6. The stretch method subjects the filament to tension while it is being hardened.
7. As the spinning solution is pumped through the large-sized orifices in the spinnerette, it passes into a glass funnel through which flows de-aerated water at a constant temperature. On its way through the funnel, the filament is stretched and twisted.
8. After leaving the funnel, it enters a bath of mild sulfuric acid, which removes the copper and the ammonia. This reaction leaves a solidified filament of pure cellulose ready to be wound into skeins or onto cones for finishing and weaving or knitting purposes.
9. Final washing and bleaching are not necessary, since these were initial steps in the treatment given the cotton linters.

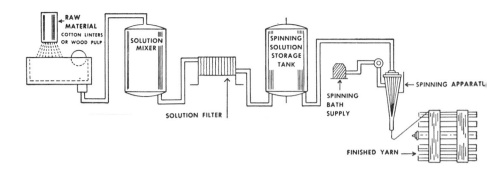

PRODUCTION OF CUPRAMMONIUM RAYON YARN

SOME WELL-KNOWN NOVELTY YARNS MADE OF BEMBERG RAYON

NUB-LITE: A short, entangled slub yarn, irregular in spacing and size, which comes in the lower deniers and is used in dress and blouse fabrics. Heavier deniers find use in bedspreads, draperies, and upholstery.

CUPIONI: A mechanically controlled, entangled slub yarn that is irregular in size and spacing. The yarn has a true Douppioni silk appearance, and is used for fabrics whose end use includes blouses, dressgoods, ladies' and men's suiting, and slacks.

LONG TYPE "A" SLUB YARN: A long, parallel, non-tangled slub yarn which gives a thick-and-thin appearance, soft in hand. Lower deniers are used in blouse and dress fabrics; heavier deniers are used in bedspreads, draperies, and upholstery.

MEASLE YARN: This is a partly tight and partly loose yarn wherein the filaments show different shrinkages that give a loop or bouclé effect. Has the same uses as Long Type "A" slub yarn.

The following yarns are used in bedspreads, draperies, and upholstery—Strata Slub, Multi-Strata Slub, Flake Slub, and Flaikona. These yarns serve as filling yarn in fabrics, with the warp yarn being acetate, silk, or Chromspun, nylon Fortisan, "Dacron," or "Orlon."

Bemberg Rayon, Properties of

Cuprammonium burns like cotton, very quickly. Decomposes around 300° F.

It will swell in alkalies, the degree of swelling depending on the concentration of the alkali solution.

Bemberg is like viscose rayon with regard to action of acids; little effect with cold diluted acids; weakens in hot diluted acids, and the yarn disintegrates at higher concentration.

It bleaches in about the same way as viscose rayon; generally insoluble in organic solvents.

May be attacked by mildew, and compares with viscose rayon in resistance to sunlight.

Specific gravity is 1.52–1.54.

Water absorbency is 27 per cent at 95 per cent relative humidity. Total retention may be 100–125 per cent.

Uses the same dyes as viscose rayon.

Identification of the fiber shows that it is disintegrated by acids similarly to cotton. It is insoluble in acetone, and dissolves in ammoniacal copper solution. Cross-section reveals a round filament.

[220]

The stretch-spinning method produces a very fine, strong yarn that is capable of taking high twist per inch. Aids in drapability.

It has greater elasticity than viscose rayon.

The fine yarns can be made into the sheerest of fabrics.

Bemberg is ideal for printed fabrics of the sheer type for summer wear.

Uses of Bemberg Rayon

These include lightweight dressgoods, crepes, sheers, gloves; ninon, marquisette, voile and other fine-denier, very lightweight fabrics; also used in knitted fabrics, neckwear, and in decorative fabrics.

TESTING

1. Explain some of the differences between viscose rayon and Bemberg rayon.
2. Discuss the principle of stretch spinning.
3. What may be said about the twisting properties of Bemberg rayon?
4. Why is it not necessary to give Bemberg yarn a final washing and bleaching?
5. Name four cuprammonium yarns.
6. Define a sheer print.

NITROCELLULOSE RAYON AND ITS MANUFACTURE

This was the first successful method of manufacture in the history of what is today known as rayon. It was the method developed by Count Hilaire de Charlonnet, the "Father of the Rayon Industry," during the years 1885 to 1889, in Besançon, France. While this rayon is no longer made anywhere in the world because of improved and better methods, its story is given in this book as a matter of record, and in the hope that it may be of some value to students interested in the history and development of manmade fibers.

Manufacture

1. Cotton linters are treated with a mixture of nitric acid and sulfuric acid.
2. The linters are then dissolved in a mixture of alcohol and ether, which forms the spinning solution. This is known as "collodion."
3. As the spinning solution is forced through the spinnerette, the alcohol evaporates and the filament hardens.
4. The nitrate element is removed by a sodium hydrosulfide treatment. Thus a filament of purified cellulose results, to complete the cycle in creating this regenerated textile fiber.

Part 2—Unit 7

TOPIC: Standard Rayon Fabrics

Following World War I, rayon and acetate fibers, filaments, and fabrics came into the textile market. At that time the fabrics were made to simulate and compete with silk materials. The only other manmade fiber to appear here prior to World War II was nylon, and it did not come into its own for use in apparel and hosiery until after the war, since it, like some other fibers, "went off to war." Rayon and acetate fabrics even had the same names as the fabrics they competed with, and still do to considerable degree. They had comparable textures in pick count and in surface effects. Filament, staple, and spun yarns were produced and kept pace with fabrics with which they competed; and after World War II they went ahead of silk in demand, and are still making rapid strides, while silk has declined very much in its use here as well as throughout the world. These fabrics from the newer fibers were engineered so that they had many of the properties and characteristics of the staple silk cloths. Spun yarns of rayon and acetate staple, when made into fabrics, more than held their own against silk goods made from spun and other waste yarns.

The old powerful Silk Association of America, organized in 1872, in time became the National Federation of Textiles, which became cognizant of the impact of the manmade fibers on silk, and joined its efforts on silk with those of the manmade fiber industry. Finally, in 1958, the Federation became a division of The American Cotton Manufacturers Institute, Inc. The advent of a host of new manmade fibers since the close of World War II had brought rapid progress in this field and continues to do so, and silk, in yardage production, is no longer considered to be a major textile segment in the industry because of the continuing growth of the cellulosic and non-cellulosic fibers. The major rayon fabrics follow:

BARONET SATIN: A satin-weave fabric made with rayon warp and cotton filling. This very lustrous material has the tendency to "catch particles." Comes in white and colors.

Baronet wears well, washes easily, and has good draping qualities. "Roughing up" in the cloth is detrimental and lessens its use.

BENGALINE: A cross-rib fabric in which the filling is coarser than the warp. Made of rayon and wool or of silk and wool. Comes in colors and is used in coating, dress goods, millinery and ribbon.

The fabric gives good wear, launders well if care is taken, and possesses good draping qualities. The pronounced filling rib cord adds much to the cloth, which comes in widths ranging from ribbon size to broad goods.

CANTON CREPE: This 46-inch-width cloth is made with a flat yarn warp and filling crepe yarn with "S"- and "Z"-twist. Pick counts range from 96 warp ends of 150-denier with 46 up to 52 picks of 200-denier.

Originally made of several-ply crepe yarn of Canton silk, the cloth is heavier than crepe de chine, possesses a pronounced pebble-effect, but is otherwise the same as the original cloth. Uses include coat lining, dressgoods, dressing gowns, negligees, pajamas, scarfs, and accessories.

CHALLIS: Spun-rayon fabric made of plain weave. Printed to simulate woolen or worsted challis; durable, launders well, drapes in satisfactory manner and is a popular staple.

CHIFFON: "S"-twist and "Z"-twist yarns are used in warp and filling, the denier size is 50. Finished at about 47 inches with textures of 60 by 60 up to 80 by 80. The word "chiffon" implies thin, diaphanous, or gauze-like fabric.

Chiffon resembles Georgette with the exception that instead of being invariably constructed with two ends and two picks of "S"-twist and "Z"-twist, it is often made with one "S"-twist and one "Z"-twist, sometimes with only one twist.

An interesting feature in the chiffon construction is that when only one twist is used, warp and filling-wise, it must be either all "S"-twist or all "Z"-twist in order to preclude a curling or rolling action which may develop when the goods are cut in tapered fashion. Uses include dressgoods, evening wear, lamp shade, millinery, trimming, and many novelty decorative effects.

CREPE: The filling is made of right-hand or left-hand twisted yarn or both. The usual size yarn employed to construct this rugged, well-wearing fabric is 100–150 denier. If pigmented, the cloth is often known as French crepe.

The textures used in crepe make it a popular staple at all times; it is usually compact and the luster is often high in surface finish. Crepe has excellent draping qualities but will have the tendency to shrink if not laundered too well. (*See* FRENCH CREPE.)

AILLE: Belongs to the bengaline group of cross-rib fabrics; the fine ribs or cords are coarse and flat, with the warp finer than the filling in construction.

Faille is difficult to launder well, has good draping qualities, and will wear well if handled with care.

FLAT CREPE: Made in the warp with flat yarn, and in the filling with "S"-twist and "Z"-twist yarn, the fabric is finished from 41–50 inches. Denier of the warp may be 150, 100, or 75; filling is of 100-denier or 75-denier yarn. Textures range from 80 by 40–48 up to 150 by 76, which is a print-cloth texture.

The origin of crepe is found in the Latin *crispare*, which means "to render crimpy." As the name indicates, the material is comparatively flat and reveals only a slight pebble or crepe effect. The use of crepe filling imparts a soft, pliable hand, which enhances drapability despite the light weight of the goods. Reed widths are from three inches to five inches wider than the finished width. The print-goods texture is extremely popular in the apparel trade and is used in garments such as accessories, blouses, dressgoods, negligees, and pajamas.

Any of the flat crepe textures may be used in the above-mentioned garments as well as in the lining trade.

FRENCH CREPE: This 39–43-inch fabric is made with flat warp yarn and voile-twist filling. Denier of warp and filling may be 150, 100, 75. Textures vary from 92 by 69 to 150 by 94. The voile-twist, which is comparatively low, affords roundness to the filling yarn to reduce its covering power and to add pliability to the goods.

Uses include negligees and underwear. Lambskin-type crepe is made of 104 ends of 100-denier and 72 picks of 150-denier. Very popular today, it comes in prints which are much used in aprons, blouses, dressgoods, and interior decoration.

GEORGETTE: Made with 75-denier, "S"- and "Z"-twist crepe yarn; widths are from 43–46 inches. Textures vary from 60 by 48 to 80 by 80. The fabric was originally made of silk and was a very popular staple; the yarn used was 13/15-denier silk with as many as 95 turns per inch in some cases. Georgette is diaphanous, airy, delicate in appearance, but rather rugged. Creped viscose rayon, from the time of its inception, spelled the death-knell for silk Georgette. The viscose fabric seemed to possess greater uniformity and other inherent advantages when compared with the silk fabric. Used in dressgoods, evening wear, lamp shades, millinery, trimming, and numerous dainty decorative effects.

MARQUISETTE: This 38-inch, leno-woven fabric is made of voile-twist warp and filling of either 150-denier or 75-denier. Pick counts run from 28 by 24 to 72 by 48. Also a popular glass-fiber material.

Fine yarn has to be used in the manufacture of the goods, as is obvious from optical inspection. The weave attracts the attention, not only because of its present achievement, but also for the promises it holds if one should ever be successful in realizing a complete turn or a turn and a half, as against the half-turn now possible with present-day leno-weaving equipment. Lenos are woven with cotton heddles, metal heddles, leno reeds and leno blades, as used on Jacquard looms. Terminal use of marquisette includes bedspreads, curtains, dresser ensembles, netting, and varied decorative purposes; high-grade fabric is used in evening wear.

MATELASSÉ, MATELLASSÉ: Name applied to figured fabrics made on dobby or Jacquard looms; the pattern stands out and gives a pouched or quilted effect. Plain, twill, and satin weaves may be used in construction to give the novelty double-weave effect. This blister-effect cloth drapes well, gives good wear, is attractive, and when in vogue, in much demand. Laundering has to be carefully done. Used chiefly in women's dressgoods and for evening wear.

MIGNONETTE and TRICOLETTE: Knitted rayon fabrics made on circular machines. Incidentally, tricolette was the first knitted fabric made of rayon to appear on the market; this was in 1924.

Properties and characteristics of these cloths include luster, great elasticit[y] some porosity, and the tendency to slip, run or creep—much care has to be exe[r]cised in the cutting and sewing of the goods. Mignonette is of finer gauge an[d] mesh when compared with tricolette. Chief uses were for underwear and dres[s] goods. Tricot-knit fabrics have now replaced them.

MOIRE: Taffeta is given the moiré or watermarking treatment to enhance its beaut[y] in a sort of shimmering effect. Moiré goods are attractive, durable, and give goo[d] service. Ideal for evening wear, vestments, decorative fabrics, bridal gowns, et[c].

PLAIN SATIN: Sometimes known as panne satin, this 39-inch fabric is made both wa[ys] with flat yarn. Warp is 150, 100, or 75-denier; filling is 300, 150, 100, or 75-denie[r]. Textures range from 110 by 52 to 300 by 80. Great luster and beauty are achieve[d] in plain satin. Incidentally, the hand in viscose rayon satin is not comparable wit[h] that of an all-acetate rayon satin; the latter seems to have the more appealing fe[el] and graciousness.

Terminal uses include cushion covers, dresses, evening wear, fur-coat linin[g], ribbon, slipper satin, slips.

POPLIN: Originally called "popeline," it was a fifteenth-century fabric made in an[d] around Avignon, France, to honor the reigning pope; used for church vestmen[ts] and hangings.

Present-day poplin is made in widths from 35–40 inches, and the warp ma[y] be any of the following denier—150, 120, 100, 75. Filling denier may be 150, 20[0], 250, 300. Textures vary from 84 by 64 to 158 by 50.

Poplin has a cord effect that runs in the filling or crosswise direction in th[e] goods, which explains the use of a rather coarse filling yarn. Higher-quality popl[in] is made with high sley, fine-count warp yarn to insure a smooth, well-rounde[d] rich-looking rib effect. Uses include day and evening wear, drapery fabric, u[p] holstery material.

RHYTHM CREPE: May be called a rayon seersucker or plissé effect type of fabric. Mad[e] of "plain-weave" variation, the crimped effect runs in warp direction. Comes i[n] white or colors.

The fabric is washable, drapes well, gives good wear, and is a rather rugge[d] type of cloth. Made to simulate seersucker.

ROUGH CREPE: Finished at 46–48 inches, the warp is of the flat type, while the fillin[g] is crepe, "S"- and "Z"-twist yarn. Warp is either 150-denier or 100-denier, fillin[g] is 200-denier or 150-denier. Pick counts range from 96 by 46–52 up to 124 b[y] 52–56.

The fabric is on the order of Canton crepe with the exception that it is allowe[d] greater shrinkage to produce a rougher cloth. The fabric is sometimes found wit[h] multi-pick fashion weaving, that is, four picks of "S"-twist, four picks of "Z"-twis[t] or eight picks of "S"-twist, eight picks of "Z"-twist; this gives a hammered effe[ct] in the goods. Chief use for the cloth is in outdoor, dressy garments of the sma[ll] variety.

SAND-WEAVE FABRIC: Finished from 45–50 inches with warp made of 100-denier fla[t] yarn or 100-denier crepe yarn; filling is made of 150-denier crepe yarn or 10[0] denier "S"-twist and "Z"-twist crepe yarn. Pick counts range from 112 by 6[0] to 135 by 72.

The repeat in sand-woven goods is spread over many ends and picks despi[te] the fact that the cloth is woven on comparatively few harnesses. An importe[d] European weave that is much used to weave the goods contains 66 ends and 4[8] picks to the repeat, with six harnesses or shafts required. No end or pick floats f[or] more than two ends or two picks. A popular cloth in the range today is made [of] 150-denier, dull-acetate flat yarn, with textures of either 108 by 68 or 116 by 6[8]. The fabric is much used in various types of dressgoods.

TACKLE TWILL: It was originally made by William Skinner & Sons, Holyoke, Mass[a] chusetts. This strong, snag-proof twill weave has a rayon-face and cotton-back co[n] struction made to maintain the desired color brilliancy on the athletic field.

[224]

Features of this popular fabric include deep, rich luster, water-repellency, vat-dyed fast colors, drycleanability; washability if handled properly; nonsusceptibility to moths and mildew if dried thoroughly before storing. Fabric weight is about 8½ ounces per square yard. Uses include football pants, softball uniforms, hockey pants, warm-up clothing, basketball uniforms, fishing garments, rainwear, golf jackets, sports jackets, and other athletic and spectator sportswear. Comes in all colors and shades. Also made with nylon.

TAFFETA: The word comes from the Persian *taftah*, which means "to spin." This flat-yarn cloth comes in widths ranging from 35 inches to about 44 inches. Warp and filling yarns are of 100-denier or 150-denier. Textures range from 68 by 44 to 140 by 64; only about one-third of the weight of the fabric is filling yarn. Taffeta is a rugged, practical fabric and is one of the genuine staples in the trade.

Pigment taffetas, which are at present very popular, have pick counts of 92 by 68 to 72 by 56. Much pigment fabric is printed. Taffeta is used in dress-goods, low-price lining, and undergarments.

TIRE FABRICS: Conditions and constructions listed here are those generally used in passenger and truck tires. Variations to meet specific performance or processing requirements are frequent.

Carcass: Cord constructions are used extensively in the carcass-fabric warp and may be either nylon or rayon. The picks only serve to maintain alignment during the adhesive treatment and the calendering.

TYPICAL FABRIC CONSTRUCTIONS (GRAY GOODS)

YARN	CORD CON-STRUCTION	TWIST RANGE SINGLES ("Z")	PLY ("S")	WARP ENDS PER INCH	FILLING PICKS PER INCH
Nylon	840/2	11.0–13.0	11.00–13.0	21–32	2–4
	1680/2	7.0– 9.0	7.0 – 9.0	18–25	2–3
Rayon	1100/2	12.0–14.0	13.5 –15.0	26–34	2.0–4.0
	1650/2	10.0–12.0	11.0 –13.0	21–26	2.0–3.0

Typical pick construction is 30s cotton count of yarn.

Breaker: Constructed the same as the carcass fabric but usually having a reduced end count.

Flipper: Usually a square-woven construction of cotton, rayon, or nylon, located in the bead area. The flipper holds the rubber in place during the cutting operation and also provides additional anchoring of the bead of the carcass.

Chafer: Similar in construction to the flipper, the chafer is located on the outside of the bead in the area next to the rim. Its purpose is the same as the flipper during the curing operation, and once cured, serves to protect the bead area from mechanical damage.

TRANSPARENT VELVET: There are many types on the market. The following will serve as a typical layout for the material, usually woven on the double-piece method of weaving, which requires two shuttle looms:

WARP	FILLING	YARN
Ground of 160		60-denier rayon, 27–30-twist
Pile of 80		150/60 viscose rayon
	2 x 92	60-denier rayon, 27–30-twist

Originally made of silk, the fabric of today gives much satisfaction when made of rayon; so much so that it is very doubtful if silk will be used again in this country to make the cloth. Crease-resistant finish is applied to the cloth; this has enhanced the value of the fabric. Chief uses include dresses, evening wear, and decorative effects. Nylon is also used to make the cloth.

[225]

TRIPLE SHEER: Finished at about 47 inches, the fabric is made with warp crepe yarn of either 100-denier or 75-denier; filling is of 100-denier or 75-denier, the latter may be "S"-twist or "Z"-twist or with no twist at all. Textures range from 90 by 68 to 104 by 72.

This extremely sheer fabric possesses a fair weight. The warp is usually given twist; the no-twist filling seems to be more popular than the twisted filling. Most triple sheer is made with Bemberg yarn but some of the material is now made with viscose rayon. Since the fabric does not seem to have much appeal in plain colors most sheer is printed with eye-appealing motifs. Used chiefly in summer wear.

TULLE, SILK NET, RAYON NET: General names for a sheer cloth made with hexagonal mesh fabric is stiff, cool, dressy, delicate, and difficult to launder. Comes in white and colors, and when used as dressgoods gives the wearer a rather stately appearance. Also used in overdraping and in ballet materials.

TWILL: This flat-yarn cloth comes in widths of 35–40 inches and is made of 150-denier in warp and filling. Textures range from 72 by 52 to 148 by 72. The weight of the warp is predominant in the cloth, which finds much use in infants' wear and lining. Made of a 2-up and 1-down twill weave, the material has smoothness and luster, which are ideal for terminal use. Dull yarn is never used. This rugged fabric is said to even outlast the average men's wear suiting fabric. It has been estimated that the lining trade, at present, uses about twenty-five million pounds of the yarn to cover annual requirements. A 2-up and 2-down twill is also used.

VELVET: A broad term which covers a wide range of warp pile cloths with the exception of chenille, corduroy, plush, terry cloth, and velveteen. Velvet is woven face to face and then cut by the cutting blade while still in the loom. Much velvet has a silk back. The texture often reveals a close pile. Transparent, chiffon, and taffeta-back effects are staple examples of velvet. Nylon is now popular for velvets.

The cloth may give brilliant surface effect; it is durable, may wash well, and is often given crush-resistant treatment.

TESTING   75 points

1. Name two rayon fabrics that are form-concealing when made into an article of apparel. Two that would be form-revealing.
2. How do you account for the popularity of moiré-finish fabrics?
3. What is the purpose of a crepe back on some satins?
4. Why should labels or tags on rayon fabrics and garments be read and understood by the consumer?
5. Name five fabrics made of rayon that have the same name as their silk counterpart.
6. Explain a simple test to distinguish between a rayon fabric and a silk cloth.
7. Why are velvets not suitable for school or business wear?
8. Why is a triple sheer ideal for summer wear?
9. What is a quick way to identify bengaline?
10. What causes a fine sheer fabric such as chiffon to withstand considerable wear?
11. Distinguish between a crepe de chine and a Georgette crepe.
12. Why is marquisette, although very sheer, such a strong fabric?
13. Discuss tire fabrics for use in automobile tires.
14. Tell why you would prefer a satin evening gown to one made of taffeta.
15. Name five uses for satin fabrics.

TRUE-FALSE QUESTIONS   25 points

1. _____ Bengaline is recognized by the rib effect in the warp direction.
2. _____ Rayon chiffon is ideal for everyday wear.
3. _____ Taffeta is made with a satin-weave construction.
4. _____ Pigmented crepe is known as French crepe.
5. _____ Baronet satin comes only in white.

6. _____ Faille dresses will withstand rugged wear.
7. _____ Triple sheers are made from triple-cloth constructions.
8. _____ Velvet is not always a pile fabric.
9. _____ Some satins appear to have a sort of metallic finish on them.
10. _____ Tricolette is an example of a woven fabric made of rayon.
11. _____ Mignonette is one of the strongest woven fabrics in the rayon trade.
12. _____ Tackle twill is ideal for evening wear.
13. _____ Canton is a cross-rib crepe on the order of silk crepe.
14. _____ Rayon net has little sizing in it.
15. _____ Tricot knit is of finer gauge and mesh when compared with tricolette.
16. _____ Rhythm crepe has a sort of seersucker effect in the goods.
17. _____ Taffeta is a form-revealing type of fabric.
18. _____ Sharkskin has the tendency to pick up considerable lint or fuzz.
19. _____ Jersey is always a woven fabric when made of rayon.
20. _____ Crepe Marocain is really a heavy dressweight crepe.
21. _____ Rayon gabardine is made only in right-hand twill.
22. _____ Some rayon fabrics are sized.
23. _____ Rayon taffeta is a weighted fabric.
24. _____ Rayon matelassé is made only in Jacquard designs.
25. _____ Rayon fabrics with a pouch or quilted effect are known as moiré or watermarked fabrics.

TOPIC: EXAMINATION ON RAYON

TRUE-FALSE QUESTIONS   25 points

1. _____ In 1864, Dr. Robert Hooke, English naturalist and scientist, in his book, *Micrographia,* mentioned the fact that an artificial or synthetic silk might be produced in due course of time.
2. _____ Rayon fabric is stronger when wet.
3. _____ Rayon leaves a hard, black bead when burned.
4. _____ René de Réaumur, English scientist of the eighteenth century, tried to imitate the filament produced by the silkworm and spider.
5. _____ George Audemars, Swiss scientist of the middle nineteenth century, hit upon the possibility of coagulation as a basic principle to use in an endeavor to produce an artificial silk filament.
6. _____ Sir Joseph W. Swan, nineteenth-century English chemist, physicist, and electrician, produced the first artificial fiber.
7. _____ Louis Pasteur is known as the "Father of the Rayon Industry."
8. _____ The cuprammonium method of making rayon was discovered by Count Hilaire de Chardonnet.
9. _____ Elsaesser is known for his development of the stretch method used in spinning rayon filament.
10. _____ Sir Joseph W. Swan developed the idea of forcing a solution through the fine openings or orifices in the spinnerette used in obtaining filament yarn.
11. _____ Cross and Bevan, English scientists, discovered and patented a viscous solution which, in time, led to the development of the viscous method of making rayon.
12. _____ Stearn and Topham are known for their contributions made in fostering the silk industry.
13. _____ More wool is used in this country than rayon today.

14. _____ Kodel is a product of Du Pont.
15. _____ Bemberg is linked with cuprammonium rayon.
16. _____ Bemberg rayon is made on the stretch system of making rayon.
17. _____ Fortisan is a product of the Celanese Corporation of America.
18. _____ "Rayon staple" and "spun rayon" are said to be synonymous.
19. _____ Cupioni is made by American Enka Corporation.
20. _____ Pfleiderer is a new type of viscose rayon.
21. _____ Pasteur was a pioneer in the development of rayon.
22. _____ The United States was the first nation to produce a textile fiber from cellulose.
23. _____ Rayon must be made with cellulose as a base ingredient.
24. _____ Cellulose xanthate is white in cast or shade.
25. _____ Cotton may be said to be the "Father of Rayon."

COMPLETION-TYPE QUESTIONS: VISCOSE METHOD OF MAKING RAYON

30 point

1. Pulp used for rayon is _____ and then pressed into a _____ form which resembles blotting paper.
2. Cellulose sheets are soaked in _____.
3. The machine used for the shredding of blotting stock is called a _____
4. Shredded stock is known as _____.
5. This is _____ in color or cast.
6. Carbon bisulfide is added to cellulose crumbs to produce the orange crumb known as _____.
7. This is then treated with a dilute solution of _____, after proper aging of the crumbs.
8. One of the great secrets in the making of rayon is _____.
9. The bath into which viscous solution is forced in rayon manufacture is _____ in nature.
10. Viscous solution is _____ in nature.
11. The openings in a spinnerette are referred to as _____.
12. Spinnerettes are made from _____ and _____.
13. The rayon _____ is formed in the revolving feed box in rayon manufacture.
14. The openings in the spinnerette are interesting because of the fact that they are _____.
15. Acetone will _____ affect viscose rayon.

COMPLETION-TYPE QUESTIONS: CUPRAMMONIUM METHOD OF MAKING RAYON

30 point

1. The base used in making cuprammonium rayon is _____.
2. This base is boiled with caustic soda and _____.
3. Bleaching with _____ follows.
4. Dried pulp is dissolved in copper oxide and _____.
5. The color of the viscous solution in cuprammonium rayon is _____.
6. The stretch system of spinning cuprammonium rayon was brought out by _____.
7. In the stretch method, the filament is subjected to _____ while it is being drawn out.
8. _____ acid is used to remove the copper and the ammonia in cuprammonium manufacture.
9. Final washing is _____ in this method of rayon manufacture.
10. The cuprammonium method is also known as _____ rayon.

Place the number of your choice from the second column on the blank line before the first column to match the statements.

1. ____ Cutting device	1. Often spun on cotton system of spinning
2. ____ Longer than a fiber	2. Used to deluster rayon filament
3. ____ Fibro	3. Spinnerette
4. ____ 4,464,528 yards	4. Very strong filament
5. ____ Titanium dioxide	5. Spun rayon to simulate worsted
6. ____ Mildew will attack	6. Orifice
7. ____ Spun rayon	7. Regenerated cellulose rayons
8. ____ Regain of 11 per cent	8. Regain in acetate
9. ____ Fortisan	9. Filament
10. ____ Regain of 6.5 per cent	10. Regain in rayon
	11. Used in making spun-rayon staple
	12. Number of yards in one pound of a 1-denier filament

Part 2—Unit 9

TOPIC: ACETATE AND ITS MANUFACTURE

Acetate, like viscose rayon and cuprammonium rayon, has cellulose as its base cotton linters, or chips of pine, spruce, or hemlock. Acetate differs from rayon in the method of manufacture; different chemicals are used to digest the cellulose. Thus the burning test for acetate as well as the dyeing properties are different.

Cellulose is a white, shapeless, or amorphous substance classed as a carbohydrate. Chemically it comes from the following formula:

$$(C_6H_{12}O_6) \text{ n or x times—Glucose}$$
$$\underline{H_2O} \qquad\qquad \text{—Water is removed}$$
$$(C_6H_{10}O_5) \text{ n or x times—Cotton}$$

About 96 per cent of cotton is cellulose; it is the substance that forms the cell walls of plant life, as cotton, flax, kapok, etc.

The substance is isomeric with starch, which means that it is a compound having the same molecular weight and formula as starch but with a different structure and different properties.

A carbohydrate is any one of a group of compounds which contain carbon in combination with hydrogen and oxygen, the latter being in the same proportion as in water. A carbohydrate is essential in the metabolism of plants and animals. Carbohydrates include cellulose, starches, and sugars.

THE MANUFACTURE OF ACETATE, CELLULOSE-DERIVATIVE FIBER

Acetic anhydride is used for the acetylation or combining with cellulose. This anhydride is obtained by allowing chlorine gas to act on anhydrous sodium acetate. To produce this, a special plant is designed for heavy duty and to withstand corrosive materials. The product is a clear liquid.

Cellulose pulp is steeped in acetic acid under controlled temperature.

At a point in the process, the pulp is mixed with acetic anhydride in a heavy kneading machine. In this step, the cellulose loses its identity and forms a new compound, cellulose acetate. This is a clear, viscous, nearly white liquid.

Precipitation follows when the acetic acid is drawn off and the solid cellulose acetate is recovered in the form of small, solid, white particles.

5. Thorough washing follows, to free particles from the acid. After drying, the cellulose acetate is ready for spinning in the spinning solution.
6. The solution or dope is delivered into one end of a hollow tube through which the filaments are formed and pass on their way to the spindle; a current of warm air in the tube causes the evaporation of the acetone from the spinning dope.
7. The evaporation of the solvent leaves a solidified residue of cellulose acetate in the form of yarn, which can then be wound onto a bobbin. In this condition the yarn is then ready for use, requiring no such washing or bleaching as noted in the manufacture of viscose rayon. Handling in skein form is not necessary, since it can be put up or packaged in the form desired by the weaver or the knitter.
8. Outline of the manufacture of acetate:

WOOD PULP OR LINTERS		CHEMICAL		MACHINERY		THE TEXTILE FILAMENT
Cellulose	plus	Glacial Acetic Acid Acetic Anhydride Acetone	plus	Spinnerette	yields	Cellulose Acetate or Acetate

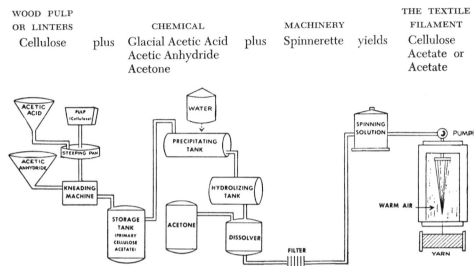

PRODUCTION OF ACETATE YARN

Properties and Characteristics of Acetate

Acetate, when burned, will melt and give off drippings that can be very painful if allowed to fall on the person doing the test. The odor noted is acrid and may be compared with the odor of vinegar or comparable acids. The residue is a curled, hard blackish-brown bead, difficult to crush between the fingers.

Acetate becomes sticky at 350° F.; softens at 400° F. to 450° F. It melts at 500° F. In strong alkalies it will saponify into regenerated cellulose.

Concentrated solutions of strong acids cause decomposition.

Bleaches attack it in strong oxidizing agents. Not damaged by weak sodium hypochlorite or peroxide bleaching. After-bleach rinsing should be done with utmost care.

As to organic solvents, acetate is soluble in acetone and in certain other solvents of this type.

Has resistance to mildew, and in sunlight there is a slight weakening of tensile strength but no discoloration.

Specific gravity is 1.32, while the water absorbency is 14 per cent at 95 per cent relative humidity.

It may be dyed with disperse dyes, and in some instances with basic dyes. Acetate can also be dyed under special conditions with some vat dyes, azoic acid, mordant pigment, and solvent dyes.

Acetate is resistant to moisture, and the normal amount of moisture ranges from 3.5 per cent to about 6.5 per cent.

It dries rapidly, does not deteriorate from salt air or mold, and does not rot.

Acetate is not a substitute for, nor imitation of, silk or any other fiber.

The basic process changes solid cellulose into a liquid, then back into a solid in the form of filaments, which are textile fibers. Cellulose for acetate comes from wood pulp or cotton linters. Both forms must be broken up into small, fluffy particles. Cotton linters go through a picking machine, shown here.

Fluffy pulp, packed in aluminum pans, goes to the steeping room, where acetic acid is added. The steeped pulp is aged in the conditioning room.

The steeped and conditioned pulp is mixed with acetic anhydride in a heavy-duty kneading machine called an "Acetylator." The solid cellulose becomes liquid cellulose acetate, held in solution by acid.

The solution is clear, almost water-white, and known as "acid dope." It is emptied into aging tanks known as "eggs." Hydrolysis then takes place, which makes the cellulose acetate soluble in acetone.

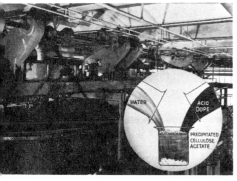

The solution is formed into precipitating tanks, water is added, and cellulose acetate in the form of solid white particles is precipitated from the acid dope. The solid particles are washed until free of acetic acid.

The wet mass of particles is dropped into a tank known as a "stabilizer," where hot water and acid remove any impurities. The wet mass then goes over a screen where the cellulose acetate is separated from the hot water.

Courtesy: American Viscose Corporation, New York

[231]

The damp cellulose acetate is fed into a dryer and emerges in dry, granular form. Various batches are blended together to insure uniformity.

The dry granules go into mixers and are dissolved in acetone into a liquid known as "spinning dope."

The spinning dope is forced through a series of high-pressure filters to remove all undissolved material. It is then stored in tanks, ready for spinning.

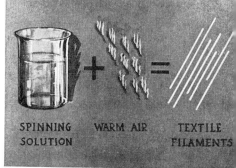

SPINNING SOLUTION   WARM AIR   TEXTILE FILAMENTS

When the spinning dope comes in contact with warm air, the acetone evaporates rapidly leaving solid cellulose acetate fibers.

The tiny spinnerette, the key factor in spinning the liquid into yarn, is about the size of a thimble and contains a number of very fine holes.

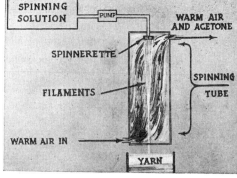

The spinning dope is drawn from the tanks and forced through spinnerettes vertically downward into a hollow tube through which warm air passes. This is known as the spinning tube.

 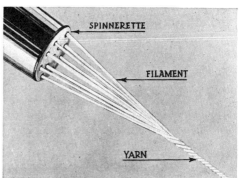

In the spinning tube the fine streams travel downward against a current of warm air, which evaporates the acetone, leaving solid filaments.

The filaments are withdrawn from the bottom of the spinning tube and twisted and wound on a bobbin in the form of finished continuous filament acetate yarn. No washing or bleaching processes are necessary.

Here is a view of the acetate spinning room at the American Viscose Corporation plant in Meadville, Pa.

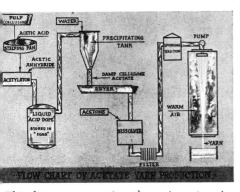 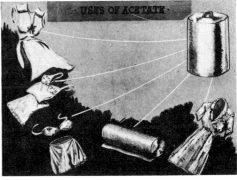

This diagram summarizes the various steps in the production of acetate.

Acetate gives good draping qualities and hand, and is used in dress fabrics, especially crepes, linings, woven and knitted lingerie.

It is not a weighted or adulterated fiber.

Its hygienic qualities are excellent.

Because of its insulating properties, acetate may be thought of as a fiber for all season wear.

It comes in continuous filament or short fibers of specified length and diameter. May be bright or dull.

Remains a permanent white, and textures may be soft and have a pleasant feel to the skin.

Suppleness gives excellent draping qualities.

Has no natural tendency to stretch or shrink.

May be given special finishes.

Acetates can be laundered and drycleaned provided care and attention are given.

Acetate is much used in cross-dyeing with other major fibers to give two-tone and iridescent effects.

When wet, it has less loss of strength than rayon.

Fabrics of acetate will take a good crease and pleat well.

Suggestions in Handling Acetates

1. Ironing of acetate fabrics or garments should be done on the back or wrong side of the material. The fabric should be slightly damp. Use a warm iron, not hot, to prevent adverse reaction to the fabric's instability at higher temperatures.
2. Always keep the end use of the fabric in mind.
3. Avoid home dyeing of acetate fabrics.
4. Exercise care in the manipulation of the material. If so done, there should be no possibility of a tendency toward slippage or splitting. Knitted fabric should be handled carefully to prevent possible snagging or drop-stitching.
5. Use care in handling fabrics cut on the bias.
6. Perspiration will not affect the fabric.
7. One of the high points in acetate is its ability to provide excellent drape.
8. Acetate is a "fabric of beauty" and is always a good buy from an economic angle.

Uses of Acetate

These include dressgoods of many types, evening wear, fused fabrics, linings, lingerie. The staple fiber is much used in carpeting and rugs, blankets, and upholstery.

Because of the excellent blending qualities of the staple fiber with other major fibers, a great use of the resultant fabric is in men's, women's, and children's wear of many types.

TESTING

1. Define cellulose, carbohydrate, isomeric.
2. How is the natural luster of acetate made semi-dull or dull?
3. What are the basic raw materials used to make acetate?
4. Why is acetate not classed as a regenerated textile fiber?
5. Describe the burning test on acetate.
6. Who were the pioneers for the manufacture of acetate in the United States?
7. Why would you say that acetate is a "fabric of beauty"? Give one or more specific examples to support the statement.
8. Give three selling points for acetate fabrics.
9. Why is acetate fabric a very good lining material?
10. Why should acetates be ironed on the reverse side of the goods?
11. Define iridescent effect in fabrics.
12. Why is acetate an ideal fiber to use in cross-dyed fabrics?
13. Give three important points as to taking care in the handling of acetate fabric or garments.
14. Describe the acetone action on acetate.
15. Why would acetate be ideal for use in bathing suits?

TOPIC: Standard Acetate Fabrics

The name of a fabric does not necessarily give a hint as to its composition. For rayon, acetate, and silk fabrics, names such as Canton, satin, moiré, taffeta, panne satin, crepe, sharkskin, and so on, are noted. Some of these names are used for pure-silk fabrics or for acetate or rayon, or for all of these in some instances. Several of these materials are made from combinations of acetate and rayon. The easiest and best test to use, incidentally, to determine whether the fabric is acetate, rayon, or a combination of these, is to place a few drops of acetone on the cloth in question. Acetone destroys acetate yarn or fabric immediately; it has no effect on rayon. This test will reveal whether there is a rayon warp and acetate filling, or whether, as in the case of staple stock, the spun yarn contains both acetate and rayon fibers in either the warp or the filling, or in both systems of yarn.

Warp yarns and filling yarns should be tested separately after a preliminary test has been made on the fabric by the use of acetone. Fiber content is vitally important in both systems of yarn which go into the fabric.

Fabrics made of acetate can be readily tested by ironing. They will stick to the iron if the temperature is just above the regular ironing level. The burning test may also be used for distinction between a rayon cloth and an acetate material. Rayon burns like cotton or linen; acetate will curl, melt, and form a hard bead difficult to crush between the fingers. Moiré or watermarked treatment is permanent on acetates while rayons cannot be given this treatment.

The standard acetate fabrics follow:

ACETATE CREPE: Finished from 45 inches up to 49 inches, the warp yarn is of the flat-type acetate, while the filling is viscose-crepe yarn with "S"-twist and "Z"-twist. The choice for warp may be 150, 120, and 100-denier; filling is chosen from 200, 150, or 100-denier. Textures range from 96 by 46 up to 114 by 64.

Cross-dyeing, known sometimes as two-tone dyeing, gives beautiful coloring in the goods. The fabric is also singular in that the acetate warp provides luxury of feel while the viscose yarn, with its ability to crepe, together with the shrinkage and resulting build-up caused by the action of the crepe filling, provides a genuine public appeal.

Variations in the fabric may be had by multi-pick arrangements such as four "S"-twist and four "Z"-twist, or eight "S"-twist and eight "Z"-twist. A hammered effect results from this construction. Incidentally, the larger the group of one-way twist picks together, the more sensitive will be the fabric.

Terminal uses include dress coats, lining in sportswear, suiting. A texture of 96 by 48 is ideal for clothes of this type. A texture of 136 by 64 is popular for the so-called higher-class trade in women's blouses, dressgoods, and negligees.

ACETATE CREPE-BACK SATIN: Finished at 43.5 inches, the warp is flat acetate while the filling is viscose-crepe yarn. Denier of the warp is 100 or 75; the filling is 150 or 100-denier. Textures range from 200 by 72 or 320 by 88. The warp is high in sley with comparatively high pickage to produce a dull, slightly creped back. The warp weight acts as a foundation for drapiness to the goods, which have a decided richness and suppleness. Used for dressgoods and fur-coat lining.

ACETATE GAMZA: This 48-inch finished fabric is made with flat-acetate warp and viscose-crepe filling made of "S"-twist and "Z"-twist. Denier in the warp is 150 or 120; in the filling it is 200 or 150. Texture ranges from 96 by 56 to 110 by 52.

Fancy weaves bring out the surface appeal in gamza. The crepe filling also enhances the appeal. Warp sley is quite low, comparatively speaking. It should be noted that the warp side is the back of the cloth. Used in the outerwear trade, gamza is not as popular as formerly.

ACETATE NINON: Made in voile-twist yarn each way, 75-denier is used in textures of 64 by 64 to 80 by 80. This sheer, glass-like fabric is simple in construction, has appeal, and is highly suitable for curtaining. The washability of the goods is of interest to the housewife. Accessories, curtains, and evening wear are the uses for ninon.

ACETATE PANNE SATIN: Finished from 39 inches to 41.5 inches, this flat-yarn fabric is made with 100-denier or 75-denier in the warp, and with 150-, 100-, or 75-denier yarn. Pick counts range from 100 by 60 to 320 by 96. Comparable with viscose rayon satin, the acetate satin seems to possess greater suppleness. The texture, 200 by 72, is popular for lining in ladies' sports coats and dress coats. Other uses include blankets, candy-box lining, dressgoods, labels, trimmings, underwear.

ACETATE SHARKSKIN: Finished around 41 inches and made with flat yarn, the warp is made from 150-denier or 300-denier; filling is of the following denier—300, 450, 600. Pick count is from 52 by 52 to 176 by 36. This popular sportswear cloth is firm, rather stiff, and solid. The cloth is usually made from the plain, taffeta, or tabby weave; occasionally fancy weaves which effect short floats are used. Viscose sharkskin is too stiff for acceptance in the trade at present.

End uses of sharkskin include nurses' uniform fabric, sportswear of many types, and resort clothes for warm climates.

ACETATE TAFFETA: Finished from 39 inches to about 41 inches, this flat-yarn cloth is made from the following denier—150-, 120-, 100-, 75-denier; filling is of 300-, 150-, 120-, or 75-denier. Textures range from 84 by 60 to 200 by 64. There is a wide range in taffeta fabrics. While acetate was not approved by consumers as early as viscose rayon, it has, nevertheless, made rapid strides, since it has a distinctive and very appealing hand. Variations with viscose yarn in the warp are ideal for cross- or two-tone dyeing. The 84 by 60 and the 200 by 64 numbers are very popular in the apparel trade. Other uses include bedspreads, blouses, hangings, ribbon, and trimmings.

ACETATE TWILL LINING: Made with flat yarn and finished from 37 inches to 41 inches, the warp and the filling are made from 150-denier or 75-denier yarn. Pick count ranges from 84 by 72 to 150 by 88. This fabric has a better hand than its counterpart, viscose twill lining; however, the cloth is less rugged but seems to be more luxurious. In abrasion testing, viscose rayon is superior to acetate-twill lining. The chief use of the lining is for garments which require a rich-looking cloth with a luxurious feel; durability is secondary.

Handling and Care of Rayon and Acetate Fabrics and Garments

These materials can be washed by hand or drycleaned, but attention should be given to the construction of the cloth, the finish on the material, and the dyes used to color the fabric. Usually the washing or laundering instructions come with the article. The consumer should read the instructions well and be guided accordingly. If perchance the article may not have a label or hang-tag, the following general instructions should be followed:

Pure, mild soap should be dissolved in warm (not hot) water before dipping the fabric into the solution.

The sudsy water should be gently squeezed through the material. Rough or rigid handling should be avoided. Do not soak colored fabrics.

Colored fabrics should be washed apart from white materials.

Careful rinsing should be done in clear lukewarm water. Do not wring or twist the material. Excess water should be removed by rolling the garment in a towel.

The great majority of rayon and acetate fabrics are ironed best when almost dry; a slightly dampened condition should suffice.

Pressing should be done on the wrong side or back of the material with a warm iron. Be sure to check the setting on the iron: rayon, acetate, or low.

TESTING

1. Why may it be stated that some acetate fabrics are made to resemble silk materials? Give some examples.
2. What are some reasons for using "S"-twist and "Z"-twist yarns in some acetate fabrics?
3. Why may a crepe-back acetate satin be called a reversible fabric?
4. Give some reasons for the continued popularity of the staple fabric, taffeta.
5. Name three uses for acetate-crepe fabric.
6. How do you account for the great use of some acetate fabrics for garment lining?
7. Of what value is cross-dyeing in fabrics which contain acetate and rayon fibers or filaments?
8. Discuss the handling and care of acetate and rayon fabrics in washing and laundering.

Part 2—Unit 11

TOPIC: CONTINUOUS FILAMENT, SPUN-RAYON, AND COMBINATION-YARN FABRICS OF VISCOSE RAYON AND ACETATE

Before a study is made of very many blended yarns and fabrics on the market today, there are certain symbols and figures that should be understood by the reader when considering the structures of these materials. The following list should enlighten the student with regard to interpreting the data found on approval samples and head ends:

128 x 64. This is the actual count of the number of warp ends and filling picks per square inch in the material.

150/40. This means that the denier is 150 and that there are 40 filaments in the yarn.

25/1 50/50 viscose-acetate. This implies that the warp-yarn size or count is a single 25s, in either the cotton count or the worsted count. Both systems use yarn of this size. If the cotton standard of 840 yards in one pound of the number-one yarn is used, the yardage per pound of the yarn is found by multiplying the 25 by 840, which equals 21,000 yards of yarn. If worsted, multiply the 25 by 560, the number of yards in one pound of a number-one worsted yarn, to give 14,000 yards of yarn per pound.

The 50/50 means that the filling is made of 50 per cent viscose rayon and 50 per cent acetate.

30/2. This means that the count or yarn size is composed of two single yarns of 30s, to make this a 30/2 yarn. The single equivalent of this yarn would be a 15/1 or single 15s. (Dividing 30 by 2 gives 15-ply, the basis of the count.) If figured on the system used for cotton, there would be 840 times 15, or 12,600 yards of yarn to the pound. The 30/2 would be the same as the 15/1 in diameter and in yardage of yarn to the pound.

Terms and expressions constantly met with in regard to fabrics of this type include the following: pigment yarn, slub yarn, bright yarn, dull yarn, nub yarn, spun rayon, spun acetate, rayon staple, blended yarn, combination yarn; reed width or loom width, finished width; greige or gray goods; shrinkage; "S"-twist, "Z"-twist.

CONTINUOUS FILAMENT AND SPUN YARN FABRICS OF RAYON AND ACETATE

FABRIC	TEXTURE	WARP		FILLING
Faille	128 x 46	150/40 Acetate yarn	25/2	50/50 Viscose-acetate
	Used in men's sportswear fabrics			
Fuji-type	120 x 68	120/40 Acetate yarn	15/1	50/50 Viscose-acetate
	150 x 62	75/20 Acetate yarn	25/1	50/50 Viscose-acetate
	Used in blouses, children's dress-goods, men's shirting			
Luana-type	108 x 48	150/40 Acetate yarn	25/2	50/50 Viscose-acetate
	Used in blouses, dressgoods, en-sembles, men's shirts and slacks, two-piece dresses, women's slacks			
Print dressgoods	100 x 52	100/60 Pigment	18/1	Viscose nub yarn
	114 x 54	100/40 Dull acetate	22/1	Viscose nub yarn
	108 x 68	120/40 Dull acetate	30/1	Viscose yarn
	Used in dress trade in plain colors and prints			
Shantung	114 x 54	100/28 Dull acetate	22/1	Viscose slub yarn
	120 x 50	120/36 Dull acetate	17/1	Viscose slub yarn
	Used in children's dresses, dress-goods, men's shirts, and two-piece dresses			
Spun-Rayon Linen	42 x 42	14/1 Spun-rayon slub yarn	14/1	Spun rayon slub yarn
	Used in prints for the dress trade			
Tackle twill	240 x 72	150/40 Viscose	45/3 or 30/2	Viscose or cotton
	Used in coating, hatwear for men, rainwear, sportswear			

COMBINATION YARN FABRICS OF RAYON AND ACETATE

FABRIC	REED WIDTH	TEXTURE OR PICK COUNT	DENIER-FILAMENT	YARN SIZES
Alpaca	48	36 x 34	75/100	4-ply, all one twist
Alpaca	48	44 x 38	150/150	2-ply, all one twist
Cynara	47	52 x 40	100/150	2-ply, all one twist
Magic Hour	48	54 x 44	100/150	2-ply, all one twist
Mock Romaine	47	52 x 46	100/150	2-ply "S"-twist and "Z"-twist in warp, 200-denier acetate with voile-twist in filling
Romaine	48	52 x 44	100/150	2-ply "S"- and "Z"-twist in warp, 75/100-denier acetate filling

These are fabrics strictly for the dressgoods trade which differ in type from regulation viscose or acetate fabrics on the market today. These materials are made of fairly coarse, pliable yarns which unite viscose-rayon crepe and acetate. The materials weigh from 26 to 32 pounds per 100 yards. Reed widths are 47–48 inches, with finished widths of about 39–41.5 inches.

The staple material, Fortune, has met with universal approval. Made with combination yarns, the layout follows: Texture is 72 by 54; warp is two ends of 150-denier acetate voile twist and one end of 100/150 combination; filling is two picks of 150 acetate voile twist and two picks of 100/150 combination.

SPUN RAYON MANUFACTURE

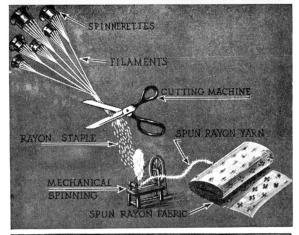

Rayon filaments are cut into short, predetermined lengths known as "rayon staple." Rayon staple must be spun mechanically, like natural fibers, to make yarn. This is known as spun rayon yarn.

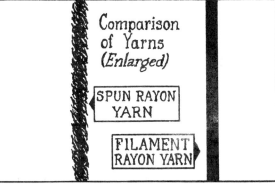

Note the fuzzy, irregular appearance of spun rayon yarn compared with continuous filament rayon yarn.

Because of the nature of spun rayon yarn, spun rayon fabrics have different textures from filament rayon fabrics. They are also somewhat spongier and more absorbent.

The initial steps in making rayon staple are the same as in making continuous filament rayon. The main difference is in the handling of the filaments when and after they are extruded.

Courtesy: American Viscose Corporation, New York

Larger spinnerettes with many mo[re] holes are used. Filaments from sever[al] spinnerettes are drawn together, with[out] twist, into a continuous loose ro[pe] known as tow, which is cut to the d[e]sired length by an automatic knife.

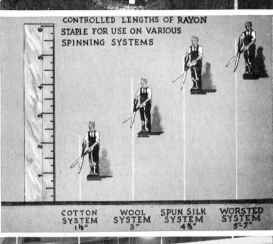

CONTROLLED LENGTHS OF RAYON STAPLE FOR USE ON VARIOUS SPINNING SYSTEMS

COTTON SYSTEM 1½"   WOOL SYSTEM 3"   SPUN SILK SYSTEM 4½"   WORSTED SYSTEM 5"-7"

Rayon staple for spinning on cotto[n] silk, wool, and worsted systems is c[ut] into lengths varying from one to sev[en] inches.

The rayon staple is now washed, c[de]sulfurized, bleached, and dried. T[he] washing and bleaching machines a[re] seen here.

After washing and bleaching, the ray[on] staple is dried and conditioned in lo[ng] tunnel dryers.

This is finished rayon staple.

When the rayon staple arrives at the mills, it is clean and ready to be carded, gilled, and combed before spinning.

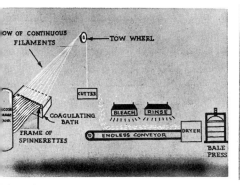

This chart summarizes the steps in making rayon staple.

Spun rayon is very versatile. It is particularly adaptable to blending with short natural fibers such as wool and cotton, producing yarns and fabrics of different types and textures.

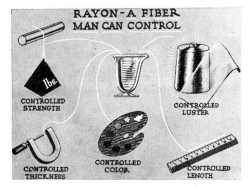

Rayon can be controlled for strength, thickness, color, luster, and length, and can be specifically planned and designed for its intended use.

TESTING

1. Explain the following data as to correct interpretation:
   - a) 150 x 62 pick count
   - b) 120/40 acetate yarn
   - c) 25/2 yarn
   - d) 50/50 viscose-acetate yarn
   - e) 22/1 viscose slub yarn

2. Define the following:
   - a) Union fabric
   - b) Cross-dyed fabric
   - c) Blended yarn
   - d) Combination yarn
   - e) Rayon staple
   - f) Spun-rayon yarn
   - g) Bright acetate
   - h) Dull viscose
   - i) Pigmented rayon
   - j) "S"-twist and "Z"-twist

3. What does the term "texture" mean with regard to cloth construction? As to surface effect on a fabric?
4. How would you identify a rayon fabric from an acetate material?
5. How would a union fabric differ from a combination-yarn cloth?
6. How would you identify a spun-rayon material?
7. Define reed width; finished width.
8. Describe a spun-rayon linen cloth.

TOPIC: EXAMINATION ON RAYON AND ACETATE FILAMENTS, FIBERS, YARNS, AND FABRICS

TRUE-FALSE QUESTIONS   20 point

1. _____ Rayon jersey is usually knitted.
2. _____ Moiré effect on rayon gives a permanent effect.
3. _____ Acetate leaves a soft black bead when burned.
4. _____ Ninon is a sheer fabric made from either plain weave or leno weave.
5. _____ Perspiration has little or no effect on acetate fabrics.
6. _____ More acetate yarn is produced than cuprammonium yarn annually.
7. _____ Wood pulp cannot be used as a base for rayon or acetate.
8. _____ Lint cotton fiber is much used as a base for making rayon.
9. _____ Cotton linters are used as a base in the manufacture of acetate.
10. _____ Acetate is not attacked by mildew.
11. _____ Manmade fiber fabrics can withstand rather high ironing temperatures
12. _____ Viscose rayon burns the same as cotton, kapok, linen, and wool.
13. _____ Japan is considered as a major rayon-producing nation.
14. _____ Moisture has little effect on viscose and Bemberg rayons.
15. _____ Acetate fabrics are dissolved by acetone.
16. _____ The nitrocellulose method of making rayon is still considered as a majo method in the manufacture of rayon filaments and fibers.
17. _____ A rayon or acetate matelassé fabric is recognized by its "quilted effect."
18. _____ Spun-rayon fabrics are made from rayon staple.
19. _____ Viscose rayon is classed as a regenerated type of fiber.
20. _____ Rayon and acetate fabrics are considered to be substitutes for silk fabric of like nature.

MULTIPLE-CHOICE QUESTIONS   15 points

Underline your choice from second column wherever you think there is a definite link with the word or words listed in the first column:

1. Viscose rayon — Natural, regenerated, animal, modified
2. Acetate — Cellulose derivative, regenerated, bast fiber
3. Cuprammonium rayon — Vegetable, bast, regenerated, acrylic
4. Three major rayon-producing countries — Peru, Turkey, Russia, Japan, Italy, Brazil, Ireland, Colombia, Scotland
5. Nitrocellulose method — Hooke, Swan, Réaumur, Chardonnet, Pasteur
6. Burns without a bead — Silk, wool, worsted, acetate, viscose rayon
7. Greatest in length — Linen, rayon staple, acetate filament, silk
8. May be watermarked — Taffeta, jersey, spun-rayon fabrics, challis
9. Acidic odor when burned — Bemberg rayon, acetate, viscose rayon
10. Used to make yarn dull — Chlorox, titanium dioxide, acetic acid, acetone
11. Closely related to faille — Bengaline, grosgrain, taffeta, Fuji, luana
12. Orifice — Spinnerette, xanthate, minute hole, needle
13. Longest in denier yardage per pound of yarn — 150, 100, 75, 300, 600, 10, 15, 20, 30
14. Largest in diameter size in terms of denier yarn — 12, 20, 300, 600, 100
15. Dissolved by acetone — Bemberg sheer, rayon voile, acetate satin

MATCHING QUESTIONS   10 points

Place the number of your choices from the second column on the blank line provided before the terms or words in the first column where you think there is a definite link or matching connection:

1. _____ Viscous solution
2. _____ Rayon "cake"
3. _____ A cutting device
4. _____ Pfleiderer
5. _____ Acetate fiber
6. _____ Union fabric
7. _____ Reversible fabric
8. _____ Texture
9. _____ Viscose rayon fiber
10. _____ Cellulose

1. Shreds "rayon blotter stock" into flakes.
2. White, shapeless, amorphous substance.
3. Is thermoplastic-type fiber.
4. Is not a thermoplastic-type fiber.
5. Ends and picks in cloth or surface effect.
6. Forced through orifices of a spinnerette.
7. A pigmented taffeta fabric.
8. Rayon warp and acetate filling.
9. Necessary to make staple form of stock.
10. Crepe-back satin fabric.
11. Made by revolving motion of the feed box in a rayon spinning machine.

GENERAL QUESTION   5 points

List five precautions to keep in mind when handling rayon or acetate fabrics or garments.

GENERAL ESSAY QUESTIONS   50 points

Choose any two of the following for a value of 25 points each:
1. a) How did rayon receive its name?
   b) List five conditions essential to running a successful rayon plant.
   c) List five advantages derived from the use of acetate or rayon fabrics.
   d) Why is acetate called "the fabric of beauty"?
   e) Name five fabrics made of acetate or rayon.

2. Give the contributions of five scientists or pioneers who have made rayon and acetate possible for use today.

3. For business or office wear, state your preference: a dress made of silk, acetate satin, spun rayon, Bemberg sheer, or a silk satin. Consider as major points in making your choice and write about the following—serviceability, weight of the article, comfort, season of the year, and laundering or drycleaning properties.

4. Would you prefer a dress made of viscose rayon, cuprammonium rayon, or acetate, for evening wear? Base your answer on a single or particular occasion. Be specific in all essay writing.

TOPIC: Brief History of the Newer Manmade Fibers, and Definitions and Terms Used in the Manufacture of Manmade Filaments and Fibers

The cellulosic fibers, rayon and acetate, were discovered and developed by the English scientists Cross and Bevan during the years 1892 to 1896. During this time, Dr. Arthur D. Little was doing comparable work in Boston, Massachusetts. These three contemporaries exchanged data and ideas and worked together in further research and development of the fibers. Following World War I, both filaments had reached the stage where it was definitely apparent that they would soon take their place in the textile fiber kingdoms. Today the two terms "rayon" and "acetate" are household words, as well as the names of some of the newer fibers, such as nylon, Dynel, Acrilan, "Orlon," "Dacron," etc. A chronological résumé of these newer fibers follows:

1926–1939: Dr. C. M. A. Stine, Chemical Director of E. I. du Pont de Nemours & Co., Inc., Wilmington, Delaware, laid the groundwork for what was to be known in time as "nylon." The word is a generic term, such as "cotton" or "wool," and is not a trademark or trade name. The term refers to and is associated with polyamide fibers. Nylon was not a planned discovery but was a development from studies made on polymers and the principles of polymerization. By 1929, after three years of research, it became the goal of the company to perfect a distinctly new textile fiber different from rayon and acetate in its physical and chemical properties. At this time another Du Pont chemist, Dr. Wallace H. Carothers, was achieving success in the field of polymerization by condensation and in determining the structure of high-molecular-weight compounds. Dr. Stine had been working chiefly on cellulose derivatives such as ethers, new types of esters, and on the amino groups. Dr. Carothers had been working on different structures and reactions. With much information at hand, Dr. Carothers and his staff began to make progress. A fiber was developed that was known as "Polymer 66." Later on it was referred to as "Fiber 66." The first "6" indicated the number of carbon atoms in the diamine, and the second "6" the number of carbon atoms in dibasic acid, of which the substance was composed.

The name "nylon" was finally given to the fiber, and it was announced to the world on October 27, 1938. The name nylon evolved from "no-run," since the company felt that it would be an ideal yarn for stockings and hosiery. This proposed name, however, was not acceptable because of the vulnerability of a nylon stocking in showing runs. Then "no-run" was spelled backwards: "nuron." Finally, the term "nylon" was decided upon, since it was short, distinctive, and a good-sounding name. On May 15, 1940, the first nylon stockings were placed on sale in stores throughout the nation. The simultaneous World's Fairs in New York and San Francisco in 1940 showed the stockings in the Du Pont Building at each fair. By the end of the summer many other nylon articles were on display at the New York World's Fair.

The promotion of nylon was done in a superb manner, the timing was well conceived, the public at once became intensely interested, and it was not long until nylon joined acetate and rayon as a household word. In fact, "nylons" and "stockings" were practically synonymous. Thus, finally, nylon was born to survive, after thirteen years of research and an expenditure up to 1939 of $27,000,000.

Four plants produce Du Pont nylon—at Seaford, Delaware (1939); Martinsville, Virginia (1941); Chattanooga, Tennessee (1948); and Richmond, Virginia (1958). Tricot lingerie made of nylon made its debut in 1940; foundation garments were produced in 1941.

One of the strongest fabrics on the market today is tackle twill, and it has an interesting background. In 1929 Knute Rockne, the famous football coach at the University of Notre Dame, decided that he would dress his squad in something that would have flash and color and would be different from the drab football pants worn up to that time; he also figured that the material he wanted had to be slippery so that it would make his players more difficult to tackle. So he thought of satin football pants. William Skinner & Sons, Holyoke, Massachusetts, developed the new togs for Rockne. The fabric was made from shoe satin, a silk-face, cotton-back satin. A new trend began, of adding color to football squads and their uniforms. Nylon in due course of time came into the picture. Its tough properties, especially its ability to withstand abrasion, made it ideal for these pants. Tackle twill, first made of nylon, made its debut on November 1, 1941, when Notre Dame met Army in its annual game in Yankee Stadium, New York City. Nylon tackle twill surpassed in "wear-and-tear" quality the twill of rayon or acetate, which was first shown in 1937.

The original pants lasted the Notre Dame squad for a full six years, although guaranteed for only one year. This fabric is now standard equipment in football. Other uses for tackle twill include warm-up suits for athletic squads, rainwear, and jackets.

At present there are thirty nylon plants in this country.

1937: The original patent on Vinyon was assigned at this time to Union Carbide and Chemicals Corporation, a division of Union Carbide Corporation, New York City.

1938: Although Fiberglas Corporation, Newark, Ohio, introduced its glass fiber in 1931, it was not until 1938 that the company perfected the product to the point where it would bend like rubber, could be tied into a knot, and woven into a fabric.

Perlon, which was made in Germany and is comparable with nylon, was announced.

1939: Vinyon came into the market as a product of the American Viscose Corporation.

Kuralon, "Japanese nylon," was assigned to Gosci-Ichigo Company, in Japan.

1940: Saran came into the market as a base product of The Dow Chemical Company, Midland, Michigan.

1941: Terylene polyester fiber, under the direction of Dr. Whinfield, was announced in England. It was the result of the study of polyesters originally made by Dr. Carothers of Du Pont. The patents and rights, in time, were bought by Du Pont; the polymer is a condensation of the ethylene glycol and dimethyl terephthalate. The Du Pont product is the well-known "Dacron" polyester fiber. It was first made in a plant in Kinston, North Carolina, which was opened in 1953.

1941: Celanese Corporation of America announced its Fortisan fiber, a super-strong rayon with great dimensional stability.

1943: Elastic-type Vinyon announced by American Viscose Corporation.
Soybean protein fiber came into being, a product of The Drackett Company.

1944: The Dow Chemical Company, Midland, Michigan, brought out its polystyrene fiber, Polyfibre.
Polyethylene announced by Union Carbide Corporation.
Stainless-steel filaments became an actuality.

1948: "Orlon," the trademark for the acrylic fiber of Du Pont, was announced. In July, 1953, the plant for its manufacture was opened in Camden, South Carolina.
Within the decade following 1948 there have been several other new fibers introduced to the textile market and consuming public. These include Acrilan, Arnel, Caprolan, Creslan, Dynel, Kodel, Mylar polyester film, Taslan, Teflon, Vycron, Verel, Zefran, etc. The end, of course, is not in sight, since progress is being made constantly in the manufacture of new textile filaments and fibers.
It is estimated that there are one thousand manmade trade name fibers throughout the world today, some major, some minor. Several are worldwide in scope, reputation, and use; others are provincial and rather isolated, and find use only in the country of origin, or in local areas. Many fibers in this field are short lived, since they do not seem to possess the physical and chemical properties that admit of their competing with better and more firmly established fibers now on the market.

1959–1960: Many of the non-cellulosic fibers have received much aid from the fact that solution- or dope-dyeing is ideal for coloring them. The color is bonded into the filament as it is being made in the solution form and remains, generally speaking, throughout the life of the filament, fiber or fabric. Clearer color effects are obtained in this method of dyeing, and greater durability is possible.
In this time span, Du Pont brought out several new products in nylon. Type 82 is a textured yarn used in sweater goods; Type 91 is an "extra-white" variety which has its color locked in by solution dyeing. Its laundering and washing properties are excellent. Type 109 is a heat-resistant yarn used for industrial purposes, while Type 228 is a textured yarn. Type 420 is a high-tenacity, high-modulus staple fiber used with cotton and rayon in blends. Type 501 is a filament nylon, trilobal in cross-section, and very popular in the carpeting trade.

Nylon staple and tow were first used in floor covering in 1946, and after much research and development, the company brought out its Du Pont BCF nylon, a trilobal cross-section, bulk-textured continuous filament made available in staple and tow for this use. The constructions used in the carpeting determine whether Du Pont BCF or staple should be used. "Antron" became the first trade-marked nylon in the Du Pont family of nylon yarns. Introduced in 1959, it differs from regular nylon in that fabrics made from it have a unique, interesting luster, more opacity, and a very dry hand. Sparkling nylon is a 15-denier hosiery monofilament announced in 1959.

The patent rights on nylon, which began in 1938, expired in 1955. Under license from Du Pont, the Chemstrand Corporation began making nylon 66 in 1951. Since 1955 several other companies have entered the nylon field. The twenty-fifth anniversary of nylon was celebrated far and wide in this country in 1963. Du Pont may well be extremely proud as "The Father of Nylon" in the United States; this polyamide fiber, nylon, became a household word shortly after it came on the market in the hosiery world. In fact, for several years, "nylon" and "hosiery" were practically interchangeable words.

"Dacron" also made news during these two years. "Dacron" 61 is a high-shrinkage type which was engineered for industrial uses. Type 64 is ideal for blending with wool and worsted fibers in dressgoods and suitings. Type 62 was developed to obtain brighter colors and clearer prints on materials.

Du Pont unveiled Cantrece, now a filament nylon yarn for women's hosiery and apparel, and Sayelle, the certification mark for fabrics and garments having specified amounts of "Orlon" bi-component acrylic staple fiber in them.

Other companies were also busy with new products. Allied Chemical Corporation brought out its Golden Caprolan nylon tire yarn in 1959. American Enka unveiled its "Blanc de Blanc" extra-white nylon in 1960. Beaunit Corporation announced its Vycron polyester fiber, while Chemstrand Corporation introduced Cadon, a multilobal cross-section nylon, FRN nylon, which has an increased fatigue resistance so necessary in many industrial uses, and Cumuloft, a staple nylon fiber used in carpeting, in textured form.

Eastman Chemical Products, Inc., announced its modacrylic fiber, Verel, in 1957, and in 1960, Verel H.B., a high-bulk staple for the floor-covering trade. Verel H.B. and Dynel are now much used in pile fabrics, fake fur, and similar materials; both are modacrylic fibers.

Reeves Brothers, Inc., New York City, brought out its polypropylene bristles for use in brushes, and Prolene, a polypropylene fiber in filament and tow forms was announced by Industrial Rayon Corporation.

1961–62: Du Pont brought out "Dacron" Type 99, a polyester fiberfill which is extremely soft, resilient, resists mildew, is very white in cast, has no odor and non-allergic properties. The company also introduced Teflon FEP, a fluorocarbon monofilament for use in brake lining, packing, and insulation.

Eastman Chemical Products, Inc., announced that the Kodak trademark would be used on its Kodel polyester fiber. Hang-tags now have the trademark of the parent company on them, Eastman Kodak Company, Inc. American Cyanamid Company brought out Creslan 61, a bright and semidull staple and tow, and Type 63, a filament yarn for use in dressgoods and lingerie; both are acrylic fibers.

1963: Courtaulds North America, Inc., presented its Sarille, a modified rayon staple, crimped and with improved bulk, and Teklan, a flame-resistant fiber, a modacrylic fiber, and a copolymer with equal weight of vinylidene chloride and acrylonitrile, and with a small but important unnamed ingredient. It is used in household textiles and garments. British American Spandex Co., Ltd., a joint venture of Courtaulds, Ltd., and Firestone Tire and Rubber Company, brought out Spanzelle, a spandex elastomeric yarn for use in foundation garments, support stockings, swimwear, etc. Firestone also introduced a spandex multifilament yarn.

Du Pont announced "Orlon" Type 29, a yarn which has the feel and appearance of loop-mohair yarn, high luster, low crimp, and is ideal for cross-dyeing purposes. Fiber H, a monofilament nylon for hosiery, also made its debut. Chemstrand Corporation presented EO2 Chemstrand nylon yarn with improved dyeing qualities; it is much used in seat belts.

Definitions and Terms Used in the Manufacture of Manmade Filaments and Fibers

The rise of new textile fibers in this synthetic age has produced a new vocabulary of terms that are met with daily in the industry. These reference terms should be of value to the reader, since all, at some time or other, have played their part in the study and development of manmade fibers. It is realized that most of the terms are technical in nature; but they may be of some aid to the student of textiles, particularly to one having a textile or scientific background. The definitions follow:

ACRYLIC: Designating an acid—$C_3H_4O_2$—which has a sharp, acrid odor; prepared from acrolein or from certain derivatives of propionic acid. Used in organic synthesis in the manufacture of plastics. Also known as propenoic acid.

"Orlon" fiber, for example, is a true manmade filament or fiber made with an acrylic base and is a polyacrylonitrile fiber. Acrilan and Dynel, as well as some of the newer fibers, are partly acrylic in composition.

ATOM: The smallest part of an element that can enter into the composition of a molecule. It is not a particle of a chemical compound; a compound must have at least two atoms.

CATALYST: A substance which hastens a chemical change in other chemicals when mixed together with them. The catalyst itself undergoes no permanent change, and may be recovered when the action terminates. In the manufacture of plastics, for example, catalytic agents include acetone, alcohol, caustic soda, distilled water, and sulfuric acid.

CONDENSATION: Water is separated from milk by the evaporation of one constituent from a mixture of materials—really the opposite of condensation. For example, water is evaporated from a wet towel, but water is condensed from hot air as moisture on a cold towel or cold wall. Many types of plastic are made by condensation. This action is not a separation as in taking water from milk, but is the actual splitting off of the hydrogen from one compound and the OH from another compound. The H and the OH unite to form water. Water does not become present until actual condensation takes place. After one chemical has lost its H, and the other its OH, the two molecules can then unite by combining their terminals that are now left "hungry" for a partner.

Incidentally, the two compounds can be molecules of the same chemical structure as long as that structure has terminals which can lose either the H or OH radicals.

DIMENSIONAL STABILITY: The quality which enables a fabric or a garment to withstand any type of change in measurement through repeated launderings. The generally accepted standard is that the garment should not shrink out of fit (that is, shrinkage should be less than 3 per cent) or become distorted after five launderings by the appropriate methods. Note, however, that worsted trousers that shorten or lengthen with changes in relative humidity, or carpets that ripple or tear with changes in humidity, would have poor dimensional stability regardless of laundering.

ETHYL: The hypothetical radical of the carbon series (C_2H_5), the base for common alcohol, ether, acetic acid, and a rather large number of compounds—hydride, chloride, iodide, alcohol.

ETHYLENE: The diatomic hydrocarbon or olefin of the ethyl series, C_2H_4.

FORMALDEHYDE: A colorless gas obtained from wood alcohol (methanol). Finds much use as a preservative and disinfectant. This formic aldehyde is an important reagent in some phases of textile chemistry.

FURFURAL: Obtained from cottonseed hulls, it is used with phenol to form thermosetting plastics comparable with the phenol formaldehyde group of plastics.

HYDROCARBON: One of a large group of compounds that contain hydrogen and carbon only. There are several classes and types, including the aliphatic, aromatic, saturated, and unsaturated.

INHIBITOR: An agent which slows down, checks, diminishes, or prevents a physical or chemical change.

INORGANIC: Not having in its structure the carbon element as found in animal and vegetable matter. It should be observed, however, that carbolic acid, ether, and nylon, for example, are not exactly animal or vegetable matter, nor are they inorganic or formed from living organisms or substances.

INORGANIC SOLVENT: A solvent which lacks the carbon element: for example, water, or a water-miscible noncompound which possesses solvent properties; other examples include dilute hydrochloric acid used on rust stains, and hypo used on iodine stains.

KETONE: From the German, a modification of acetone: the name given to a class of chemical compounds formed by the oxidation of the secondary alcohols or carbinols, to which they stand in some respects in the same relation as aldehydes. The lowest of the series, dimethyl-ketone, is common acetone.

MICA: Any of a class of silicates which crystallize in the monoclinic system and which can be separated into very thin, tough scales, colorless to jet-black. Used as a filler material in some plastic products. The transparent variety is known as isinglass.

MOLECULES: The smallest unit of an element or a compound that retains chemical identity with the same element or compound in the mass. In modern chemistry, the molecules of each element or compound are assumed to be of uniform size and mass, representing the smallest portion into which the substance can be divided without losing its chemical identity.

NATURAL RESIN: A family of solid or semi-solid organic substances of vegetable origin. Found, for example, in resin; and used in soaps, varnishes, and drying agents. Another example, lac, is obtained from the lac bug of India, and is much used in the manufacture of shellac and similar products. The resins, which are brittle and have a waxlike luster, are insoluble in water.

OLEFIN: The name for a series of hydrocarbons homologous with olefiant gas or ethylene; general formula is C_nH_{2n}.

ORGANIC: A broad term, applied to substances obtained from living organisms, or any substances which consist largely of hydrogen, oxygen, and carbon. The other general class of substances is the inorganic or mineral group.

ORGANIC ACID: One which contains carbon, such as acetic, formic, oxalic acids. All organic acids contain carbon; all inorganic acids are devoid of carbon.

[249]

ORGANIC SOLVENT: Contains the element carbon, the only known chemical element for which there is no known solvent. The symbol for carbon, C, will appear in the formula. This type of solvent is used in the removal of stains greasy in nature. Since the vapors are injurious when inhaled in large quantities, all organic solvents should be used in well-ventilated quarters. Some organic solvents are wood alcohol, ether, benzene, gasoline, carbon tetrachloride, benzol, acetic acid, chloroform.

pH: A term used to express acidity or alkalinity of solutions. For solutions which are on the acid side, the pH is less than 7; on the alkaline side, it is more than 7.

PLASTICIZER: A chemical added to plastics to soften, increase malleability, or to make more readily deformable. There are several plasticizers on the market, and they are ideal when used with thermoplastic plastics such as camphor, high-boiling esters, and polynaphthalenes.

POLYMER: A comparatively large molecule produced by linking together many molecules of a monomeric substance. Such a reaction is known as polymerization. If two or more different monomeric substances are mixed prior to polymerization, the product of the reaction is known as a copolymer. Nylon is an example of a copolymer.

RADICAL: Taken from the Latin, and means "root." It is an element or an atom, or a group of these, forming the base of a compound, and remaining unaltered during the ordinary chemical reactions to which it is subject.

RESIN: An amorphous organic substance exuded by plants, and soluble in alcohol and ether. Any of various substances which have properties similar to true resin and which are made by chemical synthesis—especially those substances used in the manufacture of plastics.

RESINOID: Implies that the product is a synthetic resin.

SOLVENT: A liquid in which substances will easily dissolve. Water is often referred to as the universal solvent, since it will dissolve almost anything to some degree. The textile industry uses a very large range of solvents depending upon the specific operation involved.

STAPLE FIBER: Filaments which have been cut to a predetermined length. This stock may be spun on the cotton, woolen, worsted, flax, or spun-silk systems, and finds much use in dressgoods and suiting fabrics.
Staple fiber is often mixed with other major textile fibers in varying amounts to bring about a new yarn and a new fabric effect. Practically all the manmade filaments are cut into staple length for use alone or for mixing with other fibers.

TAR: It is found in cigarettes, oil, wood, cotton, bituminous coal, etc. The distillation of bituminous coal produces a dark-brown liquid of very heavy viscosity; it is used to make coal tar used in certain plastics, dyes, and explosive materials.

THERMOPLASTIC PLASTIC: One that will soften when exposed to heat and will harden again when the source of heat is removed. Plastic material which is permanently fusible is known as thermoplastic.

THERMOSET PLASTIC: Plastic set permanently into shape or form by the use of heat; heat applied later may produce a charred formation without causing the plastic to melt or lose shape.

TOW: A large group of continuous filaments, such as acetate or rayon, Kodel, nylon, etc., without any definite twist. The tow stock is cut into definite set lengths and is known as staple fiber. It is used to make blended or mixture-type yarns in which two or more different fibers (natural and/or manmade) are used. Staple fiber also may be used alone in making a spun yarn such as spun acetate, spun rayon, or spun nylon.

VINYL: The compound univalent radical, CH_2CH, isomeric with many derivatives of ethylene—the hydride of vinyl.

TESTING

1. What seems to be the present status of the terms "manmade" and "synthetic," with regard to the naming of textile fibers in each group?
2. Name two cellulosic fibers; four non-cellulosic fibers.
3. Who discovered the first commercial manmade textile filament?
4. What is the name of this filament, and where were fabrics made from it first shown to the world?
5. Identify the following persons who were pioneers in the field of manmade fibers: 1. Dr. C. M. A. Stine. 2. Dr. Wallace H. Carothers. 3. The Dreyfus Brothers. 4. Dr. Whinfield. 5. Cross and Bevan. 6. Arthur D. Little.
6. What fiber is said to be the first "true manmade fiber"?
7. Name "five textile fibers" of Du Pont.
8. What company produces the following:
    a) Fortisan? b) Dynel? c) Vinyon HH? d) Arnel? e) Verel? f) Saran? g) Creslan? h) Zefran? i) Kodel? j) Fiberglas?

Part 2—Unit 14

TOPIC: Acrilan, Arnel, Creslan

ACRILAN—ACRYLIC FIBER, POLYMER OF ACRYLONITRILE

This product of the Chemstrand Corporation, New York City, is made from a polymer of acrylonitrile. The solution is made and then extruded, the solvent is eliminated, and the resultant yarn is then stretched. Filament form is easily cut into staple length.

Properties

There is a loss of 2.5 per cent in shrinkage when boiled. Shrinkage in dry heat at 487° F., is 5 per cent; at 511° F., it is 10 per cent.

There is fair to good resistance to alkalies; good to excellent resistance to acids; excellent resistance to hypochlorites and other bleaching agents.

Acrilan is not harmed by the common solvents, nor is it affected by sunlight; in fact, its sunlight-resistance is excellent in common with other acrylics.

Specific gravity is 1.17, and water-absorbency shows retention of 5 per cent after centrifuging.

This round-cross-section fiber does not have a melting point; it burns and leaves a hard black bead that may be gummy or brittle in parts. Further identification reveals that Acrilan is not affected by glacial acetic acid, chloroform, acetone, or 90 per cent formic acid. It is soluble in dimethylformamide.

Possesses medium tenacity and abrasion-resistance, has high extensibility and low absorption.

Washes easily, dries rapidly, and has high resistance to wrinkling.

Has high bulking qualities and capacity; greater bulk for weight of material used.

Acrilan has a warm, full feel, and its crimping property is excellent.

May be ironed up to temperature of 300° F. Use rayon setting for iron heat.

This staple fiber may be used alone or in blends with other fibers.

Dyes used include acid, premetalized, chrome, acetate, basic and vat. Usually dyed by ordinary procedures and dyeing times.

[251]

Uses

Carpets and rugs, pile fabrics, blankets, fine jersey fabrics, dressgoods, suitings and other staple apparel in men's, women's and children's wear. Also used in sweaters, draperies and upholstery, work clothing, and chemical-resistant materials.

TESTING

1. Define acrylic fiber.
2. List five properties of Acrilan.
3. What may be said of the bulking properties of Acrilan?
4. In what chemical is Acrilan soluble?
5. Name five uses for this fiber.

ARNEL—CELLULOSE TRIACETATE FIBER

This thermoplastic triacetate fiber is made by the Celanese Corporation of America, producers of acetate, Celaperm, bulked acetate, crystal yarn, Quilticel, Fortisan, Fortisan-36, rayon filament yarn, and continuous filament tow.

Properties

Arnel burns rapidly, and shows small sparks and considerable sputtering. The odor is that of burning sugar with a "resin odor" noted. The residue is hard, dark, gritty, and rather easily crushed or flecked. Arnel melts around 582° F. When heated it will not stick at a temperature of 482° F.

Arnel is unaffected by dilute solutions of weak acids. Strong acids may cause deterioration.

Strong oxidizing agents such as potassium permanganate will attack it. Ordinary laundry bleaches such as hypochlorites and peroxides do not injure the fiber, if used in the accepted standard procedures and proper amounts.

Common solvents will not affect the fiber; it is swollen by some ketones and trichlorethylene. It is soluble in methylene chloride.

High in resistance to mildew and sunlight.

Specific gravity is 1.3, and water absorbency is 10–11 per cent—100° relative humidity, centrifuge method, for heat-treated Arnel.

As for identification of Arnel, it is soluble in methylene chloride-alcohol mixture.

It is not as absorbent as cotton or rayon.

In dyeing Arnel, a proper selection of dispense dyes is used. Colors will not change or stain other fibers when washing is done at 160° F.

Under normal conditions for dyeing, alkalies have little or no effect at 9.5 pH and 200° F., for 16 hours. It is saponified by high-alkaline concentrations.

It can be dyed to give wash-fast fabrics in a wide range of colors.

When constructed properly and heat-set, Arnel can be used in fabrics that are known for their colorfastness, crease and pleat retention, and dimensional stability. Heat-setting must be done with care.

When heat-treated, it is resistant to glazing; the iron can be set at the cotton setting. Washes easily and dries quickly.

Gas-fading may develop in some garments; therefore, proper selection of dyestuffs and inhibitors is very important.

Trichlorethylene should not be used as a drycleaning agent or spotting agent, since it will cause Arnel to bloat or swell.

Uses

Arnel may be used by itself or in blends with other fibers. When properly blended with other fibers, it is ideal for specific fabrics such as challis, crepe, faille, flannel, gabardine, sharkskin, taffeta, and comparable materials—cloths that can be used for daily wear. It has appeal in woven and knitted fabrics of many types, in addition to the above fabrics. Industrially, it finds use in laundry pads and press covers.

1. Name three textile products of the Celanese Corporation of America.
2. Describe the burning test for Arnel as to flame, odor, and residue.
3. List five properties or characteristics of Arnel.
4. What type of dyes are best to use on Arnel?
5. Name five fabrics in which Arnel is used.

CRESLAN—ACRYLIC FIBER

Creslan is classed as a true acrylic fiber because it is composed of 85 per cent or more of acrylonitrile. It is a product of the American Cyanamid Company, New York City. It can be used alone or in blends with natural and other man-made fibers. It is especially good for union dyeing in wool blends.

Properties

Creslan does not flash-burn, and its sticking point is 433° F. It will melt and burn, leaving a hard, black bead.

There is no loss of its strength in weak acids; good resistance to strong organic acids; some strong inorganic acids will dissolve Creslan.

In alkalies, fair to good resistance to weak alkalies; poor resistance to strong alkalies; will turn yellow.

Creslan can be bleached with some of the common bleaches.

The product is insoluble in acetone; soluble in dimethylformamide.

Not attacked by mildew, and effect of sunlight is negligible.

Specific gravity is 1.17, while water absorbency is 1.5 per cent at 70° F., and 65 per cent relative humidity.

Moth-resistant, non-irritating to the skin, and not dangerously flammable.

Dyes used for Creslan include acetate, basic, chrome, direct, developed, direct-after-treatment, neutral milling, neutral metalized. Dyes in a wide range of colors.

For identification of the fiber use Calco Identification Stain No. 2, American Cyanamid Company. Creslan can be creased and durably pleated, launders easily and well, and irons quickly.

Some Creslan fabrics combine light weight and soft hand, thus providing for the use of yarns and fabrics of great bulk for their weight. This makes possible its use for strong, light, cool fabrics for summer, or very light yet bulky and warm fabrics for winter wear.

Uses

These include brushed, napped or pile fabrics; blanketings; suitings and overcoatings; jersey and other knit fabrics; sweaters; sportswear; and work clothing.

TESTING

1. List five properties of Creslan.
2. Describe the burning test for Creslan.
3. Discuss the bulking properties of Creslan.
4. Name five possible uses for this fiber.
5. Differentiate between a napped fabric and a pile fabric.

TOPIC: "DACRON," DARVAN-TRAVIS, DYNEL

"DACRON" POLYESTER FIBER

"Dacron" polyester fiber is the trademark for the polyester fiber manufactured by E. I. du Pont de Nemours & Co., Inc., Wilmington, Delaware. Technically, the base for this fiber is a polymer called polyethylene terephthalate, developed and discovered in 1941 by Dr. J. R. Whinfield and J. T. Dickson, in the laboratories of the Calico Printers Association in Lancashire, England. The trademark is Terylene. The ground work for the fiber was done by Dr. Wallace H. Carothers, in whose name the original nylon patent rights were issued. In 1946, Du Pont purchased the United States patent application on the polymer and the fiber from this polymer.

"Dacron" comes in continuous filament, which is easily cut into tow for staple. The filament is not produced as such at the present time. Chemically, "Dacron" is made from a composition of ethylene glycol and terephthalic acid, and it is melt-spun in a manner comparable with nylon.

Polymerization of these chemicals is carried out at high temperatures using a vacuum. This polymer is then spun from the melt, and the filaments are stretched several times their original length, the exact number of filaments depending on the end use of the product.

Properties

In the burning test, "Dacron" burns slowly and does not flash. Melting point is 480° F. Very black smoke is given off while it burns, and a hard black mass residue, formerly molten, is observed. Sticking temperature is around 460° F.

Good resistance to mineral acids. Dissolves with partial decomposition in concentrated solutions of sulfuric acid.

Good resistance to weak alkalies; moderate resistance in presence of strong alkalies at room temperature; disintegrates at the boiling point.

It is not soluble in acetone or concentrated formic acid. It is soluble in some hot phenolic compounds.

Specific gravity is 1.38, while water absorbency is 0.5 per cent at 95 per cent relative humidity.

There is some loss of strength in sunlight on long exposure, no discoloration. It is much more resistant behind glass than in direct sunlight.

Does not absorb perspiration well. Not degraded by moths.

Too hot an iron may affect the fabric. Use rayon setting on iron.

Static electricity may be created unless treated to prevent it.

"Dacron" is noted for its crease-retention and crease-resistance.

Creases and pleats can be heat-set into the fabric, and they are lasting in nature. "Dacron" does not shrink or stretch under normal use. Crispness and strength are features of "Dacron."

It stands quick, easy removal of water-borne spots and stains such as coffee, tea, or lemonade.

Easy washing, quick drying, and little ironing are attributes of the fiber.

The dyes that may be used are disperse (acetate) and developed (azoic), with a carrier or at high temperatures.

Uses

These include cravat fabric, dresses, shirtings, socks, suitings, blouses, curtains, slacks, sewing threads. In industrial applications it finds use in V-belts and ropes.

The use of "Dacron" in blends, combinations, and mixes has been very well received in the trade, particularly for its strength and crease-retention. It is one of the most popular fibers used for blending.

"DACRON" TYPE 64: This supplements but does not replace the standard polyester fiber. It is made to increase the use of the fiber in winter apparel for men, women, and children. The yarn is spun on the worsted, and the American or rayon spinning systems. Features of the product include improved resistance to pilling, higher tenacity and abrasion properties, greater versatility in that disperse and selected cationic dyes may be used. Wrinkle-recovery, crease-retention, and wash-and-wear properties are very good in apparel made with this type of "Dacron." Its chief use is for worsted- and rayon-type fabrics such as Bedford cord, basket-weave constructions, plain and sheen gabardine, mill-finished and unfinished worsteds, and for selected worsted- and rayon-type flannel.

Courtesy: E. I. du Pont de Nemours & Co., Inc., Wilmington, Delaware.

TESTING

1. What are the common basic ingredients for "Dacron" polyester fiber?
2. In what two forms is the present-day fiber produced?
3. Discuss five chemical and/or physical properties of "Dacron."
4. Name three characteristics of "Dacron" which make it ideal for the housewife.
5. Give some reasons as to why "Dacron" is an asset when mixed with other major textile fibers.

DARVAN-TRAVIS—NYTRIL FIBER (called Travis in Europe)

Manufactured by Celanese Corporation of America. Darvan is a composition of matter whose basic constituent is vinylidene dinitrile; United States Patent Number 2,615,866 for Darvan was first assigned to the B. F. Goodrich Company, Cleveland, Ohio; now belongs to present manufacturer.

Properties

Darvan retains 100 per cent strength after 195 days in the air at 300° F. Sticking point is 340° F.

For identification, Darvan may be separated from cellulosic or protein fibers by dissolving it in dimethylformamide. It is stained a pale mint green using Identification Stain GDC (General Aniline & Film Corporation) or light purple gray using Calco Identification Stain No. 2 (American Cyanamid Company).

Concerning acids, Darvan has good to excellent resistance to hot and cold acids. With alkalies, it has fair resistance to cold dilute caustic; strong alkalies will degrade the fiber. Dry temperatures above 315° F. or wet temperatures above 250° F. should be avoided.

Darvan may be bleached using acidic sodium or calcium hypochlorite. It is not affected by acidic hydrogen peroxide.

Insoluble in acetone and soluble in dimethylformamide.

No evidence of failure in standard tests used for resistance to mildew.

There is an outstanding resistance to outdoor weathering in direct sunlight; 88 per cent strength is retained after two years of direct Florida exposure.

Specific gravity is 1.18 and moisture regain is 2–3 per cent at 65 per cent relative humidity, 70° F.

As to dyeing properties, disperse or cationic dyes with a carrier are used for medium to deep shades. Pastels can be obtained with disperse dyes. Good deep shades are best obtained with azoic dyes, developed with beta-oxynaphtholic acid. There is a limited affinity for vat, solubilized vat, or selected acid dyes, the latter being applied by the cuprous ion method. There is no affinity for direct, acid, metalized, or chrome dyes.

Uses

Men's and women's wear apparel, pile fabrics, hand-knitting yarns; sweaters, and industrial fabrics of several types. It finds much use in fabrics of wool and Darvan made for apparel.

TESTING

1. What company manufactures Darvan?
2. List five properties of this fiber.
3. Give three uses of Darvan.

DYNEL—MODACRYLIC FIBER, COPOLYMER OF ACRYLONITRILE AND VINYL CHLORIDE

Dynel is a light cream-colored fiber made from a copolymer of 40 per cent acrylonitrile and 60 per cent vinyl chloride, in tow or staple form. It is a product of Union Carbide Chemicals Company, a division of Union Carbide Corporation, New York City.

Properties

Dynel will burn on contact with an open flame but is self-extinguishable when the flame is removed. It does not melt or drip.

It is resistant to attack from acids, alkalies, moths, fungus, and bacteria.

Dynel can be immersed in a concentrated (up to 95-per-cent) sulfuric acid bath without any effect. It is weakened by boiling, concentrated hydrochloric acid, phosphoric acid, and concentrated sodium hydroxide, but there is little effect by these reagents up to and including 50° C. Acetone and other ketones will soften the fiber.

Possesses excellent resilience, warmth, and dimensional stability, permitting washing and quick drying with pleat-retention and without loss of shape or size.

Specific gravity is 1.3 at 25° C. Moisture regain is below 0.4 per cent.

It is non-felting and non-shrinking below 212° F. It will begin to shrink and stiffen at 250° F., and will soften at about 315° F.

Because of its initial shrinkage point of 250° F., it can be ironed with a naked iron only at temperatures below the acetate setting. It can be boiled, and piece-dyed fabrics are generally subjected to boiling above 205° F., for 1–1½ hours.

Sunlight will bleach the fiber very slightly, and prolonged exposure at high temperatures will darken and weaken the fiber to some small degree.

Uses

Dynel is ideal for blending with cotton or other fibers, for warmth and softness in sportswear, suitings, and underwear.

The most important use for Dynel is in pile coatings. In knit pile cloths, a Dynel backing is stabilized to minimize distortion and to provide drape. In knit and woven pile fabrics, Dynel is used to increase softness and luster.

When blended with wool, Dynel in men's suitings affords improved crease-retention and improved wear-resistance.

Other uses for the fiber are in pile and fur-type fabrics for collar and cuff trimmings, paint-roller covering, filter cloth; and it is also used in the manufacture of wigs for dolls.

Because Dynel is pliable under heat, 100-per-cent Dynel fabrics can be heat-shaped or molded. Men's summer suits are made by this process, and it has possibilities for many other items such as packaging, pocketbooks, and upholstery.

TESTING

1. What company produces Dynel?
2. List five properties of Dynel.
3. Describe the burning test for Dynel.
4. How do acids, generally speaking, react on Dynel? Alkalies?
5. Give five uses for Dynel.

TOPIC: NYLON, "ORLON," SARAN

NYLON—A POLYMER FIBER

After thirteen years of research and development, E. I. du Pont de Nemours & Co., Inc., Wilmington, Delaware, introduced this polyamide fiber, "nylon." The word is a generic term. The patents for nylon were issued in 1939 to the late Dr. Wallace H. Carothers of that company.

Nylon is extruded from a molten state, resembles silk to considerable degree, and can be spun to exceptionally fine filaments. It was introduced to the public on May 15, 1940, and was originally known as "coal-air-water" filament.

MANUFACTURE OF NYLON

1. Nylon is made from four elements—carbon, hydrogen, nitrogen, and oxygen. The basic raw materials are a hydrocarbon obtained from coal, petroleum, or natural gas; nitrogen and oxygen from the air; and hydrogen from water. By means of high-pressure synthesis, the hydrocarbon and other intermediates are converted into chemicals known as adipic acid and hexamethylene diamine.
2. The hydrocarbon, oxygen, nitrogen, and hydrogen are then processed to form nylon salt, which is sent to one of the Du Pont plants.
3. The nylon salt is conditioned in evaporators which take care of the solution and prime it for the next step.
4. SOLIDIFYING AND CHIPPING: The ordinary molecules of nylon polymer are joined together in giant chains of super-molecules, in molten solution. On a large casting wheel, the solution is solidified into a hard white ribbon which is later chapped into flake form.
5. MELTING OF THE FLAKES: The flakes are melted into a viscous liquid which is extruded through spinnerettes. On exposure to the air, these individual nylon filaments form immediately.
6. FILAMENTS: A pound of single nylon filament, like that of other filaments, would have a total length of 4,464,528 yards, or about 2,500 miles. In the processing, the filaments are gathered into a single strand form and wound at high speed onto a spinning bobbin. The bobbins are then transferred to the drawing frame.
7. COLD-DRAWING: The nylon filaments are then "cold-drawn" about four times the original length, and then wound on a suitable shipping package; this arranges the molecules in parallel lines comparable with the sticks in a package of spaghetti.
8. FINISHED NYLON: The yarn is now ready for final inspection, wrapping, packaging, and shipping to destination.

Nylon 66 is made by the Du Pont Company and The Chemstrand Corporation. Nylon 6 is made by Industrial Rayon Corporation, Allied Chemical and Dye Corporation, American Enka Corporation, Beaunit Corporation, and Firestone Tire & Rubber Company.

Courtesy: E. I. du Pont de Nemours & Co., Inc.

Nylon salt moisture control
Polymerizing nylon molecules
Control instruments
Blending nylon flakes

Adding pigment for dull yarns
Controlling polymerization
Molten nylon formed into ribbon
Spinning nylon into filaments

Courtesy: E. I. du Pont de Nemours & Co., Inc.

Checking the yarn denier	"Twist setting oven"
Sizing nylon yarn	Twisting filaments together
Air conditioned plant	Twisting nylon yarn
Finished nylon yarn	Final inspection of yarn

[259]

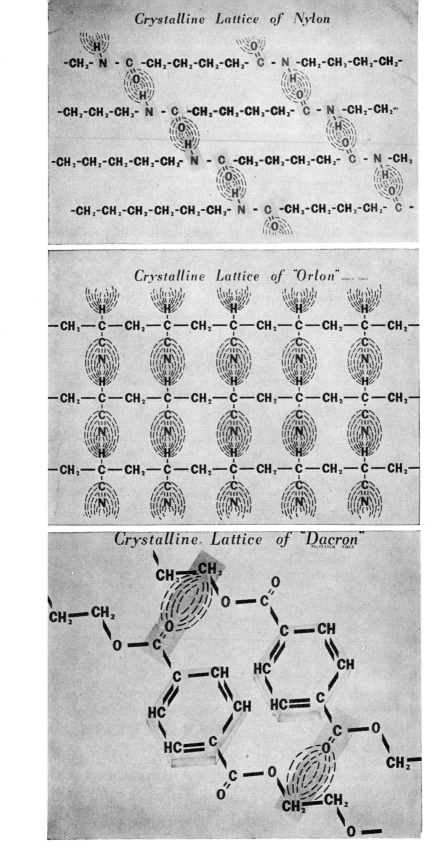

Crystalline Lattice of Nylon

$-CH_2- N - C -CH_2-CH_2-CH_2-CH_2- C - N -CH_2-CH_2-CH_2-CH_2-$

$-CH_2-CH_2-CH_2- N - C -CH_2-CH_2-CH_2-CH_2- C - N -CH_2-CH_2-$

$-CH_2-CH_2-CH_2-CH_2-CH_2- N - C -CH_2-CH_2-CH_2-CH_2- C - N -CH_2$

$-CH_2-CH_2-CH_2-CH_2-CH_2-CH_2- N - C -CH_2-CH_2-CH_2-CH_2- C -$

Crystalline Lattice of "Orlon" ACRYLIC FIBER

$-CH_2-C-CH_2-C-CH_2-C-CH_2-C-CH_2-C-CH_2-$

$-CH_2-C-CH_2-C-CH_2-C-CH_2-C-CH_2-C-CH_2-$

$-CH_2-C-CH_2-C-CH_2-C-CH_2-C-CH_2-C-CH_2-$

Crystalline Lattice of "Dacron" POLYESTER FIBER

Properties

In a burning test, there is no flame; there is a melting and dripping. The odor is like that of celery, and the residue is a very hard black bead; there is a sticking before actual hardening.

Nylon 66 (polyamide) is insoluble in acetone or boiling caustic-soda solution. It is soluble in concentrated formic acid and xylenol. Nylon 6 (polyamide caprolactam) is insoluble in acetone or boiling caustic-soda solution. It is soluble in concentrated formic acid and xylenol, and dissolves slowly in chloral hydrate.

Nylon 66 melts at 482° F., and yellows slightly at 300° F., when held for five hours. Nylon 6 melts at 420° F., and yellows at 300° F., when held for five hours.

Both types have good resistance to bleaches such as hypochlorite and peroxide. Both are generally insoluble in organic solvents. They are the same in specific gravity, 1.14.

In alkalies there is little effect and they are substantially inert.

On long exposure there is loss of strength in sunlight.

Water absorbency is 8 per cent at 95 per cent relative humidity.

Disperse and acid dyes are the best to use on nylon. Chrome and premetalized dyes are also used.

Absorbency and coolness depend primarily on the yarns used in the construction of the fabrics.

Nylon has very high abrasion-resistance, washes easily, dries quickly, needs little ironing, holds the shape well, and does not stretch or shrink. Press at rayon setting to prevent possible fusing.

It takes creases very well and pleats exceptionally well; the pleats may be heat-set in a fabric for durability.

Its wet strength is excellent, and elasticity and flexibility are outstanding.

Uses

One of its greatest uses is in hosiery and socks. Other uses include curtains, draperies, dressgoods of many types, floor coverings, lingerie, sportswear, evening wear, summer suitings, sweaters, slips, upholstery, uniforms, transportation fabric. It is also used in bristle form (Exton) for toothbrushes. Surgical thread, lace, net, tire cord, sailcloth, filter cloth, rainwear, tarpaulins, and bullet-proof vests are some other uses for nylon.

Nylon staple is ideal for blending with other fibers, and it is used in a great many fabrics for the apparel trades.

Courtesy: E. I. du Pont de Nemours & Co., Inc., Wilmington, Delaware.

TESTING

1. Name two of the prominent types of nylon.
2. Who received the first patents granted on nylon?
3. What are the basic raw materials used to make nylon?
4. Name five properties of nylon.
5. Give five uses of nylon.
6. What care should be given nylon stockings? (Daily washing and care to prevent "snagging" caused by rough fingernails.)
7. How might nylon be a "warm fiber"? A "cool fiber"?
8. Name an outstanding property of nylon with regard to long wear in a garment.

"ORLON" ACRYLIC FIBER

"Orlon" acrylic fiber is made from a polymer of acrylonitrile. The solution is then made and extruded, the solvent is eliminated, and the yarn obtained is then stretched. The filament is easily cut into tow and staple forms. It is made only in the staple form at the present. The fiber is manufactured by E. I. du Pont de Nemours & Co., Inc., Wilmington, Delaware.

The term "acrylic" designates an acid—$C_3H_4O_2$—which has a sharp, acrid odor. It is prepared from acrolein or certain of its derivatives or propinoic acid, also known as propenoic acid. This acid is used in organic synthesis and in the manufacture of plastics. "Orlon" is a type of acrylic and is classed as a polyacrylonitrile fiber.

Properties

This non-cellulosic fiber burns with a glowing flame which is easily extinguishable. The residue is a hard, black bead; odor is that of broiled fish. Its sticking point is 455° F., on the copper-block method. While "Orlon" will burn, it does not have a practical melting point. "Orlon" will retain 100 per cent strength after 32 days in air at 257° F.

It is not affected by glacial acetic acid, chloroform, acetone, or 88 per cent formic acid. Its solvent is dimethylformamide.

Specific gravity is 1.14; it has a low regain of 1½ per cent at 65 per cent relative humidity. Very little loss of strength when wet.

It is not harmed by the common solvents, greases, neutral salts, oils, and some acid salts. "Orlon" has good to excellent resistance to mineral acids.

Fair to good resistance to weak alkalies.

Water-absorbency is 2.5 per cent at 95 per cent relative humidity.

The cross-section of the fiber resembles a dog bone.

Dimensional stability is such that garments will retain original size, fit, and shape when drycleaned.

"Orlon" used alone or when blended with other fibers provides a soft, appealing hand, good drape, ease of washing and quick drying, and good covering quality.

Outstanding features of the fiber include crease-retention, wrinkle-resistance, and wash-and-wear properties, bulkiness.

Too hot an iron may glaze or discolor fabrics.

"Orlon" does not come in clear white (chalk).

There may be a build-up of static electricity. Inhibitors on the market may control this property.

"Orlon" is dyed with cationic and disperse dyes. Acid dyes can be used by the cuprous ion method.

NOTE: As "Dacron" polyester fiber, "Orlon" acrylic fiber is a trademark term of the Du Pont Company. Nylon is a generic term such as "cotton," "wool," and "water."

Uses

Ideal for use in outdoor fabrics and garments in cold temperatures. "Orlon" sweaters are very popular. It is much used in dressgoods, suiting, and other apparel items. Its pleating qualities are very good. It is used in workclothes.

The fiber is very good in fabrics where strength and low stretch are vital. Much used in curtains and drapes, since it withstands varying temperatures very well.

In industrial fabrics, "Orlon" is used in aprons and laboratory coats—particularly where there is a chance of contact with acids, corrosive chemicals, and substances that would normally deteriorate cotton garments.

Courtesy: E. I. du Pont de Nemours & Co., Inc., Wilmington, Delaware.

TESTING

1. Describe the burning test for "Orlon" acrylic fiber.
2. State three ways in which "Orlon" resembles nylon.
3. What is a solvent for "Orlon"?
4. List five properties of the fiber when used alone or with other fibers in fabric blends.
5. Why is it possible for "Orlon" to provide bulk without added weight to a fabric?
6. Name five fabrics in which "Orlon" may be used.

SARAN—A VINYL DERIVATIVE FIBER

The Dow Chemical Company, Midland, Michigan, licenses companies to produce the monofilament and the multifilament. In the manufacture of the product, the vinylidene chloride monomer is prepared by chlorinating ethylene. This monomer is mixed with approximately 10–15 per cent vinyl chloride monomer, and polymerized.

This copolymer is in the form of a powder which is melted and then extruded in filament form. The filaments are oriented to give the desirable tensile properties. A staple length can be made somewhere in the neighborhood of 1 to 6 inches.

Properties

It is self-extinguishable. Softens at 240° F. to 280° F. It melts between 340° F and 350° F.

Saran has excellent resistance to acids, and outstanding resistance to alkalies with the exception of ammonium hydroxide.

In bleaches it is safe to use temperatures as low as 120° F.

In organic solvents, it is not affected by alcohols or aromatic hydrocarbons, halogenated hydrocarbons, or ketones. Esters and ethers may be detrimental in varying degrees.

Mildew-resistance is high, and in sunlight there is only slight darkening. Moisture absorption is less than .001 per cent after a 24-hour immersion.

Specific gravity is 1.70 plus/minus 0.05.

In the identification of the fiber, when exposed to a flame it will soften and char only. When combined with flammable fibers, saran acts as a fire-retardant. For example, a yarn spun of 50 per cent saran and 50 per cent flammable fiber will not support a flame. The flameproof properties of saran conform to the standards of the flammable fabrics act. Saran is insoluble in acetone; dissolves in dioxan at elevated temperatures.

In dyeing, saran fibers can be mass-pigmented, colors are built in during the fiber manufacture. Each fiber is colored solidly throughout. This factor contributes to increased color stability and stronger fade-resistance in the finished fabric.

Production

First produced in 1939, saran monofilament has a minimum diameter of four millimeters; multifilament and staple stock have a diameter of less than four millimeters. This stiff, plastic-type yarn comes chiefly in monofilament form, but staple and heavy-denier multifilament yarns are also made. Saran comes in regular and high-shrinkage forms. In longitudinal appearance it is rodlike with a smooth surface and profile; in cross-section it is round or nearly round.

The National Plastic Products Company, Inc., Odenton, Maryland, manufactures the following: "Saran 25 S," a polyvinylidene chloride (saran) which comes in tow and staple; "Saran by National," made in filament, staple, and tow forms; "Saranspun," a yarn made from saran and with not more than 30 per cent of spun-dyed viscose rayon.

The Vectra Company, a division of the above company, manufactures monofilament and yarn, which is sold as "Saran by Vectra."

Rovana, a flat monofilament, is made by the Dow Chemical Company Fibers Department, a division of the parent company located in Williamsburg, Virginia.

Firestone Synthetic Fibers Company, a division of the Firestone Tire & Rubber Company, Inc., located in Hopewell, Virginia, makes the monofilament, Velon. Southern Lus-Trus Corporation, Jacksonville, Florida, manufactures the monofilament, Lus-Trus.

Uses

The multifilament is used for carpet pile, protective clothing, blankets, outerwear, imitation fur, scouring pads, upholstery, and drapery fabrics.

The monofilament is used in automotive upholstery, curtains, heavy-mesh open cloths, screening, auto seat covers, filter cloth, decorative fabric, luggage, outdoor furniture, and car seats.

TESTING

1. What company licenses other companies to manufacture saran?
2. What may be the staple length of saran fibers?
3. Explain the method of coloring saran fibers.
4. In what two forms is saran produced?
5. List five uses for saran yarns.

Part 2—Unit 17

TOPIC: Verel, Vinyon HH, Zefran

VEREL—A MODACRYLIC FIBER

This fiber is produced by Tennessee Eastman Company, a division of Eastman Kodak Company, and sold through its sales representative, Eastman Chemical Products, Inc.

The stabilized or non-shrinkable form of the fiber will show only a small percentage of shrinkage (2–3 per cent) when subjected to boiling water or to hot air (250°–275° F.).

There are two other forms of Verel: Type 1 Verel has moderate shrinking characteristics (10–12 per cent) under the conditions noted above. Yarns made from this type are adapted to pile fabrics, upholstery, backing, etc. Type 2 Verel is the high shrinking member (20–25 per cent) and is applicable for high-bulk needs.

Verel, in its initial condition, is white, thereby not requiring any bleaching.

Properties

This staple fiber, thermoplastic in nature, will not support combustion. Exposure to excessive pressure or to temperatures over 300° F. causes stiffening and discoloration.

There is little or no effect if placed in hydrochloric or nitric acids, phenol, or aqua regia, even at high temperatures.

In alkalies there is a slight effect on the tensile properties from sodium hydroxide and comparable alkalies, even if at high concentrations. There is, however, some discoloration.

For bleaching properties, hydrogen peroxide at 30-per-cent concentration will show no effect. Chlorox at 5-per-cent concentration will show a slight bleaching effect.

Verel is unaffected by the common organic solvents such as used in drycleaning. Soluble in warm acetone. It is not soluble in acetic acid at room temperature or in cyclohexanone.

Highly resistant to mildew and micro-organisms and also to sunlight, it suffers no appreciable loss in strength or coloration.

Specific gravity is 1.37. Moisture regain is 3.5–4 per cent under standard conditions.

An excellent test to use for the qualitative detection of Verel is to place a small amount of scoured fiber in a test tube that contains pyridene. Heat the tube over a steam bath for two or three minutes. If Verel is present, the fiber will turn deep reddish-brown and the solution will become pale pink. Verel is not soluble in this specific test.

Verel has a soft, pleasant, and appealing hand. It possesses good wrinkle-retention as well as shape- and press-retention. It withstands repeated launderings very well.

Dimensional stability is good and there is little tendency to pilling.

[264]

The fiber may be used alone or blended with other major fibers for particular end uses.

The dyes used include neutral, premetalized, disperse (acetate); and in some cases basic or cationic dyes are used.

Uses

In blends it is ideal for woven and knitted fabrics such as dress and sportswear materials, sweaters, men's hosiery, and men's flannel-type suitings. In pile cloths Verel may be used for either the face or the back of the fabric.

When mixed with cotton, it can produce lightweight fabrics on the order of batiste; and with wool, dense materials for industrial use.

In the non-apparel field, it is used in blankets, paint rollers, wash mitts, toys, and polishing fabrics because of its high resistance to chemicals and its non-flammability. Draperies, fire-curtain shields, and work clothing are also made from Verel.

TESTING

1. What company produces Verel?
2. Discuss two types of Verel.
3. What is the resistance of Verel to mildew, micro-organisms, and sunlight?
4. List five properties of the fiber.
5. State three uses for Verel in the apparel field. In the non-apparel field.

VINYON HH—A VINYON FIBER—THERMOPLASTIC COPOLYMER FIBER

This staple fiber is a thermoplastic copolymer of vinyl chloride and vinyl acetate. Of low strength and high sensitivity to heat, its principal function is to act as a binder agent to bring about yarn shrinkage, or in end uses where resistance to chemicals is highly vital. It is successful for heat-sealing purposes, in fiber mats, and is also used in the paper industry. It is not produced in filament form by any American company at present.

In 1937, the original patent, number 2,161,766 for Vinyon, was assigned to Carbide and Chemicals Corporation, New York City. Vinyl resin, which comes in powder form and is soluble in acetone, forms the base. It is now made by Union Carbide Chemicals Corporation, New York City, which makes the well-known fiber, Dynel. The copolymer is dissolved in acetone, well filtered, and then spun, somewhat on the order of acetate filament. It is made in tow form and then cut as desired into staple form. Vinyon HH is produced by American Viscose Corporation.

Properties

The fiber has a circular cross-section, softens at low temperatures, does not support combustion, will not mildew, and bacteria, fungi, and mold will not grow on it. It softens around 135° F., shrinkage temperature is around 150° F.; tacky temperature is 185° F. to 215° F.; and its melting temperature is around 260° F.

It is as strong when wet as when dry and has only 0.1 per cent moisture. It is actually water-repellent but can be surface-wetted by various wetting agents.

Highly resistant to acids and alkalies; it is insoluble in gasoline, mineral oils, alcohols, and glycols. Salt solutions and cuprammonium have no effect on it.

Specific gravity is 1.34 to 1.36; poor conductor of electricity.

Ketones will dissolve it, and it is softened by or partly dissolved by esters, ethers, aromatic hydrocarbons, and some amines and halogenated hydrocarbons. At high temperatures, mineral acids may char and embrittle the fiber.

Most important is its ability to soften, shrink, and bond to other fibers under pressure in the presence of heat and certain solvents. Thus it can be used in the manufacture of rubber-coated elastic fabrics, embossed carpets, pressed felts, bonded fabrics, and heat-sealable paper.

Because of its low strength and high extensibility, the staple is not a good fiber to spin into yarn.

Disperse dyes used with certain swelling agents; solvent methods; pigment dyeing.

Uses

It is used extensively as a bonding agent, and may be blended with other fibers. This is a limited-use fiber.

TESTING

1. What company manufactures Vinyon HH?
2. Define thermoplastic fiber.
3. Why is Vinyon HH classed as a thermoplastic fiber?
4. Discuss the burning test on Vinyon HH.

ZEFRAN—ACRYLIC FIBER, NITRILE ALLOY FIBER BASED ON ACRYLONITRILE

The Dow Chemical Company, Midland, Michigan, manufactures this fiber in (Lee Hall) Williamsburg, Virginia. This nitrile alloy fiber is based on acrylonitrile. A solution of the polymer is extruded and the resulting yarn is then stretched. The initial color of the fiber is white, and it comes in tow and staple forms.

Properties

Zefran melts and burns, leaving a hard black bead. Sticking temperature is 490° F.

It has good to excellent resistance to acids, and its resistance to alkalies is fair; good in weak alkalies.

In bleaching, an excellent white is obtained with sodium chlorite. Peroxide bleaching is not recommended.

Not affected by organic solvents.

It is not attacked by mildew or moths.

Has good resistance to sunlight.

Specific gravity is 1.19, while moisture regain is 2.5 per cent at 70° F. and 65 per cent relative humidity.

In a solvent test for Zefran, the result is like that of other acrylics. Ammonium thiocyanate is used to separate the acrylics, and in this test it is insoluble.

In a staining test it should be noted that it is dyed at room temperature for three minutes with 1.0 per cent (owf) Fastusol Pink BBA. Other fibers are left white or only stained slightly.

Naphthol, sulfur, and vat dyes provide a wide range of colors. After-treated direct colors and neutral pre-metalized colors are also used.

Zefran contributes high bulking properties, has good wrinkle recovery, good press-retention, good dimensional stability, and crease-resistance.

The fiber is non-allergic, and non-irritating.

Uses

In general apparel fabrics, especially in suiting, sportswear, dresswear, and knitwear. It also finds use in rainwear, blankets, coating, fabric, carpeting, pile fabrics, and in industrial fabrics.

1. What company produces Zefran?
2. Define tow; staple stock.
3. What is the initial color of Zefran when produced?
4. What color does Zefran show in an identification test in 1.0% Fastusol Pink BBA?
5. Name five properties of Zefran.
6. List three uses for the fiber.

Part 2—Unit 18

TOPIC: POLYOLEFIN FIBERS—POLYPROPYLENE, POLYURETHANE

This class of textile fibers belongs in the group of "non-cellulosic fibers from synthetic long-chain polymers." The fibers in variously allied categories made from synthetic long-chain polymers are made from coal or petroleum plus the addition of other elements derived from air, salt, water, and similar abundantly available ingredients.

This "long-chain polymer group" includes nylon, consisting of polyamides; modacrylics (Dynel and Verel) consisting of acrylonitrile, to which specific amounts of modifying chemicals are added; acrylic (A-Acrilan, Creslan, "Orlon," Zefran) consisting essentially of acrylonitrile; and polyesters, made up chiefly of esters of a dihydric alcohol terephthalic acid. Also in the group are the olefins (polypropylene, polyethylene), saran, spandex, vinyon and synthetic rubber and some others now under development but not yet on the market.

A polymer is defined as a comparatively large molecule produced by linking together many molecules of a monomeric substance. Monomeric, in this sense, means a single substance. If two or more different monomeric substances are mixed prior to polymerization, the product of the reaction is known as a polymer. Nylon is an example, although the monomer is the reaction product of two different compounds.

The Federal Trade Commission, Washington, D.C., decreed in 1961 that an "olefin" is a manufactured fiber in which the fiber-forming substance is any long-chain polymer composed of at least 85 per cent by weight of ethylene, propylene, or other olefin units. Thus, polyethylene and polypropylene, for example, are polymers designated as polyolefins from which the name "olefin" is taken. Both are related chemically to paraffin; they share with it a resistance to moisture and have a high degree of inertness to chemical reactions.

Olefins are defined as any of a series of hydrocarbons with ethylene having a general chemical formula of C_nH2_n, with the "n" representing "the variable." They are also known as "olefines" and "alkenes." The olefins are actually compounds of carbon and hydrogen which, unlike paraffins, are unsaturated.

The term "unsaturated" means that the substance in question is chemically capable of taking on an element by direct chemical combination without the liberation of other elements or compounds. An unsaturated radical is an organic radical with a double or a triple bond linking two carbon atoms.

The olefins therefore have two carbon atoms connected by a double bond which can be opened or activated so as to link a carbon atom of one molecule to an unsaturated carbon of a second molecule, then to a third, and so on. The carbon chain can be theoretically lengthened without limit. For fiber production, polyolefins have between one thousand and five thousand carbon atoms in the chain.

Polyolefin fibers are manufactured by melt-extrusion, the same as nylon, "Dacron," "Orlon," Kodel, and comparable textile fibers. The filaments thus formed in processing do not have any strength and must be cooled below the melting point and then drawn in order to orient the molecular chains parallel to the filament axis. Strong fibers result from this action.

Properties of polyolefins show that they have a water absorbency of zero, are chemically inert, odorless, resist mildew, and are stable at room temperature. They burn slowly, but the fibers are self-extinguishing by melting, and the addition of a retarding agent, such as a chlorinated wax, will improve flame resistance.

They have high electrical insulation properties. Coloring can be achieved by several methods, either by compounding into the "melt-bath" before extrusion occurs, or by introducing dye-receptive groups into the polymer.

POLYPROPYLENE FIBERS

In 1954, Professor Giulio Natta and his coworkers announced that their pioneer and developmental work had borne fruit with the birth of what is known today as polypropylene. His patents were assigned to Montecatini-Soc. Generale per L'Industria Mineraria e Chimica (Montecatini Chemical and Mining Company), Milan, Italy. The Chemore Corporation, New York City, represents Montecatini in the United States. On November 26, 1963, two patents were awarded the company by the Patent Office, Washington, D.C. Company claims are covered by U.S. Patents Nos. 3,112,300 and 3,112,301 for their product claims on the invention of isostatic polypropylene.

Chemically, propylene is a colorless, unsaturated, gaseous hydrocarbon with a formula of $CH_3CH=CH_2$. The product is a low-cost polymer which has many desirable properties—low density, good strength, good dimensional stability, and excellent resistance to abrasion and chemicals. The gas ingredient is obtained from petroleum, and Professor Natta discovered the stereospecific coordinated anionic polymerization process to make it possible to prepare polymers of high regularity in structure, from both chemical and geometrical standpoints.

This "isotactic" polymer of polypropylene, as it is commonly called, is highly crystalline and has a sufficiently high melting point of 345° F. to justify transformation into a commercial textile fiber.

The name of the Montecatini product in Italy is "Meraklon," which comes in filament and staple forms. It can compete with the regenerated cellulosic fibers—cuprammonium (Bemberg) rayon and viscose rayon, among others. Meraklon fiber is extruded from the isotactic polypropylene polymer, a white powder-like substance in the melt-spinning system. The extruded fibers, still in the molten state, solidify on cooling in the air. The fibers are then passed through a finishing process that includes stretching and various heat treatments.

This spun-dyed fiber is the lightest of existing fibers at present, gives a higher yield in the yardage of fabric on a pound-for-pound basis than any other commercial textile fiber now on the market. Outstanding properties of the fiber include high tensile strength and wrinkle resistance, exceptional resistance to abrasion and wear, as well as to chemicals, insects, and mold. It causes no allergenic phenomena, resists soil, and cleans easily and well. It burns very slowly.

Some Properties of Polypropylene Fiber

Specific gravity	.90–.91	Tenacity, wet-dry	4–7 gpd
Water absorbency	.03%	Extensibility	15%–45%
Melting point	330°–345° F.	Shrinkage	4%–8% at 165° F.
Decomposes at	550° F.		10%–15% at 212° F.

Uses include auto seat covers, transportation fabrics, nonwoven fabrics, pile cloths, carpets, some knitgoods, cordage and ropes, filter cloths, anode bags in electrical plating, etc.

POLYETHYLENE FIBERS

Polyethylene is defined as a plastic polymer of ethylene used in the manufacture of so-called monofilaments, containers, electrical insulation, packaging, film, etc.

These materials are very light, will float on water, dissolve in carbon tetrachloride, toluene, and xylene at 160° F. Moths and mildew have no effect on the fiber. Dyeing is done prior to extrusion of the filaments from the melt-spinning bath. They are non-chlorine retentive, non-nitrogenous, and being a solid substance resist dirt and soil readily. There is no discoloration, and their resistance to sunlight is good when properly stabilized. No rancidity is encountered on aging; hand and tear strength are good, and resistance to abrasion and crease recovery are very good. Storage stability is good, since there is not any wetting-out problem. It burns very slowly.

Some Specific Properties of Polyethylene Monofilaments

Specific gravity	.92–.96	Tenacity in low density, branched type, wet/dry	1.0–3.0 gpd
Water absorbency	.01%		
Melting point	230°–280° F.		
Decomposes at	over 600° F.	Tenacity in high density, linear type, wet/dry	4.5–8.0 gpd
Extensibility, low density, branched type	20%–40% and can go to 100%	Normal tenacity	.5–2.00 gpd
		Shrinkage at 212° F.	40%–60%
Extensibility, high density, linear type	10%–25%		

Uses include braids, cords, ropes, and webbings; upholstery goods, handbag fabrics, filter cloths, and tow target fabrics. It is also used for defense purposes, where there are many uses for this product.

Courtesy: Dr. Victor L. Erlich, Vice-President in charge of Research and Development, Reeves Brothers, Inc., New York City.

TESTING

1. Name two modacrylic fibers. Four acrylic fibers.
2. Define "polymer"; "olefin"; "long-chain polymer."
3. Describe briefly the rise of polypropylene fibers.
4. Give three properties of polypropylene fibers.
5. List three properties of polyethylene fibers.
6. List six uses or products of polyolefin fibers.

POLYURETHANE—FOAM LAMINATE

In discussing polyurethane, it should be borne in mind that, technically, "urethane" is any derivative of carbamic acid, NH_2COOR, a colorless crystalline compound, the ethyl ester of carbamic acid used in the synthesis of organic compounds, those which contain the element "carbon."

In textiles, polyurethane, a foam form, is used for lamination to all types of fabrics. The fabric pores are not blocked and good air permeability is retained after lamination has been completed. The urethane foam size generally used is $3/32$ inch thick, which fuses with an approximate $1/16$-inch finished thickness.

Foam that is $1/16$ inch in thickness weighs about 1.5 ounces a square yard. Much used in quilted combinations, it gives about the same insulation as six ounces of reprocessed wool batting. The $3/32$-inch foam weighs about 2.25 ounces per square yard and provides insulation equivalent to 8–10 ounces of reprocessed wool batting.

Foam Laminate

The term designates in general a combination of multiple layers, at least one of which is a foam, bonded firmly together into one sheet. Many textile-foam laminates consist of one layer of a thin foam sheet which is bonded to one side, usually the backside of a fabric; they are, therefore, called "foambacks."

Polyurethane Foam

Urethane is a chemical group related to urea, which consists of the four basic elements—nitrogen, carbon, oxygen, and hydrogen, and has been known for more than one hundred years. Polyurethane is a class of polymers formed by the reaction of two types of organic chemicals. The basic component, a so-called isocyanate, supplies the nitrogen bonded to carbon and oxygen—which may be a polyalcohol or an organic acid. These polymers originated in the laboratories of Dr. Otto Bayer, Leverkusen, Germany, as early as 1937 and encompass a rather broad line of plastics.

In another type of polymer formation, carbon dioxide gas evolves as a by-product of the reaction. This is a particularly efficient means to create the cellular structure of the polyurethane foam expanded to 30–40 times the initial volume. These polyurethanes have melting points between 490° and 550° F., when they begin to decompose. Thus they are no longer true synthetics.

Manufacture of Polyurethane Laminates: Basically there are three ways of manufacturing these laminates, as follows:

1. HEAT-FUSION PROCESS: In 1954, Curtiss-Wright in this country obtained U.S. Patents Nos. 2,957,793 and 3,057,766 for applications and patents all over the world. The process exposes the foam for an extremely short time to intensive heat well above the melt-point temperature, such as can be obtained by a gas flame. This partly decomposes a thin layer of foam surface to make it tacky, and in this form it is brought immediately in contact with the fabric. The laminate can be rolled up continuously and is ready for use. No additional adhesive is required. By 1962 the rise of the method and its product, in three short years, had become sensational. The usual width of the product is 52 by 54 inches.

2. CEMENTING OR WET PROCESS: Special adhesives, either in the form of a water emulsion or as a solution in organic solvents, are applied either to the fabric or the foam. The equipment is rather conventional. The water or the solvent is evaporated, and the bond may be set by drying or curing at elevated temperatures.

3. FROTHING PROCESS: This consists of foaming the material directly onto the base materials such as films or impervious fabrics. The foam, in this method, is usually

sandwiched between the two backing surfaces. Vinyl foam, which is made by applying a so-called vinyl plastisol paste to one side of a thin vinyl film, then blowing and jelling it by application of heat, has become very popular in the apparel trade for use in artificial-leather jackets, handbags and luggage. These products, however, lack some of the desirable properties of urethane foam laminates.

Curon

A laminate urethane foam for fabrics made from most of the textile fibers, when correctly bonded either by heat fusion or with adequate adhesives, will show good resistance to laundering and drycleaning. It will survive any washing or drycleaning recommended for its fabric partner. Other properties include ease of dirt and soil removal, and no shrinking on the foam part of laminates.

An outstanding urethane multicellular foam on the market today is Curon, a product of Reeves Brothers, Inc., New York City. The lamination process is known as "Curon-izing," but the name is used only when the process involves flame lamination of Curon foam made by the company. The method is licensed to companies which may laminate other makes of foam, but the finished products must meet the standards of Reeves Brothers, Inc.

Curon was introduced into the American market in 1954 by Curtiss-Wright Corporation, based on a West German formula for combining polyester resin and toluene diisocyanate. Originally, it was trademarked "Curifoam," but in 1956 the name was changed to "Curon."

In 1958, urethane foam was successfully laminated to nylon-tricot knit fabric. Since that time the advance of the foam has been meteoric. Reeves was licensed to laminate Curon in January, 1960, and in October of the same year acquired from Curtiss-Wright all their rights and patents to manufacture and laminate Curon.

Curon is made from a special formula wherein various chemicals are combined and baked into "cakes" or blocks usually 60 feet long and 15–25 inches thick, and of varying widths. These in turn are sliced into different degrees of thinness or thickness, ranging from $\frac{1}{16}$ inch to $5\frac{1}{2}$ inches, depending on the intended end use. The $\frac{1}{16}$-inch Curon, which is the most popular for laminating to apparel fabrics, is practically weightless. The $\frac{3}{32}$-inch thickness is much used for extra warmth protection in winter, and 620 Cloud $\frac{1}{4}$ inch is used for infants' and children's wear, where bulk and softness are important.

THE CURON-IZING PROCESS

The bond strength of the process approaches and usually surpasses the strength of Curon itself. Curon resists cleaning fluids, water and washing compounds, and it is not affected by steam ironing. The process causes the Curon to combine well with all types of fabrics and plastic films (vinyl should contain a polymeric-type plasticizer).

The Curon-ized bond remains flexible, does not harden with age, and there is not any "strike-through" on fabrics or on thin sections of the foam; no color is added. The products are odorless and do not support bacteria life which causes odors. The process does not affect resilience of Curon foam; and the end product will not wrinkle permanently or crease because of handling, use, or folded storage.

Two major methods are used for the laminating of urethane foam to fabrics.

Under the Wet System, adhesives or wet cement are used to bond the foam to the fabric, a very simple, mechanical procedure.

Curon-izing is the Dry System whereby the urethane, which is a thermoplastic, is naturally bonded to the fabric through heat and pressure. In this method of laminating by heat fusion, the goods are sent to a Curon-izing plant after having been dyed, finished, and set up into lots for the treatment. Curon itself, after having been cut into desired sizes, is ready for processing. There may be as many as 500 yards on a roll or tube.

After unpacking and preparing the fabrics for steaming, and splitting to provide smoothness and freedom from creases and wrinkles, they are then subjected to rigid inspection for flaws before being rolled onto tubes. Two rolls of Curon in a width corresponding to that of the fabric being used are placed in the laminating machine, and adjustments are made as to the correct width and the various thicknesses and densities of the foam. The two loose ends of the Curon from the rolls are butted together by a special heavy pressure machine which is set in front of the laminating equipment. Thus the Curon is fed in in one continuous flow throughout the process of lamination.

As the foam flows in from the one end, the fabric is fed into the frame from the other end. The Curon passes over a water-cooled cylinder and is exposed for just an instant, in the space of six to eight inches, to a hot butane gas flame which decomposes the outer surface to make it sticky or tacky. Foam and fabric meet at this point and pass together under a nip which exerts the pressure that establishes a permanent bond, with the foam being its own bonding agent. Thereafter, no amount of washing or drycleaning can pull the foam and the fabric apart.

ADVANTAGES OF THE CURON-IZING PROCESS
1. Superior insulation against both dry and moist cold or heat.
2. Extreme light weight, approaching virtual weightlessness.
3. Provides excellent drape; does not bunch, mat, shrink, or stretch.
4. Complete washability and drycleanability. Drip-dries for wash-and-wear.
5. Unaffected by ironing or pressing, perspiration or other mild acids.
6. Complete flexibility at high or low temperatures.
7. Does not support bacteria, fungus growth, or mildew; is non-allergenic and non-toxic; fully odorless and will not retain odors.
8. In addition to being flame-resistant, there is not any deterioration or aging of the laminate or the fabric to which it has been attached.

USES OF LAMINATED FABRICS: These include apparel linings, interlinings, shell laminates, bulky cotton or wool knits, lightweight jerseys, cotton tapestries, poplins, tweeds and comparable fabrics, outdoor garments, dress, and sportswear garments. Quilted effects in many apparel items have become very popular and provide excellent wear and performance.

Courtesy: Dr. Victor L. Erlich, Vice-President in charge of Research and Development, Reeves Brothers, Inc., New York City.

TESTING

1. Define laminate. Laminate foam. Laminated fabric.
2. Name three basic elements used as the basis for polyurethane foam.
3. There are three methods in the manufacture of polyurethane laminates—Heat Fusion, Cementing or Wet Process, and the Frothing Process. Discuss one of these methods.
4. Trace the history of urethane foam to the present time.

5. Define Curon-izing. Explain the Curon-izing process which is achieved by the Dry System of application to fabrics.
6. List five characteristics, properties, or advantages of lamination.
7. List five uses of laminated fabrics.
8. Discuss your reaction to laminated garments you have worn. In your discussion state as to why you like or do not like them, giving specific reasons in your answer.

TOPIC: OTHER MANMADE FIBERS

Other fibers have met with favor by the consumer public, and have some particular use in apparel, decorative, or industrial fabrics. Many of these have acetate or rayon as their base, being modified for a specific use.

ACETATE STAPLE, RAYON STAPLE, HIGH-STRENGTH VISCOSE, STRONG FIBRO, STRONG OR HIGH IMPACT ACETATE: This general group may be used alone or blended, if necessary, with other fibers for some specific end use.

AVISCO RAYON: Viscose-rayon filament or staple; thick and thin, with a latent crimp and crimped staple. Product of the American Viscose Company, a unit of FMC Corporation.

AVRON: This product of American Viscose Company is a rayon staple fiber with improved wet to dry strength ratio, and is non-shrinkable in water. The fiber can be used in spun-rayon fabrics finished without a resin treatment and still be washable. Noted for its high strength.

CASHMILON: A copolymer fiber composed chiefly of polyacrylonitrile which is wet-spun from solution form in an inorganic acid, usually nitric acid. Developed in 1955 by Asahi Chemical Company, Ltd., it took four years to bring the product into commercial production in the plant in Shizuoka, Japan. The filaments are washed in water, hot-stretched, then dried and finished into a staple or tow form. It has positive characteristics in about all respects and may be used alone or cross-woven with any of the major natural or other manmade fibers. It is used in knitted and woven apparel goods as well as in blankets and robes.

CELAPERM: Registered trademark of the Celanese Corporation of America for color-pigmented acetate yarn with "sealed-in color." Fabrics made with Celaperm come in a wide color range and are light-fast, washable, drycleanable, and they also withstand perspiration, gas-fading, crocking, and seawater.

CELATOW: The acetate tow of Celanese Corporation of America. Used for cigarette filter.

CELCOS: Product of the Celanese Corporation of America, this acetate fiber has a 20 per cent degree of surface saponification in order to give it a core of acetate and a surface of viscose rayon. Thus the yarn or fabric has affinity for both acetate and rayon dyes. Properties of Celcos are between those of acetate and rayon. For example, it has less absorbency than viscose but more than acetate; is less thermoplastic and has less static than acetate and a better crush- and shrink-resistance than viscose.

CHROMSPUN: A color-locked acetate fiber or filament obtainable in tow, staple fiber, and filament. Product of Eastman Chemical Products, Inc.

COLORAY: Solution-dyed viscose rayon staple. Product of Courtaulds, North America, Inc.

COLOR-SEALED: Solution-dyed acetate filaments in staple colors. Product of E. I. du Pont de Nemours & Co., Inc.

"CORFAM": A manmade "breathable shoe-upper material for use in high-fashion shoes." Following two hundred man-years of research by Du Pont, this poromeric material is neither plastic nor coated fabric but a complex, interrelated chemical structure that varies in character within its own composition, allowing it to breathe freely and wear well while flexing easily. It is noted for its ease of care, scuff and abrasion resistance, indifference to weather, colorfastness, lightness of weight, and shape retention. It comes in continuous lengths and is supplied in rolls of smooth surface, textured grain, or napped surface, soft to the touch. "Corfam" is made in Old Hickory, Tennessee.

CRYLOR: An acrylic fiber that comes in staple and filament forms manufactured by Société Crylor S.A., France. Shrinkable filaments find much use as an effect fiber in the filling in woven goods. The fiber is soft, has good bulking properties, and is very light in weight. Insulation properties are good as well as abrasion resistance. Has excellent resistance to exposure and sunlight. Fabrics or garments can be washed in cold water; they drip-dry rapidly.

CUPIONI: Machine-made slubbed Bemberg rayon sold under the trademark of American Bemberg Corporation, a division of Beaunit Corporation. Comes in long, thick uniform slub form, in uneven slub dimensions, and in thin slub formation. Simulates douppioni (doupion) silk yarn. Much used in dressgoods.

DICEL: British Celanese, Ltd., United Kingdom produces this continuous-filament acetate product. "Duracol" is the name given the spun-dyed yarn. "Fluorescent High Life Colors" are filament that is spun-dyed, fluorescent shades with very high brightness for use in apparel goods. "Slubs" is the name for the thick-and-thin yarns which find use in dressgoods, including linenlike-finished goods. "KN" is the name for the crimp yarns to provide coverage in goods used for apparel, dressing gowns, scarves, et al.

DRALON: Acrylic filament, staple, and tow manufactured by Farbenfabriken Bayer A.G., West Germany. "Dralon HB" is the name for the high-bulk staple; "Dralon Continu" is the filament product, and "Dralon Neu" signifies the acrylic staple with improved dyeability. One of the great uses of Dralon is in the headgear industry as an effect fiber, and it is ideal for blending with fur fibers used in the hat industry.

ELASTOMERIC FIBERS: All are based on polyurethane, but the pure fibers, because of their brittleness, have to date not been too important in the textile industry. These are used in bristles, screen fabrics, and artificial horsehair. The fibers come in mono- or multifilaments, and are processed as bare fibers or wrapped with other textile yarns such as cotton, nylon, Perlon, etc. They are light and porous and have much greater strength than rubber threads of the same thickness, and are more resistant to light, perspiration, and cosmetics. The present fibers in this category include "Lycra" of Du Pont, Vyrene of United States Rubber Company, I-Filament made in West Germany, Blue-C of Chemstrand Corporation, Spanzelle of Courtaulds, and Glospan of the Globe Elastic Company. Collectively they are known as Spandex Fibers. (*See* Polyurethane Fiber, Spandex, and Urethane Form Specifications.)

ELASTOMERIC YARNS: A continuous filament or spun yarn which, by virtue of the chemical structure of the fiber, is characterized by a high break elongation, a low modulus of extension, and a high degree and rate of recovery from a given elongation. (Definition includes rubber fiber.)
(NOTE: Definition from Section 1, of Sub-Committee B-8 of the American Society for Testing and Materials, March, 1963.)

ESTRON: Acetate tow, staple fiber, and filament of Eastman Chemical Products, Inc.

FIBRO: Viscose staple fiber of Courtaulds, North America, Inc.

FORTISAN: Trademark of the Celanese Corporation of America for a very strong yarn that is made by subjecting suitable cellulose acetate yarn to mechanical treatment to obtain a parallel molecular structure, and then giving it a saponification treatment for a regenerated cellulose yarn (rayon), which chemically is similar to cotton. Uses include parachute fabric, core threads for tinsel conductors, sewing thread, shroud lines, high-strength coated fabrics.

FORTISAN-36: Registered trademark for the highly oriented regenerated cellulose (rayon) made by Celanese Corporation of America. Fortisan-36 differs from Fortisan in that it has a higher strength and is made by an entirely new and different process which produces yarns with a high degree of uniformity, and at the same time is suitable especially for the production of heavy denier sizes required in industrial applications. At present it is made in continuous filament form in 800-denier/800 filament. The product is exceptionally strong, unusually high in resistance to stretching under tension, and has good dimensional stability.

FORTREL: The counterpart of Terylene made by Imperial Chemical Industries, Ltd., London, England, and sold throughout the world under this name, with the exception of the United States, where it is known as Fortrel. This polyester fiber comes in staple and yarn forms. Terylene was discovered in 1941 by J. R. Whinfield and J. T. Dickson in the laboratories of the Calico Printers Association in Lancashire, England.

To enter the American market with Fortrel, Imperial Chemical Industries, Ltd., and Celanese Corporation of America formed Fiber Industries, Inc., a jointly owned enterprise, to sell this polyester textile fiber, comparable with "Dacron" polyester fiber of E. I. du Pont de Nemours & Co., Inc., Wilmington, Delaware. The product comes in filament and staple forms and is used in blends with cotton, wool, and worsted. The plant is in Shelby, North Carolina.

Celanese Corporation, deep in the chemical field in addition to textiles, manufactures acetate and rayon fibers, Fortisan yarns, Arnel, the triacetate fiber, chemicals and plastics. Imperial manufactures dyestuffs, pharmaceuticals, fertilizers, paints, explosives, and non-ferrous metals.

JETSPUN: Solution-dyed viscose filament of American Enka Corporation.

KODEL: A registered Eastman trademark, and a product of the Tennessee Eastman Company, corporate associate of Eastman Chemical Products, Inc., a division of Eastman Kodak Company.

This polyester fiber is different from other fibers in this category both in chemical composition and in the internal molecular structure of the fiber. It is spun to fine counts of yarn on the cotton, woolen, or worsted systems of spinning. Properties show outstanding resistance to pilling, high resistance to heat, high crease retention and wrinkle resistance, excellent dimensional stability even without heat-setting or other special processing. This naturally white fiber has a low specific gravity of 1.22.

Polyester dyes are recommended for dyeing, and all fabrics made with Kodel should have at least 50 per cent of the fiber in them. Kodel launders easily and well, and is suited for wash-and-wear fabrics and garments. Used in many articles of outerwear for men, women, and children.

KOLORBON: A staple rayon fiber, solution-dyed fabric used in upholstery and in other home furnishings. Registered trademark of the American Enka Corporation, New York City.

LIRELLE: Originally called SM-27 and now known as Fiber W-63 and marketed under the name of "Lirelle," this fiber is based on the relaxation of the stresses introduced during the wet processing of the fabrics. The degree of this type of shrinkage is obviously related to the ease of deformation of wet fibers and fabrics. Lirelle is produced as a rayon fiber with a wet stress of 5 per cent elongation of over 2 grams per denier, compared with 0.3 gram for regular rayon and 1.2 grams for cotton.

The product shows very high dry and wet tenacities at low elongation and superior resistance to caustic soda. It has distinct cotton-like properties and is an ideal fiber for blending with cotton. High luster can also be a feature of fabrics in which it is used. Much used in various types of apparel in men's, women's and childrens' wear. Product of Courtaulds North America, Inc., New York City.

MERINOVA: A casein fiber produced by Snia Viscosa Company of Italy, which has replaced the old-time—and the first—casein fiber to be marketed, Lanital. This fiber was made in Italy up to the end of World War II. It is now produced in Belgium.

MYLAR: This product is a polyester film made from polyethylene terephthalate, the polymer formed by the condensation reaction between ethylene glycol and terephthalic acid. It has a combination of physical, electrical, and chemical properties which make it suitable for a series of new industrial uses. Strong, tough, and durable, it has excellent insulating properties. It retains its flexibility at very low temperatures. Mylar retains its physical and electrical properties under a wide range of heat and humidity changes. Possesses excellent resistance to attack by chemicals.

It may be transparent or metalized and comes in extremely thin sections; the maximum width of a sheet or roll is 50–55 inches. Tensile strength is 17,000–25,000 pounds per square inch. Its elongation break ranges from 70–130 per cent.

Mylar is used in electrical and industrial tapes, electrical insulation, fabric backing, packaging, and for decorative purposes. In the textile field, it finds much use with metallic yarns in fabrics such as lamé using Mylar in foil or in metalized structure. Some of the metallic yarns it is used with include Fairtex of Metal Film Company, Inc.; Lamé, produced by Standard Yarn Mills, Inc.; Lurex-MM, made by The Dobeckman Company a Division of The Dow Chemical Company; and with Malora of the Malina Company. This versatile product is manufactured by E. I. du Pont de Nemours & Co., Inc.

PERLON: The trademark of the PERLON-Warenzeichenverband e. V., Frankfurt am Main (PERLON-Trademark Association), registered in all important countries of the world, and related to polyamide threads, fibers, filaments, and bristles manufactured by the following licensed users:

Badische Anilin- & Soda-Fabrik AG., Ludwigshafen-am-Rhein;
Farbenfabriken Bayer Aktiengesellschaft, Leverkusen-Bayerwerk;
Farbwerke Hoechst AG, vormals Meister Lucius & Bruening, Frankfurt/Main-Hoechst;
Phrix-Werke Aktiengesellschaft, Hamburg;
Spinnstoffabrik Zehlendorf Aktiengesellschaft, Berlin-Zehlendorf;
Vereinigte Glanzstoff-Fabriken AG., Wuppertal-Elberfeld.

In 1938, Dr. Paul Schlack realized for the first time the polymerization of caprolactam; the result was the Poly-ε-Amino-Caprolactam which by further processing in the melting and spinning procedures could finally be turned into PERLON. Raw materials for PERLON are carbon, hydrogen, oxygen, and nitrogen. After complicated chemical reactions and when mixed in the exact proportions, these elements will form the snow-white crystalline substance caprolactam. This consists of six carbon atoms, eleven hydrogen atoms, one oxygen atom, and one nitrogen atom.

When exposed to heat, this polyamide becomes liquid, in which form it is forced through close spinning nozzles; the fine filaments leaving the orifices in the spinnerette become solid as soon as exposed to the air. The polyamide filament still possesses high dilatability so that in the subsequent elongation process it is stretched to four times the length it had before. By this process the filament acquires extraordinary resistance to tearing or rupturing. PERLON filament or the staple fiber may have wool-like or cotton-like properties, dependent on the end requirements.

It should be borne in mind that nylon and PERLON are classed as polyamide fibers, that they are similar to each other in chemical properties, and that nylon is a generic term while PERLON is a trademark which belongs to PERLON-Warenzeichenverband e. V., Frankfurt/Main, Germany, and that this word is their exclusive property.

POLYNOSIC: From the French *polynosique,* this is the generic term for regenerated cellulosic fibers of high wet modulus property. The term, first used in 1959, applies to fibers that differ fundamentally in some respects from ordinary viscose rayon staple. The first fiber in this group, Toramomen, invented by the Tachikawa Institute in Japan, appeared in 1942. The fiber was practically unknown outside Japan for seventeen years, until 1959, when some other countries began to take an interest in polynosic fibers. At present there are about fifteen fibers in the group, no two of them identical. For example, air-dry tenacity ranges from 3.2 grams per denier to 5.2 grams per denier; wet extensions vary from 8 per cent to 20 per cent. Improved properties of polynosics are caused by the very fine structure of the fibers—high crystallization, orientation, and lateral order. They are not produced in the same way as viscose rayon. It is now possible to divide these fibers into three groups:

1. *Fibers of high dry-air and wet tensile strengths*—"Super Polyflex," "Junion," and "W63."
2. *The so-called standard types*—"Z54," "Vincel," "Polyflex," "Koplon," "Polyno," "Hipolan," "Polycot," "Tufcel," and "Zantrel." The latter is the trademark name for the polynosic fiber owned by American Enka Corporation, New York City, as well as the term, in the United States, "Polynosic." Zantrel is a modified rayon fiber.
3. *Fibers with high elongation, dry and wet*—"Fiber 40," and "Superfaser."
   Uses of "all-polynosic" fibers include blouses, knit and woven shirtings, and knit outerwear and underwear garments. When mixed with cotton, an ideal combination, end uses include dressgoods, furnishings, and sheetings.

P.V.C. OR POLYVINYL CHLORIDE FIBER: In 1838, Henri Regnault, noted French scientist, developed polyvinyl chloride, which was further developed into polymerized polyvinyl chloride, a source for manmade textile fibers. The trouble with P.V.C. was that it had a very low softening point, from around 70° to 80° C. Nothing of note came from the findings of Regnault until 1913, when German scientists brought out an experimental fiber known as P.V.C., which in 1936 was developed into the Pe Ce fiber made from chlorinated P.V.C., in Germany. These findings gave much food for thought to subsequent research groups. In 1940, French scientists found that P.V.C. would dissolve in a combination of acetone and carbon disulfide, thereby making P.V.C. suitable for manufacture on a commercial basis. Thus, Vinyon was born, and the fiber is made in France under the trademark name of Rhovyl. (*See* RHOVYL.)

RHOVYL: This polyvinyl chloride (PVC) staple fiber is used for blending with other fibers. Its properties include warmth, ease of washing and laundering, permanent pleating after repeated launderings, rapid drying and non-felting or shrinking; it does not need ironing. Rhovyl may be colored by dope-dyeing; by naphthol, acetate, and indigosol dyes. The fiber or filament is not affected by acids, alkalies, or salts, and is non-flammable. Other trade names include Thermovyl, Fibravyl, and Isovyl (yarn and fabric). Product of Société Rhovyl, Tronville-en-Barrois (Meuse), France, and Rhodia, Inc., New York, New York.

ROYALENE: A group of polyethylene and polypropylene fibers produced by the United States Rubber Company. These fibers are "tailored" for a wide variety of uses. There are six types of Royalene, as follows:

High-Tenacity Linear Polyethylene: Known as *Type A,* it has the highest strength, and the greatest heat, abrasion, and chemical resistance of the fibers in the group.

Type C: Polyethylene fiber compounded for shrinkage and for heat and chemical resistance; it is used for unusual effects, such as three-dimensional fabrics.

Type E: This fiber has very high shrinkage in boiling water; therefore it is useful for certain effects either alone or with other fibers.

Type L: This polyethylene fiber possesses an electrical grade for applications requiring conformity to Bell Laboratories' specifications for insulation.

Polypropylene Fiber: This is used for higher heat resistance and for resistance to creeping under sustained loading. This *Type P* fiber lends itself to multifilament applications.

High-Density Copolymer Polyethylene: This *N* fiber has superior resistance to creepage under load, and retains physical properties of the highest-grade linear polyethylene.

Suggested end uses for the fibers include nautical ropes, auto seat covers, filter cloths, decorative screening, shoe webbings, flat ropes, tow targets, handbag fabrics, upholstery, and outdoor furniture webbings. Types C and E compounded for shrinkage are used to make Trilok, the three-dimensional fabric which is used for decorative and special-purpose industrial fabrics, such as air filters.

SUPER CORDURA: The very strong or high-tenacity rayon of E. I. du Pont de Nemours & Co., Inc. Ideal for tire cord fabric and other industrial uses.

TEFLON: Trade name for a tetrafluoroethylene polymer fiber of E. I. du Pont de Nemours & Co., Inc. This is the sixth manmade fiber produced by the company. It has outstanding resistance to high frequencies and high temperatures; possesses the highest degree of chemical inertness of any commercial plastic, and nothing will stick to it. Teflon finds much use in industrial fabrics, primarily for filtration. It has also found considerable use in gaskets, laundry fabrics for pads, press and roll covers, conveyor belts and other beltings, and tapes.

TERGAL: Trade name for the polyethylene terephthalate (polyester) fiber produced by Société Rhodiaceta S.A., France; comes in filament and staple forms.

TETORON POLYESTER FIBER: Polyester fiber manufactured in Japan; in the same classification as "Terlenka," made in Holland, "Terylene" is the British polyester and its counterpart is "Fortrel" made by Fiber Industries, Inc., Shelby, North Carolina. Outside the United States "Fortrel" is known as "Terylene," with Fiber Industries, Inc., being a joint venture of Celanese Corporation of America and Imperial Chemical Industries, Ltd., of Great Britain. "Dacron," "Kodel," "Vycron," and polyesters are manufactured by E. I. du Pont de Nemours & Co., Inc., Eastman Chemical Products, Inc., and Beaunit Corporation, respectively. The fiber is called "Diolen" and "Trevira" in West Germany; "Montecatini," and "Terital" in Italy; "Tergal" in France.

"TORAMOMEN": S. Tachikawa, Japanese scientist, developed a modification of viscose rayon in the early 1950's. He brought about a rayon with high-wet modulus, and the term "Polynosic" was applied to this type of rayon. He gave the name "Tora-momen" to his fiber, which in due time brought about the creation of fibers such as Fiber HM, Vincel, and Zantrel, now a product of American Enka Corporation, New York City.

TYREX: The name for "super-super" or "super-2" high-tenacity rayon tire cord. It is the name given to the yarn; and American Tyrex Corporation, a nonprofit organization with headquarters in New York City, promotes the product. Fiber producers that make up the corporation include American Enka Corporation, American Viscose Division of FMC Corporation, Beaunit Corporation, Courtaulds North America, Inc.; IRC Fibers Division of Midland-Ross Corporation.

ULSTRON: Polypropylene fiber of the olefin group made by Imperial Chemical Industries, Ltd., United Kingdom. It comes in staple, multifilament yarns, and in monofilament form as per an agreement between Imperial and Montecatini Società Generale per l'Industria Mineraria e Chimica, Milan, Italy. It is made by the melt-spinning of the molten polymer, which is then stretched to orientate the fiber molecules.

Uses include filter cloths, laundry bags, ropes, protective clothing, pile cloths, floor coverings, candlewickings, upholstery, et al.

[278]

TESTING

Matching Questions

Place the number of the group of words or terms in the second column on the blank line before the first column of words or terms where there is a definite relation.

1. ____ Chromspun	1. A textured yarn
2. ____ Coloray	2. Beaunit Mills, Inc.
3. ____ Super Cordura	3. American Enka Corporation
4. ____ Royalene	4. High-tenacity rayon tire yarn
5. ____ Cupioni	5. United States Rubber Company
6. ____ Celaperm	6. Product of Eastman Chemical Products, Inc.
7. ____ Fortisan	7. Velon
8. ____ Merinova	8. Trademark for polyamide fiber
9. ____ Perlon	9. Solution-dyed viscose-rayon staple
10. ____ Saran	10. Saponified-treated fiber
	11. Protein fiber made in Belgium
	12. Color-pigmented acetate with "sealed in color"

Part 2—Unit 20

TOPIC: POPULAR BLENDED FABRICS IN USE AT THE PRESENT TIME

In this age of blends and their far-reaching scope in the fabric field, there are many terms that should be understood. These include fiber, filament, tow, staple, yarn, yarn-twist, blend, mixture, combination, sandwich blend. In the matter of coloring fabrics, there are several terms that should be well understood, such as gray goods, dyeing, printing, union fabric, cross-dyeing, union-dyeing, piece-dyeing, stock-dyeing, and yarn- or skein-dyeing.

In considering the texture of a fabric, the number of warp ends and filling picks per inch in the cloth is important. Texture in its secondary meaning should be kept in mind: the surface effect or the face effect of the goods. In addition, terms such as bright yarn, full yarn, semi-dull yarn, and pigmented yarn are of value.

Following a great amount of research, experimentation, time and labor, sample weaving, pilot plant work, sample finishing, and wear-testing, blended fabrics at present are one of the most important segments of the textile industry. Discussed below are some of the representative blends which have found wide acceptance by the consumers.

"DACRON" AND WOOL: Many factors determine the performance of fabrics and garments made from blends of "Dacron" and wool. Among these are yarn count, yarn twist, fabric construction, and finishing techniques. Of great importance is the percentage of this polyester fiber and wool in the particular blend. For example, 50 per cent or more "Dacron" in both warp and filling should be used to derive the benefits of "Dacron." Exceptions to this are the wash-and-wear fabrics, which should have a minimum of 70 per cent or more of "Dacron."

"DACRON" AND RAYON: A properly constructed and finished fabric containing 55 per cent or more "Dacron" blended with rayon yields excellent wash-and-wear performance. Rayon contributes to the reduction of static, while the "Dacron" brings crease retention, wrinkle resistance, and ease-of-care properties to this blend.

[279]

"DACRON" AND COTTON: Fabrics made in this combination have found wide acceptance in such end uses as shirtings, blouses, dresses, rainwear, jackets, pajamas, slacks and suits. Here again, the "Dacron" contributes to the wash-and-wear performance and/or to good crease retention, excellent wrinkle resistance, and long wear with outstanding comfort. Cotton reduces the static propensity of these fibers. Look for high-quality garments which contain 65 per cent or more "Dacron" with cotton to insure complete satisfaction. Always make sure that the percentages of fiber content are on the label when buying garments of "Dacron" polyester fiber and cotton.

NYLON AND RAYON: At least 15 per cent nylon, in both warp and filling, should be used to insure a good minimum performance. The nylon component in this blend is responsible for the good abrasion-resistance of these fabrics. To translate this for the practical man, this means longer wear and greater saving. Pilling protection comes from the proper fabric design and construction, and the correct, careful finishing of the goods.

NYLON AND ACETATE: The best range to use is 60 per cent nylon and 40 per cent acetate. Nylon will definitely add launderability to the acetate in the particular fabric. Women's suiting fabric in this range gives good service.

"ORLON" AND WOOL: The percentage of "Orlon" acrylic fiber used in the fabric depends to a large degree on the desired performance. For example, in woolen spun suitings and coating fabrics, i.e., flannels, coverts, tweeds, and comparable materials, 30–40 per cent "Orlon" is often used, while in the case of wash-and-wear flannel-type slacks, 70 per cent or more "Orlon" is required. For knit fabrics, 80 per cent "Orlon" is necessary to obtain wash-and-wear performance in such garments as sport shirts, blouses, and dresses. "Orlon" is noted for its bulking properties without any added weight, and it produces luxuriously soft garments with good shape-retention.

"ORLON" AND RAYON: Knit fabrics should contain 80 per cent or more of "Orlon" to achieve optimum dimensional stability and aesthetic appeal. In woven fabrics, the percentage of "Orlon" may range from 50–90 per cent, depending on whether you want ease-of-care dresses, blouses, and sport shirts, or hard-finished fabrics for men's washable uniforms.

TESTING

1. Which of the manmade fibers covered in this unit is noted for the following: (a) Abrasion? (b) Bulkiness without added weight? (c) Crease retention and crease resistance?
2. Name two fibers that could be used with "Orlon" acrylic fiber, nylon, or "Dacron" polyester fiber to cut down the effect of possible static electricity in a fabric.
3. Define, relate, and discuss some occurrence you may have had with pilling in a fabric or garment.
4. Would you prefer an all-worsted tropical suiting or one with, say 55 per cent "Dacron" and 45 per cent wool yarn in it? Disregard price and merely consider the garment from the standpoint of performance and comfort.

Part 2—Unit 21

TOPIC: TEXTURED YARNS

Made of continuous filaments, textured yarns are modifications of these filaments in that the filaments do not lie parallel to one another. Fabrics made of these yarns have more cover and are softer than fabrics made from untreated filament yarns.

Stretch yarns are also modified versions of continuous filament yarns and are classified as textured yarns. Some of these, however, do not have stretchability.

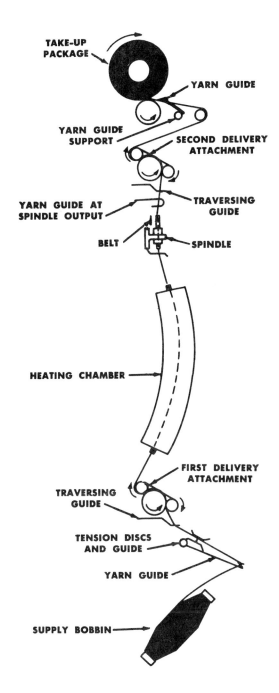

TAKE-UP PACKAGE

YARN GUIDE

YARN GUIDE SUPPORT

SECOND DELIVERY ATTACHMENT

YARN GUIDE AT SPINDLE OUTPUT

TRAVERSING GUIDE

BELT

SPINDLE

HEATING CHAMBER

FIRST DELIVERY ATTACHMENT

TRAVERSING GUIDE

TENSION DISCS AND GUIDE

YARN GUIDE

SUPPLY BOBBIN

Courtesy: Whitin Machine Works,
Whitinsville, Massachusetts

Schematic string-up diagram of Whitin A.R.C.T.,
type FT-1 machine for false twist in textured yarn.

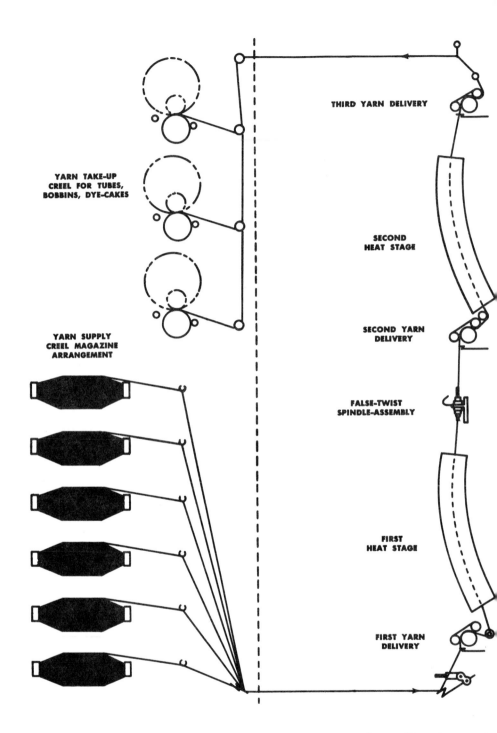

THIRD YARN DELIVERY

YARN TAKE-UP
CREEL FOR TUBES,
BOBBINS, DYE-CAKES

SECOND
HEAT STAGE

SECOND YARN
DELIVERY

YARN SUPPLY
CREEL MAGAZINE
ARRANGEMENT

FALSE-TWIST
SPINDLE-ASSEMBLY

FIRST
HEAT STAGE

FIRST YARN
DELIVERY

Courtesy: Whitin Machine Works,
Whitinsville, Massachusetts

Schematic string-up diagram of Whitin A.R.C.T., type FTF machine. For most stretch-woven fabrics the stretch yarn is produced using the first process stage only with the second heat zone inoperative.

TYPE F.T.3.

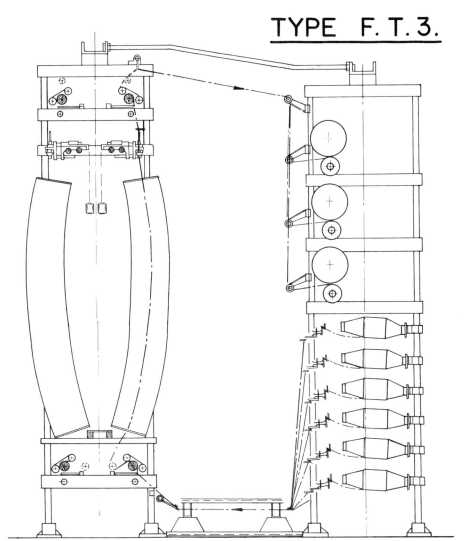

Courtesy: Whitin Machine Works,
Whitinsville, Massachusetts

Advanced stretch yarn machine for production of high modulus yarns at speeds of 250,000 rpm. Equipped with separate yarn supply and take-up creels; magazine tailed for uninterrupted production. Has yarn-cutting device to prevent yarn lap-ups and minimizes operator's patrol duties. Stop motions are at each spindle position, and optional spindle drive arrangement permits simultaneous production of S-twist and Z-twist on each machine. Type FT-3 machine.

High-bulk yarns are spun yarns made by blending high-shrinkage staple fibers with staple fibers of low shrinkage. Strictly speaking, they are not textured yarns, since they are made from staple stock and not from continuous filament. Bulk yarns provide a soft, fluff-like effect or an opaque effect on certain woven and knitted fabrics.

Articles made from the foregoing yarns are form-fitting to the body without pressure. The yarn effects are obtained in a number of ways—twisting, untwisting, false-twisted stretch, and by the use of air jets, heat, dry heat, crimping, curling, straining, and looping. Some of the major yarns in the group follow:

AGILON: The texturing method is done by heat-setting over a blade. There is alteration of strain within the filaments so that when released from tension they have a tendency to curl. The yarn is made on modified standard textile equipment, of a non-torque nylon or "Dacron" filament yarn used alone or in combination with other yarns, chiefly cotton. A product of Deering Milliken Research Corporation, Spartanburg, South Carolina.

BAN-LON: This is a crimped yarn in which unprocessed filaments are textured or crimped and then thermo-set in a stuffer box. The principle of stretch yarn is not involved, and the yarn presents a smooth surface texture. Applied to any of the thermo-plastics, Ban-Lon gives a soft, appealing hand. Joseph Bancroft & Sons Company, Wilmington, Delaware, owns and controls the patents associated with the yarn (Textralized) and the fabrics and garments made from yarn under specific standards (Ban-Lon).

FLUFLON: Of high bulk and high stretchability, the method may be applied to any thermoplastic fiber. The method of manufacture is continuous, taking the raw yarn as received all the way through to produce finished ply yarns for the trade. Licensor of the method is Leesona Corporation, Warwick, Rhode Island.

HELANCA: The first of the commercial stretch yarns to be introduced—in 1947. The yarn is highly twisted, set, and then detwisted in separate operations. It can also be prepared in one continuous operation. Product of Heberlein Patent Corporation, New York City.

SOME EXAMPLES OF TEXTURED YARNS

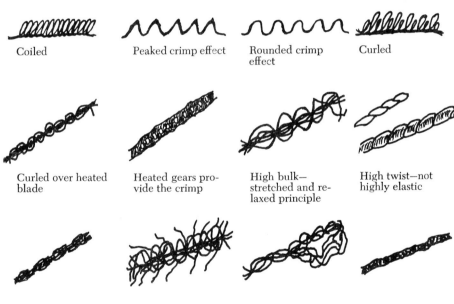

Coiled

Peaked crimp effect

Rounded crimp effect

Curled

Curled over heated blade

Heated gears provide the crimp

High bulk—stretched and relaxed principle

High twist—not highly elastic

Lofted effect from use of air jet

Stretch core—retains good elasticity

Synfoam—twist and untwist method

Stuffing box used for crimp

MYLAST: The crimp is inserted into the yarn, to give a surface effect that may be either smooth or creped. Product of Clarence L. Meyers & Co., Philadelphia, Pennsylvania

SAABA: Obtained by an annealing process on the Universal down-twister, which is equipped with a heating chamber and feed rolls. Involves the removal of stretc from a false-twist stretch yarn. Surface texture may be bouclé, chenille-like, c smooth. Licensor is Leesoma Corporation, Warwick, Rhode Island.

STEVETEX: Announced in August, 1964, by J. P. Stevens & Company, Inc., New Yor City, this textured yarn affords more bulkiness in the yarn than has theretofor been possible and provides improved wearing comfort in knitted and woven good used in lingerie, dressgoods, sportswear, etc. The greater bulkiness is achieved by crimping the individual filaments that make up the individual yarn. The method reduces skin contact, and allows for greater capillary space for air insulation in winter and evaporation in warm weather. Stevetex has more crimps per inch than comparable yarns, and the depth of the crimps can be controlled. Fine merino wool has from 30 to 40 crimps per inch; Stevetex runs to 80 or more crimps per inch.

This product absorbs more dye than non-crimped yarns and provides more clarity and better color depth or intensity. The yarn has a very soft, appealing hand and excellent draping properties.

SUPERLOFT: This highly twisted yarn is made in continuous process in which dry heat is used. False twist spindles reverse the direction of the twist as the yarn is being wound onto a bobbin or cone. Comes in single and ply yarn. Licensor is Leesona Corporation, Warwick, Rhode Island.

SYNFOAM: Owned by Synfoam Yarns, Inc.; the yarn is made on the twist-and-untwist method. Nylon and "Dacron" crepe fabrics are made from the yarn, which also finds much use in upholstery fabrics.

TASLAN: Produced through a bulking process which imparts a particular texture different from standard textile yarns. The hand, loftiness, covering power, yarn texture are such that these properties are permanent and do not require special handling or care. As a full-textured yarn, it is distinctively different when compared with regulation spun yarns or continuous filament yarns. The method can be applied to any thermoplastic fiber. A product of E. I. du Pont de Nemours & Co., Inc.

TYCORA: This trademark of Textured Yarn Company is applied to several processes used in the modification of continuous-filament yarn. Tycora yarns have soft hand, high dye affinity, strength and durability, bulkiness without added weight, and they are non-pilling.

ADVANTAGES OF BULKED AND STRETCH YARNS

These include a soft, appealing hand, retention of air, absorbency conductivity of perspiration, rather dull surface effect, varying amounts of stretchability, low specific gravity, ease of washing and rapid drying, and good resistance to wear and abrasion. Most products which use these yarns come in one size, thus making them economical for both the manufacturer and the consuming public.

Generally speaking, these yarns have about the same uses in the trade, such as for men's, women's, and children's stockings and socks, undershirts, T-shirts, men's shorts, light winter-wear fabrics, blankets, swimsuits, decorative fabrics, leotards, carpeting, foundation fabrics; and for certain industrial fabrics.

TESTING

1. What is the name of the first stretch yarn to be produced?
2. Define stretch yarn; bulked yarn.
3. Differentiate between a coiled yarn and a curled yarn.
4. List three principles used to make these yarns.

TOPIC: GLASS FIBERS; FIBERGLAS TEXTILES

Glass fibers and yarns used in the textile trade are produced from glass, which, when drawn fine enough, can be woven into strong, flexible fabrics. The raw materials used for making ordinary glass are refined and shaped into glass marbles which are remelted and formed into more than a hundred glass filaments, simultaneously attenuated into a single yarn of minute diameter. Glass fibers have been produced as fine as 100s cotton count of yarn in this field of spun glass.

When a glass rod is heated in a flame, it will become soft, pliable, and mal-

[285]

leable, and can be drawn into a long, fine filament. Fibers of glass are not a new discovery. Thousands of years ago nomads on the desert unknowingly pulled the first glass fiber when they poked a stick into the molten sands upon which they built their fires.

During the Renaissance, glassblowers pulled glass into fine strands for raised decoration on glassware. These strands were used experimentally to simulate some of the textile fibers known in those days, and some of the strands were broken into short lengths to be used in a wool-like substance for certain felt products. This practice was the forerunner of the manufacturing of our present-day insulating wool.

IMPORTANT DATES IN THE HISTORY OF FIBERGLAS

1893: The World's Fair in Chicago exhibited the much publicized Glass Dress, one of the first experiments in the fabrication of a glass fabric. People who swarmed into the Libby Glass Building were naturally hoping to find the dress transparent, but they were disappointed. It was, moreover, found to be very stiff and quite unlovely. It did, however, serve to stimulate the imagination of many as to what might be perfected in the future.

1938: In this year the independent research efforts of the Owens-Illinois Glass Company at Alton, Illinois, and the Corning Glass Works at Corning, New York, had reached a stage of sufficient success to warrant the establishment of the Owens Corning Fiberglas Corporation located in Toledo, Ohio, with a factory and laboratory in Newark, Ohio.

The parent companies turned over to the new company their knowledge of commercially producing fibers of glass and the possible uses for the new basic material.

Fiberglas textile yarns had been perfected to a point where they were extremely pliable, could be knotted, and were quite acceptable for normal textile processing such as wrapping, braiding, knitting, and weaving.

It was in this year that the production of Fiberglas yarns began and a program of commercial application was initiated.

1949: The Textile Products Division of the Owens-Corning Fiberglas Corporation was formed. Headquarters were established in New York City, with yarn-producing plants in Huntingdon, Pennsylvania, and Ashton, Rhode Island. A Development and Textile Process Laboratory is also located in Ashton.

Both yarn-producing plants continued to be supplied with their principal raw material—the glass marble—as made in the company factory in Newark, Ohio.

The new division was formed to handle exclusively the production, the development, and the sales of the entire range of the corporation textile products as differentiated from other, non-textile, products such as thermal insulating wool mats, air filters, etc., also made from fibrous glass.

Such specialization was highly warranted in view of the increasing and diversified acceptance of Fiberglas textile products during World War II and the post-war period.

FIBERGLAS PRODUCTION PROCESSES—THE MARBLE, CONTINUOUS FILAMENT-TYPE YARN, STAPLE-TYPE YARN

The Marble

Both the continuous filament and the staple types of yarn employ a ¾-inch diameter solid glass marble as the beginning point in their process of production. The formation of these marbles is a prior operation where non-organic substances such as silica (sands) are combined with other inert chemicals such as sodium, potassium, borate, etc., in the granular form and in very accurate and delicate proportions.

1. The batch plant where the basic ingredients are mixed.

2. Marble inspection.

3. The single strand forming operation—continuous filament. The bushing is above while the forming tube is below.

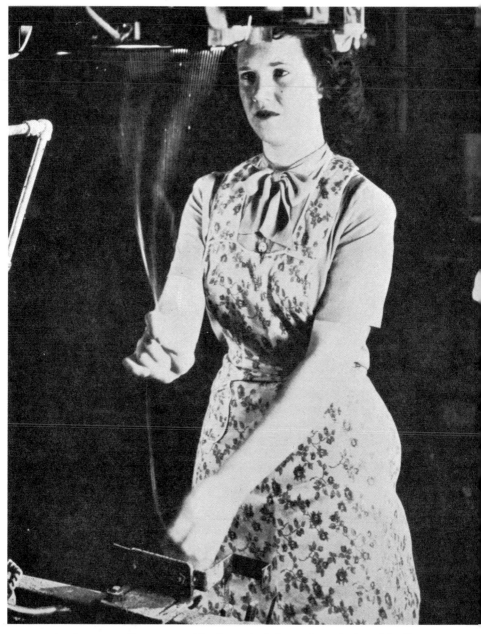

4. Continuous filament strand bushing which shows the gathering of the filaments.

5. Close-up view of the take-up.

These are all melted together in a "batch tank" and the resultant molten glass i drawn off and chopped into marbles which are rounded when soft. In effect, eacl marble becomes a measured quantity of glass of a type most workable into filament later on and best adapted to the ultimate use that these filaments will experience.

The marbles are supplied to the various yarn-producing plants to undergo remeltin; there as the first step in the extrusion process. Each marble can account for approxi mately ninety miles of continuous filament when melted.

Continuous Filament-Type Yarns

A two-floor, vertical operation is necessary in order to draw the filaments from th molten glass provided for by the remelted marbles. On the second floor a continuou procession of marbles is fed by gravity into a small boxlike tank (a "bushing"), wher they are melted at high temperature.

The bottom of the bushing contains small holes (either 102 or 204) from which th molten glass flows downward. Each hole emits a single filament of glass which, as it i drawn away at a speed of better than 100 m.p.h., becomes much smaller in diamete than the orifice from which it flows.

The consistency of the molten glass, the size of the orifice, and rate of drawin; speeds constitute the variables which permit regulation of the ultimate filament desirec

The molten glass filaments solidify at less than a foot away from the bottom of th "bushing," and the 102 or 204 filaments are gathered together in a "strand" at a poin shortly beyond, where it runs over a felt wick which deposits a size or lubricant o the untwisted strand.

The strand is then guided through a floor opening, located directly under the "bush ing," where it is directed to a high-speed take-up or "forming" tube. Once filled, th tube is then removed and transported to conventional type twisting-plying frames.

Fiberglas strands or filaments can be twisted, plied, tubed or coned in the sam manner as silk or rayon. The Owens-Corning Fiberglas Corporation sells the yarn plie and packaged to specification and ready for the individual use of the customer.

The yarn is supplied to weavers on approximately two-pound rayon-type cone: Packages are made up to the individual needs required in the braiding industry an other customers' wants.

Fiberglas Continuous Filament Nomenclature

Since a yard of X-diameter Fiberglas weighs about twice as much as a comparabl diameter rayon yarn, on a yard basis, it is therefore necessary to use a different count tha the denier method used in rayon, acetate rayon, and similar filaments.

The finest Fiberglas filament in theoretical diameter will run to a little less than one-third denier (approximately 13-million yards to the pound). A single filament : about 15 times finer in diameter when compared with a single hair strand on the hea of a human being.

The finest continuous filament strand (single) approximates a 30-denier, and commercial fabric which uses this strand in both directions is being made with a thicl ness of about 0.0015-inches. Most of the commercial fabrics, however, are composed c 60-, 120- and 230-denier (diameter) plied yarns.

"Fiberglas filament" is the individual solid glass fiber which comes from one of th holes at the "bushing."

"Basic strand" is composed of the 102 or 204 filaments drawn together from th same bushing, running in parallel direction and not twisted with one another. At later operation each strand may receive a certain twist.

"Plied fiberglas yarn" consists of a number of basic strands.

A typical plied fiberglas yarn may be described as ECD 450-2/2. This gives a dire approximation as to the number of yards contained in a pound of that particular plie yarn.

Multiply the prefix number 450 by 100 and then divide by the number of individu strands (2/2), which is 4. This will give a final result of 11,200 yards of the yarn t the pound.

Prefix letters (example is ECD 450-2/2) are used to help describe the character of the filament used in the particular plied yarn involved.

The first letter (either E or C will be used) designates the type of glass used to make up the marble itself. "E" represents a type of glass especially formulated to give optimum characteristics for high temperature and electrical applications of the yarns made from this type marble. Yarns from the "C" type glass are not made in the continuous filament form and are used only in limited quantity in staple type yarn.

The second letter (either C or S will be used) indicates the character of the filament Continuous Filament or Staple Filament.

The third letter (either D, E or G will be used) indicates relative diameters of the individual filament (or staple fiber) employed. Letters have arbitrarily been assigned to represent various fraction-of-inch diameter measurements (D- .00023" ave.; E- .0028" ave.; G- .00038" ave.).

The prefix numbers 90, 350, 225, and 150 are used to represent approximately the number of 100-yard lengths per pound of the single untwisted strand involved.

Table of Most Commonly Used Fiberglas Continuous Filament Yarns

150–1/0	225–1/0	450–1/0	900–1/2
150–1/2	225–2/0	450–2/0	900–1/0
150–1/3	225–3/0	450–3/0	
150–2/2	225–1/2	450–4/0	
150–3/2	225–1/3	450–1/2	
150–3/3	225–2/2	450–1/3	
150–3/4	225–3/2	450–2/2	
	225–3/3	450–3/2	
	225–4/3	450–3/3	
		450–3/5	
		450–4/3	
		450–4/5	

Staple Fiber Yarn

The consumption of this type of yarn is relatively small, but it is ideally suited for fabric uses where texture bulk is a factor, combined with the other advantages of fiberglas. Examples include use in chemical filtration fabrics, electrical cable filler, electrical plastic laminates, etc.

The production operation consists of blowing fibers directly onto a revolving drum similar to a card delivery roll, where the web is taken off in sliver form. Because the fibers in the web itself are in a jack-straw pattern, the sliver also has a tendency toward this pattern rather than the exact parallel usually found in ordinary card sliver.

From this point on it is twisted and plied in the ordinary or conventional manner. There is no necessity for carding, drafting, or spinning.

Staple Fiber Facts

Individual fibers run to about ⅔ of a denier (in diameter) and to about 1-plus denier on the yards per pound basis.

Fiber length is not uniform and runs anywhere from about four inches to about thirteen inches in length.

No crimp exists in the individual fibers.

In general, the fiber diameter range in staple yarn products is slightly larger than those employed in the continuous filament yarn products.

By a modified method, fibers of a much smaller diameter (⅕ denier) can be made, and these resulting yarns are now in the research and development stages.

The staple yarns are designated, for example, as ESE 70/2, which means that the yardage per pound is (70 x 100 divided by 2) 3,500 yards of yarn to the pound. This size, equivalent to an approximate ⅙s (single 6s) cotton yarn in diameter, is the finest commercial staple weaving yarn.

For weaving purposes most of the fine-diameter staple yarns are reinforced by strand of continuous filament yarn.

The staple yarns can be furnished by employing either one of two basic types of fibers:

a) Those drawn from superior chemical-resistant glass.
b) Those drawn from glass formulated to give superior electrical insulation prop erties. Selection of the type desired is made by the customer.

Coronizing, Coronized Finish

This development of the company is an outstanding advance in the dyeing and finishing of Fiberglas fabrics. Marquisette greige goods, for example, a padded with a formula which combines metallic oxide dyestuffs with a hig temperature curing weave-set. The material is then Coronized, which is essential an exposure to approximately 1200° F. heat for a few seconds.

This temperature-time cycle serves not only to permanently glaze or fuse th coloring and the weave-set to the fabric but also to greatly alter and impro the hand or drapability of the greige goods. In effect, the heat sets the crimp the yarn, thereby giving the fabric a pliability heretofore unknown. It is th feature which accounts for the non-wrinkling characteristic of the Fiberglas fabri so processed and eliminates the need for ironing.

Hess, Goldsmith & Company, a unit of Burlington Industries, Inc., develope a new process in the finishing of glass-fiber fabrics whereby multiple colors an unusual textures and motifs are possible. Under the trademark of Dy-Cor, th process is an important one, since it made possible an important breakthrough f decorative glass-fiber fabrics.

Uses for glass-fiber fabrics include curtains, draperies, ironing-board cover non-burning Christmas decorations, coated glass auto-top fabric and awning mate rial, wire and cable electrical insulation fabrics and tapes. Glass-fiber reinforce plastic items include plastic fishing rods, aircraft parts, commercial bread tray etc.

OTHER GLASS FIBER COMPANIES

The Carborundum Company, Niagara Falls, New York. Fiberfrax products (alum num-silicate ceramic fiber).

Ferro Corporation, Fiber Glass Division, Huntington Beach, California, and Nas ville, Tennessee. Trade names of Unifab, Uniformat, Unirove.

L. O. F. Glass Fibers Company, Waterville, Ohio; Parkersburg, West Virgin Laurens, South Carolina. Products known as Garon and Vitron. Now a unit of John Manville Corporation.

Modiglass Fibers, Inc., Bremen, Ohio. Trade name is Modiglass.

Pittsburgh Plate Glass Company, Fiber Glass Division, Shelbyville, Indiana, a Shelby, North Carolina. Trade names of Pittsburgh and PPG.

Courtesy: Owens-Corning-Fiberglas Corp., Textile Division. Plants are located in Asht R. I.; Anderson, S. C.; and Huntingdon, Pa. New York City address: 717 Fifth Avenue.

TESTING

1. What is the molded shape of the solid glass just before melting it into filament for
2. List five Fiberglas products; five uses of Fiberglas yarn or fabric.
3. What company makes Fiberglas products? Give the location of its plants.
4. How many yards in one pound of a Number 450-2/2 Fiberglas yarn?
5. How many individual filaments are used to make up the yarn base strand?

. Discuss the manufacture of Fiberglas continuous filament yarn.
. What is the meaning of the symbol ESE 70/2 used to designate a particular Fiber-
glas yarn?
. About how many miles of single filament may be obtained from a single glass
marble?
. Discuss Coronizing of Fiberglas fabrics.

TOPIC: ASBESTOS MINERAL FIBER

This very important mineral fiber is found in veins of solid rock formation of
the earth's crust. Asbestos is found chiefly in the Province of Quebec, where the
largest deposits are located; in Russia, where the next greatest veins are found;
and in New York, Vermont, Arizona, South Africa, and the Savoy district in Italy.
Thetford, Quebec, is the asbestos capital of the world.

CHRYSOTILE is the best grade, a fibrous, silky, white hydrous silicate; it is known as
"white asbestos." CROCIDOLITE is blue to green in color cast. The third grade is
called AMOSITE.

Asbestos will not burn, is a poor conductor of heat and electricity, and can be
used where no other material will serve. It provides greater safety and longer-lived
and better products in countless fields of industry. Outstanding properties are its
ability to withstand very high temperatures with little or no alteration, its non-
combustibility and excellent insulation.

CARDED FIBERS OF ASBESTOS: The raw asbestos fiber stock is received in the plant in a
semi-opened condition, where it is then opened, cleaned, and blended with varying
percentages of cotton, rayon, or both fibers, depending on its textile end uses. The
blend is then carded, processed into roving form from the sliver condition, and
then spun into yarn. The carded fiber itself is used for chemical filtration purposes,
thermal or heat packing, and for heat-resistant filters. The fibers are also much used
in electrical insulation purposes, padding, stuffing, or wipers where thermal en-
durance is vital.

ASBESTOS CLOTH: This comes in a wide variety of style, texture, grade, weight, and
thickness. The standard fabric width is forty inches, but any width can be made
to serve some particular purpose. Asbestos is woven in plain, twill, or herringbone
effects, and in either metallic or non-metallic construction yarns. Fabric weight
is from a few ounces to several pounds per square yard. The thickness varies from
0.015 inches to 0.100 inches for the single-ply fabric.

Uses include conveyor belting, draperies, automobile, airplane, and locomotive
equipment; passenger, sleeping, express, mail, and freight-car equipment; electrical
insulation for toasters, broilers, coffee makers, sweepers, fans, refrigerators, washing machines, et al. It is also used for friction materials, fire blankets, fireproof
curtains for theaters, ironing-board covers, jackets for pipe insulation, laminated
plastics, packings, safety clothing, welding, etc.

ASBESTOS CORD: This is multi-ply yarn of uniform diameter and superior tensile strength.
It is used extensively as sewing thread, mantle yarn, tying cord, core for wire-
wound electrical elements, gaskets, packing, and as a braided wall in the manufacture of steam hose.

ASBESTOS LACE: The name for lace which has been treated chemically to make it non-
flammable.

ASBESTOS PAPER: Fireproof paper made by adding the mineral amianthus to the wood
pulp. A very poor conductor of heat, it is used to cover steam pipes.

ASBESTOS ROOFING: Roof material combining the chrysotile types of asbestos and cotton
or some other type of organic fiber.

[295]

ASBESTOS ROVING: A composition of chrysotile asbestos and cotton or other organic fiber. Reinforced roving is composed of a core of yarn consisting of organic fiber covered with a mixture of chrysotile asbestos and organic fiber.

ASBESTOS TAPE: Also called "listing," it comes in plain or non-metallic type and in the asbestos-metallic product which is the wire-inserted variety. Plain type ranges from 0.010 inch to 0.030 inch in thickness. Its greatest use is in electrical insulating for motor windings. Its low heat conductivity, thermal resistance, and its property of absorbing a high percentage of heat are important assets.

Heavier plain tapes find use in thermal insulation, flameproofing of sheathed cables, and as a component part of gaskets and packings.

Asbestos metallic tape is used when service conditions require a high tensile strength or a high coefficient of friction. Where excessively high temperatures are encountered, woven tape is reinforced with special alloy wire. Much of this finds use in fabrication of woven brake lining and clutch facing. Oil-burner wicking and conveyor belting are two types of this tape.

ASBESTOS TUBING: It is woven or braided, and is used chiefly as a flexible sleeve lining for insulating electrical conductors, and as a jacket for high-temperature packing. Woven asbestos tubing is used as flexible heat ducts and as the filtration medium in dust collectors.

ASBESTOS YARN: This is used as a basic component in the manufacture of cord, tape, tubing, and fabric for innumerable applications. Asbestos yarn, which is made by spinning the roving, is used chiefly in braiding and weaving where thermal resistance, electrical insulating properties, fire protection, and durability are necessary engineering requirements of the textile product.

Generally speaking, there are comparatively few asbestos companies today. Johns-Manville Products Corporation (Manville, New Jersey) has plants in several locations, and is the world's largest producer and processor of asbestos. The Asbestos Textile Institute has its headquarters in the Philadelphia College of Textiles & Science, Philadelphia, Pennsylvania.

TESTING

1. Name five world sources for asbestos.
2. Define chrysotile; crocidolite; amosite.
3. Describe carded fibers of asbestos for their use in various products.
4. Give five uses for asbestos fabric.
5. Define asbestos cord; asbestos roving.
6. List four uses of asbestos yarn.

Part 2—Unit 2

TOPIC: RUBBER THREADS AND ELASTIC YARNS; METALLIC YARNS

RUBBER THREADS AND ELASTIC YARNS

There are two types of rubber thread—rubber itself, and Spandex. Rubber is defined as a manufactured fiber in which the fiber-forming substance is comprised of natural or synthetic rubber. Spandex is a manufactured fiber in which the fiber-forming substance is a long-chain synthetic polymer comprised of at least 85 per cent of a segmented polyurethane.

A polymer is a comparatively large molecule produced by linking together many molecules of a monomeric substance. Such a reaction is called polymeriation. If two or more monomeric substances are mixed prior to polymerization, the product of the reaction is known as a copolymer. Nylon is an example of a copolymer.

Elastomer is a synthetic-rubber product which has the physical properties of natural rubber such as high stretchability and recovery. According to the American Society for Testing Materials, an elastomer should be capable of being stretched repeatedly to at least three times its original length, and on release of the stress to return with force to its approximate original length. An elastomer should not be confused with a stretch yarn which obtains its elasticity from some modification of a filament yarn structure.

Rubber thread may be of the extruded type such as Lactron made by the United States Rubber Company, or cut from a sheet such as Darleen made by Darlington Fabrics Corporation, New York City.

The first "miracle yarn," Lastex, was produced in 1930 by the United States Rubber Company. Elastic yarns include cut-rubber yarn, which was the original core yarn cut to size from a rubber-sheet form.

The high position that rubber thread and elastic yarn have in industry is the result of many factors, such as research, development, competition, functional uses, time and labor expended, the economic importance of the products to the consuming public, sound promotion, and advertising.

Types of Rubber Threads and Elastic Yarns

UNITED STATES RUBBER COMPANY PRODUCTS

LACTRON: An extruded thread which is the original latex thread. It is much used for braids and elastic webbings, is heat-resistant and non-discoloring.

LASTEX: This is an elastic yarn whose base is latex, the raw material from which rubber is made. The yarn is made by wrapping a filament of fine rubber thread with cotton, nylon, silk, etc. It comes in complete ranges of size, modulus, and covering for weaving, knitting, and shirring all types of elastic fabrics. Its application by stitching imparts stretch or creates novel elastic fabrics for foundation garments, hosiery, swimwear, and many other products.

LATON: An elastic yarn uniquely covered to produce extra-light, extra-soft, extra-fine knitted and woven elastic fabrics. This soft-tension yarn is used chiefly for slips, swimsuits, underwear, and other light-weight elastic fabrics.

REVERE: For generations this cut-rubber thread has been used for all kinds of narrow elastics; and it is heat-resistant and non-discoloring. Revere rubber tension tape is a cut-rubber tape that comes in various sizes, for waistbands, legbands, hems, and all types of elastic edges.

CONTRO OR ROLLED LATEX: This product of Firestone Tire & Rubber Company, Inc., is first formed as a flat strip and then rolled on itself much in the same manner as one would roll paper into a tube form. Stretching straightens the molecules and adds strength. A fine core thread results, which is covered with nylon for use in foundation fabrics, swimsuits, hosiery, cushions.

DARLEEN: A cut-rubber yarn in which the original core is cut into proper size from a rubber sheet form. A silk or nylon hosiery yarn will have about 15,000 yards to the pound. This product of Darlington Fabrics Corporation, New York City, is an outstanding cut-rubber yarn which is especially good for foundation fabrics.

FILATEX: A grooved wheel collects the latex from the bath used. Solidification follows, and the core is then drawn off. The product is classed as a flat-oval type. This product of Filatex Corporation, Waxhaw, North Carolina, runs to about 14,000 yards per pound. Its greatest use is for stocking tops.

VYRENE: Classed as a Spandex fiber, it is the trademark of the United States Rubber Company for its synthetic elastomer to supplement and extend the range of its Lastex yarn. It is a super-fine elastic yarn ideal for use in sheer elastic fabrics. Vyrene has toughness, high tensile strength, and good resistance to chafing; it is resistant to light, ozone, and solvents, even in very fine sizes. Other properties include a good modulus of retention, very rapid stretch return, and the ability to withstand standard scouring, finishing, and dyeing procedures, and wash-and-wear tests.

Vyrene is a complete yarn in itself, with a fine elastic core or elastic monofilament covered with nylon or some other manufactured fiber. Compared with Lastex, which is much used in constructions with core sizes about $\frac{1}{100}$ inch in diameter, Vyrene is made with the elastic element $\frac{1}{150}$ inch in size. In woven or knitted fabrics, its extra fineness creates soft and sheer fabrics not heretofore obtainable. Uses include swimwear, golf jackets, sportswear, and foundation items of all types.

LYCRA: A Spandex fiber of the elastomer type and a product of E. I. du Pont de Nemours & Co., Inc. It is the original Spandex fiber.

NEOPRENE: A trademark name for a type of synthetic rubber produced by E. I. du Pont de Nemours & Co., Inc. It is like crude rubber in appearance and properties. Neoprene is sold to rubber concerns who mix it with other ingredients, process it, and vulcanize it for use in a great many products. It is wrapped with nylon for use in elastic yarns.

TESTING

1. Define rubber thread; Spandex; polymer; elastomer; extrusion.
2. What is the name of "the first miracle fiber"?
3. Differentiate between a rubber thread and an elastic yarn.
4. Name a base for rubber threads.
5. Why are Vyrene and Lycra classed as Spandex fibers?
6. Discuss Neoprene and its uses.
7. Name two rubber threads; two elastic yarns.
8. List five uses for fabrics or garments in which rubber threads or elastic yarns have been employed.

METALLIC YARNS

Metallic yarns have had considerable rise in recent years, and they are now made with an acetate film or a mylar ("Dacron") film to enhance the finished yarn. Use of these yarns is now widespread in many fields of the textile and apparel industries.

Some leading manufacturers of metallic yarns include:

Metal Film Co., Inc., New York City: the Chromeflex products.
Fairtex Corp., Charlotte, North Carolina: the Fairtex products.
Standard Yarn Mills, Inc., Glendale, Long Island, New York: the Lamé products.
The Dobeckmun Co., a Division of Dow Chemical Co., Lurex Yarn Division: the Lurex products.
Malina Co., New York City: the Malora products.
Metlon Corp., Subsidiary of Acme Backing Corp., New York City: the Metlon products.
E. I. du Pont de Nemours & Co., Inc., Wilmington, Delaware. Their product, Mylar, polyester film, is much used in conjunction with the above metallic yarns such as Lamé with Mylar (metalized), Metlon with Mylar, Fairtex with Mylar, etc.

Some Major Metallic Yarns and Fabrics

METALLIC YARNS OR THREADS: These are lustrous yarns or threads of metal strands, and they have been popular since the Middle Ages. These strands have brilliancy, particularly when placed on a plain background material. They are used in brocade, brocatelle, damask, and other decorative fabrics, and in evening apparel. They have also found favor in daytime wear in the women's wear field.

Woven screening of many types for doors and windows, Pullman screening, fencing, chicken wire, ranch fencing and garden wire are also made with metallic threads or yarns.

METALLIC CLOTH: Any fabric, usually silk, that has gold, silver, tinsel, or other metal threads interspersed throughout the motif in a fabric, hanging, cloth, or tapestry. Lamé is a metallic fabric. Cloths of this type usually have a cross-rib or repp effect, are rather stiff, harsh, stately, formal, prone to tarnish, and quite durable. Ideal for evening wear, these fabrics come in many varying grades and qualities.

METLON: This is a non-tarnishing metallic yarn made by laminating an extremely bright aluminum foil between two plies of specially formulated plastic film. Registered trademark of Metlon Corporation, New York City.

METALLIC YARNS MADE WITH ACETATE AND MYLAR COMPARED: Acetate and Mylar film (Dacron) are used in the manufacture of the present-day yarns. Mylar base yarn will withstand higher temperatures and more rugged fabric-finishing and laundering than the acetate type.

Some metallic yarn is made of thin aluminum foil sandwiched between layers of film; another type uses metalized aluminum (vaporized in vacuum) sprayed on the binder between the layers of film.

Mylar film is stronger and thinner and will give a larger yield than the acetate-film yarn. Its cost per thousand yards is not much higher when compared with the acetate type. There is, however, at present a rather substantial price difference between the two on the pound basis, acetate being the less expensive. Width of the film and its thickness vary as does the price per pound.

A large variety of colors and combinations of two or more colors are available. These narrow ribbons of glittering metallic yarns are finding increasing use in many types of apparel and household furnishings, and in some industrial fabrics.

TESTING

1. Define lamination.
2. What two products can be used to make metallic yarns of the laminated type?
3. List four properties of Mylar film.
4. Name three manufacturers of metallic yarns or threads.
5. Name five fabrics in which metallic threads may be used.

Part 2—Unit 25

TOPIC: PLASTICS

A plastic is defined as a material which is capable of being molded or modeled, according to its softness and pliability, into some particular shape. There are two types of plastic used in textiles:

1. **THERMOSETTING PLASTICS:** These have been set permanently into some shape or form by the use of heat. Heat applied later on may produce a charred formation without causing the object or item to lose its shape.
2. **THERMOPLASTIC PLASTICS:** These will soften when exposed to certain heats and will harden again when the source of the heat has been removed.

Generally speaking, there are five major steps in use today to process plastics from the raw material to the finished article. These are molding, casting, extruding, calendering, and laminating.

[299]

Processing from Raw Material to Finished Product

MOLDING: A base powder (thermosetting or thermoplastic) is poured into steel molds heat or pressure is applied, or both may be used in the treatment.

CASTING: This involves the pouring of liquid plastic into a mold or onto a belt or whee where it is allowed to harden without the use of pressure.

EXTRUDING: Heat-softened plastic is forced through a spinnerette or opening cut to th cross section of the product; a continued or extended formation is produced.

CALENDERING: Heavy rollers are used to form thin sheets or film and to apply the plasti to fabric or to paper.

LAMINATING: Layers of cloth, metal, paper, plastic or plywood are held together b plastic adhesives. Laminated plastic comes in plain or cut-to-shape form.

THERMOSETTING PLASTICS INCLUDE:

CASEIN TYPE: This can take a very high polish and comes in a wide range of opaqu and translucent colors and shades. Properties include great strength, non-flamma bility, ability to withstand drycleaning, and resistance to chemicals and solvents Examples include Ameroid and Galorn.

CAST PHENOLIC TYPE: This is available in opaque, transparent, and translucent color It is much used for general decorative purposes and does not have the strength c the molded phenolic type of plastic. Examples are Catalin and Marblette.

MELAMINE PLASTIC TYPE: This is heat-resistant up to 210° F.; other properties includ light weight, colorfastness, scratch resistance, and resistance to chemicals, oils, an water. It is available in a full color range. The product is nontoxic, odorless, an tasteless. Examples include Melmac, Plaskon Melamine, and Resimene.

MOLDED PHENOLIC TYPE: This type will resist heat up to 300° F. Properties include ligh weight, hardness, great strength, and ability to hold a given shape, as well a resistance to water and chemicals. The color range is limited to dark or mottle colors and effects. Examples include Bakelite, Indur, and Resinox.

POLYESTER TYPE: This very tough product is heat-resistant up to 400° F. It is resistan to scuffing and abrasion and comes in clear to translucent colors. It is used i laminates, since they set at low or room temperatures with low or contact pressure Examples include Laminac, Paraplex, Plaskon, Selectron, and Vibrin.

UREA TYPE: This type comes in full color range and is colorfast; it is very hard, scratch resistant, odorless, tasteless, nontoxic, and will resist common chemicals and oils This product is light in weight and does not possess the heat-resistance of th melamine type. Examples are Beetle, Plaskon Urea, and Sylplast.

THERMOPLASTIC PLASTICS INCLUDE:

ACRYLIC TYPE: The term acrylic is used to designate an acid—$C_2H_4O_2$—which has sharp, acrid odor. It is prepared from acrolein or from certain derivatives or fror propionic acid. It is used in organic synthesis and in the manufacture of plastics also known as propenoic acid. Orlon, for example, is one type of acrylic and i classed as a polyacrylonitrile filament.

Properties of the acrylic type include lightness of weight, great breakage resistance, and lack of odor and taste. This type is nontoxic. It comes in opaque translucent, and transparent colors, all in a wide range. Acrylic plastic is nc resistant to scratching, to very hot water, lighted cigarettes, alcohol, cleaning fluids and nail polish. Examples include Lucite and Plexiglas.

CELLULOSIC TYPE: This type has five major groups:
Cellulose acetate: Examples include Fibestos, Lumarith, Kodapak I, Plastacele Tenite I, and Vuepak.
Cellulose acetate butyrate: Examples include Kodapak II.
Cellulose nitrate: Examples include Kodaloid, Nitron, and Pyralin.
Cellulose propionate: Example is Forticel.

Ethyl cellulose: Example is Ethocel.

Characteristics and properties of these types include low cost in mass production and uniformity in size, lightness of weight, toughness and resistance to breakage; wide color range and high-luster finish.

Cellulosics will resist heat to about 135° F.

The nitrate type is highly flammable and its abrasion resistance is limited. This type is injured by nail polish.

The acetate and butyrate types are affected by alcohol and alkalies.

The ethyl type is affected by cleaning fluids, fats, and oils.

NYLON THREAD TYPE: Properties include strength, toughness, long wear, resistance to most chemicals, and boiling without resoftening. Available in all colors. The representative name is nylon.

POLYETHYLENE TYPE: This will show heat resistance to 200° F. It is flexible at low temperatures, odorless, tasteless, nontoxic, moisture-proof, heat-sealable and resistant to food acids and common chemicals. This type will show a milk-like translucence in molded objects and is transparent in film form. Pastel shades are used to a considerable degree for coloring. Examples include Bakelite Polyethylene, Polyethene.

POLYSTYRENE TYPE: This comes in transparent form and in a wide range of clear, opaque, and translucent colors. It is light in weight, tasteless, odorless, and nontoxic; when tapped it has a metallic resonance. Other characteristics include resistance to ordinary chemicals; it is weak to cleaning fluids, nail polish, and citrus fruit oils. Examples include Bakelite, Catalin Polystyrene, Lustrex, Plexene M, and Styron.

VINYL TYPE: This very important type has a wide range of uses: in the rigid form it is used for drawing instruments, floor tiles, and phonographic records; in the flexible form it is used for fabric coating, garment bags, shower curtains, upholstery and upholstery thread, and wallpaper. Properties include the following: great strength and toughness, lightness of weight, resistance to sunlight, to food action, alcohol, and common chemicals. Vinyl must be given protection from boiling water, hot cooking utensils, moth-repellents, and lacquered surfaces. Examples include Geon, Koroseal, Krene, Marvinol, Pliovic, Saran, and Vinylite.

TESTING

1. Define the following terms: plastic, thermosetting plastic, thermoplastic plastic.
2. The five steps used in processing plastics from the raw material are molding, casting, extruding, calendering, and laminating. Define these terms and explain the function of each in sequence as outlined in this question.
3. Define the following types of thermosetting plastics:
   (*a*) Casein type; (*b*) cast phenolic type; (*c*) melamine plastic type; (*d*) molded phenolic type; (*e*) polyester type; (*f*) urea type.
4. Define the following types of thermoplastic plastics:
   (*a*) acrylic type; (*b*) cellulosic type; (*c*) nylon thread type; (*d*) polyethylene type; (*e*) polystyrene type; (*f*) vinyl type.
5. List five plastics trade names and identify which class of plastics each one belongs to.

Part 2—Unit 26

TOPIC: EXAMINATION ON MANMADE FIBERS AND FILAMENTS

This test is to serve the purpose of a wide or narrow survey of the material covered in the units on manmade fibers and filaments. Much depends on the background of the reader, technologist, or student. These questions are varied so that if a teacher wishes to apply this test to a group of textile students, the questions which are at the level of the group should be the only ones used.

TRUE-FALSE QUESTIONS   20 points

1. _____ Acetate, rayon, and nylon can be made from the same base materials.
2. _____ The scientist who perfected nylon was Dr. Arthur D. Little.
3. _____ A core thread is one that is wound on the outside of the yarn.
4. _____ Lastex is the raw material from which latex is made.
5. _____ Filatex is used for stocking tops.
6. _____ Dynel is known as a copolymer of acrylonitrile and vinyl chloride.
7. _____ Celanese acetate is a regenerated textile fiber.
8. _____ The word *xanthate*, from the Greek, implies a blue color.
9. _____ There is more cuprammonium rayon produced than viscose rayon.
10. _____ The word "viscose," by itself, refers to the bath or solution used to make viscose rayon.
11. _____ Any fabric made of viscose rayon should be known as viscose-rayon cloth.
12. _____ Viscosity of the solution used is necessary in a spinning bath to make manmade fibers.
13. _____ The opening in an orifice is known as a spinnerette.
14. _____ A filament made from marbles is glass fiber.
15. _____ Acrilan and Celcos have much in common.
16. _____ Nylon bristles are known as Exton.
17. _____ Cold-drawn nylon may be stretched to four times its original length.
18. _____ Vinyon HH has several uses in industrial fabrics and in apparel.
19. _____ Arnel and Verel are manufactured by the same company.
20. _____ A hydrophobic fiber is one that absorbs water or moisture rapidly.

COMPLETION-TYPE QUESTIONS   10 points

1. Fortisan and Fortisan-36 are products of _____.
2. A Coronized finish is applied to _____ fabrics.
3. Crease retention and wrinkle resistance are features of _____.
4. Acrilan and "Orlon" provide extra bulk without _____.
5. A filament made from marbles is _____.
6. Nylon is classed as a poly-_____ fiber.
7. "Orlon" is classed as a poly-_____ fiber.
8. "Dacron" is classed as a poly-_____ fiber.
9. Celcos is a viscose-acetate fiber made by _____.
10. Saran and _____ have much in common.

MULTIPLE-CHOICE QUESTIONS   10 points

Underline your choice:

1. Father of the Rayon Industry   Jacquard, Chardonnet, Swan, Little.
2. "The coal-air-water" fiber   Fiberglas, "Orlon," nylon, acetate.
3. Fireproof filament   Asbestos, Fiberglas, latex, Kodel.
4. Fireproof fiber   Verel, Creslan, asbestos, "Dacron."
5. The original core yarn   Arnel, Zefran, nylon, cut rubber.
6. Copper sulfate and ammonia   Viscose, acetate, Bemberg, Fortisan-36.
7. Estron   Avisco, latex, Filatex, acetate.
8. Acrylic fiber   Asbestos, "Dacron," nylon, "Orlon."
9. A short fiber   "Orlon" staple, silk, linen, filament.
10. Used in making rayon   Vinyl chloride, linters, petroleum.

MATCHING QUESTIONS   10 points

Place the number of your choice from Column Two on the blank line before Column One where you think there is a definite connection.

1. ____ Vinyon HH		1.	Eastman Chemical Products Company.
2. ____ Kodel		2.	Bath for cuprammonium.
3. ____ Used to dull luster		3.	Same strength, wet or dry.
4. ____ Verel		4.	Important in rayon manufacture.
5. ____ Blue in color		5.	Polyester fiber.
6. ____ Carbon bisulfite		6.	Shredder of cellulose blotter stock.
7. ____ Spun-rayon yarn		7.	Titanium dioxide.
8. ____ Pfleiderer		8.	Rayon staple.
9. ____ Nylon		9.	Cold-drawn four times its length.
10. ____ Spinnerette		10.	Coronized.
		11.	Made of platinum and iridium.

WRONG-WORD QUESTIONS   10 points

In each of the following questions, one of the words or groups of words is out of place and does not belong with the other terms. Place the number of the "out-of-place" term on a line provided at the left of the page:

1. ____ Du Pont fiber	1. Nylon. 2. "Dacron." 3. Verel. 4. Taslan.
2. ____ Celanese product	1. Estron. 2. Fortisan. 3. Arnel. 4. Celaperm.
3. ____ Eastman product	1. Acetate. 2. Kodel. 3. Arnel. 4. Verel.
4. ____ Rubber	1. Mylar. 2. Lastex. 3. Filatex. 4. Contro.
5. ____ Polyester fiber	1. "Dacron." 2. Fortrel. 3. Lactron. 4. Kodel.
6. ____ Acrylic fiber	1. Acrilan. 2. Creslan. 3. Acele. 4. Zefran.
7. ____ Rayon fiber	1. Avril. 2. Avron. 3. Velon. 4. Bemberg.
8. ____ Acetate fiber	1. Fibro. 2. Celanese. 3. Colorspun. 4. Estron.
9. ____ Metallic yarn	1. Lurex. 2. Lamé. 3. Saran. 4. Metlon.
10. ____ Nylon types	1. Perlon. 2. Chemstrand. 3. Fortrel. 4. Du Pont.

TABULATION QUESTION   10 points

In one column make a list of ten manmade fibers. In a second column place the name of one manufacturer of each of the fibers you have listed.

ESSAY QUESTION   30 points

Write an essay of not more than 250 words on a manmade fiber of your choice. Include in the effort any experiences which you may have had with the fiber, fabric, or garment which may or may not have appealed to you. Also give the reason as to why you selected to write about this fiber.

Part 2—Unit 27

TOPIC: MAJOR NATIONWIDE AND WORLDWIDE PRODUCERS OF MANMADE OR MANUFACTURED FIBERS

RAYON GROUP

NAME	TYPE	SOURCE
Aristocrat	Cuprammonium tow, staple and yarn	Beaunit
Avisco rayon, including Avicron, Avlin, Avril, Avron, Avicolor	Viscose—filament, staple, crimped, textured	AVC/FMC Corporation

NAME	TYPE	SOURCE
Belastra, Belastraw	Viscose—filament, staple	American Enka
Bembella	Two ends of (Bemberg) Parfé special textured filament yarn	Beaunit
Bemberg	Bemberg or cuprammonium rayon filament, staple, yarn	Beaunit
Briglo	Viscose—bright filament	American Enka
Celanese	Viscose—filament, tow, staple	Celanese
Coloray	Viscose—solution-dyed rayon filament, staple	Courtaulds
Colorspun	Viscose—solution-dyed filament and/or yarn	AVC/FMC Corporation
Comiso	High-strength cuprammonium tow	Beaunit
Cordura	Viscose—medium and high tenacity	Du Pont
Cotron	Yarn of viscose and cotton—Avisco rayon staple used	AVC/FMC Corporation
Covinair, Covingtone	Viscose—medium and high tenacity	IRC/Midland-Ross
Cupersil	Special textured, dye-slub cuprammonium filament	Beaunit
Cupioni	Thick-thin shantung-type cuprammonium filament yarn	Beaunit
Cupracolor	Solution-dyed cuprammonium filament	Beaunit
Cuprasheer	Cuprammonium filament yarn	Beaunit
Drapespun	Viscose rayon yarn for draperies	IRC/Midland-Ross
Dream slub	Cuprammonium, novelty torpedo slub yarn	Beaunit
Dull-fast, Dul-tone	Viscose—medium and high tenacity	IRC/Midland-Ross
Dy-Lok	Viscose—solution-dyed filament	IRC/Midland-Ross
Englo	Viscose—dull luster filament	American Enka
Enka	Rayon (and nylon) filament yarns	American Enka
Enkor	High-modulus viscose rayon staple	American Enka
Fiber HM	High-modulus, dimensionally stable viscose rayon staple	American Enka
Fiber 700	High-modulus, dimensionally stable viscose rayon staple	American Enka
Fibro	Viscose-rayon staple fiber	Courtaulds
Flaikona	Cuprammonium filament flake yarn	Beaunit
Flake slub	Cuprammonium yarn with short entangled slubs	Beaunit
Fortisan, Fortanese	High-tenacity saponified acetate to give rayon filament	Celanese
Fortisan, Fortisan 36	High-denier saponified acetate to give rayon filament	Celanese
Hi-Narco	High-tenacity viscose filament	Beaunit
Hygram	High-tenacity viscose filament	Celanese
IRC Rayon	Viscose filament, medium and strong	IRC/Midland-Ross
I.T.	Improved tenacity viscose rayon staple	American Enka
Jetspun	Solution-dyed viscose filament	American Enka
Kolorbon	Solution-dyed, heavy-denier, crimped viscose rayon staple	American Enka
Krispglo	Flat viscose-rayon filament yarn	American Enka
Lektroset	Twist-set viscose rayon filament	IRC/Midland-Ross
Lirelle	High-modulus, dimensionally stable viscose rayon staple	Courtaulds

NAME	TYPE	SOURCE
Long Type "A" Slub	Cuprammonium filament, parallel non-entangled slubs	Beaunit
Matesa	Delustered cuprammonium filament	Beaunit
Measle Yarn	Cuprammonium, taut and loose filament	Beaunit
Multi-Cupioni	Douppioni-type multi-entangled slub-filament Bemberg yarn	Beaunit
Multi-Strata Slub	Novelty Bemberg rayon yarn with torpedo-shaped slubs	Beaunit
Narco	Viscose filament, medium with regular tenacity	Beaunit
Narcon	Viscose—strong staple filament	Beaunit
Newbray—bright Newdull—dull Newlow—semi-dull	All three are viscose rayon yarns	New Bedford Rayon Company of Mohasco Industries
Nublite	Cuprammonium thick-and-thin filament	Beaunit
Ondelette	Viscose rayon, randomly spaced with entangled slubs, irregularly spaced and shaped	Beaunit
Parfé	Cuprammonium space-dyed by pigment padding	Beaunit
Perlglo	Viscose—semi-dull luster yarn	American Enka
Polynosic	High-modulus, dimensionally stable rayon staple	American Enka
Premier	Viscose-rayon filament	IRC/Midland-Ross
Rayflex	High-strength viscose rayon filament	AVC/FMC Corporation
Semi-dull	Partially delustered viscose rayon	Beaunit
Skendo, Skenendoa	Viscose-rayon filament	Beaunit
Skybloom	Bulked viscose rayon staple for tufting yarns	American Enka
Skyloft	Viscose—bulked filament for carpeting	American Enka
Softglo	Semi-dull rayon filament yarn for carpeting	American Enka
Spun-black	Viscose rayon, solution-dyed	IRC/Midland-Ross
Spun-Lo	Viscose-rayon filament	IRC/Midland-Ross
Strata-Slub	Bemberg—thick-and-thin filament	Beaunit
Stratella	Bemberg rayon yarn, thick-and-thin	Beaunit
Strawn	Flat, strawlike monofilament rayon for drapery fabrics	IRC/Midland-Ross
Sunspun	Bemberg or cuprammonium rayon yarn	Beaunit
Super L	Smooth, soil-resistant viscose rayon carpet staple	AVC/FMC Corporation
Super-Narco	Strong viscose rayon filament	Beaunit
Super Rayflex	High-strength viscose-rayon filament; 40% stronger than Rayflex	AVC/FMC Corporation
Suprenka	Extra-high-tenacity viscose-rayon filament	American Enka
Suprenka Hi Mod	High-modulus viscose-rayon yarn	American Enka
Tubize	Viscose rayon—filament, bright and dull; continuous-filament tow	Celanese
Tufton	Viscose-rayon staple, crimped	AVC/FMC Corporation
Tusson	Shantung-type, dull-luster slubbed rayon-filament yarn	Beaunit

NAME	TYPE	SOURCE
Tyrex	Viscose rayon—filament with high tenacity; "Super-super" and "Super-2," used for rayon tire-cord yarn	Tyrex, Inc., 350 Fifth Avenue, New York City
Tyron	High-tenacity viscose-rayon filament	IRC/Midland-Ross
Veri-Dul	Viscose rayon, delustered or dull	Beaunit
Xtra-Dul	Viscose rayon, very dull in cast	Beaunit
Zantrel	High-modulus viscose rayon, dimensionally stable staple	American Enka

TYPES OF ACETATE FIBERS PRODUCED IN THE UNITED STATES

NAME	TYPE	SOURCE
Acele	Acetate filament yarn	Du Pont
Arbel	Acetate staple	Celanese
Arnel, Arnel 60	Triacetate fibers, tow, staple, and filament	Celanese
Avicolor	Solution-dyed acetate filament; also used to color rayon staple and filament	AVC/FMC Corporation
Avisco Acetate	Acetate staple and filament	AVC/FMC Corporation
Celacloud	Crimped acetate staple	Celanese—yarns and fibers of various types including acetate, triacetate, and rayon
Celacrimp	Textured acetate filament yarn	
Celafil	Abraded acetate yarn	
Celaire	Twist-set acetate yarn	
Celairese	Dull acetate staple	
Celaloft	Bulked acetate yarn	
Celaperm	Solution-dyed acetate filament	
Celarandom	Intermittently saponified filament yarn	
Celaspun	Yarn spun from acetate staple	
Celatow	Acetate tow	
Celcos	Saponified acetate staple	
Chromspun	Solution-dyed acetate filament	Eastman
Cycloset	Acetate yarn treated to have weavability at zero twist	Du Pont
Estron, Eastman Estron	Acetate filament; tow used for cigarette filters	Eastman
Estron SLR	Dull acetate yarn resistant to sunlight and weather degradation	Eastman
Eastman 50	High-bulk acetate filament	Eastman
Lanese	Acetate staple fiber	Celanese
Loftura	Acetate slub-effect yarn	Eastman
Type F	Crimped acetate staple	Celanese
Type K	Crimped acetate staple	Celanese

NON-CELLULOSIC MANMADE FIBERS PRODUCED IN THE UNITED STATES

NAME	TYPE	SOURCE
A-Acrilan	Acrylic tow, staple, fiberfill	Chemstrand, Division of Monsanto Chemical Company
A-Acrilan 16	Whiter than A-Acrilan	
A-Acrilan Spectran	Solution-dyed Acrilan staple	
Antron	Nylon filament and staple with trilobal cross section	Du Pont

NAME	TYPE	SOURCE
Avisco Vinyon HH	Copolymer of vinyl chloride and vinyl acetate, dissolved in acetone, filtered and then extruded; staple form	AVC/FMC Corporation
Blanc de Blanc	Extra-white nylon for foundation garments	American Enka
Boltaflex (Saran)	Vinylidene chloride monofilament	Bolta-Saran, Lawrence, Mass.
Bristand	88% vinyl chloride and 12% vinyl acetate, dry spun	Polymers, Inc., Middlebury, Vt.
Cadon	Nylon yarn, multilobal cross-section	Chemstrand
Cantrece	Nylon filament yarn, silklike luster; knitwear, hosiery	Du Pont
Caprolan	Nylon 6 fiber and yarn, polycapramide; tow, staple, fiber	Allied Chemical
C-Chemstrand 66	Nylon 66, polyamide condensation from hexamethylene diamine and adipic acid	Chemstrand
Crepeset	Crinkled nylon filament	American Enka
Creslan	Acrylic filament, tow, staple	American Cyanamid
Cumuloft	Filament nylon yarn, textured	Chemstrand
"Dacron" polyester fiber—many types	Polyester condensation polymer from ethylene glycol and terephthalic acid; filament, tow, staple, fiberfill	Du Pont
Darvan/Travis	Nytril fiber made from vinylidene dinitrile; staple; not made now in U.S.A.	Celanese
Dynel	Modacrylic fiber of copolymer of acrylonitrile and vinyl chloride; comes in staple form	Textile Fibers Department, Union Carbide Corporation, New York City
Enkaloft	High-bulk, modified cross-section nylon filament for carpets	American Enka
Enkalure	Modified cross-section sparkle nylon, filament yarn	American Enka
Enkatron	Untextured, modified nylon filament yarn for carpets	American Enka
Enlon	Polypropylene monofilament and multifilament; also staple	National Plastic Products Co., Inc., Charlotte, N.C.
Firestone Polyethylene	Polyethylene resin is used; filaments are hot-extruded and sometimes annealed	Firestone Plastics Company, Hopewell, Va.
Fortrel	Polyester filament, tow, staple. Counterpart of Terylene made by Imperial Chemical Industries, Ltd., in filament and staple forms	Fiber Industries, Inc., Shelby, N.C.
Golden Caprolan	Nylon 6 tire yarn	Allied Chemical
Kodel	Polyester fiber in staple, tow, fiberfill. Different from comparable fibers in chemical composition and in internal molecular structure	Eastman
Lus-Trus	Saran, polyethylene, and polypropylene monofilaments	Southern Lus-Trus Corporation, Jacksonville, Fla.
Monosheer	Nylon yarn for hosiery	American Enka
Mylar polyester film	Polymer of ethylene glycol and terephthalic acid	Du Pont
Nomex	High-temperature-resistant nylon fiber	Du Pont

[307]

NAME	TYPE	SOURCE
Nylenka	Staple fiber of nylon	IRC/Midland-Ross
Nylon 6	Polyamide polymer from caprolactam	Allied Chemical; American Enka; Firestone Synthetic Fibers Co.; Beaunit
Nylon 6,6 (66)	Hexamethylene diamine and adipic acid used as base. Polyamide is melted and extruded in several filaments from spinnerette and then stretched	Du Pont; Chemstrand
Nylon 6, IRC	Condensation of e-amino caprolactam, extrusion of melt through spinnerette, then stretched; staple	IRC/Midland-Ross
Nylon (700)	An improved industrial-type nylon	Du Pont
Nylon (701)	High breaking strength and very high abrasion nylon for cordage, rope	Du Pont
Nylon Elastic	Copolymer of Nylon 610 with small amount of condensation product from sebacic acid and alky-substituted hexamethylene diamine	Du Pont
"Orlon" acrylic fiber, many types	Polymer of acrylonitrile; solution is made and extruded solvent is then eliminated and resultant yarn is then stretched	Du Pont
Polycrest	Olefin fiber, polypropylene, used to make yarn	U.S. Rubber
Polyethylene (Olefin)	Monofilament from polymerization of ethylene under heat and pressure. Color pigments incorporated in resin prior to extrusion; strength and elongations controlled in variable degrees of stretch	Dawbarn Division of W. R. Grace & Co.; Firestone Synthetic Fibers Co.; Reeves Brothers, Inc.; Southern Lus-Trus Corporation; The Vectra Company
Polypropylene (Olefin)	Polymerization of propylene in solution in presence of specific catalysts (monofilaments). Multifilament staple and yarn produced by melt spinning method NOTE: Staple and yarn produced by Beaunit Corporation; Dawbarn Division of W. R. Grace & Co.; Firestone; Reeves Brothers, Inc.; U.S. Rubber Co.	Dawbarn Division of W. R. Grace & Co.; Firestone; Reeves Brothers, Inc.; Southern Lus-Trus; The Vectra Company
Proloft	Textured olefin (polypropylene) yarn	Firestone
Reevon	Olefin polypropylene fibers and yarns, tow, staple, and multifilaments in fine deniers and yarns; bristles in monofilaments	Reeves Brothers, Inc., New York City
Rovana (Saran)	Filament yarn of vinylidene chloride copolymer. Monofilament in form of flat film tape of uniform thickness	Dow Chemical Company, Midland, Mich., and Williamsburg, Va.
Saran	Chlorine and ethylene combined to form vinylidene chloride. Made into copolymer with 10% vinyl chloride. Heated, extruded to form filaments, then extruded Velon is the trademark name used by Firestone Tire & Rubber Company, Firestone Plastics Company, Hopewell, Virginia	Dawbarn; Bolta-Saran; National Plastic Products Co.; Oriented Plastics, Inc.; Saran Yarns Company; Southern Lus-Trus Company

NAME	TYPE	SOURCE
Taslan	Loop-type, non-stretched bulk yarn	Du Pont
Teflon (Saran)	TFE-fluorocarbon and FEP-fluorocarbon staple, monofilament and multifilament tow, flock, and yarn	Du Pont
Vectra	Olefin (polyethylene and polypropylene) monofilaments tow, staple, and yarn	The Vectra Division, National Plastics Products Co., Inc., Odenton, Md.
Velon	*See* Saran	*See* Saran
Verel	Modacrylic tow and staple	Eastman Chemical Products, Inc., New York City
Verel Type A	High crimp, good retention	
Verel Type B	High crimp, less permanent than Type A	
Verel Type C	Medium crimp, non-permanent	
Verel Type D	Low crimp, removed in pile fabric cloth	
Verel Type F	High crimp, removed in pile fabrics	
Verel Type III	High-shrinkage modacrylic fiber	
Vycron	Polyester filament, tow, staple, and fiberfill	Beaunit
Zefkrome	Colored acrylic staple fiber	Dow Chemical Company
Zefran	Acrylic staple and tow	Dow Chemical Company

STRETCH-TEXTURED YARN GROUP

NAME	TYPE	SOURCE
Agilon	High-stretch, non-torque (non-twist) bulk-textured yarn	Deering Milliken Research Center, Spartanburg, S.C.
Antron 24	Bulked trilobal continuous-filament nylon yarn. Yarn changed in process of manufacture prior to molecular structure being set up	Du Pont
Ban-Lon (owns and controls patents and trademarks associated with the yarn, Textralized and fabrics, Ban-Lon— licensed	Made on stuffer-box principle; can be finished soft or harsh and from flat to nubby effect. Textralized nylon, Textralized "Dacron." Used in woven, knit, and lace goods of a great many types	Joseph Bancroft & Sons Company, Wilmington, Del. A division of Indian Head Mills, Inc., New York City
BCF Nylon	Bulked trilobal continuous-filament nylon yarn for use in carpeting. Yarn is changed during manufacture before final molecular structure is set up	Du Pont
Cumuloft	Textured filament nylon yarn used in carpeting	Chemstrand
Cuprel, Cuprino	Cuprel is textured filament yarn; Cuprino is a special textured filament and slub yarn	Beaunit
Diane	Stretch-nylon multifilament yarn	Sauquoit Fibers Company, Scranton, Pa.
Duclé	Uses either nylon or "Dacron" base. Also made in acetate; many uses	Clarence L. Meyers & Co., Inc., Wyncote, Pa.
Dynaloft	"Dacron" or nylon textured filament yarn	Leon Ferenbach, Inc., New York City
Enkaloft	Textured multilobal continuous nylon yarn for carpeting	American Enka

[309]

NAME	TYPE	SOURCE
FF, FTF	FF is false-twist stretch yarn; FTF is same but stabilized	Deering Milliken
Fluflon	Any thermoplastic yarn highly twisted in heated zone in continuous process using dry heat. Leesona Corporation is licensor of method	Marionette Mills, South Coatesville, Pa.
Hazel	Monofilament stretch-nylon yarn	Sauquoit Fibers Company
Helanca	High-stretch torque yarn	Patents, licenses, and nature and quality all controlled by The Heberlein Patent Corporation, 350 Fifth Avenue, New York City
Helanca Hi-Test	Stretch yarn—"clinging" apparel, hosiery, swimwear, tights, leotards	
Helanca NT	Non-torque textured yarn with soft hand and excellent stretching properties	
Helanca SP	Stretch yarn for weaving purposes—ski pants, etc.	
Helanca SPZ	Stretch torque, false-twist yarn	
Helanca SS	Highly bulked yarn, soft in hand, limited in stretch properties	
Helanca SW	Limited stretch for use in bouclé and comparable yarns	
Leferon	Crimped, textured yarn	Leon Ferenbach, Inc.
Mylast	Crimp-type, non-torque textured yarn	Clarence L. Meyers & Company, Inc.
Saaba	False-twisted stretch yarn is modified by after-treatment involving heat	Licensor is Leesona Corporation, Warwick, R.I.
Shape-2-U	Textured yarn obtained by a twisting and untwisting method	Burlington Industries, Inc., New York City
Spunized	Filament yarns crimped in batch form and equipment used has a heat-setting chamber	Spunize Company of America, Inc., Unionville, Conn.
Superloft	Highly twisted yarn made in a continuous process in which dry heat is used. A false-twist type	Licensor is Leesona Corporation, Warwick, R.I.
Synfoam	Twist and untwist methods used on this nylon and "Dacron" base to be used in crepe fabrics and upholstery	Synfoam Yarns, Inc., Lowell, Mass.
Taslan	A mechanical treatment by air jet changes the loft, texture, hand, and covering power. Many uses	Du Pont
Textralized	Crimp-type, stretch, non-torque yarn used in Ban-Lon garments, etc.	Patents, quality, and licensing controlled by Joseph Bancroft & Sons Company, Wilmington, Del.
Type A	Crimp-type, stretch, non-torque, sparkle crepe or bouclé effect for Ban-Lon garments, etc.	
Type B	Crimp-type, stretch, non-torque yarn subtle sheen or silklike effect for use in Ban-Lon garments	
Tycora	Embodies several techniques, much used in knitgoods, upholstery and carpeting. Term covers continuous-filament textured yarns—acrylic, nylon, polyester, polypropylene	Textured Yarn Company, New York City
Welderstretch	Twisted combination of stretch nylon with cotton, rayon, worsted, spun nylon, and "Orlon-dyed," and in the natural condition	Blackwelder Textile Company, Inc., Cherryville, N.C.

NAME	TYPE	SOURCE
Whitin ARCT-FT-1, Whitin ARCT-FT-3, and Whitin ARCT-FTF	Any thermoplastic yarn highly twisted, heat-set, untwisted, relaxed and heat-set a second time in continuous process. Stretch yarns of nylon, polyester, polypropylene, acrylic, acetate, triacetate. Ideal for knitted and woven fabrics. Many uses	The Whitin Machine Works, Whitinsville, Mass. This company sells the necessary machinery. Developed in conjunction with Deering Milliken Research Corporation, Spartanburg, S.C.

SPANDEX GROUP

NAME	TYPE	SOURCE
Blue "C"	Can be used for practically all end uses which require stretch. Made from polymer consisting of segmented polyurethane. Is exceptionally white in cast	Chemstrand
Duraspan	Cut monofilaments of spandex fiber; well meets requirements for stretch garments	International Latex Corporation, Dover, Del.
Glospan	Monofilaments and yarn	Globe Mfg. Company, Fall River, Mass.
Lycra	Dog-bone cross-sectional shape, individual fibers, host of uses	Du Pont
Rheeflex	Comes in cut monofilament form	Rhee Industries Division, Rohm & Haas, Warren, R.I.
Spandelle	Ideal in knit fabrics; provides good union-dyed fabric with either Type 6 nylon or Type 6,6 nylon as an ingredient	Firestone Synthetic Fibers Company, Inc., Hopewell, Va.
Vyrene	Host of uses in knit and woven fabrics. Ideal as core yarn	United States Rubber Company, New York City

METALLIC GROUP

NAME	TYPE	SOURCE
Alistran	Used in loom-finished goods only— grill cloths, braids, trimmings, upholstery fabrics, narrow goods	Multi-Tex Products Corporation, Newark, N.J.
Dura-stran	Used with other textile fibers; non-tarnishing, washable and drycleanable	Multi-Tex Products
Fairtex	Good for use in non-dyeable fabrics; automotive fabrics, upholstery, dressgoods, novelties	Fairtex Sales, Riegel Paper Corporation, Charlotte, N.C.
Lamé (and with Mylar)	Used in woven and knitgoods; and comes in foil, metalized, and non-laminated forms	Standard Yarn Mills, Inc., Woodside 77, New York City
Lurex (butyrate, with polyester film, and with aluminum foil)	Host of uses; cannot flake off; non-tarnishing, woven and knitgoods	The Dow Chemical Company, Williamsburg, Va.
Malora (with Mylar, Mylar M.L., Foil, Mylar M-200 and M-300)	Aluminum foil laminated between two films of acetate butyrate. Comes unsupported or supported with various fibers	Malina Company, New York City

NAME	TYPE	SOURCE
Metlon (F, P-75, LMP, C)	Made by laminating a clear viscose cellophane film to aluminum foil. Comes unsupported or supported with various fibers	Metlon Corporation, subsidiary of Acme Backing Corporation, New York City

GLASS FIBER GROUP

NAME	TYPE	SOURCE
Aercor	Air-bulked fiber glass yarns	Owens-Corning Fiberglas Corporation, New York City
Fiberglas	Textile glass fiber; has host of uses in many fields	Owens-Corning Fiberglas Corporation
Modiglass	Glass fibers for many uses in the home, industry, furnishings, sports; decorative and utility purposes	Modiglass Fibers, Bremen, Ohio
PPG	Much used for decorative purposes and in industry	Pittsburgh Plate Glass Company, Pittsburgh, Pa.
Unifab	Textile glass fibers in fabric form	Ferro Corporation, Fiber Glass Division, Nashville, Tenn.
Uniformat	Glass fibers in a mat formation	
Unirove	Glass fibers in a roving form	
Unistrand	Fibers in a roving strand formation	
Unitape	Fibers woven into edge tapes	
Uniglass	Fabrics made of glass fibers for many uses—upholstery, drapes, decorative cloths, etc. Much used in various industries	United Merchants Industrial Fabrics, New York City

TYPES OF ACETATE AND RAYON PRODUCED IN FOREIGN COUNTRIES

NAME	TYPE	SOURCE
Alastra	Viscose, filament	Fabelta, Brussels, Belgium
Albene	Acetate, dull	Société Rhodiaceta, Lyon-Vaise (Rhône) France
Albula	Viscose filament, dull	Snia Viscosa, Rome, Italy
Amplum	Viscose	Algemene Kunstzijde, Unie, N.V., Arnhem (Arnheim), Netherlands
Argentea	Viscose filament	Snia Viscosa, Milan, Italy
Arma Flisca	Viscose, high-tenacity	Société de la Viscose, Albi (Tarn) France
Arma Flisca-Dull	Viscose, high-tenacity, dull	Société de la Viscose, France
Arma Lamo	Viscose, high-tenacity	Société de la Viscose, France
Belimat	Viscose filament, dull	Fabelta, Brussels, Belgium
Bemberg	Cuprammonium rayon, filament	British Bemberg, Ltd., Doncaster, Yorkshire, England
Bobina	Viscose—bristle, hair, and thread	Kunstseidefabrik, Bobingen, Germany
Bobol	Viscose staple	Snia Viscosa, Italy
Breda	All-inclusive trademark for all textiles of Hollandsche Kunstzijde Industrie	N.V. Hollandsche Kunstzijde Industrie, Breda, Netherlands (Holland)
Bredanese	Viscose, semi-dull	N.C. Hollandsche Kunstzijde Industrie, Breda, Netherlands (Holland)
Britbem	Cuprammonium rayon, filament form	British Bemberg, Ltd., Doncaster, Yorkshire, England

NAME	TYPE	SOURCE
Cantona	Viscose, semi-dull	Algemene Kunstzijde Unie, N.V., Arnhem, Netherlands
Celafibre	Acetate staple	British Celanese, Ltd., Spondon, Derbyshire, England
Celafil	Acetate, ruptured-filament type yarn	British Celanese, Ltd.
Celanese	Acetate filament	British Celanese, Ltd.
Cheviot	Viscose filament	North British Rayon, Ltd., Jedburgh, Scotland
Chinsang	Viscose multifilament	Hollandsche Kunstzijde Industrie, N.V., Breda, Holland
Cisalfa	Viscose staple, animalized with 10% protein	Snia Viscosa, Rome, Italy
Conyma	Viscose, bright filament	Nyma Rayon Works, Ltd., Nijmegen (Nimeguen) Holland
Conymex	Viscose, bright filament	Nyma Rayon Works, Ltd.
Cordenka	Viscose	Algemene Kunstzijde Unie, N.V., Arnhem, Netherlands
Cordulla	Viscose, dull	Courtaulds, Ltd., London, England
Courtaulds	Viscose staple	Courtaulds, Ltd., London, England
Crinol	Viscose filament	Snia Viscosa, Milan, Italy
Crispella	Viscose	Hollandsche Kunstzijde Industrie, N.V., Breda, Holland
Croneka	Viscose	Algemene Kunstzijde Unie, N.V., Breda, Holland
C.S. Yarn	Viscose filament	Harbens, Ltd., Colborne, Lancashire, England
Cuprama	Cuprammonium filament	Farbenfabriken Bayer, Düsseldorf, Germany
Cupresa	Cuprammonium rayon	Farbenfabriken Bayer, Düsseldorf, Germany
Delustra	Viscose, dull	Courtaulds, Ltd., London, England
Emera	Viscose, high twist	Hollandsche Kunstzijde Industrie, N.V., Breda, Holland
Enka	All-inclusive trademark for all Algemene Kunstzijde Unie fibers	Algemene Kunstzijde Unie, N.V., Arnhem, Netherlands
Extrema	Viscose, dull	Hollandsche Kunstzijde Industrie, N.V., Breda, Holland
Fabelmat	Viscose filament, dull	Fabelta, Brussels, Belgium
Fibrelta	Viscose	Fabelta, Brussels, Belgium
Fibramine	Viscose	Fabelta, Brussels, Belgium
Fibrenka	Viscose	Algemene Kunstzijde Unie, N.V., Arnhem, Netherlands
Fibro	Viscose staple	Courtaulds, Ltd., Cornwall, Ontario, Canada
Fibro	Viscose staple	Courtaulds, Ltd., London, England
Fibroceta	Acetate staple	Courtaulds, Ltd., London, England
Fibrolane	Viscose staple with special dyeing properties	Courtaulds, Ltd., London, England
Flatessa	Viscose, semi-dull	Hollandsche Kunstzijde Industrie, N.V., Breda, Netherlands
Flimba	Viscose, high-tenacity and crimped	Société de la Viscose Suisse, Emmenbrucke, Switzerland

NAME	TYPE	SOURCE
Flisca	Viscose	Société de la Viscose Suisse, Emmen-brucke, Switzerland
Flox	Viscose staple	Spinnfaser A.G., Elberfeld, Germany
Glanzstoff	Viscose filament	Vereinigte Glanzstoff-Fabriken, A.G., Elberfeld, Germany
High 10	Viscose filament, high-tenacity	Fabelta, Brussels, Belgium
Ivorea	Viscose filament, dull	Snia Viscosa, Milan, Italy
Jedmat	Viscose filament	North British Rayon, Ltd., Jedburgh, Scotland
Jedpak	Viscose filament for crepes	North British Rayon, Ltd., Jedburgh, Scotland
Kasilga	Viscose filament	Kunstsilkefabrikken, Notodden, Norway
Kirksyl	Viscose yarn and viscose crepe yarn	Kirklees, Ltd., Bury, Lancashire, England
Lacisana	Viscose staple	Snia Viscosa, Rome, Italy
Lamita	Viscose	Société de la Viscose, Albi (Tarn) France
Lamo	Viscose	Société de la Viscose, Albi (Tarn) France
Lansil	Acetate	Lansil, Ltd., Lancaster, Lancashire, England
Lanusa	Viscose	Badische Anilin & Soda Fabrik, Ludwigshafen, Germany
Lucisa	Viscose filament	Snia Viscosa, Rome, Italy
Matenka	Viscose, dull	Algemene Kunstzijde Unie, N.V., Arnhem, Netherlands
Matenkanese	Viscose multifilament	Algemene Kunstzijde Unie, N.V., Arnhem, Netherlands
Matenkona	Viscose, dull	Algemene Kunstzijde Unie, N.V., Arnhem, Netherlands
Matesa	Cuprammonium rayon filament, delustered	British Bemberg, Ltd., Doncaster, Yorkshire, England
Mattesco	Viscose filament dulled by titanium	Courtaulds, Ltd., Cornwall, Ontario, Canada
Neoplex	Viscose, dull	Harbens, Ltd., Colborne, England
Nerane	Acetate, dyed fast black	Société Rhodiaceta, Lyon-Vaise (Rhône) France
Nobricella	Viscose, semi-dull	Hollandsche Kunstzijde Industrie, N.V., Breda, Netherlands
Nyma, Nymella, and Nymex	Viscose filaments	Nyma Rayon Works, Nijmegen, Netherlands
Nymata, Nyatco, and Nymellamat	Viscose filaments, dull	Nyma Rayon Works, Nijmegen, Netherlands
Nymcord	Viscose filament for industrial purposes	Nyma Rayon Works, Nijmegen, Netherlands
Oceane	Acetate, dyed fast black	Société Rhodiaceta, Lyon-Vaise (Rhône) France
Opaceta	Acetate, dull	Courtaulds, Ltd., London, England
Paramount	Viscose filament	North British Rayon, Ltd., Jedburgh, Scotland
Rayolanda	Viscose rayon staple with special dyeing properties	Courtaulds, Ltd., London, England
Rhodia	Acetate	Société Rhodiaceta, Lyon-Vaise (Rhône) France

NAME	TYPE	SOURCE
Sava	Viscose filament	Fabelta, Brussels, Belgium
Scaldyna	Viscose, high tenacity	Fabelta, Brussels, Belgium
Seraceta	Acetate	Courtaulds, Ltd., London, England
Setilmat	Acetate filament, dull	Fabelta, Brussels, Belgium
Setilose	Acetate filament	Fabelta, Brussels, Belgium
Setina	Acetate	Fabelta, Brussels, Belgium
Spunenka	Viscose	Algemene Kunstzijde Unie, N.V., Arnhem, Netherlands
Standard	Viscose	North British Rayon, Ltd., Jedburgh, Scotland
Summum, Superarnum	Viscose	Algemene Kunstzijde Unie, N.V., Arnhem, Netherlands
Super Breda	Viscose	Hollandsche Kunstzijde Industrie, N.V., Breda, Holland
Supral	Viscose staple	Atkieselskapet Borregaard, Norway
Suprasta	Viscose filament, high-tenacity	Fabelta, Brussels, Belgium
Swina	Viscose	Fabelta, Brussels, Belgium
Tenasco	Viscose, high-tenacity	Courtaulds, Ltd., London, England
Tenax	Viscose, high-tenacity	Algemene Kunstzijde Unie, N.V., Arnhem, Netherlands
Tubastra	Viscose filament	Fabelta, Brussels, Belgium
Tudenza	Viscose filament	Courtaulds, Ltd., London, England
Ultrenka	Viscose multifilament	Algemene Kunstzijde Unie, N.V., Arnhem, Netherlands
Viscol	Viscose	Snia Viscosa, Milan, Italy
Viscose	Viscose	Svenska Rayon, Aktiebolaget, Sweden
Viscocord	Viscose, high-tenacity	Courtaulds, Ltd., Cornwall, Ontario, Canada

MANMADE FIBERS, NON-CELLULOSIC IN NATURE, MADE IN FOREIGN COUNTRIES

NAME	TYPE	SOURCE
Polyacrylonitrile		
Crylor	Filament and staple	France
Dolan	Tow and staple, both may be pre-dyed	Germany
Dralon	Staple	Germany
Nitrilon	Filament and staple	Russia
PAN-endlos-Faser	Filament and staple	Germany
Redon	Staple	France, Germany
Polyamide		
Amilan	Filament and staple	Japan
Bayer-Perlon	Filament	Germany
Bayer-Perlon-Borsten	Monofilament and ribbon	Germany
Bayer-Perlon-Faser	Staple, not pre-dyed	Germany
Bobina-Perlon	Filament	Germany
Bobina-Perlon-Borsten	Monofilament and ribbon	Germany
Bobina-Perlon Draht	Monofilament	Germany
Bobina-Perlon-Faser	Staple, pre-dyed	Germany
Ducilo Nylon	Filament and staple	Argentina
Enkalon	Filament	Netherlands
Frilon	Staple	Spain

NAME	TYPE	SOURCE
Grilon and Grilon-Faser	Filament, staple, and mono-filament	Germany
Kapron	Filament	Russia
Lilion	Filament	Italy
Nailon	Filament	Italy
Niplon	Filament	Japan
Perlon	Staple	Germany
Perlon-Borsten	Monofilament	Germany
Perlon-Cordseide	Filament	Germany
Perlonseide	Filament	Germany
Rhodia-Nylon	Filament	Germany
Rilsan	Monofilament	France
Sanderit-Faden	Monofilament and ribbon	Germany
Steelon	Filament and monofilament	Poland
Supron-Band	Ribbon	Germany
VGF-Perlon-Faser	Filament and staple	Germany

Polyester

Enkalene	Staple	Germany
Tergal	Staple	France
Terital	Staple	Italy
Terylene	Filament	England
Terylene Staple Fiber	Staple	England

Polyethylene

Courlene	Filament and monofilament, latter may be pre-dyed	England
Northylen	Monofilament	Germany
Polyethylene	Monofilament	Belgium
Polythene	Monofilament	England

Polystyrene

Styroflex-Faden	Monofilament	Germany

Polyurethane

Perlon-U	Filament and staple	Germany
Perlon-U-Borsten	Monofilament	Germany

Polyvinyl Alcohol

Cremona	Filament and staple	Japan
Kanebiyan	Filament and staple	Japan
Kuralon	Filament and staple	Japan
Newlon	Filament and staple	Japan
Synthofil	Monofilament	Germany
Vinylan	Filament and staple	Japan
Woolon	Filament and staple	Japan

Polyvinyl Chloride

Bayer Pe-Ce-U-Borsten	Monofilament	Germany
Chlorin	Filament	Russia
Fibrovyl	Staple	France
Isovyl	Staple	France, Germany
Kurehalon	Monofilament	Japan
Movil	Staple	Italy
Rhovyl	Staple	France, Germany

NAME	TYPE	SOURCE
Rhovyl-Fibra	Staple	Germany
Rhovyl-Thermo	Staple	France, Germany
Pe-Ce-Faser	Staple	Germany
Pe-Ce-Kunstseide-Faser	Staple	Germany
PCU-Faser	Staple	Germany
Pe-Ce-U-Flach-Runddraht	Staple	Germany
Thermovyl	Staple	France, Germany

Polyvinylidene Chloride

NAME	TYPE	SOURCE
Bexan	Monofilament	England
Bolta-Saran	Monofilament	Germany
Draka-Saran	Monofilament	Netherlands
Kurehalon	Monofilament	Japan
Pe-Ce-120	Filament	Germany
Pe-Ce-120-Borsten	Monofilament	Germany

PROTEIN FIBERS, WORLDWIDE PRODUCERS

NAME	TYPE	SOURCE
Alginate	Calcium-alginate, staple	Courtaulds, Ltd., London, England
Casein	Casein	Fabelta Union des Fabriques Belges de Textiles Artificiels, S.A., Brussels, Belgium
Courtaulds Standard	Alginate	Courtaulds, Ltd., London, England
Enkasa	Casein	A.K.U. Algemene Kunstzijde Unie N.V., Arnhem, Netherlands
Fibrolane—A, B, C, BC, and BX	Casein, staple	Courtaulds, Ltd., London, England
Lanital, Lanital S	Casein, staple	Les Textiles Nouveaux; Le Lanital Belge, Anvaing, Belgian Frasne-Buiznol, Belgium
Melkwol, Merinova	Casein, staple	Snia Viscosa, Milan, Italy
Silkool, Silkoon, Silkwool	Soybean	Shawa Sangyo Kaisha, Japan

Courtesy: Stanley B. Hunt, editor of Textile Organon, *Textile Economics Bureau, Inc., 10 East 40th Street, New York City.*

HOME SALES OFFICES OF SOME OF THE MAJOR PRODUCERS OF MANMADE TEXTILE FIBERS AND YARNS IN THE UNITED STATES

Allied Chemical Corporation, Allied Chemical Tower, New York, N.Y. 10016.
American Cyanamid Company, Inc., Berdan Avenue, Wayne, N.J.
American Enka Corporation, Enka, N.C. 28728.
American Viscose Division of FMC Corporation, 1617 Pennsylvania Boulevard, Philadelphia, Pa. 19103.
Joseph Bancroft & Sons Company, Division of Indian Head Mills, Wilmington, Del. 19899.
Beaunit Fibers Division, Beaunit Corporation, 261 Madison Avenue, New York, N.Y. 10016.
Celanese Corporation of America, 522 Fifth Avenue, New York, N.Y. 10036.
Chemstrand Company, Division of Monsanto Chemical Company, Inc., 350 Fifth Avenue, New York, N.Y. 10001.
Courtaulds North America, Inc., 104 West 40th Street, New York, N.Y. 10018.
Dawbarn Division, W. R. Grace & Company, Waynesboro, Va.

The Dow Chemical Company, Textile Fibers Department, Williamsburg, Va. 23185.

E. I. Du Pont de Nemours & Company, Inc., Textile Fibers Department, Wilmington, Del. 19898.

Eastman Chemical Products, Division of Eastman Kodak Company, Kingsport, Tenn. 37662.

Ferro Corporation, Fiber Glass Division, Fiber Glass Road, Nashville, Tenn. 37211.

Fiber Industries, Inc., Shelby, N.C. 28150.

Firestone Synthetic Fibers Company, Inc., 45 Rockefeller Plaza, New York, N.Y. 10020, and Hopewell, Va. 23860.

Heberlein Patent Corporation, 350 Fifth Avenue, New York, N.Y. 10001.

Hercules Powder Company, 900 Market Street, Wilmington, Del. 19899.

IRC Division of Midland-Ross Corporation, 660 Union Commerce Building, Cleveland, Ohio 44114.

Johns Manville Fiber Glass, Inc., River Road, Waterville, Ohio 43566.

Leesona Corporation, Warwick, R.I. 02887.

Metlon Corporation, 432 Park Avenue South, New York, N.Y. 10016.

Clarence L. Meyers & Company, Inc., The Wyncote House, Wyncote, Pa. 19095.

Modiglass Fibers, Division of Reichhold Chemicals, Inc., Bremen, Ohio 43107.

National Plastic Products Company, Inc., Odenton, Md.

New Bedford Rayon Division, Mohasco Industries, Inc., New Bedford, Mass. 02746.

Owens-Corning Fiberglas Corporation, 717 Fifth Avenue, New York, N.Y. 10022.

Pittsburgh Plate Glass Company, Inc., Fiber Glass Division, One Gateway Center, Pittsburgh, Pa. 15222.

Reeves Brothers, Inc., 1071 Sixth Avenue, New York, N.Y. 10018.

Southern Lus-Trus Corporation, 1048 Escambia Street, Jacksonville, Fla. 32208.

Spunize Company of America, Inc., 45 South Main Street, Unionville, Conn. 06085.

Textured Yarn Company, Inc., 40 East 34th Street, New York, N.Y. 10016.

Tyrex, Inc., 350 Fifth Avenue, New York, N.Y. 10001.

Union Carbide Corporation, Textile Fibers Department, 270 Park Avenue, New York, N.Y. 10017.

United States Rubber Company, Inc., 1230 Sixth Avenue, New York, N.Y. 10020, and 350 Columbia Road, Winnsboro, S.C.

The Vectra Company, Division of National Plastic · Products Company, Inc., Odenton, Md., and 1300 Baxter Street, Charlotte, N.C. 28202.

Two Outstanding Sources for Information on Manmade Textile Fibers; Without Their Aid This Book Would Not Have Been Possible:

1. Man-Made Fiber Producers Association, Inc., 350 Fifth Avenue, New York City. A. "Manmade Fiber Industry Fact Book." B. "Man-made Fibers—Summary of Origins, Characteristics and Uses." C. "Index for Educational Material on Man-made Fibers."

2. *Textile Organon* of the Textile Economics Bureau, Inc., 10 East 40th Street, New York City. Stanley B. Hunt, editor. "The monthly 'bible' for authentic market data important to the United States Man-made Fiber Industry, published in the interests of good business."

TEXTILE BIBLIOGRAPHY

OUTLINE OF TOPICS

COTTON GROWING

Cotton, George Bigwood. Constable and Company, Ltd., London, 1919.

Cotton, Brown. I.C.S., Scranton, Pennsylvania.

Cotton, Harry B. Brown. McGraw-Hill Book Co., Inc., New York, 1938.

Cotton, Edna Turpin, 266 pages. American Book Company, New York, 1924.

Cotton and Cotton Manufacture, James P. Warburg, 61 pages. First National Bank, Boston, Massachusetts, 1921.

Cotton and Its Production, W. H. Johnson, 536 pages. Macmillan and Company, Ltd., London, 1926.

Cotton and Other Useful Fibers, N. B. Allen, 368 pages. Ginn and Company, Boston, Massachusetts, 1929.

Cotton and Other Vegetable Fibers, production and utilization, E. Goulding, 231 pages. Handbook for The Imperial Institute, Number Four, John Murray Company, Ltd., London, 1917.

Cotton and the A.A.A., Brookings Institute, 722 Jackson Place, N.W., Washington, D.C.

Cotton from Raw Material to Finished Product, Cotton Textile Institute, 320 Broadway, New York, 1944.

Cotton from the Raw Material to the Finished Product, R. J. Peake, 134 pages. Pitman and Sons, Ltd., London, 1934.

Cotton from Seed to Loom, Dana, New York, 1878.

Cotton Goes to Market, A. H. Garside, 411 pages. Growing and marketing of cotton. Frederick A. Stokes Company, New York, 1935.

Cotton, History of, Donnel, New York, 1872.
Cotton, Its Uses, Varieties, etc., C. P. Brooks, Spon and Chamberlain, New York, 1898.
Cotton Plant, Flatters, London, 1906.
Cotton, The Universal Fiber, W. D. Darby, 63 pages. Dry Goods Economist, New York, 1932.
Cotton Under the Agricultural Adjustment Act, to July 1934, H. I. Richards, 129 pages. Brookings Institute, Washington, D.C., 1934.
Cotton Waste, Thomas Thornley. D. Van Nostrand Company, Princeton, N.J., 1921.
Damaged Cotton, J. A. McKee. Graham Printing Company, New Orleans, Louisiana, 1937.
Development and Properties of Raw Cotton, W. L. Balls. A. & C. Black Company, Ltd., London, 1915.
Facts About Cotton, Leaflet Number 167, 8 pages. Bureau of Agricultural Economics, U.S. Department of Agriculture, Washington, D.C., 1938.
Fundamentals of Fiber Structure, W. T. Astbury. Oxford University Press, Oxford, England, 1933.
King Cotton, M. L. Rutherford, 22 pages. Athens, Georgia, 1922.
La Culture de Coton, Borain. Brussels, Belgium, 1875.
La Culture de Coton à la Coté Française des Somalis, Arloz. Marseilles, France, 1906.
La Culture de Cotonnier dans les Colonies Françaises, Brenier. Paris, 1903.
La Production de Coton en Egypte, Charles-Roux. Paris, 1909.
Le Coton, Deschamps. Paris, 1885.
Le Coton, Ganeval. Lyon, France, 1881.
Le Coton en Algerie, Brunel. Paris, 1910.
Le Coton en Egypte, Cordemoy. Paris, 1897.
Methods of Cellulose Chemistry, C. Doree. D. Van Nostrand Company, Princeton, N.J., 1933.
Origin of Egyptian Cotton, Fletcher. Cairo, 1908.
Researches on Cellulose IV, C. F. Cross and C. Doree. Longmans, Green Company, New York, 1922.
Story of King Cotton, H. Dickson. Funk and Wagnalls, 354 Fourth Avenue, New York, 1937.
Structure of the Cotton Fiber, F. H. Bowman. Macmillan and Company, Ltd., London, 1908.
Studies of Qualities in Cotton, W. L. Balls. Macmillan and Company, New York, 1928.
Textbook of Cellulose Chemistry, E. Heuser. Translated by C. J. West and G. G. Esselen. D. Van Nostrand Company, New York, 1938.
The Cotton Plant, A. Flatters, 92 pages. Sherrat and Hughes, Ltd., London, 1906.
The Cotton Plant in Egypt, W. L. Balls. Macmillan and Company, Ltd., London, 1912.
The Great Cottonseed Industry of the South, L. A. Ransom. Oil Paint and Drug Publishing Corporation, 1911.
The Heritage of Cotton, M. D. C. Crawford, 244 pages. G. P. Putnam's Sons, New York, 1931.
The Production of Cotton, G. H. Collings, 256 pages. John Wiley and Sons, New York, 1926.
The Story of Cotton, D. Scarborough, 99 pages. Harper and Brothers, New York, 1933.
The Story of Cotton and the Development of the Cotton States, E. C. Brooks, 370 pages. Rand, McNally and Company, New York, 1911.
The Story of the Cotton Plant, F. Wilkinson. D. Appleton and Company, New York, 1915.
The Structure of the Cotton Fiber in Its Relation to Technical Application, F. H. Bowman, 470 pages. Macmillan and Company, Ltd., London, 1908.
The Textile Fibers, J. Merritt Matthews, 1133 pages. John Wiley and Sons, New York, 1947.
The Wild and Cultivated Cotton Plants of the World, Sir George Watt. Longmans, Green Company, Ltd., London, 1907.
Three Textile Raw Materials and Their Manufacture, 127 pages. International Acceptance Bank, Inc., New York, 1924.
Uplands Cotton, Fibers of Long Staple, Allard. Bulletin 111, U.S. Government Printing Office, Washington, D.C.
You Have Seen Their Faces, E. Caldwell and M. Bourke-White. Viking Press, New York, 1937.

RAW COTTON MARKETING

Agricultural Industries, Malot and Martin. McGraw-Hill Book Company, Inc., New York, 1939.
Biographical Sketches of Prominent Men and Historical Résumé, J. H. Lamb. Lamb's Textile Industries of the United States, J. H. Lamb, 1911.
Cotton, Harry B. Brown, 517 pages. McGraw-Hill Book Company, Inc., New York, 1927.
Cotton and Cotton Manufacture, James P. Warburg, 61 pages. First National Bank, Boston, Massachusetts, 1921.
Cotton and the Cotton Market, W. H. Hubbard, 503 pages. Meredith Press, Inc., New York, 1927.

Cotton Classing Manual, Willis, Gage and Moore. Textile Foundation, Washington, D.C., 1938.
Cotton Exchanges and Their Economic Functions, pages 253–80 in Volume XXXVIII, Number 2, American Academy of Political and Social Sciences, September, 1911.
Cotton Facts, A. B. Shepperson. Shepperson Publishing Company, New York, 1904, 1913, 1920.
Cotton Futures, A. B. Shepperson, 66 pages. Shepperson Publishing Company, New York, 1911.
Cotton Futures, C. Stewart, 20 pages. C. Stewart, London, Liverpool, 1921.
Cotton Goes to Market, A. H. Garside, 411 pages. Frederick A. Stokes Company, New York, 1935.
Cotton in Australia, R. Harding. Longmans, Green Company, Ltd., London, 1924.
Cotton, The Universal Fiber, W. D. Darby, 63 pages. Dry Goods Economist, New York, 1932.
Cotton Trade Guide and Students' Manual, T. S. Miller, 450 pages. Austin Printing Company, 1910.
Cotton Under the Agricultural Adjustment Act, H. I. Richards, 129 pages. Brookings Institute, Washington, D.C., 1934.
Cotton Yearbook, A. H. Garside. New York Cotton Exchange, New York.
Credit and International Trade, Barnard Ellinger, 189 pages. Macmillan and Company, Ltd., London, 1934.
Distribution of Textiles, Harvard University, Cambridge, Massachusetts, 1926.
Factors Affecting the Prices of Cotton, B. B. Smith. B. B. Smith, 1928.
Future Trading Upon Organized Commodity Markets in the United States, G. Wright Hoffman, 482 pages. University of Pennsylvania Press, Philadelphia, Pennsylvania, 1932.
Human Factors in Cotton Culture, R. B. Vance. University of North Carolina Press, Chapel Hill, N.C., 1929.
King Cotton, cotton and the cotton gin, M. L. Rutherford. Athens, Georgia, 1922.
King Cotton Diplomacy, F. L. Owsley, 617 pages. Foreign Relations of the Confederate States of America. University of Chicago Press, Chicago, Illinois, 1931.
King Cotton Is Sick, C. T. Murchison. University of North Carolina Press, Chapel Hill, N.C., 1930.
Memoir of Samuel Slater, G. S. White. Philadelphia, Pennsylvania, 1836.
Merchandising of Cotton Textiles, M. T. Copeland and E. P. Learned, Harvard University Press, Cambridge, Massachusetts.
Modern Cotton Economics, Thomas Thornley. Scott, Greenwood and Sons, Ltd., London, 1923.
Study of Cotton Hedging for a Grey Goods Mill, 1921–1926, Bureau of Business Research, Harvard University Graduate School of Business Administration, Cambridge, Massachusetts, 1928.
Textile Industries, An Economical Analysis, H. E. Michl. Textile Foundation, Washington, D.C., 1938.
Textile Unionism in the South, G. S. Mitchell. University of North Carolina Press, Chapel Hill, N.C., 1931.
The American Cotton System Historically Treated, T. S. Miller, Sr., Austin Printing Company, Austin, Texas, 1909.
The Cotton Industry, J. H. Crabtree. Lockwood and Sons, Boston, Massachusetts, 1922.
The Cotton Trade and Industrial Lancashire, 1600 to 1780, A. P. Wadsworth and Julia Del Mann. Manchester University Press, Manchester, England, 1931.
The Marketing of Cotton, from grower to spinner, J. A. Todd, 250 pages. Pitman and Sons, Ltd., London, 1934.
The Story of Cotton. Callaway Mills, La Grange, Georgia, 1939.
The Story of King Cotton, Harris Dickson. Funk and Wagnalls, New York, 1937.
World Resources and Industries, E. W. Zimmerman. Harper and Brothers, New York, 1933.

RAW COTTON STATISTICS

Bibliography of the Cotton Industry, C. J. H. Woodbury, E. L. Barry, Waltham, Massachusetts.
Cotton and the New Orleans Exchange, J. E. Boyle. Country Life Press, New York.
Samuel Slater and the Early Development of Cotton Manufacture in the United States, William R. Bagnall. Stewart Company, Middletown, Connecticut, 1890.
The Cotton Growing Countries, Present and Potential—Production, Trade and Consumption, International Institute of Agriculture, Bureau of Statistics. P. S. King and Sons, Ltd., London, 1926.
The Textile Industries of the United States of America, William R. Bagnall. Riverside Press, New York, 1893.

RAW COTTON UTILIZATION

American Cotton System, History of, T. S. Miller, Sr. Austin Printing Company, 1909.

Cotton Industry of Japan and China, A. S. Pearce. International Spinners, 1930.

Cotton Yearbook of the New York Cotton Exchange, Van Rees Press, New York.

Forecasting the Yield and Price of Cotton, H. L. Moore, 173 pages. Macmillan Company, New York, 1917.

Rise of the Cotton Mills of the South, Broadus Mitchell. Johns Hopkins Press, Baltimore, Maryland, 1921.

Texas Cotton from Seed to Mill, Anderson. Clayton Company, Houston, Texas, 1937.

The Cotton Trade of Great Britain, Thomas Ellison. E. Wilson, Ltd., London, 1886.

The Cotton World, survey of the World's Cotton Supplies and Consumption, J. A. Todd, 236 pages. Pitman and Sons, Ltd., New York, 1927.

COTTON CLOTH MANUFACTURING

A Cotton Fabrics Glossary, 739 pages. Frank P. Bennett and Company, Inc., Boston, Massachusetts.

A Practical Detail of the Cotton Manufacturer of the U.S.A., James Montgomery. D Appleton Company, New York, 1840.

Analysis of Cotton Fabrics, C. P. Brooks. International Library of Technology, volume 81.

Annual Proceedings of the American Cotton Manufacturers Association, Charlotte, North Carolina.

Automatic Weaving, W. A. Hanton. E. Benn, Ltd., London, 1929.

Card Grinding in Theory and Practice. Dronsfield Brothers, Ltd., Oldham, England, 1926.

Clark's Weave Room Calculations, W. A. G. Clark, 262 pages. Clark Publishing Company, Charlotte, North Carolina, 1926.

Computing Cotton Fabric Costs, F. H. Hill, Jr., 122 pages. McGraw-Hill Book Company, Inc., New York, 1929.

Cotton, George Bigwood, 206 pages. Henry Holt and Company, New York, 1919.

Cotton, Edna Turpin, 266 pages. American Book Company, New York, 1924.

Cotton and Cotton Manufacture, James P. Warburg, 61 pages. First National Bank, Boston, Massachusetts, 1921.

Cotton and Its Treatment, Butterworth. Manchester, England, 1881.

Cotton and Linen, E. B. Thompson, 199 pages. Ronald Press, New York, 1922.

Cotton Carding, Brickett. I. C. S., Scranton, Pennsylvania.

Cotton Carding, H. H. Willis and V. B. Moore, 153 pages. Textile Foundation, Washington, D.C., 1936.

Cotton Carding, Drawing, Spinning, Twisting, etc. International Textbook Company, Scranton, Pennsylvania.

Cotton Classing Manual, H. H. Willis, G. Gage and V. B. Moore. The Textile Foundation, Department of Commerce Building, Washington, 1938.

Cotton Combing Manual, Willis, Blair and Moore. Textile Foundation, Washington, D.C., 1938.

Cotton Combing Machines, Thomas Thornley. Scott, Greenwood and Sons, Ltd., London, 1902.

Cotton Combing Machines, W. S. Taggart. Macmillan Company, Ltd., London, 1902.

Cotton Fabrics Directory by Constructions and Sources, 96 pages. The Textile Committee, National Association of Purchasing Agents, 1933.

Cotton from Plant to Product, 64 pages. Pepperell Manufacturing Company, Boston, Massachusetts, 1929.

Cotton from the Raw Material to the Finished Product, R. J. Peake, 134 pages. Pitman and Sons, Ltd., New York, 1934.

Cotton Goods, Sizing of, Thomson. Manchester, England, 1875.

Cotton Loom Fixing, John F. Reynolds. Bragdon, Lord and Nagle, Textile World, New York City, 1924.

Cotton Manufacturing, Brooks. Blackburn, England, 1886.

Cotton Manufacturing, E. Posselt. Philadelphia College of Textiles and Science, Philadelphia, Pennsylvania, 1903 and 1919.

Cotton Mill Handbook, 168 pages. Textile World, New York City, 1932.

Cotton Mill Management, W. S. Taggart, 268 pages. Macmillan Company, Ltd., London, 1932.

Cotton Mill Mathematics, T. H. Quigley and W. S. Smith. Smith, Hammond and Company, Atlanta, Georgia, 1930.

Cotton Opening, Cleaning, and Picking, H. H. Willis and Vernette B. Moore, 131 pages. The Textile Foundation, Commerce Building, Washington.

Cotton Sample Book of Fabrics, John Hoye. John Hoye Company, 112 Franklin Street, New York.

Cotton Spinning, Brickett. I.C.S., Scranton, Pennsylvania.

Cotton Spinning, Thomas Thornley. D. Van Nostrand Company, Princeton, N.J., 1901, 1920.

Cotton Spinning, A. S. Wade, 104 pages. Pitman and Sons, Ltd., London, 1921.

Cotton Spinning, Walmsley, 1883.

Cotton Spinning, H. H. Willis, G. H. Dunlap, and V. B. Moore, 141 pages. Textile Foundation, Commerce Building, Washington, D.C.

Cotton Spinning, Student's, Nasmith. Heywood, Ltd., Manchester, England.

Cotton Spinning Calculations and Yarn Costs, J. Winterbottom. Longmans, Green Company, New York, 1907, 1921.

Cotton Spinning Machinery and Its Uses, W. S. Taggart, 110 pages. Pitman and Sons, Ltd., London, 1922.

Cotton Spinning, The Science of, Hyde. Manchester, England.

Cotton Spinning, The Science of, Leigh. Manchester, England, 1877.

Cotton, The Universal Fiber, W. D. Darby, 63 pages. Dry Goods Economist, New York, 1932.

Cotton Weaving and Designing, J. T. Taylor. Longmans, Green, Ltd., London, 1909.

Cotton Yarn Manufacture, W. E. Winchester, 311 pages. Philadelphia College of Textiles and Science, Philadelphia, Pennsylvania, 1902, 1914.

Cotton Yarn Manufacturing Problems, S. E. Smith. McGraw-Hill Book Company, Inc., New York, 1928.

Descriptions, Finishes and Uses of Staple Cotton Fabrics, John Hoye. John Hoye, 112 Franklin Street, New York City, 1935.

Drawing and Roving, G. R. Merrill. G. R. Merrill, 1935, 1941.

Drawing Frames, H. H. Willis and V. B. Moore, 52 pages. Textile Foundation, Washington, D.C., 1937.

Early New England Cotton Manufacture, Caroline F. Ware. Houghton Mifflin Company, New York, 1931.

Encyclopedia of Cotton Fabrics for Students and Others in the Cotton Trade, W. Hough, 84 pages. Manchester, England, 1927.

Fabric Analysis Covering Wool, Worsted, Silk, Cotton, Artificial Silk, E. A. Posselt, 231 pages. Textile Publishing Company, Philadelphia, Pennsylvania, 1920.

Fine Cotton Spinning, J. W. Lomax. Emmott and Company, Ltd., Manchester, England, 1913.

Finishing Materials, J. A. Clark, 113 pages. W. R. Smith Publishing Company, Atlanta, Georgia, 1934.

From Cotton Field to Cotton Mill, H. Thompson. Macmillan Company, New York, 1906.

Greer's Spinning Rules, J. A. Greer. Charlotte, N.C., 1915.

Hand Loom Weaving, Plain and Ornamental, Luther Hooper. London, 1910.

Handbook for Cotton Manufacturing Students, Brooks. London, 1889.

Handbook on Cotton Manufacture, Geldard, New York, 1867.

High Drafting in Cotton Spinning, C. Barnshaw, 127 pages. E. Benn, Ltd., London, 1930.

High Drafting in Cotton Spinning, J. Noguera. Charley and Pickersgill, 1934.

History and Principles of Weaving by Hand and by Power, A. Barlow. Sampson, Ltd., London, 1884.

History of Cotton Manufacture in Great Britain, Baine. London, 1835.

Industrial Fabrics, Handbook of, G. B. Haven. Wellington Sears Company, 111 W. 40th Street, New York City, 1941.

King Cotton Is Sick, C. T. Murchison, 190 pages. University of North Carolina Press, Chapel Hill, N.C., 1930.

La Filature du Coton, Du Pont. Paris, 1901.

Labor and Textiles, R. W. Dunn and J. Hardy, 256 pages. International Publishers, New York, 1931.

Lappet and Dobby Looms, Thomas Roberts. Emmott and Company, Ltd., Manchester, England, 1920.

Manufacture of Narrow Woven Fabrics, E. A. Posselt, 198 pages. Textile Publishing Company, Philadelphia, Pennsylvania, 1917.

New England Cotton Textile Industry, J. H. Burgy. Waverly Press, Boston, Massachusetts, 1932.

Overlooker's and Student's Guide to the Ring Spinning Frame, N. Booth. Scott, Greenwood and Sons, Ltd., London, 1912.

Power Loom, Introduction of the, N. Appleton. Information on the Origin of Lowell, Massachusetts. Lowell, Massachusetts, 1858.

Practical Loom Fixing, Thomas Nelson. Ray Printing Company, Charlotte, N.C., 1917.

Principles of Cotton Manufacturing, William King. Dominion Textile Company, Ltd., Montreal, 1938.

Processing and Finishing Cottons, James F. Monoghan, 1008 pages. J. F. Monoghan, Wiltham, Massachusetts, 1935.

Production Costs in Cotton Spinning Mills, A. H. Hardman. Emmott and Company, Ltd., Manchester, England, 1912.

Profits and Losses in Textiles—Cotton Textile Financing Since World War One, S. J. Kennedy, 257 pages. Harper and Brothers Company, New York, 1936.

Progress of Cotton Manufacture in the United States, Introduction and, Sam Batchelder. Boston, Massachusetts, 1863.

Roving Frames, H. H. Willis, R. K. Eaton, and V. B. Moore, 103 pages. Textile Foundation, Washington, D.C., 1937.

Sam Crompton, The Inventor of the Spinning Mule, Dobson and Barlow, Ltd., Bolton, England, 1927.

Single Process Cotton Lapping, W. Hardman. D. Van Nostrand Company, Princeton, N.J., 1927.

Standard Cost Control for Cotton Spinning, J. Ryan and J. S. Taylor.

Standard Cotton Cloths and Their Construction, H. W. Nichols and W. H. Broomhead, 160 pages. Illustrated with samples. H. W. Nichols, Fall River, Massachusetts, 1927.

Standard Tables for Strength of Cotton Yarns, W. S. Kelley. Lowell, Massachusetts, 1887.

Staple Cotton Fabrics, John Hoye. McGraw-Hill Book Company, Inc., New York, 1943.

Students' Cotton Spinning, Nasmith. D. Van Nostrand Company, Princeton, N.J., 1904.

Study of Cotton Hedging for a Grey Goods Mill, 1921–1926. Harvard University Press, Cambridge, Massachusetts, 1928.

Testing Strength of Materials, Cotton and Linen, G. R. Smith, 122 pages. E. Marlborough and Company, Ltd., London, 1922.

Tests on Cotton, Cobb. Bulletin 62, U.S. Government Printing Office, Washington, D.C.

Textile Chemistry for the Cotton Industry, F. G. Cooper, 235 pages. Methuen and Company, Ltd., London, 1923.

Textile Handbook, Cotton Edition, Research Staff of E. F. Houghton and Company, Philadelphia, Pennsylvania, 1925.

Textile Raw Materials and Their Conversion Into Yarns, J. Zipser, revised by D. T. Nisbet. Scott, Greenwood and Son, Ltd., London, 1921.

Textile Tests for Cotton Manufacturers, 360 pages. Draper Company, Hopedale, Massachusetts, 1917.

The American Cotton Industry, I. M. Young, 150 pages. Charles Scribner's Sons, New York, 1903.

The Cotton Industry, J. H. Crabtree, 126 pages. G. Lockwood and Sons, Ltd., London, 1922.

The Cotton Industry and Trade, S. J. Chapman, 175 pages. Methuen and Company, Ltd., London, 1905.

The Cotton Manufacturing Industry of the United States, M. T. Copeland, 415 pages. Harvard University Press, Cambridge, Massachusetts, 1917.

The Cotton Textile Worker's Handbook, 367 pages. I.C.S., Scranton, Pennsylvania, 1920.

The Cotton Weaver's Handbook, H. B. Heylin. Griffin and Company, Ltd., London, 1908, 1923.

The Cotton Yarn Manufacturer's Problems, Stephen E. Smith, 191 pages. Textile World, McGraw-Hill Book Company, New York, 1928.

The Determination of Cotton and Linen by Physical, Chemical, and Microscopic Methods, A. Herzog, 32 pages. Teachers College, Columbia University, New York, 1916.

The Early English Cotton Industry, George W. Daniels. University Press, Manchester, England, 1920.

The Fabric of Civilization. Guaranty Trust Company, New York, 1919.

The Middle Processes of Cotton Mills, Thomas Thornley. Scott, Greenwood and Son, Ltd., London, 1923.

Wages and Labor in Cotton Spinning, Jewkes and Gray. University of Manchester Press, Manchester, England, 1935.

Weaving, Plain and Fancy, Thomas Nelson. Edwards and Broughton Company, 1907.

Yarn and Cloth Making, An Economic Study, M. L. Kissel. Macmillan Company, New York, 1918.

COTTON YARN AND CLOTH MARKETING

Cotton and Cotton Manufacture, brief analysis for the layman, James P. Warburg, 61 pages. First National Bank, Boston, Massachusetts, 1921.

Cotton as a World Power, study in the economic interpretation of history, J. A. B. Scherer, 452 pages. F. A. Stokes & Co., New York, 1916.

Cotton, the Universal Fiber, from raw material to finished product, manufacture and marketing methods and dictionary of cotton goods, W. D. Darby, 63 pages. Dry Goods Economist, New York, 1932.

King Cotton Diplomacy, Foreign Relations of the Confederate States of America, F. L. Owsley. University of Chicago Press, 1931.

King Cotton Is Sick, C. T. Murchison, 190 pages. University of North Carolina Press, 1930.

Merchandising of Cotton Textiles, M. T. Copeland and E. P. Learned, 92 pages. Harvard University, Graduate School of Business Administration, Bureau of Business Research, Soldiers Field, Boston, Massachusetts. Under a grant from the Textile Foundation, Inc., 1933.

The Cotton and Linen Departments, Eliza B. Thompson, 182 pages. Ronald Press, New York, 1917.

The Cotton Industry and Trade, S. J. Chapman, 175 pages. Methuen & Company, London, 1905.

The Cotton Manufacturing Industry of the United States, M. T. Copeland, 415 pages. Harvard University Press, Cambridge, Massachusetts, 1917.

Twenty-Five Years, the Association of Cotton Textile Merchants of New York, 1918 to 1943, the Story of Worth Street, 62 pages. The Association of Cotton Textile Merchants of New York. Parker Allston Associates, New York, 1944.

World Developments in the Cotton Industry, with special reference to the cotton piecegoods industry, Louis Bader, 187 pages. New York University Press, New York, 1925.

COTTON YARN AND CLOTH UTILIZATION

Annual Proceedings of the American Cotton Manufacturers Association, Charlotte, North Carolina.

Management of a Textile Business, C. C. Balderston and V. S. Karabasz. Textile Foundation, Department of Commerce, Washington, D.C., 1938.

Managing Cotton Cloth Inventories in the Cotton Textile Industry, Harvard University Press, Cambridge, Massachusetts, 1934.

World Developments in the Cotton Industry, with special reference to the cotton piecegoods industry, Louis Bader, 187 pages. New York University Press, New York, 1925.

COTTON CLOTH UTILIZATION

Textile Fabrics, George H. Johnson, 385 pages. Harper and Brothers, New York, 1927.

COTTON LINTERS

Cotton-Cellulose, Its Chemistry and Technology, A. J. Hall, 228 pages. E. Benn, Ltd., London, 1924.

Cotton Waste, Its Production, Manipulation and Uses, Thomas Thornley, 400 pages. D. Van Nostrand Company, New York, 1921.

Textile Waste Treatment and Recovery, J. C. Geyer and W. A. Perry. Textile Foundation, Department of Commerce, Washington, D.C., 1938.

The Chemical Properties of Cotton Linters, W. F. Henderson, 11 pages. Easton, Pennsylvania, 1923.

The Great Cottonseed Industry of the South, L. A. Ransom. Oil and Drug Publishing Company, 1911.

BAST FIBERS OTHER THAN COTTON

A Treatise on the Cultivation of Flax, Hemp and Jute, Campbell. Sydney, Australia, 1868.

Cordage Fibers, Carter. London, 1909.

Cotton and Linen, E. B. Thompson, 199 pages. Ronald Press, New York, 1922.

Culture du Lin, Ferrage. Toulouse, France, 1907.

Culture du Lin, Ladureau. Lille, France, 1878.

Etude sur la Ramie, Benoit. Paris, 1901.

Etudes sur la Culture de Lin, Cherot. Paris, 1845.

Flax, H. H. Willis, 32 pages. Textile Foundation, Commerce Building, Washington, D.C., 1936.

Flax, Hemp and Jute Products, Stanwood. U.S. Census Reports, U.S. Government Printing Office, Washington, D.C.

How to Weave Linens, E. F. Worst, 166 pages. Bruce Publishing Company, Milwaukee, Wisconsin, 1926.

Jute, an account of its growth and manufacture, 112 pages. Ludlow Manufacturing Associates, Ludlow, Massachusetts, 1928.

Jute and Its Manufacture, H. R. Carter, 192 pages. J. Bale, Sons, and Danielsson, Ltd., London, 1921.

Jute and Jute Spinning, T. Woodhouse and Peter Kilgour, two volumes, Macmillan and Company, Ltd., London, 1929.

Jute and Linen Weaving, T. Woodhouse and Thomas Milne, two volumes, Macmillan and Company, Ltd., London, 1931.

L'abaca aux Iles Philippines, Desleyez. Paris, 1902.

La Ramie, Bothier. Paris, 1902.

La Ramie, Bray. Paris, 1879.

La Ramie, Fremey. Paris, 1884.

La Ramie, Graugnard. Marseilles, France, 1878.

Le Lin et sa Culture, Veret. Paris, 1866.

Linen and Bedding, F. J. Ringo, 119 pages. A. W. Shaw Company, New York.

Linen, from the Raw Material to the Finished Product, A. S. Moore, 132 pages. Pitman and Sons, Ltd., New York, 1914.

Linen, The Emblem of Elegance, W. D. Darby, 79 pages. Dry Goods Economist, New York, 1926.

Modern Flax, Hemp, and Jute Spinning and Twisting, a handbook, H. R. Carter, 244 pages. Scott, Greenwood and Son, London, 1925.

Note Industrielle sur la Ramie, Favier. Avignon, France, 1882.

Ramie and China-Grass, Carter. London, 1910.

Ramie, China-Gras und Nesselfaser, Bouce and Grother. Berlin, 1884.

Spinning, Weaving and Finishing of Flax and Jute, Thomas Woodhouse and Peter Kilgour, 206 pages. Pitman and Sons, Ltd., New York, 1929.

Summary of the Origin and Processes of Linen Manufacture, Combe. Belfast, Ireland, 1868.

Testing Strength of Materials, cotton and linen, G. R. Smith, 122 pages. E. Marlborough and Company, London, 1922.

The Cotton and Linen Departments, E. B. Thompson, 182 pages. Ronald Press, New York, 1917.

The Determination of Cotton and Linen by Physical, Chemical, and Microscopic Methods, A. Herzog, 32 pages. Teachers College, Columbia University Press, New York, 1916.

The Finishing of Jute and Linen Fabrics, Thomas Woodhouse, 326 pages. Macmillan and Company, Ltd., London, 1928.

The Jute Industry from Seed to Finished Cloth, T. Woodhouse and P. Kilgour, 133 pages. Pitman and Sons, Ltd., New York, 1921.

The Manufacture of Linen, Hemp, and Jute Fabrics, H. R. Carter, 89 pages. J. Bale and Sons; and Danielsson, Ltd., London, 1909.

The Spinning and Twisting of Long Vegetable Fibers, flax, hemp, jute, tow, and ramie, H. R. Carter, 434 pages. C. Griffin and Company, Ltd., London, 1919.

The Story of Linen, William F. Leggett, 103 pages. Chemical Publishing Co., Brooklyn, New York, 1945.

The Theory and Practice of Jute Spinning, W. Leggett, 284 pages. W. Kidd, Dundee, Scotland, 1902.

RAYON AND OTHER MANMADE FIBERS—MANUFACTURING

About Du Pont Nylon, E. I. du Pont de Nemours & Co., Inc., Wilmington, Delaware.

Acetate Silk and Its Dyes, C. E. Mullin. D. Van Nostrand Company, Princeton, New Jersey, 1927.

Artificial Silk, V. Hottenroth, 421 pages. Pitman and Sons, Ltd., New York, 1928.

Artificial Silk, Dr. Otto Faust, 184 pages. Pitman and Sons, Ltd., New York, 1929.

Artificial Silk and Its Manufacture, Joseph Foltzer, 255 pages. Pitman and Sons, Ltd., 2 West 45th Street, New York, 1926.

Artificial Silk Handbook, F. Nasmith. Heywood, Ltd., London, 1927.

Artificial Silk Industry, Schlesinger, Berlin.

Artificial Silk or Rayon, Its Manufacture and Uses, Thomas Woodhouse, 245 pages. Pitman and Sons, Ltd., New York, 1929.

Artificial Silks, S. R. Trotman and E. R. Trotman, 274 pages. Griffin and Company, Limited, London, 1931.

Better Buymanship. Household Finance Corporation, Chicago, Illinois, 1937.

Celanese Family, The. Celanese Corporation of America, New York.

Celanese in War. Celanese Corporation of America, New York.

Cellulose, Cross and Bevan. London, 1895.

Cellulose Acetate, A. G. Lipscomb. E. Benn, Ltd., London, 1933.

Cellulose Chemistry, E. J. Heuser. McGraw-Hill Book Company, Inc., New York, 1924.

Cellulose, Researches on, Cross and Bevan. London, 1901, 1906, 1912.

Chemical Technology of Silk and Rayon Throwing, D. S. Chamberlain, 60 pages. Warwick Chemical Company, West Warwick, Rhode Island, 1935.

Chemistry and Technology of Artificial Silk, A. J. Hall. London, 1928.

Cleaning and Dyeing of Celanese and Rayon, E. Foster. 1929.

Die Zellulose, Piest. Stuttgart, Germany, 1910.

Dissecting and Calculating Silk and Rayon Fabrics, Horace Nield. 1928.

Dyeing of Viscose with D. C. Dyestuffs, Courtaulds, Ltd., London, 1927.

Eastman Acetate Rayon, The Story of, Eastman Chemical Products, Inc., New York.

Fabrication de la Soie Artificielle, Joseph Foltzer. Paris, 1905.

Facts About Fabrics, E. I. du Pont de Nemours & Company, Inc.

Fiberglas. Owens-Corning Fiberglas Corporation, Newark, Ohio; New York.

Home Economics and Rayon. American Viscose Company, Marcus Hook, Pennsylvania.

Information Regarding Rayon. American Viscose Company, Marcus Hook, Pennsylvania.

Instructional Material on Rayon Hosiery of Celanese Yarn. Celanese Corporation of America, New York.

Knitted Fabrics. Beaunit Corporation, 261 Fifth Avenue, New York.

Latex in Industry, Royce J. Noble, 334 pages. Palmerton Publishing Company, Inc., New York, 1935.

Manufacture of Artificial Silk, E. Wheeler. London, 1929, 1930.

Methods of Cellulose Chemistry, C. Doree. D. Van Nostrand Company, Princeton, New Jersey, 1933.

Nitrocellulose Industry, Worden. New York, 1911.

Physical and Chemical Properties and Processing of Nylon Textiles. E. I. du Pont de Nemours and Company, Inc., Wilmington, Delaware, 1943.

Practical Rayon Sizing, J. J. Sussmuth. Rayon Publishing Company, 303 Fifth Avenue, New York.

Preparation and Weaving of Artificial Silks and Rayons, Thomas Woodhouse. Pitman and Sons, Ltd., New York, London, 1929.

Production and Distribution of Silk and Rayon Broadgoods, M. T. Copeland and W. H. Turner, 109 pages. Textile Foundation, Inc., and the National Federation of Textiles, Inc., New York, 1935.

Questions and Answers on Rayon. Rayon Publishing Company, 303 Fifth Avenue, New York, 1938.

Rayon and Other Synthetic Fibers, W. D. Darby, 65 pages. Dry Goods Economist, 239 West 39th Street, New York, 1929.

Rayon and Synthetic Yarn Handbook, E. W. K. Schwarz and Herbert R. Mauersberger, 558 pages. Rayon Publishing Company, 303 Fifth Avenue, New York, 1936.

Rayon Dyeing and Finishing, B. L. Hawthorne. Howes Publishing Company, New York, 1934.

Rayon Fabrics. American Viscose Company, Marcus Hook, Pennsylvania.

Rayon Fabrics, Jessie Caplin. Riverside Press, St. Paul, Minnesota, 1939.

Rayon Today. E. I. du Pont de Nemours and Company, Inc., Wilmington, Delaware.

Rayon, a Beautiful New Fiber Synthetically Produced, 54 pages. Green, Ellis, and Anderson, New York, 1925.

Report on the Development and Use of Rayon and Other Synthetic Fibers. Department of Agriculture, Washington, D.C., 1938.

Romance of Celanese. Celanese Corporation of America, 522 Fifth Avenue, New York.

Silk and Rayon Directory. Issued annually by the Harlequin Press Co., Ltd., Manchester, England.

Silk and the Silk Industry, Joseph Schober, 375 pages. Includes information on rayon. Constable and Company, Ltd., London, 1930.

The Manufacturing of Artificial Silk, chiefly on the Viscose Process, E. Wheeler, 177 pages. D. Van Nostrand Company, Princeton, New Jersey, 1931.

The New Fibers, J. V. Sherman and S. L. Sherman, 538 pages. D. Van Nostrand Co., Princeton, New Jersey, 1946.

The Rayon Industry, M. H. Avram, 893 pages. D. Van Nostrand Company, Princeton, New Jersey, 1929.

The Story of Artificial Silk, H. N. Casson. London, 1928.

The Story of Rayon, 95 pages. For the American Viscose Corporation by Moore Press, Inc., 461 8th Avenue, New York City, 1937.

The Textile Fibers, J. Merritt Matthews, 1053 pages. John Wiley and Sons, Inc., New York, and Chapman and Hall, Ltd., London, 1924. Fourth edition, rewritten and enlarged,

1924. Fifth Edition, Matthews-Mauersberger Edition, rewritten and enlarged, 1133 pages, 1947.

Uniformity Rides the Rails. Industrial Rayon Corporation, Cleveland, Ohio, 1947.

Vinyon. American Viscose Corporation, 350 Fifth Avenue, New York.

Viscose Rayon Production, D. L. Pellatt, 236 pages. Emmott & Co., Ltd., Manchester, England, 1931.

What Is Rayon? American Viscose Company, Marcus Hook, Pennsylvania.

What You Should Know About Rayon. E. I. du Pont de Nemours and Company, Inc., Wilmington, Delaware.

Your Guide to Rayon. American Viscose Company, Marcus Hook, Pennsylvania.

RAYON AND OTHER MANMADE FIBERS—DYEING

Acetate Silk and Its Dyes, C. E. Mullin, 473 pages. D. Van Nostrand Company, Inc., 1929.

Dyeing Silk, Mixed Silk Fabrics and Artificial Silk, Dr. A. Gandswindt, 220 pages. On the dyeing of silk and rayon. D. Van Nostrand Company, New York.

Rayon and Synthetic Yarn Handbook, E. W. K. Schwarz and H. R. Mauersberger, 558 pages. Rayon Publishing Company, 303 Fifth Ave., New York, 1936.

Rayon Dyeing and Finishing, B. L. Hawthorne. Howes Publishing Co., New York, 1934.

The Cleaning and Dyeing of Celanese and Rayon, A brief history of rayon and its manufacture, L. E. Foster, 216 pages. L. E. Foster, York, Nebraska, 1929.

RAYON AND OTHER MANMADE FIBERS—MARKETING

Production and Distribution of Silk and Rayon Broadgoods, production and distribution of silk and rayon, M. T. Copeland and W. H. Turner, 109 pages. Textile Foundation, Inc., and the National Federation of Textiles, Inc., 1935.

Rayon and Other Synthetic Fibers, origin, development, use and manufacture of rayon with information on merchandising and care of rayon fabrics. W. D. Darby, 65 pages. Dry Goods Economist, 239 West 39th St., New York, 1929.

Silk and the Silk Industry, with material on rayon, manufacture and trade, Joseph Schober, 375 pages. Constable & Co., Ltd., London, 1930.

RAYON AND OTHER MANMADE FIBERS—MISCELLANEOUS

Artificial Silk Industry, report of the League of Nations, Economic and Financial Section, International Economic Conference, Geneva, May, 1927, 51 pages. World Peace Foundation, 1927.

Cellulose Acetate, Its Manufacture and Applications, A. G. Lipscomb, 308 pages. E. Benn, Ltd., London, 1933.

Cotton-Cellulose, Its Chemistry and Technology, A. J. Hall, 228 pages. E. Benn, Ltd., London, 1924.

Dissecting and Calculating Silk and Rayon Products, H. Neild, 196 pages. American Silk Journal, 1928.

Rayon Year Book (Contains directory of rayon yarn producers.) Textile World, 330 West 42nd St., New York.

Rayon, A New Influence in the Textile Industry, 31 pages. Metropolitan Life Insurance Company, New York City, 1929.

Report on Development and Use of Rayon and Other Synthetic Fibers, 50 pages. U.S. Department of Agriculture, Washington, D.C., 1938.

The Methods of Cellulose Chemistry, C. Doree, 499 pages. D. Van Nostrand Company, Princeton, New Jersey, 1933.

The Romance of Rayon, A. H. Hard, 76 pages. Whittaker and Robinson, Ltd., Manchester, England, 1934.

The Story of Rayon, 63 pages. American Viscose Corporation, Empire State Building, New York, 1929.

Zellwolle, a German book on textile fiber, H. G. Bodenbender, 534 pages. Rayon Publishing Company, 303 Fifth Avenue, New York, 1936.

WOOL RAISING

American Wool Handbook, Von Bergen and Mauersberger, 864 pages. American Wool Handbook Co., 303 Fifth Avenue, New York, 1938.

Range Sheep and Wool in the Seventeen Western States, Hultz and Hill, 374 pages. John Wiley and Son, New York, 1931.

The Story of Wool, William F. Leggett, 304 pages. Chemical Publishing Co., Brooklyn, New York, 1947.

Three Textile Raw Materials and Their Manufacture, how cotton, wool, and silk are produced, International Acceptance Bank, Inc., New York, 127 pages. 1924.

Wool, Stanley H. Hart, 249 pages. Philadelphia College of Textiles and Science, Philadelphia, Pennsylvania, 1924.

Wool and Wool Manufacture, J. P. Warburg, 50 pages. First National Bank, Boston, Massachusetts, 1920.

Wool Carding, James Bradley, 344 pages. Emmott and Company, Manchester, England, 1921.

Wool Carding and Combing, With Notes on Sheep Breeding and Wool Growing, A. F. Barker and E. Priestley, 264 pages. Cassell and Company, Ltd., London, 1912.

Wool Fibers, Structure of, Bowman. Macmillan Company, New York. .

Wool, The World's Comforter, wool from raw material to finished product, includes dictionary of wool fabrics, W. D. Darby, 107 pages. Dry Goods Economist, New York, 1922.

Woolen and Worsted Raw Materials, J. R. Hind, 213 pages. E. Benn, Ltd., London, 1934.

WOOL MANUFACTURING

A Comprehensive History of the Woolen and Worsted Manufactures and the Natural and Commercial History of Sheep, J. Bischoff. Smith, Elder and Company, Ltd., London, 1842.

A Handbook of Weaves, Gustave H. Oelsner. Macmillan Company, New York, 1915.

A Manual of Weave Construction, I. Kastanek. Guild and Lord, Boston, Massachusetts, 1903.

A Way Forward for the Wool Industry, E. Kaplan. The Business Bourse, New York, 1933.

American Wool Handbook, Von Bergen and Mauersberger, 864 pages. American Wool Handbook Company, 303 Fifth Avenue, New York, 1938.

Analysis of the Production of Worsted Yarn Sales, A. H. Williams, M. A. Brumbaugh, and H. S. Davis, 116 pages. Data for the years 1911–1913 to 1919–1929. University of Pennsylvania Press, Philadelphia, Pennsylvania, 1929.

Burring and Carbonizing. I.C.S., Scranton, Pennsylvania.

Calculations in Yarns and Fabrics, F. Bradbury. F. King and Sons, Ltd., Halifax, England.

Carpets and Rugs, Robert Beaumont. 400 pages. London.

Cloth Finishing, Woolen and Worsted, J. and J. C. Schofield. Huddersfield, England, 1927.

Cost Finding in Woolen and Worsted Mills, Dale. Textile Publishing Company, Boston, Massachusetts.

Costs and Costings for Woolen Manufacturers, J. N. Todd. London, 1924.

Elementary Textile Microscopy. Howes Publishing Company, New York, 1930.

Fabric Analysis, Covering Wool, Worsted, Silk, Cotton, Artificial Silk, E. A. Posselt, 231 pages. Textile Publishing Company, Philadelphia, Pennsylvania, 1920.

Fibers and Fiber Production, Boeken. Department of Agriculture, New Zealand, Bulletin Number 45, Wellington, New Zealand.

Fur, A Practical Treatise, M. Bachrach. Prentice-Hall, Inc., New York, 1936.

History of the Woolen and Worsted Industries, E. Lipson. London, 1921.

History of Wool Combing, J. Burnley. Sampson Low, Inc., London, 1889.

How to Make a Woolen Mill Pay, J. Mackie. D. Van Nostrand Company, Princeton, New Jersey, 1904.

Imperial Wool Research Conference, 107 pages. Report of the Proceedings, London, 1930. Report Published, 1931.

Labor and Textiles, R. W. Dunn and J. Hardy, 256 pages. International Publishers, New York, 1931.

Leeds Woolen Industry, W. B. Crump. Covers the years 1780–1820. Thoresby Society, Leeds, England, 1931.

Post-War Trends in Worsted Spinning Capacity, World War One, 11 pages. Industrial Research Department, Wharton School of Finance and Commerce, University of Pennsylvania, Philadelphia, Pennsylvania, 1931.

Practical Weaving, T. R. Ashenhurst. J. Broadbent and Company, Ltd., Huddersfield, England, 1895.

Practice in Finishing, F. H. Greene. Philadelphia, Pennsylvania, 1886.

Practice in Wool Carding, Joseph Brown. Philadelphia, Pennsylvania, 1886.

Principles of Wool Combing, H. Priestman. Harcourt Brace Company, New York, 1904, 1924.

Principles of Woolen Spinning, H. Priestman. Longmans, Green Company, New York, 1908, 1924.

Principles of Worsted Spinning, H. Priestman, 300 pages. London, 1908, 1921.

Production and Equipment Trends in American Worsted Yarn Manufacture, H. S. Davis and G. T. Brown, 50 pages. Covers 1919–1932. University of Pennsylvania Press, Philadelphia, Pennsylvania, 1933.

Sheep, A. B. Gilfillan. Little, Brown and Company, Boston, Massachusetts, 1936.

Spinning and Weaving Calculations, with Special Reference to Woolen Fabrics, N. Reiser, 160 pages. D. Van Nostrand and Company, New York, 1904.

Standard Cloths, Roberts Beaumont. London.

Textile Raw Materials and Their Conversion into Yarn, J. Zipser. Scott, Greenwood and Sons, Ltd., London, 1921.

The American Wool Manufacturer, George C. Burns, 136 pages. G. C. Burns, Central Falls, Rhode Island, 1872.

The Age and Size of Worsted Spinning Frames and Mules, 15 pages. Wharton School of Finance and Commerce, University of Pennsylvania Press, Philadelphia, Pennsylvania, 1931.

The American Wool Manufacture, A. H. Cole, two volumes. Harvard University Press, Cambridge, Massachusetts, 1926.

The Commercial Problems of the Woolen and Worsted Industries, Paul T. Cherrington. Textile Foundation, Washington, D.C., 1932.

The Development of Wool Manufacture in the United States of America, George W. Bond, 1887.

The Finishing of Wool Goods, J. and J. C. Schofield. Huddersfield, England, 1935.

The Finishing of Textile Fabrics, Roberts Beaumont. London, 1909, 1926.

The Fleece and the Loom, John L. Hayes. Boston, 1865.

The Manufacture of Woolen and Worsted Yarns, J. W. Radcliffe, 353 pages. Emmott and Company, Ltd., Manchester, England, 1924.

The New England Wool Manufacture, S. N. D. North. Edited by W. T. Davis. Boston, Massachusetts, 1897.

The Processing of Wool and Wool Fabrics, John D. Haerry. Two Volumes, Textile Library, 1926.

The Romance of Commerce. Silk and Wool treated. Little, Brown Company, Boston, Massachusetts.

The Wool Carder's Vade Mecum, W. C. Bramwell. Boston, Massachusetts, 1881.

The Wool Industry, Paul T. Cherrington. A. W. Shaw Company, Chicago, Illinois, 1916.

The Woolen Manufacturer's and Overlooker's Guide, George Ibberson. London, 1853.

The Worsted Industry, J. Dumville and S. Kershaw. Pitman and Sons, Ltd., London, 1924.

The Worsted Spinner's Practical Handbook, H. Turner, 135 pages. Scott, Greenwood and Son, Ltd., London, 1915.

The Yorkshire Woolen and Worsted Industry, H. Heaton. Yorkshire, England, 1920.

Three Textile Raw Materials and Their Manufacture, 127 pages. International Acceptance Bank, New York, 1927.

Treatise of Advanced Worsted Drawing, H. Edmondson. E. Benn, Ltd., London, 1928.

Wool, Frank Ormerod, 217 pages. London, 1918.

Wool and Cotton in All Forms, 177 pages. William Whitman Company, Inc., New York, 1921.

Wool and Manufacturers of Wool, W. C. Ford. U.S. Government Printing Office, Washington, D.C., 1894.

Wool and Wool Manufacture, J. P. Warburg, 50 pages. First National Bank, Boston, Massachusetts, 1920.

Wool and the Wool Weaver, W. Claxton. Blackie and Son, Ltd., 286 Fifth Avenue, New York, 1936.

Wool Carding and Combing, Baker and Priestley. Cassell and Company, Ltd., London, 1912.

Wool from the Raw Material to the Finished Product, J. A. Hunter, 5th edition. Pitman and Sons, Ltd., London, 1937.

Wool Handling and a Revised Glossary of Wool Terms, 75 pages. Eavenson and Levering, Camden, New Jersey, 1942.

Wool Quality, S. G. Barker, 333 pages. His Majesty's Stationery Office, London, 1931.

Wool Scouring, from Drying to Spinning, inclusive, Number 79. I.C.S., Scranton, Pennsylvania, 1906.

Wool Substitutes, Roberts Beaumont, 190 pages. London, 1922.

Wool, A Study of the Fibers, S. G. Barker. His Majesty's Stationery Office, London, 1929.

Wool, Its Origin and Uses, S. B. Hollings. 1928.

Wool, Raw Material to Finished Product, A. F. Barker. University of Leeds, Leeds, England, 1922.

Wool, The World's Comforter, W. D. Darby, 107 pages. Dry Goods Economist, New York, 1922.

Woolen and Worsted, Roberts Beaumont, 716 pages. D. Van Nostrand Company, Princeton, New Jersey, 1921.

Woolen and Worsted Fabrics Glossary, Frank P. Bennett, 348 pages. F. P. Bennett and Company, Boston, Massachusetts, 1914.
Woolen and Worsted Finishing, John F. Timmerman. American School of Correspondence, 1909.
Woolen and Worsted Spinning, A. F. Barker, 343 pages. Funk and Wagnalls Company, 354 Fourth Avenue, New York, 1923.
Woolen·and Worsted Spinning, Miles Collins, 320 pages. American School of Correspondence, Chicago, Illinois, 1909.
Woolen Yarn Production, T. Lawson. Pitman and Sons, Ltd., New York.
Worsted Carding and Combing, J. R. Hind, 205 pages. Pitman and Sons, Ltd., London, 1932.
Worsted Drawing and Spinning, J. R. Hind. E. Benn., Ltd., 154 Fleet Street, London, 1936.
Worsted Drawing and Spinning Calculations, George H. Davies, 167 pages. London, 1923.
Worsted Open Drawing, Samuel Kershaw, 131 pages. Pitman and Sons, Ltd., London, 1931.
Worsted Overlooker's Handbook, M. M. Buckley, 6th edition. F. King and Sons, Ltd., Halifax, England.
Worsted Preparing and Spinning, F. Bradbury and M. M. Buckley. Three volumes. F. King and Sons, Ltd., Halifax, England, 1910.
Worsted Yarn Manufacturing in 1933, 16 pages. University of Pennsylvania Press, Philadelphia, Pennsylvania, 1934.
Worsted, Advanced Drawing of, H. Edmondson. McGraw-Hill Book Company, Inc., New York, 1928.
Yarn and Cloth Making, Mary L. Kissell. Macmillan Company, New York, 1918.

WOOL MARKETING

American Wool Handbook, Von Bergen and Mauersberger, 864 pages. American Wool Handbook Co., Rayon Publishing Company, New York, 1938.
Distribution of Textiles, survey by Bureau of Business Research, Harvard University, Cambridge, Massachusetts, study of textile woven goods flowing through the several channels of distribution, 1926.
The Commercial Problems of the Woolen and Worsted Industry, Paul T. Cherrington, 242 pages. Textile Foundation, Inc., Washington, D.C., 1932.
The Marketing and Financing of Wool, R. L. Studley, 87 pages. J. Weber, Fernwood, Pennsylvania, 1924.
The Marketing of Wool, A. F. DuPlessis, 337 pages. Pitman and Son, Ltd., New York, 1931.
The Wool Box and Other Wool Market Helps, D. C. Rogers and W. D. McKee. Missouri State Board of Agriculture, Jefferson City, Missouri, 14 pages. 1921.
Wool, The World's Comforter, W. D. Darby, 107 pages. Dry Goods Economist, New York, 1922.

WOOL—MISCELLANEOUS

A Statistical Study of Wool Prices, T. R. Hamilton, 56 pages. Texas A. and M. Press, College Station, Texas, 1938.
A Way Forward for the Wool Industry, E. Kaplan, 236 pages. The Business Bourse, New York, 1933.
By-Products in the Packing Industry, R. A. Clemen, 410 pages. University of Chicago Press, Chicago, Illinois, 1927.
Dalgety's Annual Wool Review for Australia and New Zealand, compiled by Dalgety and Company, Ltd., London.
General Study of the Wool Industry, J. J. Weber, 33 pages. Research Committee, New England Chapter of the Robert Morris Associates, Fernwood, Pennsylvania, 1928.
History of the Woollen and Worsted Industries, E. Lipson, 273 pages. A. C. Black, Ltd., London, 1921.
National Association of Wool Manufacturers, annual, 80 Federal Street, Boston, Massachusetts.
National Wool Trade Directory, covers all data in woolen, worsted, and hair-fiber industries. National Wool Publishing Company, Boston, Mass.
The Woolen Year Book, Marsden and Company, Ltd., Manchester, England.
The Worsted Industry, J. Dumville and S. Kershaw, 127 pages. Pitman and Sons, Ltd., London, 1924.
Wool, A Study of the Fiber, S. C. Barker, 166 pages. His Majesty's Stationery Office, London, 1929.
Wool Quality, S. G. Barker, 333 pages. Rayon Publishing Company, 303 Fifth Avenue, New York, 1931.
Wool Substitutes, R. Beaumont, 190 pages. Pitman and Sons, Ltd., New York, 1922.

Woolen and Worsted Fabrics Glossary, a detailed work on every known grade and variety of woolen and worsted fabrics, 348 pages. F. P. Bennett and Company, Boston, Massachusetts, 1914.

Woolen and Worsted Raw Materials, John R. Hind, 213 pages. E. Benn, Ltd., London, 1934.

Zellwolle, H. G. Bodenbender, 534 pages. Rayon Publishing Company, 303 Fifth Avenue, New York.

RAW SILK

A Familiar Treatise on the Natural History and Management of the Common Silkworm, Dewhurst. London, 1839.

A Raw Silk Classification with Methods of Testing, 44 pages. Silk Association of America, New York, 1929.

An Examination into the Divisibility of the Silk Fiber, Wardle. Manchester, England, 1908.

A Raw Silk Classification with Methods of Testing, 44 pages. Silk Association of America, 1929.

Broad Silk Industry, Thumb Nail History of, Richardson. Davis Company.

Cocoon Silk, C. H. C. Cansdale. Pitman and Sons, Ltd., New York City, 1937.

Disease of Tradesmen, 95 pages. B. Ramazzini for the Medical Lay Press, New York, 1933.

Etude sur la Secrétion de la Soie, Blanc. Lyon, France, 1890.

General Study of the Silk Industry, 64 pages. Prepared by the Robert Morris Association, Lansdowne, Pennsylvania, 1927.

La Fabrique Lyonnaise de Soieries, Morand. Paris, 1889.

Laros Data Book, compilation of schedules, yarn tables, rules and regulations governing the purchase and throwing of raw silk, 98 pages. R. K. Laros Silk Company, Bethlehem, Pennsylvania, 1924.

L'Art de la Soie, Randot. Paris, 1885.

Le Bombyx, de Francheville. Berlin, 1874.

Les Industries de la Soie, Pariset. Lyon, France, 1890.

Raw Silk, Henry Hentz, 20 pages. Henry Hentz Company, New York, 1929.

Raw Silk, A Practical Handbook for the Buyer, Leo Duran, 216 pages. Silk Publishing Company, New York, 1932.

Raw Silk and Throwing, Warren P. Seem, 198 pages. McGraw-Hill Book Company, 1929.

Raw Silk Properties, Classification of Raw Silk and Silk Throwing, Warren P. Seem, 367 pages. Howes Publishing Company, New York.

Servalor, The Valuation of Raw Silk, Adolf Rosenzweig, 191 pages. Clifford and Lawton, New York, 1917.

Silk Culturist's Manual, The, D'Homergue. Philadelphia, 1839.

Silk in India, Geohegan. Calcutta, India.

Silk Production in China, India, and Europe from the Earliest Times, Amott. London, 1865.

Silk, Its Entomology, History, and Manufacture, Wardle. London, 1887.

Silk, Its Origin, Culture, and Manufacture, 47 pages. The Corticelli Silk Mills, Florence, Massachusetts, 1930.

Silk, Its Production and Manufacture, Luther Hooper, 126 pages. Pitman and Sons, Ltd., New York, 1919.

The Raw Silk Industry of Japan, C. J. Huber, 50 pages. The Silk Association of America, New York, 1929.

Thousand Facts About the Silk Industry of Japan, K. Isome, 27 pages. The Raw Silk Association of Japan, New York Office, 1926.

Three Textile Raw Materials and Their Manufacture, 127 pages. International Acceptance Bank, New York, 1924.

Tussah Silk, Chemistry of, Wardle. London, 1891.

Ver à Soie, Anzoux. Paris, 1849.

Wild Silks of India, Handbook of, Wardle. London, 1881.

Wild Silks, Descriptive Catalogue of, Wardle. London, 1886.

SILK MANUFACTURING

Chemical Technology of Silk and Rayon Throwing, Dale S. Chamberlain, 60 pages. Warwick Chemical Company, West Warwick, Rhode Island, 1935.

Dissecting and Calculating Silk Fabrics, Horace Nield, 196 pages. Clifford and Lawton Publishing Company, New York, 1928.

Fabric Analysis, Covering Wool, Worsted, Silk, Cotton, Artificial Silk, etc. E. A. Posselt, 231 pages. Textile Publishing Company, Philadelphia, Pennsylvania, 1920.

General Study of the Silk Industry, 64 pages. The Robert Morris Association, Lansdowne, Pennsylvania, 1927.

Laros Data Book, R. K. Laros, 98 pages. R. K. Laros Silk Company, Bethlehem, Pennsylvania, 1924.

Natural Silk Industry, 34 pages. International Economic Conference, Geneva, Switzerland, May, 1927.

Process of Winding, Warping and Quilling Silk and Other Yarns from Skein to the Loom, Samuel Kline, 155 pages. Clifford and Lawton Publishing Company, New York, 1926.

Raw and Thrown Silk for Hosiery, 16 pages. Silk Grading and Testing Laboratory, Inc., 22 West 26th Street, New York, 1935.

Raw Silk and Throwing, Warren P. Seem, 198 pages. McGraw-Hill Book Company, Inc., New York, 1929.

Silk, 47 pages. R. K. Laros Silk Company, Bethlehem, Pennsylvania, 1926.

Silk and the Silk Industry, Joseph Schober, 375 pages. Constable and Company, Ltd., London, 1930.

Silk Manufacturing and Its Problems, James Chittick, 432 pages. James Chittick, Publisher, New York, 1931.

Silk Throwing, E. A. Posselt, 205 pages. Textile Publishing Company, Philadelphia, Pennsylvania, 1918.

Silk Throwing and Waste Silk Spinning, Hollins Rayner, 196 pages. D. Van Nostrand Company, Princeton, New Jersey, 1921.

Silk, Its History and Manufacture from the Earliest Ages to the Present Time, Mary M. Davison and J. B. Wadleigh. Junction City, Kansas, 1885.

Silk, Its Origin, Culture, and Manufacturing, 47 pages. Corticelli Silk Mills, Florence, Massachusetts, 1930.

Silk, Its Production and Manufacture, Luther Hooper, 126 pages. Pitman and Sons, Ltd., New York, 1919.

Silk, the Queen of Fabrics, W. D. Darby, 71 pages. Dry Goods Economist, New York, 1922.

The Handbook of Spun Silk, 31 pages. Champlain Silk Mills, New York, 1922.

The Story of Silk and Cheney Silks, 78 pages. H. H. Manchester, Cheney Brothers, South Manchester, Connecticut, 1924.

The Theory of Silk Weaving, Arnold Woldensberger, 104 pages. Clifford and Lawton Publishing Company, New York, 1932.

Three Textile Raw Materials and Their Manufacture, 127 pages. International Acceptance Bank, New York, 1924.

SILK DYEING

Dyeing Silk, Mixed Silk Fabrics and Artificial Silks, Dr. A. Gandswindt, 220 pages. D. Van Nostrand Company, Princeton, New Jersey.

The History of the Silk Dyeing in the United States, A. H. Heusser, 604 pages. Silk Dyers' Association of America, Paterson, New Jersey, 1927.

SILK MARKETING

Distribution of Textiles, 196 pages. Bureau of Business Research, Harvard University, Cambridge, Massachusetts, 1926.

Production and Distribution of Silk and Rayon Broadgoods, M. T. Copeland and W. H. Turner, 109 pages. Textile Foundation, Inc., and the National Federation of Textiles, New York, 1935.

Silk, Eliza B. Thompson, 232 pages. Ronald Press, 1922.

Silk and the Silk Industry, Joseph Schober, 375 pages. Constable and Company, Limited, London, 1930.

Silk Manufacturing and Its Problems, comprehensive study of silk problems; published by James Chittick, New York, 1931.

Silk, the Queen of Fabrics, W. D. Darby, 71 pages. Dry Goods Economist, New York, 1922.

The American Silk Industry and the Tariff, Frank R. Mason, 182 pages. American Economic Association, Cambridge, Massachusetts, 1910.

The Silk Department, Eliza B. Thompson, 224 pages. Ronald Press, New York, 1918.

SILK—MISCELLANEOUS

Cost Accounting for Broadsilk Weavers, 263 pages. The Silk Association of America, 389 Fifth Ave., New York, 1929.

Dictionary of Silk Terms, 93 pages. Clifford and Lawton, New York.

Diseases of Tradesmen, on diseases possible from sericulture to the throwing mill for weaving, B. Ramazzini, 95 pages. Medical Lay Press, New York, 1933.

[333]

Dissecting and Calculating Silk and Rayon Products, H. Neild, 196 pages. American Silk Journal, 1928.

Economics of the Silk Industry, R. C. Rawlley, 349 pages. A study in industrial organization. P. S. King and Sons, Ltd., Westminster, S.W. 1, London, 1919.

Glossary of Silk Terms, includes a short history of silk, 95 pages. Cheney Brothers, South Manchester, Connecticut, 1915.

Silk and Rayon Directory, annual, Harlequin Press Company, Manchester, England.

Silk and the Silk Worker, W. Claxton. Blackie and Son, Ltd., 286 Fifth Avenue, New York, 1936.

Silk and Mixed Goods Analysis, Construction, Cost, Calculation, and Weaves, Arthur H. Schnell, two volumes. A. H. Schnell, 957 8th Street, Philadelphia, Pennsylvania, 1935.

Silk Essays, on various phases of the silk industry, 126 pages. Silk Association of America, New York, 1915.

Silk Screen Methods of Reproduction, B. Zahn. Second Edition, F. J. Drake and Company, 179 North Michigan Avenue, Chicago, Ill., 1935.

Silk Screen Printing Process, J. I. Biegeleisen and E. J. Busenbark. McGraw-Hill Book Company, 330 West 42nd Street, New York, 1938.

The History of the Silk Industry in the United States, and also in other countries, Schichiro Mitsui, 267 pages. Howes Publishing Company, New York, 1930.

The One Thousand Facts About the Raw Silk Industry of Japan, second edition, K. Isome, 24 pages. Raw Silk Association of Japan, New York Office, 1927.

The National Raw Silk Exchange, Inc., Julius B. Baer, 32 pages. Concise summary of functions of the silk exchange, Paul C. Gehring, New York, 1928.

The Silk Industry of the World at the Opening of the Twentieth Century, Franklin Allen, 63 pages. Silk Association of America, New York, 1904.

APPLIED TEXTILES, BASIC TEXTILES, MISCELLANEOUS BOOKS

A Guidebook for Homemaking, Evelyn M. Herrington. Appleton-Century Company, New York, 1935.

Adventures with the Microscope, J. D. Carrington, 455 pages. Bausch and Lomb Optical Company, Rochester, New York, 1934.

Air Conditioning in Textile Mills, Albert W. Thompson, 497 pages. Parks-Cramer Company, Fitchburg, Massachusetts, 1925.

America's Fabrics, Bendure and Pfeiffer, 688 pages. The Macmillan Co., 60 Fifth Avenue, New York, 1946.

American Cotton Handbook, G. R. Merrill and A. R. Macormac. Rayon Publishing Company, 303 Fifth Avenue, New York.

Antique Textiles, Tiffany Studios, New York.

Applied Textiles with Lesson Plans for Teachers, George E. Linton and Louis F. Friedman. State Department of Education, Education Building, Albany, New York, 1939, 1941.

Appliqué Design and Methods, Kathleen Mann. Macmillan Company, New York, 1937.

Art in Home and Clothing, Trilling and Williams. J. B. Lippincott and Company, Philadelphia, Pennsylvania, 1936.

Art in Industry, Richards. Macmillan Company, New York.

Art Weaving, Frieda Kean. D. C. Heath Company, New York, 1937.

Asbestos, Cirkel. Ottawa, Ontario, Dominion of Canada, 1905.

Bobbins of Belgium, Charlotte Kellogg. Funk and Wagnalls, New York, 1920.

Calculations in Yarns and Fabrics, Bradbury. Belfast, Ireland, 1906.

Clothing, Jordan. Barrows Publishing Company.

Clothing and Health, Kinne and Cooley. Macmillan Company, New York.

Clothing Construction, Brown. Ginn and Company, New York.

Cloths and the Cloth Trade, Hunter. Pitman and Sons, Ltd., London, England.

Color and Design in the Decorative Arts, Elizabeth Burris-Meyer. Prentice-Hall, Inc., Englewood Cliffs, New Jersey, 1935.

Color in Woven Design, Beaumont. Whittaker Company, London, England.

Cost Control and Accounting for Textile Mills, Eugene Szepesi, 441 pages. Bragdon, Lord and Nagle Publishing Company, New York, 1922.

Costume Design, Bradley. International Textbook Company, Scranton, Pennsylvania.

Costume Throughout the Ages, Mary Evans. J. B. Lippincott Company, Philadelphia, Pennsylvania.

Cotton, W. Johnson. Macmillan Company, New York.

Creative Chemistry, Edwin E. Slosson, 331 pages. Century Company, New York, 1919.

Credit and International Trade—How They Work in Practice; B. Ellinger, 189 pages. Macmillan and Company, Ltd., London, England, 1934.
Design and Manufacture of Towels and Toweling, Wodehouse. Pitman and Sons, Ltd., London, England.
Design in Textile Fabrics, Ashenhurst. Cassell Publishing Company.
Directory of Commercial Textile Testing Laboratories, 13 pages. Textile Foundation, Commerce Building, Washington, D.C., 1933.
Distribution of Textiles, 190 pages. Bureau of Business Research, Harvard University, Cambridge, Massachusetts, 1926.
Early American Textiles, Little. Century Company, New York.
Economics of Clothing and Textiles, William H. Dooley, 683 pages. D. C. Heath and Company, New York City, 1934.
Elementary Textile Design and Fabric Structure, John Read. Edward Arnold and Company, 1931.
Elementary Textile Microscopy, J. H. Skinkle, 144 pages. Howes Publishing Company, New York, 1930.
Embroidery Design and Stitches, Kathleen Mann. Macmillan Company, New York, 1937.
Embroidery in Wools, O. P. Couch. Sir Isaac Pitman and Sons, Ltd., London, England.
English Needlework, A. Kendrick. Black Publishing, Ltd., London, England, 1933.
Etude Sur Les Fibres Textiles, Barille. Strasbourg, 1868.
Fabric Analysis, Covering Wool, Worsted, Silk, Cotton, Artificial Silk, etc., E. A. Posselt, 231 pages. Textile Publishing Company, Philadelphia, Pennsylvania, 1920.
Finishing Materials, J. Andrew Clark, 113 pages. W. R. C. Smith Publishing Company, Atlanta, Georgia, 1926.
Finishing of Woven Fabrics, E. Midgley. Longmans, Green Company, New York, 1929.
Foot-Power Loom Weaving, E. F. Worst. Bruce Publishing Company, New York, 1943.
Fundamentals of Fibre Structure, W. T. Astbury, 187 pages. Oxford University Press, London, England, 1933.
Fundamentals of Textiles, E. A. Jacobsen and H. E. McCullough. John Wiley and Sons, Inc., 605 Third Avenue, New York, 1937.
Getting Ahead in Retailing, Nathan M. Ohrbach, 266 pages. McGraw-Hill Book Company, Inc., New York, 1936.
Handbook of Industrial Fabrics, George B. Haven, 538 pages. Wellington Sears Company, New York, 1938, 1941.
History of Manufactures in the United States, V. S. Clark, 3 volumes. McGraw-Hill Book Company, Inc., New York, 1929.
History of Silk, Cotton, Linen, and Wool, Gilroy. Harper and Brothers, New York.
History of the Basic Trades, H. Kay. Macmillan Company, 60 Fifth Ave., New York, 1936.
Home and Family, Jordan, Zeller and Brown. Macmillan Company, New York, 1935.
Home Decoration—Its Problems and Solutions, Ross Steward and John Gerald. Garden City Publishing Company, Garden City, Long Island, New York, 1938.
Home Furnishing, A. H. Ruff. John Wiley and Sons, New York, 1936.
Homespun Handcraft, Bowles. J. B. Lippincott and Company, Philadelphia, Pennsylvania, 1935.
How the World Is Clothed, Carpenter. American Book Company, New York.
How to Decorate Textiles, Branch. Dodd, Mead Company, New York.
How to Know Textiles, Cassie Paine Small, 394 pages. Ginn and Company, New York, 1932.
How We Are Clothed, Chamberlain. Macmillan Company, New York.
Industrial Fibers, Imperial Economic Committee, 113 pages. London, England, 1938.
Introduction to Textile Chemistry, H. Harper. Macmillan Company, New York, 1931.
Laboratory Manual, Stanley and Cline. Ginn and Company, New York, 1935.
Les Fibres Textiles, d'Origine Animale, Zolla. Paris, 1910.
Les Tissues Indiens de Vieux Pérou, Harcourt. Morance, France.
Management of a Textile Business, C. C. Balderston and Victor Karabasz, 228 pages. Textile Foundation, Commerce Building, Washington, D.C., 1938.
Management's Handbook, L. P. Alford. Ronald Press, New York, 1924. 1607 pages.
Manual of Winding, Warping, and Quilling, I. Kline. John Wiley and Sons, New York City, 1926.
Manufacture of Narrow Woven Fabrics, E. A. Posselt, 198 pages. McGraw-Hill Book Company, Inc., New York, 1917.
Marketing of Textiles, Reavis Cox, 390 pages. Textile Foundation, Commerce Building, Washington, D.C., 1938.
Millinery, Aiken. Ronald Press, New York.

Millinery, Brown. Ginn and Company, New York.
Millinery, Loewen. Macmillan Company, New York.
Modern Needlecraft, D. C. Minter. Blackie and Sons, Ltd., London, England, 1932.
Modern Textile Microscopy, J. M. Preston, 315 pages. Emmott and Company, Ltd., London, England, 1933.
Musée Historique des Tissues, D'Hennesel. Laurens Company.
Nomenclature Nouvelle des 550 Fibres Textiles, Bernardin. Ghent, Belgium, 1872.
Ornamentation and Textile Design, Barker. Stokes Publishing Company, New York.
One World of Fashion, M. D. C. Crawford. Fairchild Publishing Company, 7 East 12th St., New York, 1946.
Plain and Fancy Weaving, Brickett. International Correspondence Company, Scranton, Pennsylvania.
Plastics, A. J. Lockrey, 233 pages. D. Van Nostrand Company, Princeton, New Jersey, 3rd edition, 1943.
Principles of Woolen Spinning, H. Priestman. Longmans, Green Company, New York, 1924.
Prints and Patterns, Littlejohn. Pitman Publishing Company, Ltd., New York, London, England.
Problems in Textiles, Hess and Bruner. J. B. Lippincott and Company, Philadelphia, Pennsylvania, 1931.
Psychology of Dress, Hurlock. Ronald Press, New York.
Rayon Industry, M. H. Avram. D. Van Nostrand and Company, Princeton, New Jersey, 1927.
Romance of Design, Warren. Doubleday, Page and Company, New York.
Romance of French Weaving, Rodier. Tudor Publishing Company, New York.
Romance of Textiles, E. Lewis. Macmillan Company, New York, 1937.
Shelter and Clothing, Kinne and Cooley, 377 pages. Macmillan Company, New York, 1913.
Some Great Commodities, Statistical Division, National Bank of Commerce in New York, 287 pages, 1922.
Standard Cloths, Beaumont. Greenwood, Ltd., London, England.
Story Book of Cotton, Maud and Miska Petersham, John C. Winston Publishing Company, Philadelphia, Pennsylvania, 1939.
Story of Textiles, Perry Walton. Tudor Publishing Company, New York, 1936.
Story of Textiles, Watson. Harper and Brothers, New York.
Story of Weaving, L. Lamprey. Stokes Publishing Company, New York, 1939.
Student's Manual of Textiles, Wilford. Pitman and Sons, Ltd., London, England.
Study of Fabrics, Turner. Meredith Press, Inc., New York.
Stuff, Berry. Meredith Press, Inc., New York.
Shuttlecraft of American Hand Weaving, Atwater. Macmillan Company, New York.
Survey of Textile Research in the United States, United States Institute of Textile Research, Inc., 65 Franklin St., Boston, Massachusetts, 1931.
Tapestry, The Mirror of Civilization, Ackerman. Oxford Press, London, England.
Technical Testing of Yarns and Textile Fabrics, Dr. J. Herzfeld, 209 pages. D. Van Nostrand Company, Princeton, N.J., 1920.
Technology of Textile Design, E. A. Posselt. Philadelphia College of Textiles and Science, Philadelphia, Pennsylvania.
Testing of Yarns and Fabrics for Manufactures, Warehousemen, and Operatives, H. P. Curtis. Sir Isaac Pitman and Sons, Ltd., London, England, 1930.
Textile Analysis, S. R. Trotman and E. R. Trotman, 301 pages. J. B. Lippincott Company, Philadelphia, Pennsylvania, 1932.
Textile Costing an Aid to Management, J. Lockwood and A. D. Maxwell, 300 pages. Textile Foundation, Commerce Building, Washington, D.C., 1938.
Textile Design, Brickett. International Textbook, Scranton, Pennsylvania.
Textile Design, Woodhouse and Milne. Macmillan Company, New York.
Textile Design, A Bibliography and Directory, 29 pages. Textile Foundation, Commerce Building, Washington, D.C., 1932.
Textile Design, Grammar of, Nesbit. D. Van Nostrand Company, Princeton, N.J.
Textile Fabrics, Elizabeth Dyer. Houghton Mifflin Company, Boston, Massachusetts, 1926.
Textile Fabrics, Historical, Glazier. Charles Scribner's Sons, New York.
Textile Fabrics, Their Selection and Care from the Standpoint of Use, Wear, and Launderability, G. H. Johnson, 385 pages. Harper and Row, Inc., New York City, 1927.
Textile Factory Organization and Management, D. R. H. Williams, 89 pages. Emmott and Company, Ltd., Manchester, England, 1934.
Textile Fibers and Their Uses, Katherine Hess, 354 pages. J. B. Lippincott Company, Philadelphia, Pennsylvania, 1936, and revisions.
Textile Fibers of Commerce, Hannan. London, England, 1902.

Textile Fibers, Their Physical, Microscopical and Chemical Properties, J. Merritt Matthews and H. R. Mauersberger, 630 pages. John Wiley & Sons, Inc., New York (6th ed.), 1954.

Textile Fibers, Yarns, and Fabrics, Bray. Century Company, New York.

Textile Problems for the Consumer, T. N. Carver, Mary S. Woolman, and Ellen B. McGowan, 175 pages. Macmillan Company, New York, 1935.

Textile Raw Materials, Zipser. Scott, Greenwood, Ltd., London, England.

Textile Waste Treatment and Recovery, J. C. Geyer and W. A. Perry. Textile Foundation, Commerce Building, Washington, D.C., 1938.

Textiles, Barker. Macmillan Company, New York.

Textiles, Paul H. Nystrom, 335 pages. D. Appleton and Company, New York, 1916.

Textiles and Clothing, E. Sage. Charles Scribner's Sons, New York, 1930.

Textiles and Clothing, Watson. American School of Home Economics.

Textiles and Origin of Their Names, Megrew. Private printing, 1906.

Textiles and the Microscope, E. R. Schwarz, 329 pages. McGraw-Hill Book Company, Inc., New York, 1934.

Textiles for Salesmen, E. Ostick. Sir Isaac Pitman and Sons, Ltd., London, England, 1931.

Textiles, Guide to, Evans and McGowan, 233 pages. John Wiley and Sons Company, New York, 1939.

The Big Book of Needlecraft, Annie A. Patterson. Charles Scribner's Sons Company, New York.

The Conservation of Textiles, 162 pages. Laundry Owners National Association, La Salle, Illinois, 1923.

The Heritage of Cotton, M. D. C. Crawford. Grosset and Dunlap Company, New York.

The Home Economics Omnibus, Harris and Huston. Little, Brown and Company, Boston, Massachusetts, 1935.

The Instructor in Garment Cleaning, C. C. Hubbard, 318 pages. National Association of Dyers and Cleaners, Railway Exchange Building, St. Louis, Missouri.

The Location of Manufactures in the United States, 1899–1929, 105 pages. F. B. Carver, F. M. Boddy, and A. J. Nixon. University of Minnesota Press, Minneapolis, Minnesota.

The Mode in Dress and Home, D. G. Donovan. Allyn and Bacon, Boston, Massachusetts, 1935.

The New Elementary Home Economics, M. L. Matthews. Little, Brown and Company, Boston, Massachusetts.

The Printing of Textiles, R. Capel, 145 pages. Chapman and Hall, Ltd., London, England, 1930.

The Standard Handbook of Textiles, A. J. Hall, F. T. I., 296 pages. D. Van Nostrand Co., 250 Fourth Ave., New York, 1946.

The Story of Weaving, L. Lamprey, 278 pages. Stokes Publishing Company, New York, 1939.

The Textile Industries—An Economic Analysis, H. E. Michl, 304 pages. Textile Foundation, Commerce Building, Washington, D.C., 1938.

The Training of Men for the Textile Industry, 47 pages. Textile Foundation, Commerce Building, Washington, D.C., 1934.

Training in Textile Information, Research Bureau of Retail Training, University of Pittsburgh Press, Pittsburgh, Pennsylvania.

United States Testing Company, 1415 Park Avenue, Hoboken, New Jersey. Many valuable pamphlets, booklets, charts, etc., in all phases of textiles and textile testing.

Various Needlecrafts, Vera C. Alexander. Sir Isaac Pitman and Sons, Ltd., New York, London, England.

Vertical Integration in the Textile Industries, Hiram S. Davis, G. W. Taylor, C. C. Balderston, and Anne Bezanson, 132 pages. Wharton School of Finance and Commerce, and Textile Foundation, Commerce Building, Washington, D.C., 1938.

Vicuna. S. Stroock and Company, Inc., Newburgh, New York, 1937.

Weaves, Handbook of, Oelsner. Macmillan Company, New York, 1914.

What You Should Know About Rayon Yarn. Prepared by the Rayon Institute, New York, 1940.

World Resources and Industries, E. W. Zimmerman, 842 pages. Harper and Brothers, New York, 1933.

Yarn and Cloth Making, An Economic Study, Mary Louise Kissel, 252 pages. Macmillan Company, New York, 1913.

WOMEN'S READY-TO-WEAR AND INFANTS' WEAR

A Century of Fashion, Jean Philippe Worth. Little, Brown and Company, Inc., Boston, Massachusetts, 1938.

Any Girl Can Be Good-Looking, Cades. Meredith Press, Inc., New York.

Attractive Clothes, Consalus and Dooley. Ronald Press, New York.

Clothes and Personality, Ryan. Meredith Press, Inc., New York.

Clothes for Girls, Todd. Little, Brown and Company, Inc., New York, 1935.

Clothing, Friant, Turner and Miller. Collegiate Press, Ames, Iowa, 1936.

Clothing, M. Friend and Hazel Schultz. Meredith Press, Inc., 1933.

Clothing, Choice, Care and Cost, Mary S. Woolman. J. B. Lippincott and Company, Philadelphia, Pennsylvania, 1926.

Clothing, Fundamental Problems of, Louise Jordan and E. Bulger. Barrows Company, 1927.

Clothing, Introductory College Course, Latzke and Quinlan. J. B. Lippincott and Company, Philadelphia, Pennsylvania, 1935.

Clothing, Selection and Care of, Mary L. Matthews. Little, Brown and Company, Boston, Massachusetts.

Clothing, Selection and Purchase of, Lillian C. W. Baker. Macmillan Company, New York, 1932.

Clothing for Women, Laura Baldt. J. B. Lippincott and Company, Philadelphia, Pennsylvania, 1929.

Clothing for the High School Girl, Laura Baldt. J. B. Lippincott and Company, Philadelphia, Pennsylvania, 1933.

Clothing Study, A Workbook for High School Girls, Trilling and Nicholas. J. B. Lippincott and Company, Philadelphia, Pennsylvania, 1935.

Color and Design in Apparel, Bernice G. Chambers, 627 pages. Prentice-Hall, Inc., Englewood Cliffs, New Jersey, 1944.

Color and Line in Dress, Laurene Hempstead. Prentice-Hall, Inc., Englewood Cliffs, New Jersey, 1931.

Complete Dressmaker with Simple Directions for Home Millinery, Loughlin. Meredith Press, Inc., New York.

Consumer Goods, Reich and Siegler, 526 pages. American Book Company, New York, 1937.

Designing and Decorating Clothes. The Women's Institute, International Textbook Company, Scranton, Pennsylvania, 1932.

Designing Women, Margaretta Byers and Consuelo Kamholz. Simon and Schuster, New York, 1938.

Distinctive Clothes, Frances H. Consalus. Ronald Press, New York City, 1940.

Domestic Art in Women's Education, Cooley. Charles Scribner's Sons, New York.

Draping and Dress Design, Mary Evans. Edwards Company, New York.

Dress and Home Workbook, Dulcie G. Donovan. Allyn and Bacon Company, Boston, Massachusetts, 1935.

Dress and Look Slender, Wells. Personal Arts Company.

Dress Construction with the Aid of Patterns. Butterick Company, New York.

Dress Design and Selection, Margaret H. Hopkins. Macmillan Company, New York, 1937.

Dress, Blouse and Costume Clothes, Beaumont and Hill. Pitman and Sons, Ltd., New York, London, England.

Dresses, Ringo. A. W. Shaw Company.

Dressmaking, Fales. Charles Scribner's Sons, New York.

Economics of Fashion, Paul H. Nystrom. Ronald Press, New York.

Elements of Costume Design for High School Students, Downs and O'Leary. Bruce Publishing Company, New York.

Embroidery and Design in the New Stitching, Foster. Pitman and Sons, Ltd., New York, London, England.

Embroidery Design, Molly Booker. Studio Publications Company.

Embroidery or the Craft of the Needle, Townsend. Truslove and Hanson, Ltd., London, England.

Essentials of Sewing, Rosamond C. Cook. Manual Arts Press.

Everyday Living for Girls, Adelaide Van Duzer. J. B. Lippincott Company, Philadelphia, Pennsylvania, 1941.

Fabrics and Clothing, McBride. Macmillan Company, New York, 1932.

Fabrics and Dress, Rathbone and Tarpley. Houghton Mifflin Company, Boston, Massachusetts.

Fashion Drawing, H. R. Dotin. Harper and Brothers, New York, 1939.

Fashion Is Spinach, Elizabeth Hawes, 337 pages. Random House, New York, 1938.

Fashion Merchandising, Paul H. Nystrom. Ronald Press, New York.

Fashions Since Their Debut, Wilson. International Textbook Company, Scranton, Pennsylvania.

From Thimble to Gown, Van Gilder. Allyn and Bacon Company, New York.

Fundamentals of Dress, Marietta Kettunen. McGraw-Hill Book Company, Inc., 1941.

Fundamentals of Dress Construction, Manning and Donaldson. Macmillan Company, New York, 1926.

Fundamentals of Sewing, Carrie Crane Ingalls. Bruce Publishing Company, 1928.

Fur, Max Bachrach. Prentice-Hall Company, Englewood Cliffs, New Jersey, 1937.
Girls' Problems in Home Economics, Trilling and Williams. J. B. Lippincott Company, Philadelphia, Pennsylvania.
Good Looks for Girls, Cades. Harcourt Brace Company, New York.
Good Taste in Dress, F. W. McFarland. Manuel Arts Press, Peoria, Illinois, 1936.
Handbook of Elementary Sewing, A. M. Miall. Pitman and Sons, Ltd., New York, London, England.
Help Wanted—Female, Byers. Julian Messner Company, New York, 1941.
History of American Costume, Elizabeth McClennan. Tudor Publishing Company, New York, 1937.
How the Fashion World Works, Margaretta Stevenson. Harper and Brothers, New York, 1938.
How to Draw Fashion Figures, Ruth Conerly. Bridgman Publishing Company, 1936.
How We Are Clothed, James F. Chamberlain. Macmillan Company, New York, 1936.
Individuality and Clothes, Margaret Story. Funk and Wagnalls, New York, 1930.
Introduction to French Civilization, Whiting. Thrift Press, Ithaca, New York, 1938.
Junior Clothing, K. W. Kinyon and L. T. Hopkins. Sanborn Company, New York, 1937.
Language of Fashion, Mary B. Picken. Funk and Wagnalls Company, New York.
Leavers Lace, H. G. Truman and E. F. Walker. American Lace Manufacturers Association, Inc., Providence, Rhode Island.
Making Smart Clothes. Butterick Company, New York.
Mode in Dress and Home, Donovan. Allyn and Bacon Company, Boston, Massachusetts.
Modern Clothing, Laura Baxter and Alpha Latzke. J. B. Lippincott and Company, Philadelphia, Pennsylvania, 1938.
Modern Dressmaking, Mary B. Picken. McKay Publishing Company, New York.
New Butterick Dressmaker. Butterick Company, New York.
New Dressmaker. Butterick Company, New York.
One World of Fashion, M. D. C. Crawford. Fairchild Publishing Company, 7 East 12th Street, New York, 1946.
Pattern and Dress Design, Josephine Eddy and Elizabeth C. B. Wiley. Houghton Mifflin Company, Boston, 1932.
Powers Girls, John Robert Powers. E. P. Dutton and Company, Inc., New York, 1941.
Practical Dress Design, Mabel D. Irwin. Macmillan Company, New York, 1941.
Principles of Clothing Selection, Helen G. Buttrick. Macmillan Company, New York, 1936.
Principles of Dress, Winterburn. Harper and Brothers, New York.
Secrets of Distinctive Dress, Mary B. Picken. International Textbook Press, Scranton, Pennsylvania.
Sewing and Textiles, Turner. Meredith Press, Inc., New York.
Sewing Handicraft for Girls, McGlauflin. Manual Arts Press, Peoria, Illinois.
Sewing Materials, 267 pages. Women's Institute of Domestic Arts and Sciences, Scranton, Pennsylvania, 1928.
Student's Manual of Fashion Drawing, E. Young. John Wiley and Sons, New York, 1930.
Study Guide to Problems of Fabrics and Dress, L. Rathbone. Houghton Mifflin Company, Boston, Massachusetts, 1937.
Style and the Woman, Cary. Dry Goods Economist, New York.
The Story of Costume, Beele Northrup. Art Education Press, Inc., New York, 1935.
The Ways of Fashion, M. D. C. Crawford, 320 pages. G. P. Putnam's Sons, New York, 1941.
The Women's Garment Workers, Louise Levine. B. W. Huebsch, Inc., New York, 1924.
Well Dressed Woman, Rittenhouse. Harper and Brothers, New York City.
When Sally Sews, Helen Perry Curtis. Macmillan Company, New York, 1929.
Workbook for Clothing, Elnora Culbert. Economy Company, Oklahoma City, Oklahoma, 1933.
Your Clothes and Personality, Mildred G. Ryan. Meredith Press, Inc., New York, 1937.

HOME ECONOMICS AND THE HOME

Accessories of Dress, K. M. Lester and B. V. Oerke. Manual Arts Press, Peoria, Illinois.
Antique Jewelry and Trinkets, Burgess. Tudor Publishing Company, New York.
Art Metalwork, Payne. Manual Arts Press, Peoria, Illinois.
Art in Needlework, Day. B. T. Batsford, Ltd., London.
Artificial Flower Making, Baskin. Pitman and Sons, Ltd., New York.
Bedding, Hidden Value Series, Sears Roebuck Company, Chicago, Illinois.
Consumer Goods, Reich and Siegler. American Book Company, New York, 1937.
Decorating the Home, Ethel Lewis, 574 pages. Macmillan Company, New York, 1942.
Decoratively Speaking, Gladys Miller. Doubleday, Doran and Company, Garden City, New York, 1939.

Embroidery and Tapestry, Christie. Hogg, Ltd., London.
Embroidery Book, Mary Thomas. William Morrow and Company, Inc., New York, 1936.
Encyclopedia of Needlework, Therese de Dillmont, 813 pages plus appendix. D M C Library, Mulhouse, France. Printed by the Société Anonyme, Dollfus-Mieg & Cie, Mulhouse, France.
Gems and Gem Materials, E. H. Kraus and C. B. Slawson. McGraw-Hill Book Company, Inc., New York, 1939.
Hats and How to Make Them, Patty. Rand McNally Company, Chicago, Ill.
Home Fashions Reporter, monthly, Reporter Publications, 350 Fifth Avenue, New York.
Homecraft Rugs, Walker. Frederick A. Stokes Publishing Company, New York.
How to Make Lace, Roberts. Dry Goods Economist, New York City.
Individuality and Clothes, Margaret Story. Funk and Wagnalls, New York, 1940.
Interesting Art Needlework, Lukowitz. Bruce Publishing Company, New York.
Lace Book, The, Jessie F. Caplin. Macmillan Company, New York, 1932.
Lace Making, Page. J. B. Lippincott & Company, Philadelphia, Penna.
Metalcraft and Jewelry, Kronquist. Manual Arts Press, Peoria, Ill.
Period Influences in Interior Decorations, W. R. Storey. Harper and Brothers, New York, 1937.
Point and Pillow Lace, Sharp. E. P. Dutton Company, New York.
Product Standards and Labeling for Consumers, Alice L. Edwards. Ronald Press, New York, 1940.
Pottery, Cox. Macmillan Company, New York.
Selling Home Furnishings Successfully, Samuel W. Reyburn. Prentice-Hall, Inc., Englewood Cliffs, New Jersey, 1938.
Shopping Guide, E. B. Weiss. Whittlesey House, New York, 1937.
Varied Occupations in String Work, Walker. Macmillan Company, New York.

PERIODICALS FOR TEXTILE INFORMATION, TRADE JOURNALS, AND GENERAL INFORMATION

American Fabrics, quarterly, Reporter Publications, William C. Segal, Publisher, 24 East 38th Street, New York.
American Exporter, monthly, Johnston Export Publishing Company, 386 Park Avenue South, New York.
America's Textile Reporter, weekly, Frank P. Bennett Company, 286 Congress St., Boston.
Bedding and Upholstery Review, monthly, Ortner Publishing Company, Inc., 407 Park Avenue South, New York.
Cotton, monthly, W. R. C. Smith Publishing Company, Atlanta, Georgia.
Daily News Record, Fairchild Publications, 8 East 13th Street, New York.
Export Trade and Shipper, weekly, Export Shipper Publishing Company, 20 Vesey Street, New York.
Fibre and Fabric, weekly, 465 Main Street, Cambridge, Mass.
Industrial Standards and Commercial Standards Monthly. American Standards Association, 70 E. 45th Street, New York.
Packing and Shipping, monthly, Bonnell Publications, 30 Church Street, New York.
Textile American, monthly, 10 Milk Street, Boston, Massachusetts.
Textile Bulletin, weekly, Clark Publishing Company, Charlotte, North Carolina.
Textile Buyers' Economist, annual, Frank P. Bennett and Company, Inc., 286 Congress Street, Boston, Massachusetts.
Textile Colorist and Converter, monthly, Howes Publishing Co., 1 Madison Ave., New York.
Textile Industries, monthly, W. R. C. Smith Publishing Company, 1760 Peachtree Road, Atlanta, Georgia.
Textile Organon, monthly, Textile Research Institute, 10 East 40th St., New York.
Textile Review, monthly, 161 Summer St., Boston, Massachusetts.
Textile World, monthly, McGraw-Hill Book Company, Inc., New York.
The Industrial Arts Index, monthly, H. W. Wilson Company, 950 University Avenue, New York.
The New York Times Index, New York Times Monthly Publication, New York Times, Times Square, New York.
The Readers Guide to Periodical Literature, monthly, H. W. Wilson Company, 950 University Avenue, New York.
Waste Trade Journal, weekly, Atlas Publishing Company, 150 Lafayette Street, New York.

FOR COTTON

American Cotton Grower, monthly, The American Cotton Grower Publishing Company, 713 Glen Street, Atlanta, Georgia.

American Ginner and Cotton Oil Miller, monthly, Box 504, Little Rock, Arkansas.

America's Textile Reporter, weekly, Frank P. Bennett Company, Inc., 286 Congress Street, Boston, Massachusetts.

Cotton, monthly, W. R. C. Smith Publishing Company, Atlanta, Georgia.

Cotton and Cotton Oil Press, weekly, 3116 Commerce Street, Dallas, Texas.

Cotton Digest, weekly, Cotton Exchange Building, Houston, Texas.

The Cotton Oil Press, monthly, Memphis, Tennessee.

The Cotton Trade Journal, weekly, Cotton Exchange Bldg., New Orleans, Louisiana.

The Oil Mill Gazetteer, monthly, H. E. Wilson Company, Wharton, Texas.

The Oil Miller and Cotton Ginner, monthly, Oil Miller Publishing Company, Atlanta, Georgia.

FOR MANMADE FIBERS

Modern Textiles Magazine, Rayon Publishing Company, 303 Fifth Avenue, New York.

Textile Organon, monthly, Stanley B. Hunt, Textile Economics Bureau Incorporated, 10 East 40th Street, New York.

FOR MISCELLANEOUS FIBERS

American Society for Testing Materials Bulletin, monthly (A.S.T.M.), Philadelphia, Pennsylvania.

America's Textile Reporter, weekly, Frank P. Bennett Company, 286 Congress Street, Boston, Massachusetts.

Associated Wool Industries, monthly, 386 Park Avenue South, New York.

Bags, monthly, Atlas Publishing Company, New York.

Broom and Broom Corn News, weekly, Arcola, Illinois.

Brooms, Brushes, and Mops, monthly, Montgomery Bldg., Milwaukee, Wisconsin.

Cord Age, monthly, Cord Age, 114 East 32nd Street, New York.

Cordage Trade Journal, semi-monthly, 132 Nassau St., New York.

Daily Mill Stock Reporter, information on wool, burlap, cotton, and wastes, Atlas Publishing Company, New York.

Linens and Domestics, monthly, Haire Publishing Company, East Stroudsburg, Pennsylvania.

Monthly Statistics of Wool Manufacture, National Association of Wool Manufacturers, 80 Federal Street, Boston, Massachusetts.

National Canvas Goods Manufacturers Review, monthly, 532 Endicott Building, St. Paul, Minnesota.

The Bedding Manufacturer, monthly, Better Bedding Alliance of America, 608 South Dearborn Street, Chicago, Illinois.

FOR KNIT GOODS

Gloves, monthly, Gloversville, New York.

Knit Goods Weekly, Howes Publishing Company, 440 Park Avenue South, New York.

Knitted Outerwear Age, monthly, Knit Goods Publishing Corporation, New York.

Knitted Outerwear Times, weekly, National Knitted Outerwear Association, 51 Madison Avenue, New York.

Underwear and Hosiery Review, monthly, Knit Goods Publishing Company, 34 North Crystal Street, East Stroudsburg, Pennsylvania.

FOR WOMEN'S READY-TO-WEAR AND INFANTS' WEAR

American Fur Designer, monthly, American Fur Designer, 345 Seventh Avenue, New York.

American Furrier and Fur Style, monthly, American-Mitchel Style Corporation, 145 West 28th Street, New York.

American Lady's Tailor and Les Parisiennes, monthly, American-Mitchel Style Corporation, 145 West 28th St., New York.

Black Fox Magazine, monthly, 152 West 42nd Street, New York.

Central Furrier, monthly, 185 North Wabash Avenue, Chicago, Illinois.

Corset and Underwear Review, monthly, Haire Publishing Co., 1170 Broadway, New York.

Corsets and Brassieres, monthly, Bowman Publishing Company, 267 Fifth Avenue, New York.

Fur Animals, monthly, 201 B. M. A. Building, Kansas City, Missouri.

Fur Reporter, weekly, Atlas Publishing Company, Inc., 150 Lafayette Street, New York.

Fur Trade Review, monthly, 370 Seventh Avenue, New York.

Furs, monthly, Atlas Publishing Company, Inc., 150 Lafayette Street, New York.

Los Angeles Modes and Apparel Gazette, monthly, 857 South San Pedro Street, Los Angeles, California.

Midwest Retailer, monthly, Savoy Hotel, Kansas City, Missouri.

The Review, monthly, Garment Trade Review Company, 151 West 40th Street, New York.

Sportswear Magazine, monthly, Ranney Publishing Company, 1170 Broadway, New York.

Style Trend, monthly, Modes and Fabrics, Inc., 307 Fifth Avenue, New York.

The Fur Journal, monthly, 72 Columbus Street, Seattle, Washington.

The Illustrated Milliner, monthly, 105 West 40th St., New York.

Women's Wear Daily, Fairchild Publishing Company, 7 East 12th Street, New York.

FOR LAUNDRY TRADES—CLEANING AND DYEING

American Dyestuff Reporter, weekly, Howes Publishing Company, 44 East 23rd Street, New York.

Cleaning and Dyeing World, monthly, Kates-Boyleston Publishers, Inc., 1697 Broadway, New York.

Dyestuffs, quarterly, National Aniline and Chemical Company, Inc., 40 Rector Street, New York.

Laundry Year Book, annual, Laundry Age Publishing Co., New York.

National Cleaner and Dyer, monthly, National Cleaners and Dyers Publishing Corporation, 305 East 45th Street, New York.

Starchroom Laundry Journal, monthly, R. H. Donnelley Corporation, 305 East 45th Street, New York.

FOR MEN'S AND BOYS' CLOTHING

American Gentleman and Sartorial Art Journal, monthly, 1133 Broadway, New York.

American Hatter, monthly, The Hat Trade Publishing Company, 1225 Broadway, New York.

Apparel Arts, quarterly, Apparel Arts, Publications, 919 North Michigan Avenue, Chicago, Illinois.

Apparel Manufacturer, monthly, Atlas Publishing Company, 150 Lafayette Street, New York.

Biography of a Suit—from Fiber to Fashion, Boys' Outfitter, 175 Fifth Avenue, New York City, December, 1940.

Clothing Trade Journal, monthly, Clothier Publishing Company, 307 Main Street, Kutztown, Pennsylvania.

Cotton Shirts for Men and Boys, Bulletin 1837F, U.S. Government Printing Office, Washington, D.C.

How to Buy a Shirt, Cluett, Peabody and Company, Inc., 530 Fifth Avenue, New York.

Magazine of the Merchant Tailors and Designers Association of America, 400 Madison Avenue, New York.

Men's Wear, bi-monthly, Fairchild Publishing Company, 418 South Market Street, Chicago, Illinois.

Selling Men's Evening Wear, and Other Articles, Fairchild Publishing Company, 7 East 12th Street, New York.

The Hat for the Occasion, Hat Style Council, Inc., 1123 Broadway, New York.

The National Clothier, monthly, National Clothier Publishing Company, Inc., 803 Merchandise Mart, Chicago, Illinois.

GENERAL TRADE AND MANUFACTURING DIRECTORIES

American Hatter Directory, bi-annual, The Hat Trade Publishing Company, 1225 Broadway, New York.

Boy's Outfitter Directory, bi-annual, 175 Fifth Avenue, New York.

Buyers for Export, annual, Thomas Ashwell & Co., 20 Vesey Street, New York.

Corset and Underwear Review's Annual Directory, Haire Publishing Company, 1170 Broadway, New York.

Crain's Market Data Book, annual, Class and Industrial Market, 537 South Dearborn Street, Chicago, Illinois.

Davison's Cordage, Twine and Duck Trade Directory, annual, Davison Publishing Company, 50 Union Square, New York.

Davison's Knit Goods Trade, annual, Davison Publishing Company, New York.

Davison's Silk and Rayon Trades, annual, Davison Publishing Company, New York.

Davison's Textile Blue Book and Buyer's Guide, annual, Davison Publishing Company, New York.

Davison's Textile Directory for Salesmen, annual, Davison Publishing Company, New York.

Fairchild's Directory of Fabrics, Trimmings, and Supplies, bi-annual, Fairchild Publishing Company, 7 East 12th Street, New York.

Fairchild's Men's Wear Directory of Chicago, semi-annual, Fairchild Publishing Company, New York.

Fairchild's Men's Wear Directory of New York, semi-annual, Fairchild Publishing Company, New York.

Fairchild's Women's Wear Directory of New York, semi-annual, Fairchild Publishing Company, New York.

International Cotton Book, annual, The Cotton and Cotton Oil News, Dallas, Texas.

Macrae's Blue Book and Hendricks' Commercial Register, MacRae's Blue Book Company, 18 East Huron Street, Chicago, Illinois.

Official American Textile Directory, annual, McGraw-Hill Book Company, Inc., New York.

Official Handbook of Textile Corporations, annual, Frank P. Bennett Company, 286 Congress St., Boston, Massachusetts.

The Directory of Branded Textile Merchandise, Textile World for Bragdon, Lord & Nagle, McGraw-Hill Book Company, New York, 1926.

Thomas' Register of American Manufacturers, annual, Thomas Publishing, 461 Eighth Avenue, New York.

TEXTILE DICTIONARIES

Callaway Textile Dictionary, W. L. Carmichael and George E. Linton, 390 pages. Callaway Mills, Inc., LaGrange, Georgia; New York Office, 295 5th Avenue, New York, 1947.

Dan River's Dictionary of Textile Terms, Cox, Grimshaw, Hoye, Linton, Merrill, and Good Housekeeping Magazine, 128 pages, Dan River Mills, Inc., 111 West 40th Street, New York City. 10 editions from 1944 to 1964.

Dictionary of Weaves, E. A. Posselt, 85 pages with 2,000 weave constructions arranged for handy use showing the draft for each weave. S. Low, Marston & Company, Ltd., London, 1914.

Handbook of Textile Fibers (Natural and Manmade), J. Gordon Cook, Ph.D., Merrow Publishing Company, Ltd., Watford, Hirts, England, 1964. Excellent succinct coverage of all textile fibers.

Index to Manmade Fibers of the World, Peter Lennox-Kerr, Harlequin Press, Ltd., Manchester, England, 1964. Excellent for ready reference.

The "Mercury" Dictionary of Textile Terms, Staff of "Textile Mercury," Manchester, England. Excellent source book in all details, 1950.

Textile Statistics Section for the Combined Textile Industries; Annual Dictionary and Directory for data, statistics and concise information on all textile mills and plants in the United States; America's Textile Reporter Magazine, Frank P. Bennett, Inc., 286 Congress Street, Boston 10, Massachusetts. (Should be in your library.)

GENERAL GOVERNMENT PUBLICATIONS RELATING TO TEXTILES

Census of Manufacturers, bi-ennial, Bureau of the Census, U.S. Department of Commerce. Also monthly and seasonal data on cotton ginning, consumption, imports and exports.

Commerce Reports, weekly. Survey of foreign trade and industrial economic conditions in foreign countries. U.S. Department of Commerce.

Cotton and Cottonseed, Rachel P. Lane, 149 pages. Miscellaneous Publication No. 203, U.S. Department of Agriculture, 1934.

Cotton Literature, selected references, annual. Prepared in the Library of the Department of Agriculture.

Domestic Commerce, issued the 10th, 20th, and 30th of each month. Gives the latest research data on distribution problems in highly condensed form. Bureau of Foreign and Domestic Commerce, U.S. Department of Commerce.

Federal Reserve Board Indexes, monthly. Index of production, factory employment, pay rolls for textiles as a whole, and index numbers covering employment and payrolls in the fabric industry. Federal Reserve Board, Washington, D.C.

Foreign Commerce and Navigation of the United States, annual. Import and export statistics of various textiles. U.S. Department of Commerce.

Foreign Commerce Yearbook. Gives high points of trade, production, and market conditions for many important foreign countries, tabulated and analyzed. Covers comparative world statistics on climate and population, agriculture, mining and manufacturing, transportation, international trade, and finance. U.S. Department of Commerce.

Government Publications Relating to Textiles, Alvin E. Johnson, 101 pages. Bureau of Foreign and Domestic Commerce, U.S. Department of Commerce, 1931.

Market Data Handbook of the United States. Covers facts necessary to an appraisement of markets in the profitable distribution of goods. Includes statistics on the location of textile manufacturing industries by states and counties. U.S. Department of Commerce.

Monthly Labor Review. Covers all phases of labor in specific states. Bureau of Labor Statistics, U.S. Department of Labor.

Monthly Summary of Foreign Commerce of the United States. Contains import and export figures, monthly average import prices, etc. Bureau of Labor Statistics, U.S. Department of Commerce.

Statistical Abstract of the United States, annual volume of about 800 pages, 56 numbers have been issued. Covers all forms of activity and progress in this country. U.S. Department of Commerce.

Survey of Current Business, monthly records of business conditions. Bureau of Foreign and Domestic Commerce, U.S. Department of Commerce.

Wholesale Prices, monthly which gives index numbers shown for wholesale prices of cotton goods, silk, rayon, woolen and worsted goods, and other textile products. Bureau of Labor Statistics, U.S. Department of Labor.

World Economic Review, annual which contains the outstanding economic developments, with emphasis on the general trend. Also includes statistics of international trade, a chronology of important events, a summary of important legislative acts, and a table of comparative business statistics. Bureau of Foreign and Domestic Commerce, U.S. Department of Commerce.

Year Book of Agriculture, contains information on production, prices, and trade of textile raw materials. U.S. Department of Agriculture.

RHODIA: Trademark for the cellulose acetate fiber and yarn manufactured by Société Rhodiaceta whose headquarters for the Rhodiaceta group are in Lyons, France.

OFFICIAL STANDARD WOOL GRADES

(Established by the Federal Register of August 21, 1965,
Title 7, Chapter 1, Part 31)

GRADE	LIMITS FOR AVERAGE FIBER DIAMETER (MICRONS)*	LIMIT FOR STANDARD DEVIATION MAXIMUM (MICRONS)
Finer than 80s	Under 17.70	3.59
80s	17.70 to 19.14	4.09
70s	19.15 to 20.59	4.59
64s	20.60 to 22.04	5.19
62s	22.05 to 23.49	5.89
60s	23.50 to 24.94	6.49
58s	24.95 to 26.39	7.09
56s	26.40 to 27.84	7.59
54s	27.85 to 29.29	8.19
50s	29.30 to 30.99	8.69
48s	31.00 to 32.69	9.09
46s	32.70 to 34.39	9.59
44s	34.40 to 36.19	10.09
40s	36.20 to 38.09	10.69
36s	38.10 to 40.20	11.19
Coarser than 36s	Over 40.20	—

* A micron is 1/25,400 of an inch.

APPENDIX

TABLE OF CONTENTS

Important Extracts from the Textile Fiber Products Identification Act
(Announced June 3, 1959; effective March 3, 1960)

TEXTILE FIBER PRODUCTS IDENTIFICATION ACT

Public Law 85–897
85th Congress–2d Session
H. R. 469
(72 Stat. 1717; 15 U.S.C. §70)

AN ACT

To protect producers and consumers against misbranding and false advertising of the fiber content of textile fiber products, and for other purposes.

Be it enacted by the Senate and House of Representatives of the United States of America in Congress assembled, That this Act may be cited as the "Textile Fiber Products Identification Act."

DEFINITIONS

Sec. 2. As used in this Act—

(a) The term "person" means an individual, partnership, corporation, association, or any other form of business enterprise.

(b) The term "fiber" or "textile fiber" means a unit of matter which is capable of being spun into a yarn or made into a fabric by bonding or by interlacing in a variety of methods including weaving, knitting, braiding, felting, twisting, or webbing, and which is the basic structural element of textile products.

(c) The term "natural fiber" means any fiber that exists as such in the natural state.

(d) The term "manufactured fiber" means any fiber derived by a process of manufacture from any substance which, at any point in the manufacturing process, is not a fiber.

[345]

(e) The term "yarn" means a strand of textile fiber in a form suitable for weaving, knitting, braiding, felting, webbing, or otherwise fabricating into a fabric.

(f) The term "fabric" means any material woven, knitted, felted, or otherwise produced from, or in combination with, any natural or manufactured fiber, yarn, or substitute therefor.

(g) The term "household textile articles" means articles of wearing apparel, costumes and accessories, draperies, floor coverings, furnishings, beddings, and other textile goods of a type customarily used in a household regardless of where used in fact.

(h) The term "textile fiber product" means—

(1) any fiber, whether in the finished or unfinished state, used or intended for use in household textile articles;

(2) any yarn or fabric, whether in the finished or unfinished state, used or intended for use in household textile articles; and

(3) any household textile article made in whole or in part of yarn or fabric; except that such term does not include a product required to be labeled under the Wool Products Labeling Act of 1939.

(i) The term "affixed" means attached to the textile fiber product in any manner.

(j) The term "Commission" means the Federal Trade Commission.

(k) The term "commerce" means commerce among the several states or with foreign nations, or in any territory of the United States or in the District of Columbia, or between any such territory and another, or between any such territory and any state or foreign nation or between the District of Columbia and any state or territory or foreign nation.

(l) The term "Territory" includes the insular possessions of the United States, and also any Territory of the United States.

(m) The term "ultimate consumer" means a person who obtains a textile fiber product by purchase or exchange with no intent to sell or exchange such textile fiber product in any form.

CRIMINAL PENALTY

Sec. 11. (a) Any person who willfully does an act which by section 3, 5, 6, 9, or 10 (b) is declared to be unlawful shall be guilty of a misdemeanor and upon conviction shall be fined not more than $5,000 or be imprisoned not more than one year, or both, in the discretion of the court: *Provided,* That nothing in this section shall limit any other provision of this Act.

(b) Whenever the Commission has reason to believe that any person is guilty of a misdemeanor under this section, it may certify all pertinent facts to the Attorney General. If, on the basis of the facts certified, the Attorney General concurs in such belief, it shall be his duty to cause appropriate proceedings to be brought for the enforcement of the provisions of this section against such person.

EXEMPTIONS

Sec. 12. (a) None of the provisions of this Act shall be construed to apply to—

(1) upholstery stuffing, except as provided in section 4 (h);

(2) outer coverings of furniture, mattresses, and box springs;

(3) linings or interlinings incorporated primarily for structural purposes and not for warmth;

(4) filling or padding incorporated primarily for structural purposes and not for warmth;

(5) stiffenings, trimmings, facings, or interfacings;

(6) backings of, and paddings or cushions to be used under, floor coverings;

(7) sewing and handicraft threads;

(8) bandages, surgical dressings, and other textile fiber products, the labeling of which is subject to the requirements of the Federal Food, Drug and Cosmetic Act of 1938, as amended;

(9) waste materials not intended for use in a textile fiber product;

(10) textile fiber products incorporated in shoes or overshoes or similar outer footwear;

(11) textile fiber products incorporated in headwear, handbags, luggage, brushes, lampshades, or toys, catamenial devices, adhesive tapes and adhesive sheets, cleaning cloths impregnated with chemicals, or diapers.

The exemptions provided for any article by paragraph (3) or (4) of this subsection shall not be applicable if any representation as to fiber content of such article is made in any advertisement, label, or other means of identification covered by section 4 of this Act.

(b) The Commission may exclude from the provisions of this Act other textile fiber products (1) which have an insignificant or inconsequential textile fiber content, or (2) with respect to which the disclosure of textile fiber content is not necessary for the protection of the ultimate consumer.

[346]

RULES AND REGULATIONS UNDER
THE TEXTILE FIBER PRODUCTS
IDENTIFICATION ACT

RULE 1—TERMS DEFINED

As used in these rules, unless the context otherwise specifically requires:

(a) The term "Act" means the "Textile Fiber Products Identification Act" (approved September 2, 1958, 85th Congress, 2nd Session; 15 U.S.C. §70, 72 Stat. 1717).

(b) The terms "rule," "rules," "regulations," and "rules and regulations" mean the Rules and Regulations prescribed by the Commission pursuant to Section 7(c) of the Act.

(c) The definition of terms contained in Section 2 of the Act shall be applicable also to such terms when used in rules promulgated under the Act.

(d) The term "United States" means the several States, the District of Columbia, and the Territories and possessions of the United States.

(e) The terms "required information" and "information required" mean such information as is required to be disclosed on labels or invoices and in advertising under the Act and Regulations.

(f) The terms "label," "labels," "labeled," and "labeling" mean the stamp, tag, label, or other means of identification, or authorized substitute therefor, required to be on or affixed to textile fiber products by the Act and Regulations and on which the information required is to appear.

(g) The terms "marketing or handling" and "marketed or handled," when applied to textile fiber products, mean any one or all of the transactions set forth in Section 3 of the Act.

(h) The terms "invoice" and "invoice or other paper" mean a written account, order, memorandum, list, or catalogue, which is issued to a purchaser, consignee, bailee, correspondent, agent, or any other person, in connection with the marketing or handling of any textile fiber product transported or delivered to such person.

(i) The term "outer coverings of furniture, mattresses, and box springs" means those coverings as are permanently incorporated in such articles.

(j) The term "wearing apparel" means any costume or article of clothing or covering for any part of the body worn or intended to be worn by individuals.

(k) The term "beddings" means sheets, covers, blankets, comforters, pillows, pillowcases, quilts, bedspreads, pads, and all other textile fiber products used or intended to be used on or about a bed or other place for reclining or sleeping but shall not include furniture, mattresses or box springs.

(l) The term "headwear" means any textile fiber product worn exclusively on or about the head or face by individuals.

(m) The term "backings," when applied to floor coverings, means that part of a floor covering to which the pile, face, or outer surface is woven, tufted, hooked, knitted, or otherwise attached, and which provides the structural base of the floor covering. The term "backings" shall also include fabrics attached to the structural base of the floor covering in such a way as to form a part of such structural base, but shall not include the pile, face, or outer surface of the floor covering or any part thereof.

(n) The term "elastic material" means a fabric composed of yarn consisting of an elastomer or a covered elastomer.

(o) The term "coated fabric" means any fabric which is coated, filled, impregnated, or laminated with a continuous-film-forming polymeric composition in such a manner that the weight added to the base fabric is at least 35% of the weight of the fabric before coating, filling, impregnation, or lamination.

(p) The term "upholstered product" means articles of furniture containing stuffing and shall include mattresses and box springs.

(q) The term "ornamentation" means any fibers or yarns imparting a visibly discernible pattern or design to a yarn or fabric.

(r) The term "fiber trademark" means a word or words used by a person to identify a particular fiber produced or sold by him and to distinguish it from fibers of the same generic class produced or sold by others. Such term shall not include any trademark, product mark, house mark, trade name or other name which does not identify a particular fiber.

(s) The term "wool" means the fiber from the fleece of the sheep or lamb or hair of the Angora or Cashmere goat (and may include the so-called specialty fibers from the hair of the camel, alpaca, llama, and vicuña) which has never been reclaimed from any woven or felted wool product.

(t) The term "reprocessed wool" means the resulting fiber when wool has been woven or felted into a wool product which, without ever having been utilized in any way by the ultimate consumer, subsequently has been made into a fibrous state.

(u) The term "reused wool" means the resulting fiber when wool or reprocessed wool has been spun, woven, knitted or felted into a wool product which, after having been used in any way by the ultimate consumer, subsequently has been made into a fibrous state. (16 CFR §303. 1.)

RULE 2—GENERAL REQUIREMENTS

(a) Each textile fiber product, except those exempted or excluded under Section 12 of the Act, shall be labeled or invoiced in conformity with the requirements of the Act and Regulations.

(b) Any advertising of textile fiber products subject to the Act shall be in conformity with the requirements of the Act and Regulations.

(c) The requirements of the Act and Regulations shall not be applicable to products required to be labeled under the Wool Products Labeling Act of 1939 (Public Law 76-850, 15 U.S.C. 68, 54 Stat. 1128).

(d) Any person marketing or handling textile fiber products who shall cause or direct a processor or finisher to label, invoice, or otherwise identify any textile fiber product with required information shall be responsible under the Act and Regulations for any failure of compliance with the Act and Regulations by reason of any statement or omission in such label, invoice, or other means of identification utilized in accordance with his direction, *provided* that nothing herein shall relieve the processor or finisher of any duty or liability to which he may be subject under the Act and Regulations. (16 CFR §303. 2.)

RULE 3—FIBERS PRESENT IN AMOUNTS OF 5% OR LESS

In disclosing the constituent fibers in required information, no fiber present in the amount of five percentum or less of the total fiber weight shall be designated by its generic name or fiber trademark, but shall be designated as "other fiber."

Where more than one of such fibers are present in a product, they shall be designated in the aggregate as "other fibers." (16 CFR §303. 3.)

RULE 4—ENGLISH LANGUAGE REQUIREMENT

All required information shall be set out in the English language. If the required informaiton appears in a language other than English, it also shall appear in the English language. The provisions of this rule shall not apply to advertisements in foreign language newspapers or periodicals, but such advertising shall in all other respects comply with the Act and Regulations. (16 CFR §303. 4.)

RULE 5—ABBREVIATIONS, DITTO MARKS, AND ASTERISKS PROHIBITED

(a) In disclosing required information, words or terms shall not be designated by ditto marks or appear in footnotes referred to by asterisks or other symbols in required information, and shall not be abbreviated except as permitted in Rule 33(d).

(b) Where the generic name of a textile fiber is required to appear in immediate conjunction with a fiber trademark in advertising, labeling, or invoicing, a disclosure of the generic name by means of a footnote, to which reference is made by use of an asterisk or other symbol placed next to the fiber trademark, shall not be sufficient in itself to constitute compliance with the Act and Regulations. (16 CFR §303. 5.)

RULE 6—GENERIC NAMES OF FIBERS TO BE USED

(1) Except where another name is permitted under the Act and Regulations, the respective generic names of all fibers present in the amount of more than five percentum of the total fiber weight of the textile fiber product shall be used when naming fibers in the required information; as for example: "cotton," "rayon," "silk," "linen," "nylon," etc.

(2) Where a textile fiber product contains hair or fiber of a fur-bearing animal present in the amount of more than five percentum of the total fiber weight of the product, the name of the animal producing such fiber may be used in setting forth the required information, provided the name of such animal is used in conjunction with the words "fiber," "hair," or "blend"; as for example:

"80% Rabbit Hair
20% Nylon"
or
"80% Silk
20% Mink Fiber"

[348]

(3) The term "fur fiber" may be used to describe the hair or fur fiber or mixtures thereof of any animal or animals other than the sheep, lamb, Angora goat, Cashmere goat, camel, alpaca, llama or vicuña where such hair or fur fiber or mixture is present in the amount of more than five percentum of the total fiber weight of the textile fiber product and no direct or indirect representations are made as to the animal or animals from which the fiber so designated was obtained, as for example:

"60% Cotton
40% Fur Fiber"
or
"50% Nylon
30% Mink Hair
20% Fur Fiber"

(4) Where textile fiber products subject to the Act contain (1) wool, (2) processed wool, or (3) reused wool in amounts of more than five percentum of the total fiber weight, such fibers shall be designated and disclosed as wool, reprocessed wool, or reused wool as the case may be. (16 CFR §303. 6.)

RULE 8—PROCEDURE FOR ESTABLISHING GENERIC NAMES FOR MANUFACTURED FIBERS

Prior to the marketing or handling of a manufactured fiber for which no generic name has been established by the Commission, the manufacturer or producer thereof shall file a written application with the Commission, requesting the establishment of a generic name for such fiber, stating therein:

(a) the reasons why the applicant's fiber should not be identified by one of the generic names established by the Commission in Rule 7 of the Regulations;

(b) the chemical composition of the fiber, including the fiber-forming substances and respective percentages thereof, together with samples of the fiber;

(c) suggested names for consideration as generic, together with a proposed definition for the fiber;

(d) any other information deemed by the applicant to be pertinent to the application, including technical data in the form of test methods;

(e) the earliest date on which the applicant proposes to market or handle the fiber in commerce for other than developmental or testing purposes.

Upon receipt of the application, the Commission will, within sixty (60) days, either deny the application or assign to the fiber a numerical or alphabetical symbol for temporary use during further consideration of such application.

After taking the necessary procedure in consideration of the application, the Commission in due course shall establish a generic name or advise the applicant of its refusal to grant the application and designate the proper existing generic name for the fiber. (16 CFR §303. 8.)

RULE 9—USE OF FUR-BEARING ANIMAL NAMES AND SYMBOLS PROHIBITED

(a) The advertising or the labeling of a textile fiber product shall not contain any names, words, depictions, descriptive matter, or other symbols which connote or signify a fur-bearing animal, unless such product or the part thereof in connection with which the names, words, depictions, descriptive matter, or other symbols are used is a fur product within the meaning of the Fur Products Labeling Act.

(b) Subject to the provisions of subsection (a) hereof and Rule 6 of the Regulations, a textile fiber product shall not be described or referred to in any manner in an advertisement or label with:

(1) The name or part of the name of a fur-bearing animal, whether as a single word or a combination word, or any coined word which is phonetically similar to a fur-bearing animal name, or which is only a slight variation in spelling of a fur-bearing animal name or part of the name. As for example, such terms as "Ermine," "Mink," "Persian," "Broadtail," "Beaverton," "Marmink," "Sablelon," "Lam," "Pershian," "Minx," or similar terms shall not be used.

(2) Any word or name symbolic of a fur-bearing animal by reason of conventional usage or by reason of its close relationship with fur-bearing animals. As for example, such terms as "guardhair," "underfur," and "mutation," or similar terms, shall not be used.

RULE 10—FIBER CONTENT OF ELASTIC YARN OR MATERIAL

(a) Where a textile fiber product is made wholly of elastic yarn or material, with minor parts of rigid material for structural purposes, it shall be identified as to the percentage of the elastomer, together with the percentage of all textile coverings of the elastomer and all other yarns or materials used therein.

(b) Where a textile fiber product is made in part of elastic material and in part of other fabric, the fiber content of such fabric shall be set forth sectionally by percentages as in the case of other fabrics. In such cases the elastic material may be disclosed by describing the material as elastic followed by a listing in order of predominance by weight of the fibers used in such elastic, including the elastomer, where such fibers are present by five percentum or more. An example of labeling under this subsection is:

"Front and back rigid sections:
50% Acetate,
50% Cotton.
Elastic: Rayon, cotton, nylon, rubber."
(16 CFR §303. 10.)

RULE 11—FLOOR COVERINGS CONTAINING BACKINGS, FILLINGS, AND PADDINGS

In disclosing the required fiber content information as to floor coverings containing exempted backings, fillings, or paddings, the disclosure shall be made in such manner as to indicate that it relates only to the face, pile, or outer surface of the floor covering and not to the backing, filling, or padding. Examples of the form of marking these types of floor coverings as to fiber content are as follows:

"100% Cotton Pile"

"Face—60% Rayon, 40% Cotton"

"Outer Surface—100% Wool." (16 CFR §303. 11.)

Note: Where it is desired to disclose the fiber content of exempted backings of pile floor coverings, such floor coverings may be labeled in accordance with Rule 24.

RULE 14—PRODUCTS CONTAINING UNKNOWN FIBERS

(a) Where a textile fiber product is made from miscellaneous scraps, rags, odd lots, textile by-products, or waste materials of unknown, and for practical purposes, undeterminable fiber content, the required fiber content disclosure may, when truthfully applicable, indicate that such product is composed of miscellaneous scraps, rags, odd lots, textile by-products, or waste materials, as the case may be, of unknown or undetermined fiber content; as for example:

"Made of miscellaneous scraps of undetermined fiber content."

"Made of miscellaneous rags of undetermined fiber content."

"Made of miscellaneous odd lots of undetermined fiber content."

"Made of miscellaneous textile by-products of undetermined fiber content."

"Made of miscellaneous waste materials of undetermined fiber content."

No representation as to fiber content shall be made as to any textile fiber product designated as being composed of undetermined fibers. If any representation as to fiber content is made with reference to such products, a full fiber content disclosure shall be required.

(b) Nothing contained in this rule shall excuse a full disclosure as to fiber content if the same is known or practically ascertainable. (16 CFR §303. 14)

RULE 15—LABEL AND METHOD OF AFFIXING

The label required to be on or affixed to the textile fiber product shall be such as is appropriate to the nature and type of product. Such label shall be conspicuously affixed to the product or, where permitted, its package or container in a secure manner and shall be of such durability as to remain on and attached thereto throughout the sale, resale, distribution and handling of the product, and, except where otherwise provided, shall remain on or be firmly affixed to the roduct or, where permitted, its package or container when sold and delivered to the ultimate ɔnsumer. (16 CFR §303. 15.)

ULE 22—PRODUCTS CONTAINING LININGS, INTERLININGS, FILLINGS, AND PADDINGS

In disclosing the required information as to textile fiber products, the fiber content of any ɯnings, interlinings, fillings, or paddings shall be set forth separately and distinctly if such lin- ɪgs, interlinings, fillings, or paddings are incorporated in the product for warmth rather than for ructural purposes, or if any express or implied representations are made as to their fiber con- ɪnt. Examples are as follows:

> "100% Nylon
>
> Interlining: 100% Rayon"

> "Covering: 100% Rayon
>
> Filling: 100% Cotton" (16 CFR §303. 22)

ULE 23—TEXTILE FIBER PRODUCTS CONTAINING SUPERIMPOSED OR ADDED FIBERS

Where a textile fiber product is made wholly of one fiber or a blend of fibers with the ×ception of an additional fiber in minor proportion superimposed or added in certain separate ɪd distinct areas or sections for reinforcing or other useful purposes, the product may be desig- ated according to the fiber content of the principal fiber or blend of fibers, with an exception aming the superimposed or added fiber, giving the percentage thereof in relation to the total ber weight of the principal fiber or blend of fibers, and indicating the area or section which ɔntains the superimposed or added fiber. Examples of this type of fiber content disclosure, as ɔplied to products having reinforcing fibers added to a particular area or section, are as follows:

> "55% Cotton
> 45% Rayon
> Except 5% Nylon added
> to toe and heel."

> "All Cotton except 1% Nylon
> added to neckband." (16 CFR §303. 23.)

ULE 24—PILE FABRICS AND PRODUCTS COMPOSED THEREOF

The fiber content of pile fabrics or products composed thereof may be stated on the label ɪ such segregated form as will show the fiber content of the face or pile and of the back or ·ase, with percentages of the respective fibers as they exist in the face or pile and in the back ·r base, *provided* that in such disclosure the respective percentages of the face and back be given ɪ such manner as will show the ratio between the face and the back. Examples of the form of ɪarking pile fabric as to fiber content provided for in this rule are as follows:

> "100% Nylon Pile
>
> 100% Cotton Back
>
> (Back constitutes 60% of
> fabric and pile 40%)."

> "Face—60% Rayon, 40% Nylon
>
> Back—70%, 30% Rayon
>
> (Face constitutes 60% of fabric
> and back 40%)." (16 CFR §303. 24)

ULE 25—SECTIONAL DISCLOSURE OF CONTENT

(a) (Permissive) Where a textile fiber product is composed of two or more sections which ɪre of different fiber composition, the required information as to fiber content may be separated ɪ the same label in such manner as to show the fiber composition of each section.

(b) (Mandatory) The disclosure as above provided shall be made in all instances where uch form of marking is necessary to avoid deception. (16 CFR §303. 25.)

RULE 26—ORNAMENTATION

(a) Where the textile fiber product contains fiber ornamentation not exceeding five per centum of the total fiber weight of the product and the stated percentages of the fiber content are exclusive of such ornamentation, the label or any invoice used in lieu thereof shall contain a phrase or statement showing such fact; as for example:

"60% Cotton
40% Rayon
Exclusive of Ornamentation."

or

"All Cotton
Exclusive of Ornamentation."

The fiber content of such ornamentation may be disclosed where the percentage of the ornamentation in relation to the total fiber weight of the principal fiber or blend of fibers is shown; as for example:

"70% Nylon
30% Acetate
Exclusive of 4% Metallic Ornamentation."

or

"100% Rayon
Exclusive of 3% Silk Ornamentation."

(b) Where the fiber ornamentation exceeds five percentum, it shall be included in the statement of required percentages of fiber content.

(c) Where the ornamentation constitutes a distinct section of the product, sectional disclosure may be made in accordance with Rule 25. (16 CFR §303. 26.)

RULE 27—USE OF THE TERM "ALL" OR "100%"

Where a textile fiber product or part thereof is comprised wholly of one fiber, other than any fiber ornamentation, decoration, elastic, or trimming as to which fiber content disclosure is not required, either the word "All" or the term "100%" may be used in labeling, together with the correct generic name of the fiber and any qualifying phrase, when required; as for example: "100% Cotton," "All Rayon, Exclusive of Ornamentation," "100% Acetate, Exclusive of Decoration," "All Nylon, Exclusive of Elastic," etc. (16 CFR §303. 27.)

RULE 35—USE OF TERMS "VIRGIN" OR "NEW"

The terms "virgin" or "new" as descriptive of a textile fiber product, or any fiber or part thereof, shall not be used when the product or part so described is not composed wholly of new or virgin fiber which has never been reclaimed from any spun, woven, knitted, felted, bonded, or similarly manufactured product. (16 CFR §303. 35.)

RULE 43—FIBER CONTENT TOLERANCES

(a) A textile fiber product which contains more than one fiber shall not be deemed to be misbranded as to fiber content percentages if the percentages by weight of any fibers present in the total fiber content of the product, exclusive of permissive ornamentation, do not deviate or vary from the percentages stated on the label in excess of 3% of the total fiber weight of the product. For example, where the label indicates that a particular fiber is present in the amount of 40%, the amount of such fiber present may vary from a minimum of 37% of the total fiber weight of such product to a maximum of 43% of the total fiber weight of such product.

(b) Where the percentage of any fiber or fibers contained in a textile fiber product deviates or varies from the percentage stated on the label by more than the tolerance or variation provided in subsection (a) of this rule, such product shall be misbranded unless the person charged proves that the entire deviation or variation from the fiber content percentages stated on the label resulted from unavoidable variations in manufacture and despite the exercise of due care.

(c) Where representations are made to the effect that a textile fiber product is composed wholly of one fiber, the tolerance provided in Section 4(b)(2) of the Act and subsection (a) of this rule shall not apply except as to permissive ornamentation where the textile fiber product is represented to be composed of one fiber "exclusive of ornamentation." (16 CFR § 303. 43.)

RULE 44—PRODUCTS NOT INTENDED FOR USES SUBJECT TO THE ACT

Textile fiber products intended for uses not within the scope of the Act and Regulations or intended for uses in other textile fiber products which are exempted or excluded from the Act shall not be subject to the labeling and invoicing requirements of the Act and Regulations *provided* an invoice or other paper covering the marketing or handling of such products is given, which indicates that the products are not intended for uses subject to the Textile Fiber Products Identification Act. (16 CFR §303. 44.)

RULE 45—EXCLUSIONS FROM THE ACT

(a) Pursuant to Section 12(b) of the Act, the Commission hereby excludes from the operation of the Act:

(1) All textile fiber products *except:*

(i) articles of wearing apparel;
(ii) handkerchiefs;
(iii) scarfs;
(iv) beddings;
(v) curtains and casements;
(vi) draperies;
(vii) tablecloths, napkins, and doilies;
(viii) floor coverings;
(ix) towels;
(x) wash cloths and dish cloths;
(xi) ironing board covers and pads;
(xii) umbrellas and parasols;
(xiii) batts;
(xiv) products subject to Section 4(h) of the Act;
(xv) flags;
(xvi) cushions;
(xvii) all fibers, yarns and fabrics (including narrow fabrics except packaging ribbons);
(xviii) furniture slip covers and other covers or coverlets for furniture;
(xix) afghans and throws;
(xx) sleeping bags;
(xxi) antimacassars and tidies;
(xxii) hammocks;
(xxiii) dresser and other furniture scarfs.

(2) Belts, suspenders, arm bands, permanently knotted neckties, garters, sanitary belts, diaper liners, labels (either required or non-required) individually and in rolls, looper clips intended for handicraft purposes, book cloth, artists' canvases, tapestry cloth, and shoe laces.

(3) All textile fiber products manufactured by the operators of company stores and offered for sale and sold exclusively to their own employees as ultimate consumers.

(4) Coated fabrics and those portions of textile fiber products made of coated fabrics.

(5) Secondhand household textile articles which are discernibly secondhand or which are marked to indicate their secondhand character.

(6) Non-woven products of a disposable nature intended for one-time use only.

(b) The exclusions provided for in subsection ·(a) of this rule shall not be applicable if any representations as to fiber content of such articles are made, except as to those products excluded by paragraph (6).

(c) The exclusions from the Act provided in subsection (a) hereof are in addition to the exemptions from the Act provided in Section 12(a) of the Act and shall not affect or limit such exemptions. (16 CFR §303. 45.)

Promulgated and made effective by the Federal Trade Commission on March 3, 1960.

Note: The Commission on its own motion or upon the application of any interested party may initiate proceedings to revise, amend, or modify all or any part of these Rules and Regulations. Such proceedings will be conducted in accordance with the rule-making procedures prescribed in the Administrative Procedure Act (60 Stat. 237, as amended, 5 U.S.C. §§1001-1011) and in accordance with Subpart A of the rule-making procedures of the Federal Trade Commission. (16 CFR §§2.1–2.8)

AMENDMENT TO RULE 25 (c) OF THE RULES AND REGULATIONS UNDER THE WOOL PRODUCTS LABELING ACT OF 1939; "THE POINT OF ORIGIN LABEL."

RULE 25(c) AS AMENDED

(c) When any representation is made on a stamp, tag, label, or other means of identifica-tion on or attached to a wool product that the fabric contained therein is imported, the name of the country where the fabric was woven, knitted, felted, bonded, or otherwise manufactured shall be set forth on the stamp, tag, label, or other means of identification so as to clearly indicate that the fabric contained in the wool product was made in such country, as for example

"Fabric Woven in Italy."

NOTE: Nothing in this Rule shall relieve any person subject to the Act (1) from any duty or liability under Section 4(a)(1) of the Wool Products Labeling Act of 1939 which prohibit false or deceptive labeling or (2) from compliance with Section 5 of the Federal Trade Com mission Act which has been held to require disclosure of the country of origin of product or fabrics from which completed products are made where the failure to make such a disclosure has the tendency and capacity to deceive or (3) from the marking requirements of the Tarif Act and the regulations of the Bureau of Customs pursuant thereto. [16 CFR §300. 25 a amended, effective May 20, 1964]

THE TEX SYSTEM FOR DESIGNATION OF YARN NUMBER OR COUNT

Sponsored by ASTM Committee D-13 on Textiles ASA Sectional Committee L-23 for ISO/TC38 on Textiles: American Society for Testing and Materials.

A plan for the orderly introduction of the single system of numbering yarns made from all types of fibers introduced to the textile industry in most of the countries of the world United States participation has helped to keep our industry abreast of this significant develop ment.

Yarn number represents the "size," "fineness," or, more accurately, the relationship between weight and length of a yarn. The tex system has been chosen to replace the many conflicting systems now used, after extended study by the Technical Committee on Textiles of the Inter national Organization for Standardization (ISO/TC 38). Delegates representing the textile industries of twenty-one nations including the United States and four international textile associations participated in the study and unanimously adopted this proposal.

It is proposed to make the changeover in three easy stages over a period of years. Th action to be taken in each stage will be given here. The first stage began in 1960 and will run until the trade is thoroughly familiar with the new system. Dates for the second and third stages will be set when the trade becomes ready for them.

I. THREE STAGES OF ACTION

1. *First Stage.* This stage is designed to familiarize everyone working in the textile industry with tex numbers. The existing yarn count systems will continue in use, but a corresponding rounded tex number will be given in parentheses after the traditional yarn count or yarn number—for example: 18 cotton count (32 tex), 48 worsted count (18 tex), 100 denier (11 tex).

During this stage the rounded tex numbers in parentheses are illustrative or explanatory and have no legal standing. They cannot be used as the basis of claims or other disputes which must be based on the traditional yarn numbers. A note to this effect may be stamped on contracts or other documents where this is felt to be desirable or helpful.

2. *Second Stage.* Commercial transactions and manufacturing operations will be shifted to tex numbering. The equivalent traditional yarn number or count will be given in parentheses after the tex number—for example: 32 tex cotton yarn will be written 32 tex (18.5 cotton count); 18 tex worsted yarn will be written 18 tex (48 worsted count).

3. *Third Stage.* The traditional yarn number in parentheses will be deleted; only tex num bers will be given.

II. ACTION TO BE TAKEN NOW

In view of the benefits to be derived from the general use of a single yarn-numbering system throughout the industry, all textile trade associations are urged to endorse the plan for introduction of the tex system and to recommend participation in it by their members. Manu facturers, distributors, testing and research laboratories, and individuals throughout the industry re urged to give rounded equivalent tex numbers in parentheses following the traditional numbers or counts wherever they appear on orders, invoices, tags, reports, in trade literature, and in technical publications.

The rounded tex numbers can be obtained readily from short tables relating them to the numbers or counts in the system now used. Condensed tables are appended to this report for cottons, worsted, woolen, and denier numbers or counts, with directions for their use. The tex number of a yarn, fiber, or other strand is defined as the weight in grams of one kilometer of yarn. Constants have been calculated for converting yarn numbers or counts of all systems currently in use to tex numbers. For the present, however, only rounded equivalent numbers need be used.

The ISO Committee, developing plans for the introduction of the tex system, has suggested that as far as possible the rounded equivalent tex numbers listed in Table II of the Appendix should be used in preference to other intermediate numbers or to the exact tex numbers. The preferred numbers have been carefully selected to cover the entire range needed for commercial yarns in a series of steps that, in general, reflect variations observed in practical spinning operations. In the second stage, when yarns are numbered in the tex system, intermediate values can, of course, be used whenever tradition or customer's requirements indicates this to be desirable.

III. SCOPE AND BENEFITS OF THE TEX SYSTEM

Since the tex number is also applicable to yarn intermediates, it can be used for laps, slivers, and rovings as well as yarns. It can be also be used for individual fibers; the millitex unit can be used to avoid low numbers.

The success of the analogous denier system gives assurance that the proposed tex system is workable. The tex system has already been used successfully in local installations, both in cotton-spinning laboratories and in manufacturing units, so that no one need have any hesitation about its suitability as a yarn-numbering system.

Adoption of a single universal system for numbering yarns made from any fiber has the following advantages:

1. The various yarn systems now in use with different fibers—for example, English cotton counts, French cotton counts, metric counts, Yorkshire woolen skeins, American woolen runs, English worsted counts—will all be replaced with the tex system, eliminating time spent in converting units from one system to the other and avoiding mistakes that occur when technicians are forced to think in unfamiliar units.

2. Efficiency in mills spinning yarns from any fiber will be increased. Picker laps, slivers, rovings, and yarns will all be numbered in the same units, thus facilitating the calculation of drafts at all stages of spinning and eliminating confusion due to changing systems between laps and slivers, slivers and rovings, tops and gills, rovings and yarns.

3. Operating procedures will be simplified in mills simultaneously spinning yarns from fibers numbered in different systems, for example, wool and manmade fibers on both the worsted and woolen systems. Sales of these products to different customers will also be simplified.

4. The buying and selling of yarns that must meet specifications given in different traditional numbering systems will be simplified by eliminating the time spent in converting and checking results.

5. Efficiency in cost accounting and inventory control will be increased, since all yarns, regardless of the fiber used, will be based on the same yarn-numbering system.

6. Fabric design work will be simplified, since the same amount of yarn, that is, the same length of yarn of a given number or count, will be needed to make the same weight of fabric, regardless of the fibers involved.

7. Calculation of the resultant count of all plied yarns that are numbered in indirect numbering systems will be much easier, since with tex numbers the equivalent single number can be calculated by simple addition.

8. Efficiency of quality control and cost comparisons will be improved, since all derived or calculated yarn properties such as breaking tenacity or lea product will be in the same units regardless of fiber used.

9. It will be easier to interpret and use the findings of textile research workers published anywhere in the world.

10. Any spinning or blend study involving the number of fibers in a yarn will be easier to make, since the yarn and the fibers used will both be numbered in the same or closely related systems.

11. The time spent in technical textile schools teaching and practicing the use of various

yarn-numbering systems will be eventually eliminated. This time will be available for teaching other important subjects.

12. The United States textile industry will avoid being placed at a further disadvantage in production costs with respect to competition from foreign countries who are expected to adopt the tex yarn-numbering system fairly soon.

13. In addition to the ultimate lower costs resulting from all these increased efficiencies each textile scientist or executive will have the personal satisfaction of promoting the use of the universal yarn-numbering system in his own company and trade association and of knowing that, at the cost of some relatively transient personal difficulty, he is contributing to the advancement of the textile industry for the benefit of all future generations.

CONCLUSION

Agreement on the tex system for yarn numbering is a notable achievement in international standardization in a field where standardization is long overdue. It merits the support of every person, organization, and company interested in the long-range good of the textile industry.

It is urged that everyone in the textile industry participate in the general educational program leading to the introduction of the tex yarn-numbering system in his part of the industry.

Discussions of the tex yarn-numbering system have appeared in textile journals in the United States and in foreign countries from time to time. Anyone desiring more information on this international development should consult his own technical experts, his ASTM representative, or should refer to the References listed below.

B. L. WHITTIER, chairman,

ASTM Committee D-13 on Textile Materials.

W. D. APPEL, chairman,

ASA Committee L23, U. S. representative on ISO/TC 38 on Textiles.

REFERENCES

(1) Anon. letter to the editor reporting use of the tex system in the large Alpargatos Cotton Mills in Argentina and Uruguay, *Textile Age*, Vol. 8, p. 108 (1944).

(2) Tentative Recommended Practice for Use of Tex System to Designate Linear Density of Fibers, Yarn Intermediates, Yarns, and Other Textile Materials, ASTM Designation: D 861-58 T, 1958 Book of ASTM Standards, Part 10, p. 347.

(3) ASTM Yarn Numbering Conversion Table. This Table gives exact tex equivalents of normal yarn counts for all traditional yarn-numbering systems. Appendix III of Compilation of ASTM Standards on Textile Materials, published annually.

(4) A. W. Bayes, "Tex Universal Yarn Numbering System," *Journal Textile Inst.*, Vol. 48 p. 225 (1957).

(5) Canadian Advisory Committee on ISO/TC 38 "Textiles—Introduction of the Tex Yarn Numbering System," *Canadian Textile Journal*, Vol. 76, pp. 59–63 (Dec. 11, 1959).

(6) J. Corbiére, "The International Numbering of Yarns and Threads," *Textile Research Journal*, Vol. 23, p. 946 (Dec., 1953).

(7) Deutsche Normen, DIN 60905 (Official German Standard), "The Tex System for the Numbering of Textile Fibers, Yarns, and Fabrics," Melliand Textil-Berichte, Vol. 38, p. 64 (1957) (In German).

(8) R. W. Forrester, "Yarn Counts—Proposed Universal System," *Journal Textile Inst.* Vol. 40, S8–12 (1949).

(9) J. W. S. Hearle, "Tex Universal Yarn Numbering System," *Journal Textile Inst.*, Vol 48, pp. 416–17 (1957).

(10) K. Henschel, "Simplification of Yarn Numbering, Preparation for the Introduction of the International Numbering of Yarns in Germany," *Textile Research Journal*, Vol. 25, p. 140 (1955).

(11) International Cotton Federation, "Approval of the Tex Yarn Numbering System for Cotton and Allied Textile Industries," *Textile Mercury and Argus*, Vol. 139, p. 360 (1958).

(12) H. L. Röder, "The Tex System Adopted as the Universal Numbering System for Yarn and Fibers," *Enka and Breda Rayon Review*, Vol. 10, p. 133 (1956).

(13) L. Szponder, "Tex—A Universal Yarn Numbering System," *Textile Industries*, Vol 122, p. 149 (1958).

(14) A. G. Scroggie, "The Tex Universal Yarn Numbering System," *Textile Research Journal*, Vol. 28, p. 330 (1958).

(15) Spanish Government, Promulgation of the Tex System for Numbering Yarns made from all Fibers (1946) (In Spanish).

(16) B. L. Whittier, "Tex—A New Yarn-Numbering System," *Textile World*, Vol. 107, p. 88 (Aug., 1957).

(17) The Tex System of Yarn Counting, Recommendation to all members of the Federation of Master Cotton Spinners Associations Ltd., The Yarn Spinners Association and the Cotton Yarn Doublers Association in the United Kingdom, to proceed with the adoption of the Tex System, pamphlet, Federation of Master Cotton Spinners Association Ltd., Manchester , England.

APPENDIX

CONVERSION TABLES

Conversion tables giving the rounded equivalent tex numbers for various ranges of English Cotton Count (Table III), English Worsted Count (Table IV), American Woolen Run (Table V), and Denier Number (Table VI), together with instructions for their use, are given in this Appendix.

Tables for other systems can be prepared by means of the factors, given in Table I. Factors for a number of other systems can be found in Draft ISO Recommendation Document ISO/TC 38 (Sc 4-1) 210).

To prepare a conversion table, use the appropriate factor from Table I to calculate the equivalent traditional value for the limiting range of the recommended rounded tex units listed in Table II. Each calculated value forms the upper limit of one range and the lower limit of the next range as shown in Tables III through VI.

TABLE I. CONVERSION FACTORS

TO GET TEX NUMBER	
DIVIDE	BY
Denier No.	9
Spyndle No.	0.02903
4960.5	Asbestos cut [a]
590.54	Cotton count (English) [b]
4960.5	Glass cut [c]
1653.5	Linen cut [d]
1000.0	Metric No. [e]
310.03	Woolen run (American) [f]
885.8	Worsted count (English) [g]
or	
MULTIPLY	BY
Denier No.	0.1111
Spyndle No.	34.45

[a] Asbestos cut, NaA, equals 100-yd hanks per lb. [b] English cotton count, Nec, equals 840-yd hanks per lb. [c] Glass cut, NG, equals 100-yd hanks per lb. [d] Linen cut, NeL, equals 300-yd hanks per lb. [e] Metric number, Nm, equals kilometers per kilogram. [f] American woolen run, Nar, equals 1600-yd hanks per lb. [g] English worsted count, Ne, equals 560-yd hanks per lb.

TABLE II. RECOMMENDED ROUNDED TEX NUMBERS [a]

RANGE OF TEX NUMBER		RECOMMENDED ROUNDED TEX NUMBER	RANGE OF TEX NUMBER		RECOMMENDED ROUNDED TEX NUMBER
ABOVE	UP TO AND INCLUDING		ABOVE	UP TO AND INCLUDING	
9.4	9.8	9.6	31	33	32
9.8	10.25	10	33	35	34
10.25	10.75	10.5	35	37	36
10.75	11.25	11	37	39	38
11.25	11.75	11.5	39	41	40
11.75	12.25	12	41	43	42
12.25	12.75	12.5	43	45	44
12.75	13.5	13	45	47	46
13.5	14.5	14	47	49	48
14.5	15.5	15	49	51	50
15.5	16.5	16	51	54	52
16.5	17.5	17	54	58	56
17.5	18.5	18	58	62	60
18.5	19.5	19	62	66	64
19.5	20.5	20	66	70	68
20.5	21.5	21	70	74	72
21.5	22.5	22	74	78	76
22.5	23.5	23	78	82	80
23.5	24.5	24	82	86	84
24.5	25	25	86	90	88
25.5	27	26	90	94	92
27	29	28	94	98	96
29	31	30	98	102.5	100

[a] Reproduced from the draft ISO Recommendation ISO/TC 38 (SC 4-1) 210, section 3
The decimal multiples and fractions of the rounded values indicated in this table are va for the decimal multiples and fractions of the corresponding ranges.

The rounded tex number appropriate to any number in a traditional system can be obtain by following the procedure set forth in the draft ISO Recommendation, but it is more convenie to use a table in which the limits of the rounded tex numbers have been converted into those a traditional system.

TABLE III. CONVERSION OF ENGLISH COTTON COUNT INTO ROUNDED TEX NUMBER

For Use During the First Stage of Introduction of the Tex System.
Tex = 590.5/Cotton Count.

COTTON COUNT [a]		RECOMMENDED
BEGINNING WITH	UP TO BUT NOT INCLUDING	ROUNDED TEX NUMBER
57.59	60.26	10
54.91	57.59	10.5
52.47	54.91	11
50.24	52.47	11.5
48.19	50.24	12
46.30	48.19	12.5
43.73	46.30	13
40.72	43.73	14
38.09	40.72	15
35.78	38.09	16
33.74	35.78	17
31.92	33.74	18
30.28	31.92	19
28.80	30.28	20
27.46	28.80	21
26.24	27.46	22
25.13	26.24	23
24.10	25.13	24
23.16	24.10	25
21.87	23.16	26
20.36	21.87	28
19.05	20.36	30
17.90	19.05	32
16.87	17.90	34
15.96	16.87	36
15.14	15.96	38
14.41	15.14	40
13.74	14.41	42
13.13	13.74	44
12.57	13.13	46
12.05	12.57	48
11.58	12.05	50
10.94	11.58	52
10.19	10.94	56
9.524	10.19	60
8.947	9.524	64
8.436	8.947	68
7.980	8.436	72
7.571	7.980	76
7.201	7.571	80
6.866	7.201	84
6.561	6.866	88
6.282	6.561	92
6.026	6.282	96
5.759	6.026	100
5.758	5.759	105

In the left-hand columns of this table, ▪d the range that includes the cotton count ▪der consideration. On the same line as the ▪lected range and to the right of it, find ▪e corresponding rounded tex number. This ▪ the number to be placed in parentheses ▪ter the traditional number during the first ▪ge of the introduction of the tex system.

EXAMPLE: Cotton count 21 falls in the ▪nge of 20.36 to 21.87. The corresponding ▪unded tex number is 28. The recom-▪ended notation for this yarn during the ▪st stage of the introduction of tex yarn ▪mbers is accordingly: cotton count 21 ▪8 tex), or, using the European abbrevia-▪n, Nec 21 (28 tex).

When required, the values below 10 tex ▪d above 100 tex can be derived from the ▪me table simply by multiplying the values ▪ 10 or dividing them by 10. When doing ▪is, it should be noted that the decimal ▪int in the left columns moves in the ▪posite direction to that in the right column.

EXAMPLES:

COTTON COUNT		RECOMMENDED
▪GINNING WITH	UP TO BUT NOT INCLUDING	ROUNDED TEX NUMBER
▪0.36	21.87	28
2.036	2.187	280
▪3.6	218.7	2.8

[a] Cotton count (Nec) = 840-yd hanks per lb.

[359]

TABLE IV. CONVERSION OF ENGLISH WORSTED COUNT INTO ROUNDED TEX NUMBER

For Use During the First Stage of Introduction of the Tex System.
Tex = 885.8/Worsted Count.

ENGLISH WORSTED COUNT [a]		RECOMMENDE
BEGINNING WITH	UP TO BUT NOT INCLUDING	ROUNDED TE⟩ NUMBER
82.400 .... 86.419		10.5
78.737 .... 82.400		11
75.387 .... 78.737		11.5
72.310 .... 75.387		12
69.474 .... 72.310		12.5
65.614 .... 69.474		13
61.089 .... 65.614		14
57.148 .... 61.089		15
53.684 .... 57.148		16
50.617 .... 53.684		17
47.881 .... 50.617		18
45.425 .... 47.881		19
43.209 .... 45.425		20
41.200 .... 43.209		21
39.368 .... 41.200		22
37.693 .... 39.368		23
36.155 .... 37.693		24
34.737 .... 36.155		25
32.807 .... 34.737		26
30.544 .... 32.807		28
28.574 .... 30.544		30
26.842 .... 28.574		32
25.308 .... 26.842		34
23.940 .... 25.308		36
22.712 .... 23.940		38
21.604 .... 22.712		40
20.600 .... 21.604		42
19.684 .... 20.600		44
18.846 .... 19.684		46
18.077 .... 18.846		48
17.368 .... 18.077		50
16.403 .... 17.368		52
15.272 .... 16.403		56
14.287 .... 15.272		60
13.421 .... 14.287		64
12.654 .... 13.421		68
11.970 .... 12.654		72
11.356 .... 11.970		76
10.802 .... 11.356		80
10.300 .... 10.802		84
9.842 .... 10.300		88
9.423 .... 9.842		92
9.038 .... 9.423		96
8.641 .... 9.038		100
8.240 .... 8.641		105

In the left-hand columns of this table, find the range that includes the worsted number under consideration. On the same line as the selected range and to the right of it, find the corresponding rounded tex number. This is the number to be placed in parentheses after the traditional number during the first stage of the introduction of the tex system.

EXAMPLE: Worsted count 32 falls in the range of 30.54 to 32.80. The corresponding rounded tex number is 28. The recommended notation for this yarn during the first stage of the introduction of tex yarn numbers is accordingly: Worsted count 32 (28 tex), or, using the European abbreviation, Ne 32 (28 tex).

When required, the values below 10 tex and above 100 tex can be derived from the same table simply by multiplying the values by 10 or dividing them by 10. When doing this, it should be noted that the decimal point in the two left columns moves in the opposite direction to that in the right column.

EXAMPLES:

WORSTED COUNT		RECOMMENDED
BEGINNING WITH	UP TO BUT NOT INCLUDING	ROUNDED TEX NUMBER
30.54 .... 32.81		28
3.054 .... 3.281		280
305.4 .... 328.1		2.8

[a] English worsted count (Ne) = 560-y⟨ hanks per lb.

TABLE V. CONVERSION OF AMERICAN WOOLEN RUN INTO ROUNDED TEX NUMBER

For Use During the First Stage of Introduction of the Tex System.
Tex = 310.03/American Woolen Run.

AMERICAN WOOLEN RUN [a]		RECOMMENDED ROUNDED TEX NUMBER
BEGINNING WITH	UP TO BUT NOT INCLUDING	
30.247	31.633	10
28.840	30.247	10.5
27.558	28.840	11
26.386	27.558	11.5
25.309	26.386	12
24.316	25.309	12.5
22.965	24.316	13
21.381	22.965	14
20.002	21.381	15
18.790	20.002	16
17.716	18.790	17
16.758	17.716	18
15.899	16.758	19
15.123	15.899	20
14.420	15.123	21
13.779	14.420	22
13.193	13.779	23
12.654	13.193	24
12.158	12.654	25
11.483	12.158	26
10.691	11.483	28
10.001	10.691	30
9.395	10.001	32
8.858	9.395	34
8.379	8.858	36
7.949	8.379	38
7.562	7.949	40
7.210	7.562	42
6.890	7.210	44
6.596	6.890	46
6.327	6.596	48
6.079	6.327	50
5.741	6.079	52
5.345	5.741	56
5.000	5.345	60
4.697	5.000	64
4.429	4.697	68
4.190	4.429	72
3.975	4.190	76
3.781	3.975	80
3.605	3.781	84
3.445	3.605	88
3.298	3.445	92
3.164	3.298	96
3.024	3.164	100
2.884	3.024	105

In the left-hand columns of this table, find the range that includes the woolen run number under consideration. On the same line as the selected range and to the right of it, find the corresponding rounded tex number. This is the number to be placed in parentheses after the traditional number during the first stage of the introduction of the tex system.

EXAMPLE: American woolen run 11 falls in the range 10.691 to 11.483. The corresponding rounded tex number is 28. The recommended notation for this yarn during the first stage of the introduction of tex yarn numbers is accordingly: Woolen run 11 (28 tex), or, using the European abbreviation, Nar 11 (28 tex).

When required, the values below 10 tex and above 100 tex can be derived from the same table simply by multiplying the values by 10 or dividing them by 10. When doing this, it should be noted that the decimal point in the two left columns moves in the opposite direction to that in the right column.

EXAMPLES:

AMERICAN WOOLEN RUN		CORRESPONDING ROUNDED TEX VALUE
BEGINNING WITH	UP TO BUT NOT INCLUDING	
10.691	11.483	28
1.0691	1.1483	280
106.91	114.83	2.8

[a] American woolen run (Nar) = 1600-yd hanks per lb.

TABLE VI. CONVERSION OF DENIER NUMBER INTO ROUNDED TEX NUMBER

For Use During the First Stage of Introduction of the Tex System.
Tex = Denier Number/9.

DENIER NUMBER [a]		RECOMMENDED
BEGINNING WITH	UP TO BUT NOT INCLUDING	ROUNDED TEX NUMBER
88.2	92.25	10
92.25	96.75	10.5
96.75	101.2	11
101.2	105.7	11.5
105.7	110.2	12
110.2	114.7	12.5
114.7	121.5	13
121.5	130.5	14
130.5	139.5	15
139.5	148.5	16
148.5	157.5	17
157.5	166.5	18
166.5	175.5	19
175.5	184.5	20
184.5	193.5	21
193.5	202.5	22
202.5	211.5	23
211.5	220.5	24
220.5	229.5	25
229.5	243	26
243	261	28
261	279	30
279	297	32
297	315	34
315	333	36
333	351	38
351	369	40
369	387	42
387	405	44
405	423	46
423	441	48
441	459	50
459	486	52
486	522	56
522	558	60
558	594	64
594	630	68
630	666	72
666	702	76
702	738	80
738	774	84
774	810	88
810	846	92
846	882	96
882	922.5	100
922.5	967.5	105

In the left-hand columns of this table find the range that includes the denier number under consideration. On the same line as the selected range and to the right of it, find the corresponding rounded tex number. This is the number to be placed in parentheses after the traditional number during the first stage of the introduction of the tex system.

EXAMPLE: The denier number 250 falls in the range of 243 to 261. The corresponding rounded tex number is 28. The recommended notation for this yarn during the first stage of the introduction of tex yarn numbers is accordingly: 250 denier (28 tex), or, using the European abbreviation, Td 250 (28 tex).

When required, the values below 10 tex and above 100 tex can be derived from the same table simply by multiplying the values by 10 or dividing them by 10. When doing this it should be noted that the decimal point in the two left columns moves in the same direction as in the right column.

EXAMPLES:

DENIER NUMBER		CORRESPONDING
BEGINNING WITH	UP TO BUT NOT INCLUDING	ROUNDED TEX VALUE
24.3	26.1	2.8
243	261	28
2430	2610	280

[a] Denier number (Td) = grams per 9000 meters.

All items of trade science are based on some principle of one of the basic sciences—physics, chemistry, or biology. The science of physics will be better understood when thought of in terms of its various phases, as heat, light, sound, mechanics, and gases. Biology can be considered more effectively under the headings of botany and zoology.

In all phases of an analysis one should find it advantageous to examine only one division or part at a time, in order to follow the scientific information in proper sequence. In scientific problems the chemistry, the physics, or the biology of the problem has to be carefully considered.

CHEMISTRY

Chemistry is the study of the composition of substances and the changes that may take place in them. Chemistry has made it possible for us to know that ordinary table salt ($NaCl$) is composed of equal parts of the elements sodium and chlorine, that water is made by combining one part of oxygen with two parts of hydrogen, (H_2O); that sulfuric acid (H_2SO_4) is composed of two parts of hydrogen, one part of sulfur, and four parts of oxygen; and that, for example, the deadly fumes from a gas engine, carbon monoxide (CO), are made up of one part of oxygen and one part of carbon; while carbon dioxide (CO_2) so essential for plant life, is made up of one part of carbon and two parts of oxygen.

CHEMICAL CHANGE

When a substance undergoes a change in its composition it is said that a "chemical change" has taken place—for example, when iron is exposed to air for a period of time, we say it rusts; in reality, the oxygen in the air has united with some of the iron to form a new substance, iron oxide. When oxygen unites with a substance rapidly enough to release sufficient energy to produce considerable heat, we say that "combustion" takes place, or that the material is "burning." The development of power by burning gasoline in an automobile engine, or even the heat that we obtain from a gas stove, is explained by this chemical process of oxidation.

EXAMPLES OF CHEMICAL CHANGES FOUND IN TRADES

Other examples of chemical changes are found in baking of food; the generation of electricity by electrolysis; the softening of water; the dissolving of substances to form solutions such as zinc chloride for a soldering flux; preparation of dyes from coal-tar derivatives; and the manufacturing of countless manmade products such as rayon, acetate, celluloid, cellophane, mercerized fabric, nylon, Vinyon, Fiberglas, "Dacron," and rubber.

Many trade tests are chemical tests; for example, textile fibers are found to be either animal or vegetable as to origin by simple chemical tests of solubility in an alkaline or acid solution; cloth is burned to determine its contents; metals are etched to reveal their true appearance; and the presence of obnoxious gases in the air are determined by the reaction of a controlled flame.

PHYSICAL CHANGE

All changes in a substance, however, are not of a chemical nature: some are merely physical; that is, the composition has not changed although the apparent form becomes different in appearance. The melting of glass, the evaporation of water, the dissolving of salt, and the dilution of oil with gasoline are physical rather than chemical changes. The physical state has changed rather than the chemical composition even though the visual identity may be lost. In general, physical changes may be recognized by the possibility of restoring the material to its previous form; for instance, water may be frozen, but easily returned to its original state by melting the ice formed by freezing; this is a physical change. Wood once consumed by fire is forever beyond recovery in its original form; this is a chemical change.

CHECK TRADE PROCESSES FOR APPLICATIONS OF CHEMISTRY

Examine the processes and the materials of your trade, vocation, calling, or profession as a means of calling to mind instances where a knowledge of the underlying principles of science are needed by, or would be helpful to, the worker in doing his job. Think of these items in the form of units and try to recall to mind the findings.

PHYSICS

Physics includes several phases of scientific investigation and knowledge; namely, heat, light, sound, electricity, mechanics and mechanical devices, hydraulics and gases. For purposes of analyzing your work it is well to examine it with reference to each of the fields of science.

Following this examination it is well to transfer the prior learning to the subject at hand in the fields of textiles, textile testing, dyeing, chemistry, etc.

BIOLOGY

Biology is the study of living things including both plant and animal life. Those vocations which utilize plant and animal materials and whose services deal with living things must turn to biology for part of its underlying information of a scientific nature. Companies which use silk, wool, cotton, flax, ramie, jute, hemp, worsted, mohair, alpaca, asbetos, glass fibers, etc., use materials whose sources are animal, vegetable, or mineral matter.

For the purposes of classification, biology is grouped under two headings:

BOTANY: the study of plant life.
ZOOLOGY: the study of animal life.

To assist the student further in analyzing his trade or profession for items of trade science several suggestions are given under the headings of Botany and Zoology:

BOTANY:

1. The story of cotton.
2. Flax and its structure.
3. Linen and what it is made from.
4. How plants used for textiles grow.
5. Plant structure.
6. Testing of plant fibers.
7. Vegetable oils and their uses in textiles.
8. How rubber is obtained and what it is.
9. The raw materials used in rayon and acetate.
10. A study of the bast fibers.

ZOOLOGY

1. Wool, its nature, and its source.
2. The nature of vicuña.
3. A study of the hair fiber animals used in textiles.
4. Differences between woolen and worsted fibers.
5. Human hair, its characteristics and nature.
6. The story of leather.
7. The story of silk.
8. How silk differs from wool in chemical, physical, and biological testing.
9. Bacteriology: explanation of diseases peculiar to wool- and hair-bearing animals.

COMPARATIVE DATA ON MAJOR TEXTILE FIBERS FOR READY REFERENCE

ELONGATION OF MAJOR FIBERS

These will vary at varying temperatures. The following tabulations show elongation at standard atmospheric conditions of 65% relative humidity and 70° F.

FIBER, DRY CONDITION	PERCENTAGE IN ELONGATION	FIBER, DRY CONDITION	PERCENTAGE IN ELONGATION
Acetate	25.00–40.00	Nylon–(reg)	26.00–32.00
Acrilan	30.00–44.00	Nylon–(staple)	18.00–52.00
Avril (HWM)	5.00– 7.00	Nylon–(HT)	16.00–28.00
Cotton	6.00– 7.00	"Orlon"–(staple)	20.00–25.00
Creslan	32.00	Rayon–(reg)	15.00–35.00
"Dacron"–(reg)	19.00–25.00	Rayon–(HT)	9.00–20.00
"Dacron"–(staple)	25.00–36.00	Saran	15.00–25.00
"Dacron" (HT)	11.00–14.00	Silk	20.00
Dynel	30.00–36.00	Verel	33.00–35.00
Flax/linen	2.00	Vycron	25.00–35.00
Fortrel	30.00–40.00	Wool	25.00–35.00
Glass	2.00	Zantrel–(HWT)	10.00
Kodel	24.00–30.00	Zefran	33.00

FIBER STRENGTH

This is the ability to resist strains and stresses and is expressed as tensile strength (pounds per square inch) or as tenacity (grams per denier). Strength is divided into three categories—high, medium, and low. Data on the major fibers follows:

HIGH STRENGTH

FIBER	DRY	WET
"Dacron"	4.5–7.5	4.5–7.5
Flax	6.6	8.4
Fortisan	8.5	5.5
Glass	6.4	5.8
Ramie	6.7	8.7
Vycron	4.2–6.3	4.2–6.3

LOW STRENGTH

FIBER	DRY	WET
Acetate	1.1–1.5	0.8
Arnel	1.2–1.4	0.8–1.0
Rayon	1.7–5.0	1.0
Vinyon	0.7–1.0	0.7–1.0

MEDIUM STRENGTH

FIBER	DRY	WET
Acrilan	2.0–2.7	2.0
Cotton	2.0	8.0
Creslan	2.7	2.7
Dynel	2.5–3.3	2.5 –3.3
Fortrel	3.7–4.7	3.7 –4.7
Kodel	2.5–3.0	2.5 –3.0
"Orlon"	2.5	2.1
Saran	2.5	2.5
Silk	5.0	28.00
Verel	2.5–2.8	2.4 –2.7
Zefran	3.5	3.1

HEAT-SENSITIVE FIBERS

Heat will cause fibers to shrink, soften or melt, a property that is not peculiar to cellulosic and protein fibers. Chemical composition and structure varies in these fibers but those listed to have common properties in which sensitivity plays an important part in their end uses; they are thermoplastic in nature—acetate, nylon polyamide, Nytril, Modacrylic, Saran, Spandex, Vinal, and Vinyon HH:

IRONING TEMPERATURES FOR "HEAT-SENSITIVE" TEXTILE FIBERS

FIBER	TEMPERATURE FAHRENHEIT	FIBER	TEMPERATURE FAHRENHEIT
Acetate	350–445	Nylon 6	420
Acrilan acrylic	325–356	Nylon 66	482
Arnel triacetate	482	Olefin fibers	300
Cotton	425–475	"Orlon" acrylic	300
Creslan acrylic	408	Rayon	300–350
"Dacron"	400	Silk	240–300
Dynel modacrylic	225	Verel modacrylic	275
Flax/linen	300–475	Wool	212–275
Kodel	425	Zefran	350

MELTING POINT OF SOME NON-CELLULOSIC FIBERS

The heat sensitivity of textile fibers of thermoplastic base shows that they will soften on heat application. The degree of sensitivity varies with the various fibers. Melting is actually a separating of the molecules in a fiber, causing them to vibrate with such force that they become separated or melt. Cellulosic and protein fibers will not melt because of the strong attractive forces in the hydroxyl groups in them. The melting points follow:

FIBER	MELTING POINT, FAHRENHEIT	FIBER	MELTING POINT, FAHRENHEIT
Acetate—cellulosic	500	Nylon 66	482
Acrilan	Sticks at 470, no melting point	Olefin	230 to 345, depending on the type of fiber
Arnel— cellulosic base	572	"Orlon"	No practical melting point, sticks at 445
Creslan	Sticks at 468, no melting point	Rayon— cellulosic	300
"Dacron"	480	Saran	340
Dynel	Does not melt or drip	Verel	About 300
Kodel	480	Vinyon HH	275–330
Nylon 6	420	Zefran	Sticking point at 490

MOISTURE REGAIN OF SOME MAJOR TEXTILE FIBERS

Moisture is the water or some other liquid which renders anything moist. Absorbency means to take up or receive in by chemical or molecular action. Moisture regain is the percentage which the weight of moisture in a textile material represents of its bone-dry weight—sometimes referred to as content. Percentages of moisture regain in the fibers follows, in standard conditions:

FIBER	PERCENTAGE OF MOISTURE REGAIN	FIBER	PERCENTAGE OF MOISTURE REGAIN
Acetate	6.00	Nylon 66	8.00 @ 95% R.H.
Acrilan	1.50–5.00	Nytril	2.60
Arnel	3.00	Olefins	0.00
Cotton	6.00–7.00	"Orlon"	2.50 @ 95% R.H.
Creslan	1.50 @ 70 degrees	Rayon—	12.00 @ 95% R.H.
"Dacron"	0.50 @ 95% R.H.	regular	
Dynel	0.40	Rayon—high-	12.20
Flax/Linen	6.00–10.00	wet modulus	
Fortisan	10.70	Saran	.10 in 24-hour immersion
Fortrel	0.40	Silk	10.00 and may reach 28.00
Kodel	0.40	Verel	3.00–4.00
Lycra	0.30	Vycron	0.40
Mercerized	10.00–11.00	Wool	15.00–17.00
cotton		Worsted	10.00–12.00
Nylon 6	8.00 @ 95% R.H.	Zefran	2.50 @ 65% R.H.

SPECIFIC GRAVITY OF SOME MAJOR TEXTILE FIBERS

Density is defined as the mass per unit of volume. Specific gravity is the ratio of the mass of a given volume of any substance to that of the same value of some other substance taken as a standard. Water is the standard for liquids and solids, while hydrogen is the standard for gases. Density and specific gravity are expressed in terms of grams per cubic centimeter.

FIBER IN GRAMS PER CC		FIBER IN GRAMS PER CC		FIBER IN GRAMS PER CC	
Acetate	1.32	Fortrel	1.38	Silk	1.30
Acrilan	1.17	Glass	2.56	Verel	1.37
Arnel	1.30	Kodel	1.22–1.38	Vinyon HH	1.34
Cotton	1.48	Nylon 6 and 66	1.14	Viscose rayon	1.50–1.5
Creslan	1.17	"Orlon"	1.14–1.17	Wool	1.30
"Dacron"	1.38	Polypropylene	0.91	Zefran	1.19
Dynel	1.30	Saran	1.70 plus		
Flax/linen	1.50		or minus		
			0.05		

RÉSUMÉ OF THE INDUSTRIAL REVOLUTION IN EUROPE

The first machines in modern history were those used to card textile fibers, to spin these fibers into yarn, and to weave or knit the yarn into textile fabric. Many causes contributed to this revolution, which took place in the span of years from 1750 to 1850, but there were rumblings of this upheaval prior to 1750, and the Industrial Revolution is still with us and making rapid strides today. It all began in England and spread to the Continent, first to France, Belgium, and Holland, then to the many states and principalities before the German Empire was formed in 1870, and to Italy, which became a united country in the same year.

England was the leading exponent of the Industrial Revolution, and it held this position until 1890, when the United States surged ahead of the United Kingdom in world trade, money invested, exports and imports, and money dollar-value return. The United States is still the leading exponent at the present time.

Many important inventions in textiles and kindred industries had been made before 1750. The wool wheel, or high wheel, with its intermittent motion, had been known since about 1400; the flax wheel, with its constant motion, had been used in Europe and the British Isles since about 1600. The Reverend Lee invented his knitting frame in 1586; Flemish weavers introduced the inkle loom in England toward the end of the sixteenth century. The latter is a broad-ribbon or linen loom capable of weaving twelve separate narrow fabrics at one time, the forerunner of the so-called "narrow loom" of today, which is actually a broad loom capable of weaving as many as 144 pieces of fabric at the same time.

The textile industry may be said to have begun in 1248, when a group of wool merchants from the Continent settled in London. The woolen industry soon began to compete with the established linen industry thriving there. In the fourteenth century many things occurred in England in textiles: by 1339, woolen cloth was being made on hand looms in Bristol; by 1348, Norwich had an established worsted fabric industry; by 1350 there were many foreign weavers located in London; by 1376, the British had set up a woolen industry in Ireland, and many linen weavers augmented this growing industry in and around London as well as in Scotland.

In the fifteenth century further advances were made: by 1436, Coventry was a flourishing wool center noted for its fabrics and cap cloth; silk manufacture was carried on with women doing all the work in plants as operatives; in 1488 it was decreed that woolen fabrics could not be exported unless in the finished state ready for tailoring. In the sixteenth century, hemp and flax were, by statute, to be sewn in England, and shortly thereafter in Scotland. Halifax in Yorkshire was noted for its woolens by 1537; in 1549 King Edward VI encouraged foreign Protestants to come to England to work—French, German, Italian, Polish, Swiss, and the Walloons. These groups did much in a relatively short time to make England a power in the textile trades. It was not long before England was exporting woolens to the value of more than one million dollars a year. Sail cloth was first made there in 1590.

Outstanding achievements in the seventeenth century included: the manufacture of broad silk goods; by 1640, Ireland was spinning flax into yarn for use in linen fabrics, then the fabric was woven in Manchester and returned to Ireland (today Ireland and Belgium are still considered the two great flax-linen countries of the world); in 1663 over forty thousand women and children were employed in silk throwing in and around London; in 1666, a law decreed that a person had to be buried in a woolen garment.

The years from 1685 to the end of the century proved most fruitful for England and did much to lay the foundation for Britain to become the leader in the Industrial Revolution. In 1685, and for several years after that, seventy thousand refugees from France went to England because of the revocation of the Edict of Nantes, which deprived French Protestants of the freedom to practice their religion. This great loss to France was of inestimable value to the British. These artisans brought with them an extensive knowledge in many manufactures at the time practically unknown in England. About two thousand artisans of this vast group settled in Ireland, and in 1701, Louis Crommelin, an expert linen weaver, founded the industry on a firm basis, and it still thrives there today. He knew all phases in the production of flax and linen, from preparation of the soil and planting to the finished linen fabric. To this day he is known as the "Father of the Linen Industry" there. By 1710 thousands of linen workers had settled in Ireland.

In the fifteen years from 1685 to 1700 it is estimated that about 750,000 refugees fled to the British Isles. Other artisans in other fields of endeavor, such as goldsmiths, jewelers, watchmakers, carvers, and woodworkers, also came. The silk industry was settled in Spitalfields, Soho, and St. Giles, in and around the city of London. Spitalfields became a great lace center, and its products were soon known all over the world. When these localities became too crowded, the workers moved to Nottingham, now the leading lace center in the British Isles.

In the early eighteenth century there were several forerunners of the Industrial Revolution, such as the following: the steam pump to provide steam power to mills was brought out in 1711 by Newcomen, and was the main source of power in plants until the time of James Watt, Edmund Cartwright, and others. The triumvirate of coal, iron, and textiles was bound in time to make the Revolution an actuality. In 1709 Abraham Darby, a Quaker, invented the process of coking coal, but he kept his discovery to himself for almost half a century. In the third generation of the family, Abraham Darby III joined with John Wilkinson, the great ironmaster of the era, and built the first iron bridge over the River Severn in 1787.

In 1740, a clockmaker named Benjamin Huntsman produced a superior type of steel that was not much in favor during the century; but it did lay the basis for improved types of steel for the heavy industries.

The eighteenth century found England more aware of changing world conditions than other nations, and ready for a genuine Industrial Revolution, which began about 1750. By the first half of the century there were three areas well known for textiles and textile products. They were:

1. London-Norwich area: Many types of woolens were made in Blackburn, Bocking, Braintree, Bury Saint Edmunds, Colchester, Hingham, Ipswich, and Norwich.

2. West Country Area: Well before 1500 the better quality and grade of woolens were being made in Bradford-on-Avon, Exeter, and Trowbridge. During this century other towns came to the fore as well—Bristol, Barnstaple, Cheltenham, Glastonbury, Monmouth, Newbury, Reading, Taunton, and Wells.

3. West Riding Area: This Yorkshire area prior to 1500 was noted for rougher-type woolens, which were made in Bradford, Frome, Huddersfield, Kendall, Leeds, and Wakefield. Other

towns became known in the field in this century, namely Bury, Dewsbury, Halifax, Manchester, and Rochdale.

Among the fabrics made from the four natural fibers at this time were beaver, striped bengal, bombazine, bombazet, cambric, worsted cassimere, cheviot, chintz, crepe, Florence silk fabric, gingham, homespun, kersey, kerseymere, linsey-woolsey, lawn, levantine silk, mantua cloth, maritime fabrics, melton, muslin, mull mull, nankeen silk, poplin, satinette, senshaw, serge, tweed, union stripes, and ulster cloth.

The Industrial Revolution came about after the Age of Discovery in the fifteenth and sixteenth centuries, when England, France, Holland, Portugal, and Spain became aware of the great possibilities for world trade in the known world. The two outstanding waterway discoveries were those of Vasco da Gama (c. 1469–1524), who discovered the sea route from Portugal around the continent of Africa to India, and of Christopher Columbus (c. 1466–1506), the Italian navigator in the employ of Spain, who discovered what is now America. At a later date, Elizabeth I, "The Virgin Queen" (1533–1603), daughter of Henry VIII and Anne Boleyn, successor of Mary I, and the last of the Tudor line of rulers, saw the value of world trade and of creating a great maritime power, which was to rule the seas for more than three hundred years. Elizabeth left England with a great world empire, that by the beginning of the twentieth century consisted of holdings in fifty-two parts of the world, so that the statement could be made that "the sun never sets on the British Empire."

The Industrial Revolution, in addition to trade growth overseas, was caused by fundamental changes which came after the year 1750. Among these were scientific inventions in textiles with regard to carding, spinning, and weaving; the rise of factories, which gradually did away with home industries, moving the centers of industry from the cottage to the town; new and supposedly better living conditions and standards; the desire for changes in the world from what it had been for so many years; especially an increase in productivity much beyond that to which the population had been accustomed in the two preceding centuries. With increased population there was a greater demand for manufactured articles.

England was a changing world in morals, economics, religion, politics, and social amenities. There was a growing demand for more refinement, and during the era England produced many great writers who are still renowned and respected. Consider the following list of writers and authors, all of whom contributed to England's greatness in the eighteenth century—a century that takes its place with two other great centuries in world history, the thirteenth and the twentieth. It was the era of Daniel Defoe (c. 1661–1731), Jonathan Swift (1667–1745), Joseph Addison (1672–1717), Alexander Pope (1688–1744), Samuel Richardson (1689–1761), Henry Fielding (1707–1754), Laurence Sterne (1713–1768), Tobias Smollett (1721–1771), David Hume (1711–1776), Oliver Goldsmith (1728–1774), Edmund Burke (1729–1797), Dr. Samuel Johnson (1709–1784), William Cowper (1731–1800), Robert Burns (1759–1796), Sir Walter Scott (1771–1832), and Jane Austen (1775–1817).

This was the century of refinement and better living, as shown by the following craftsmen whose work and memory are still with us: Thomas Chippendale, cabinets and furniture (c. 1718–1779), Josiah Spode, pottery (1754–1827); Thomas Sheraton, cabinet maker and furniture designer (1751–1806); Josiah Wedgwood, pottery (1730–1795); George Hepplewhite, designer of cabinets and furniture (?–1786); and the four Adam Brothers, all born c. 1730, who were noted for their work in architecture, from dog kennels to palaces. Their reputations were established during the years 1760–1792.

It was the age of great British statesmen: George Grenville (1712–1770), Philip Dormer Stanhope, Fourth Earl of Chesterfield (1694–1773), William Pitt, the Elder (1708–1778), Charles Townshend (1725–1767), Lord North (1732–1792), Charles James Fox (1749–1806), and William Pitt, the Younger (1759–1806).

During this century England was on a very firm industrial basis, the foremost of all major powers. Its greatest industry was the manufacture of woolen and worsted fabrics. Cloth was the most important export. Inventors, writers, statesmen, architects, cabinet makers, and designers of all types of furniture made England the acme of perfection in better living for the affluent as well as for many of the less wealthy. The factory had supplanted the domestic system that at this time had about run its course. Thus, coal, iron, and textiles made England the strongest and the most feared nation in the world and "Britannia ruled the waves and the world," thanks to the many great men who made England supreme in all fields of endeavor.

There were two other revolutions in that century that did much to shape the destinies of men throughout the world and to lay the foundation for "this modern world and way of living"—the French Revolution and the American Revolution.

But it should be borne in mind that, with all the positive contributions and improvements brought about by these three revolutions, many negative aspects of life still prevailed—primitive conditions, poverty, labor under duress, home conditions that might be considerably better, unsanitary conditions; storm, stress, and strife among nations and races of people, injustices of many sorts and many other problems that still confront all of us to the present day.

MAJOR TEXTILE INVENTIONS OF EIGHTEENTH CENTURY ENGLAND

1730: John Wyatt brought out the first cotton machinery.

1733: John Kay received patent for his fly shuttle for use in weaving.

1738: Lewis Paul received a patent for spinning machinery supposed to have been made by John Wyatt; this was improved machinery over that for which Wyatt received his patent in 1730, and upon which eight years of labor and research had been expended. It was at this time that both inventors pooled their skills to create drawing rollers for drafting fibers so as to make them spinnable on machines. John Kay received further patents for his fly shuttle. Incidentally, the first cotton-spinning plant was set up in Birmingham in 1742. Power was supplied by donkeys, but the plant was not a success.

1748: Paul and Wyatt perfected a revolving carding cylinder for the carding frame. The patent was in the name of Paul.

1760: Robert Kay, son of John Kay, invented the drop-box loom; James Hargreaves unveiled his stock cards for use on cotton.

1762–1767: Hargreaves brought out his spinning jenny in which drawing of fibers was done by means of carriages on the frame. At first the jenny could spin only eight yarns, then twelve, twenty, and finally, one hundred yarns at one time. Mule spinning frames today are capable of spinning more than one thousand yarns at one time.

1769: Sir Richard Arkwright received rights for his spinning frame in which drawing of fibers was done by means of rollers on the frame.

1774: Edmund Cartwright produced his comber frame and power loom. In this year, England forbade export of cotton machinery of all types.

1775: Arkwright received a second set of patents for carding, drawing, and spinning of fibers.

1779: Samuel Crompton invented his famous mule spinning frame which combined the ideas of Hargreaves and his drawing by means of the carriage, and those of Arkwright, who performed his drawing by means of the use of sets of rollers. Hence, the machine was hybrid, and for want of a better name, Crompton called it "the mule," a hybrid animal. Peele obtained patents on carding, roving, and spinning machinery.

1782: James Watt had received his first patent for a steam engine in 1769. In an eight-year span, ending in 1790, he perfected his engine for commercial purposes. Watt began to make steam engines in 1776 in the Soho, Birmingham. It was around this time that England began to offer bounties for the export of certain cotton goods; this industry was making rapid progress.

1785: Cartwright received a second set of patents for his power loom; he also invented his warp stop-motion for the loom, a great aid in weaving. Bell received rights for his method of cylinder printing of textiles. The first application of steam to meet with success for textile machinery was in a mill in Popplewick Notts.

TEXTILE INVENTIONS OF THE EARLY NINETEENTH CENTURY

1803: Radcliffe, Ross, and Johnson invented dressing frames and warpers, a great boon in warp preparation for the loom.

1805: Power looms were considered a success in England.

1814: Creighton brought out his cotton opener with lap attachment on it.

1816: The textile industry was making rapid progress in the factory system of manufacture. Average-size mills employed from one hundred to about three hundred operatives. One plant in Glasgow, Scotland, had more than six thousand employees on its payroll.

1828: John Thorpe obtained patents on the ring spinning frame, while Charles Danforth obtained them for his cap spinning frame.

1830: By this time mule spinning frames were much used. It is estimated that at this time there were still a half million hand looms being used in England, with power looms showing a total of about 250,000. Hand weaving gradually died out, and by 1850 production was nil. The domestic system died in the last decade of the eighteenth century when power came into use for textile machinery—carding, spinning, weaving, and finishing of goods.

1830–1850: In this twenty-year span other inventions aided textiles: in 1830, Roberts developed the quadrant for the mule frame; in 1832, Bachelder brought out his stop motions on drawing frames; Reid and Johnson perfected their shuttle-changing device on a loom; in 1834, Hope and Ramsbottom provided a filling-fork set in the race plate of the loom so as to cause the loom to stop at once if the filling pick did not reach the filling box for which it was intended; in 1842, James Bullough unveiled his feeler stop-motion on a loom, the filling fork, also known as "the cat's whiskers." In 1846, W. W. Dutcher perfected the parallel shuttle action on a loom and with E. Dutcher received patents for the reciprocating loom temple. The great textile industry was now on its way to bigger and better things.

THE DEVELOPMENT OF CARDING, SPINNING, AND WEAVING

Carding, spinning, and weaving have been known for centuries to mankind even in prehistoric times. The following digest covers their advances down through the span of history:

1. The Family System (actual beginnings unknown; ending c. 1100 A.D.):

    Under this system carding, spinning, and weaving were carried on by members of the household to supply the family with clothing. Each class of society, from the humblest peasant to the nobleman, had its own devices and methods of producing textiles and making clothing. The system was entirely one of home consumption.

2. The Guild System (from 1100 A.D. to c. 1750):

    During this span of 650 years the world progressed and as communities became larger and cities came into being, the textile industry was of more concern than to the family alone. Better fabrics and textures were in demand. To meet it, it was necessary to have looms and parts for them accessible, an improvement over the looms of the Family System. The individual weaver who owned the looms had to build them himself. Often he needed parts that were not easily accessible. Hence, he had to turn to a more prosperous weaver for his livelihood. These conditions were applicable to carding and spinning, as well. These two phases of the industry became disjoined from weaving, and in time they separated from it altogether.

    The Guild System caused the small weaver to be driven out by the growth of labor that was now becoming organized and with the rise of capital he soon became a nonentity. In this system, the industry was carried on by a small number of men, called masters. They employed two or more artisans known as journeymen and apprentices. The masters organized the various guilds on a systematic basis and controlled the manufacturing phases to a greater extent than is possible today under existing conditions.

3. The Domestic System (from 1750 to 1800):

    By the middle of the eighteenth century the separation of carding, spinning, weaving and other branches of the industry was an accomplished fact. The rural communities showed a rise and interest in textile production. As the Domestic System rose the masters began to become of less importance, and were powerless to do much about their plight. While the work to be done was still carried on in the master's house or shop he began to receive his raw materials from the merchant and to dispose of his wares to a middleman who looked after the demands of the various markets and kept abreast of the times as to what the industry needed. He followed, so to speak, the economic law of supply and demand, of production, distribution, and consumption. And, raw material was by now a very important commodity.

    The rise of the Industrial Revolution was at hand with the first machines to come under its aegis in any field those which performed carding, spinnings, and weaving. (See Major Textile Inventions of Eighteenth Century England, p. 369.) In 1769, James Watt unveiled his fantastic steam engine which was to prove a great boon to the British inventors of the period. The aid afforded by the use of steam power was of inestimable value to them, and by 1790 steam was universally applied to textile machinery in England and abroad.

    At this time there were 30,000 English cotton workers and they made as much yarn in one year as it would have taken 30 million hand spinners to manufacture. With the advent of these machines the Domestic System was soon to cease, replaced by the Factory System that is still in vogue.

    Another invention of the times was the Jacquard loom, one of the first three automatic devices ever produced. J. M. Jacquard brought out his famous "card-punched-set-of-cards" loom in the years 1801–04. Eli Whitney is known for his famous cotton gin which he invented in 1793 and took only about ten days to build and to have in running order. One of the simplest devices ever conceived, its principles have never been improved upon. Thus, the foregoing inventions surely had a great impact on the future of the industry and they were bound to bring about changes for the better.

[370]

4. The Factory System (from about 1800 to the present time):

Necessity is the mother of invention and as time went on, this system had to come into being. The factory is a mill or plant where goods are produced by power for commercial purposes and uses. Watt and the galaxy of British inventors caused this system to become an actuality. As far as is known there are no records extant to show that the system was in vogue prior to the Watt invention.

English, Irish, Scotch, and Welsh carders, spinners, and weavers were by now very skillful, and along with the machines with which to work, the production of yarn and fabric showed a very marked increase. With the aid of the mechanical arts, one man could now do in a day's toil work that formerly required from ten to one hundred workers. Steam and water reduced manual labor, and large scale production became a great factor since there was now a combining of capital and machinery. The Factory System was an accomplished fact, the outgrowth of the Industrial Revolution.

Prior to this system there were no reasons why an industry should be centered in any particular district. With the arrival of the Factory System it became essential to subdivide the major divisions of the industry. Up to now each textile effort had been to a greater or lesser degree localized. Raw material and geographical factors came into being. Suitable areas across a country were soon taken over for this or that phase of the industry. Old time textile areas that are still noteworthy in the British Isles were established because of rivers, waterpower, climate to some degree, accessibility to markets, and other natural and positive factors. In the United States the old textile areas of New England, New York, and Pennsylvania are now more or less of a memory since the exodus from there to the South is now completed. This exodus began in the 1940's and was consummated within the next twenty years.

THE DEVELOPMENT OF THE LOOM AND WEAVING

A loom is a machine, hand-driven or power-driven, necessary to weave cloth. It consists essentially of parts that make it possible to have at least two sets of yarn or thread, called warp and filling or weft, to interlace at right angles to each other. The earliest of which there is knowledge provided a means for hanging one set of yarns in a vertical position through which the crossing or horizontal threads were interlaced with the warp. Apparently, the first improvement consisted of tightening these warp yarns by hanging weights at the bottom end of the loom or by joining the yarns in such a way as to form a loop over horizontal, parallel bars.

A warp yarn or end is in the vertical or lengthwise direction in woven cloth. A filling pick, weft, or pick is the horizontal or crosswise yarn in a fabric. Horizontal looms were used by the early Egyptians and other civilizations in the beginnings of recorded history. In the simplest form, this type of loom provided for the tethering of a bar that carried the lengthwise warp ends to a stake in the ground. A bar at the farther end was secured to the person of the weaver who had a straight set of warp yarns through which he or she could cross or interlace the weft yarn.

Primitive weavers improvised from simple materials a plain device or arrangement now known as a heddle or a heald. This device enabled the alternate warp yarns to be raised in manipulation. Thus the shed, an opening between the raised and the unraised yarns, was formed, through which the crossing or filling yarns could be easily passed.

At an uncertain date before the Middle Ages, some tribes in what is now Great Britain improved the loom by adding a frame, now known as the warp beam. This beam is used to hold the warp ends which are wound around its hub. Another beam was placed on the loom around which the newly woven fabric is wound. This is the cloth beam or roller. In time, the filling or pick, which was originally conveyed across in the form of a ball or wrapped around a twig and then interlaced with the warp yarn, was placed around a spool. This device was boat-shaped or torpedo-shaped and today is called a shuttle. The spindle, round which the weft was wound, fitted into the shuttle.

The power loom of today is substantially the hand loom adapted to rotary driving. The frame is of iron or some comparable metal, the lay sword, sley or oscillating frame is pivoted below and driven by a crank, and the picking arm is activated by a cone which turns on a vertical rod. The lift of the heddle shafts or harnesses is controlled by tappets or cams.

Loom motions are timed accurately so as to give a high rate of speed and production. The weaver, free from supplying the power, has merely to watch for warp yarn breakages (now automatically controlled so that the loom will stop as soon as an end does break), blemishes and defects in the weaving operation, and loom tensions. A weaver can now care for twenty or more looms at the one time because of the great improvements and new devices that are available. A good weaver today can take care of all details of a loom, such as piecing up ends, watching for uneven selvages in weaving, harness skips, shuttle smashes, adjusting tensions, and so on.

Down through the years looms have been constantly improved and rank with the best of any fully automatic machine or device. Some of the major improvements include warp drop-wires that will cause a loom to stop instantly when a warp end breaks; filling wires or filling fork, set in the raceplate of the loom to cause stoppage as soon as a pick breaks or does not reach the shuttle box at the other end of the raceplate at the other side of the loom; and automatic let-off and take-up motions to let off the warp and feed it into the loom as the cloth is being woven and to take up the newly woven fabric and wind it around the cloth beam or roller. Loom pickage has been greatly increased; there are now looms operated devoid of harness frames, as well as some which no longer require bobbins of filling yarn or a shuttle—shuttleless looms.

Courtesy of the Draper Corporation, Hopedale, Massachusetts. Source: *Five Generations of Loom Builders,* by William H. Chase, Draper Corporation; 87 pages, copyright © 1950. Textile Division of The Smithsonian Institution, Washington, D.C.

THE RISE OF THE INDUSTRIAL REVOLUTION IN THE UNITED STATES

In addition to the steam engine invented by James Watt in 1765, it should be noted that in 1787 the first textile factory built by Edmund Cartwright that was run by steam-driving methods appeared in England. In 1800, Richard Trevithick, another Englishman, brought out his successful reciprocal or double-acting engine, a much-desired improvement in engines. With the harnessing of steam power came the rapid growth of transportation, the development of iron and steel, and the increased importance of coal used to create steam and to refine iron and steel.

In due course of time, three other sources of power came into being: electricity, gasoline, and oil.

Electricity: The development of the dynamo by Michael Faraday in 1831 proved that electricity could be obtained by mechanical means. In 1887 Nikola Tesla, Croatian-born electrician and inventor living in the United States, proved that rotating magnetic power fields made possible the transmission of electric power over long distances. His invention of the induction motor in 1888 further proved that electric power could be used in a great many fields of endeavor.

Other great inventions in the field of electricity were the telegraph by Samuel F. B. Morse (1832); the telephone by Alexander G. Bell (1876); and wireless communication by Guglielmo Marconi, the famous Italian scientist who received the Nobel Prize in physics in 1909.

Thomas Alva Edison, the "Wizard of Menlo Park," New Jersey, invented the phonograph in 1877 and the incandescent bulb in 1879. Other inventions of his included the kinetoscope, the cinematograph, and the microphone. In the beginning coal was used to generate electricity but later on waterpower was used on an increased scale for the generation of hydroelectric power, the so-called "white coal."

Gasoline and Oil: With the invention of the internal combustion engine by Nikolaus Otto in 1876, and the development of an improved engine by Gottlieb Daimler in 1895, it was now evident that gasoline and oil could be used for motive power. Internal combustion engines were soon adapted for a wide variety of uses and their inventions were a prelude to the automobile and the airplane. In addition, oil became the substitute for coal for use in locomotives and steamships. At the present time atomic energy is the latest of the "power elements," nuclear fission.

COLONIAL BEGINNINGS OF THE INDUSTRIAL REVOLUTION IN THE UNITED STATES

Colonial industry and commerce grew from the colonists' need for manufactured goods of many types and varieties. England, the mother country, needed the raw materials of the Colonies that were there in abundance. The reasons which induced engagement in industry in the Colonies at the time were:

1. The need for finished goods in a wilderness country was so great that the Colonists were forced to manufacture them as best they could in the Colonies, despite the fact that the British Government tried very much to discourage all manufacturing activities there.
2. The abundance of raw materials there made even the most loyal sons of Britain question the

advisability of sending them three thousand miles across the sea to be made into finished products and then sent back to be sold at high prices.

3. As time went on there was an accumulation of capital as the result of engaging in commerce, and the flourishing fur trade made funds available for further development and growth of Colonial industry. The result was that ships were built for commerce shipments, iron products became plentiful, the lumber industry thrived, flour was milled, and so on.

4. The volume of Colonial industry had become so large by 1750, and its commerce had so greatly increased, that the British Parliament attempted to stifle both, stating they were making great inroads and wreaking havoc on British industries. The resistance to British restraint by the Colonists led to the great American Revolution, 1775–1783, and made possible the present United States of America.

THE EMERGENCE OF AMERICAN INDUSTRY AND THE AMERICAN INDUSTRIAL REVOLUTION

The winning of the war with Britain freed commerce, industry, and free enterprise from their former restraints. Several basic factors evolved, namely:

1. The experiments and work done by Watt and Cartwright in England were repeated by an English immigrant living in Pawtucket, Rhode Island, Samuel Slater, the "Father of the Textile Industry in the United States." Prior to the close of the century, Slater, from memory, had designed the necessary machines, made them, and then set them up in the famous Slater Mill in Pawtucket in 1793. Incidentally, the mill and the machinery are still there and the mill is now known as the Old Slater Museum, a most interesting place to visit. The machinery is still in running condition.

2. Steam was soon applied to other industries and became the backbone of the Factory System in this country.

3. During the Napoleonic Wars and the War of 1812 commerce on the high seas was interrupted and Americans came to depend on themselves for manufactured goods they had formerly imported. Thus began the emergence of American industry, and the years from 1815 to 1837, ending with the Era of Good Feeling in the Jacksonian Period of Democracy, were exceedingly fruitful for the United States.

4. New England, and to some degree upper New York State and upper Pennsylvania, became the centers of industry. The reasons for this included the availability of waterpower, investment of capital, skilled labor, the desire to produce goods of use to all, the New England philosophy of down-to-earth reasoning and producing, and the will to work to produce needed articles.

The beginnings and the desire to produce were apparent during Colonial and post-Revolutionary times. The New Englanders were hard workers and thinkers, and took intense pride in their efforts and results. Their efforts gave the nation the opportunity to lead in industrial development with all new progress emanating from New England, as the country expanded in the nineteenth century.

With raw materials at hand and ready markets for products, the student of American history will recall that tariffs were invoked to protect the infant industries. There was a wealth of skilled labor available for all industries. Unskilled labor was soon taught how to develop into skilled. Competition became keen. The issuance of many patents increased free enterprise in New England.

The growth of the great textile industry is shown by the following: in 1807, there were 8,000 spindles in New England; in 1820, there were 350,000 spindles; and by 1860, at the time of the beginning of the Civil War, there were over 5 million. In 1860, also, there were over 2,000 woolen mills in America and home-spun fabric had become a memory.

Industrial growth was aided by the building of two great canals that did much to open up trade possibilities to the expanding nation: the Erie Canal in 1825, and the Ohio River Canal in 1833. And then came the railroads to further increase the growth of the United States.

SOME EFFECTS FROM THE INDUSTRIAL REVOLUTION IN THE UNITED STATES

By the end of the nineteenth century the United States had changed from an agricultural nation to an industrial nation, and in 1890 our export world trade surpassed that of the United Kingdom, a position we still hold today.

Our government has changed from a laissez-faire philosophy to one of big business. Some of the far-reaching effects of our growth as an industrial nation are urbanization, unionization, improved living conditions, the idea of one world, and the rise of the so-called upper-middle-class in our population.

SOME NONTEXTILE INVENTIONS WHICH PLACED THE UNITED STATES IN THE FOREFRONT OF WORLD INDUSTRY

1787: Steamboat   Fitch
1835: Mower and reaper   McCormick
1837: Screw propeller   Ericsson
1844: Vulcanization of rubber   Goodyear
1846: Steam cylinder printing press   Hoe

1852: Elevator   Otis
1866: Submarine cable   Field
1868: Typewriter   Sholes and Gidden
1869: Railroad airbrake   Westinghouse
1880: Linotype   Mergenthaler

1885: Aluminum extraction   Hall
1903: Airplane   Wright Brothers
1907: Vacuum radio tubes   De Forest
1907: Plastics (Bakelite)   Baekeland
1933: Frequency modulation   Armstrong
1934: Television   Baird, Farnsworth, Zworykin

IMPORTANT LOOM INVENTIONS BY THE DRAPER CORPORATION, HOPEDALE, MASSACHUSETTS, IN THE NINETEENTH CENTURY

1816: Ira Draper received patent rights for an improved type of fly-shuttle hand loom which featured the first self-acting loom temple used to keep fabric being woven at the correct widths. Attached to the breast beam of the loom it held the cloth over a revolving star wheel and was practically automatic when in operation. This device was also instrumental in allowing one weaver to manipulate two looms instead of the customary single loom.

1829: Ira Draper made further improvements on the temple for the loom. His original invention in 1816 was notable for several reasons: it was the second invention in the textile field by an American, second only to the invention of the cotton gin by Eli Whitney in 1793; it came at a time wherein it was to contribute much to the successful progress of the factory system in the United States; the device became the keystone upon which the business of the Draper Corporation was assured for the future; the temple was a great labor-saving device for the loom weaver.

1846: W. W. Dutcher patented the first parallel under-pick shuttle motion. Used for many years in weaving fabric; in time improvements made and superseded this patent.

1857: Bartlett and Snell invented the let-off motion for looms. This Draper patent was improved and became known as the Bartlett Let-Off Motion. It is still a standard loom motion, ideal for weaving rayon and comparable yarns, fully automatic in details.

1863: George Draper perfected the "frog-with-the-loose-steel-device" first made as an attachment for the Mason Loom, and later applied to other makes of looms in the United States. By decreasing the movement required of the binder the device improved greatly the "boxing-of-the-shuttle."

1868: Metcalf perfected the first practical self-threading shuttle. This Draper invention did much to cause the demise of the "kiss-of-death" practice of threading a shuttle by sucking-in the filling through the hole in the side of the shuttle through which the filling yarn passes when the loom is in operation.

1894–1895: The date for one of the last great textile inventions, the fully automatic loom brought out by the Draper Corporation. It was perfected by James H. Northrop, an Englishman in the employ of the company. He had perfected a rotary battery for filling bobbins on a loom in 1891, and then went on to complete his truly marvelous loom about three years later. This automatic bobbin-changing loom revolutionized cloth weaving throughout the world.

    The loom, the first one to which his device was attached, was sold to the Gaffney Manufacturing Company, Inc., Gaffney, South Carolina. In 1941 the Draper Corporation was able to obtain this loom from the owners and restored it to its original condition. This loom now reposes in the Smithsonian Institution, Washington, District of Columbia.

Around this time, another Draper inventor, Charles F. Roper, unveiled his warp stop motion for use on a loom when anything in the warp went awry, an outstanding effort on his part. A weaver, at this time could now run as many as 16 automatic looms instead of the conventional four or six looms.

Source: *Five Generations of Loom Builders, a History of the Draper Corporation*, by William H. Chase, published by Draper Corporation, Hopedale, Massachusetts, 1950.

SOME OTHER LOOM INVENTIONS OF THE AMERICAN TEXTILE INDUSTRY IN THE NINETEENTH CENTURY

1665: The Colony of Massachusetts decreed that every household must spin yarn and weave it into cloth in proportion to the number of females in the family. Each family had to supply its own spinning and weaving devices and it was around this time that hand weaving looms sprang up in the colony. Incidentally, the well-known term, spinster, was born since it was generally the custom that the unmarried girls in the household did all yarn spinning. The law required each family to make at least three pounds of cotton, woolen, or linen fabric per year.

1792: Kirk and Leslie received patent rights for the first American loom to be used here.

1815–1826: Paul Moody of the Boston Manufacturing Company, Waltham, Massachusetts, brought out his Lowell loom in 1815. Soon it was being used throughout New England. By 1826, he had improved the loom very much and it was the first loom to use belt drives for power transmission instead of iron gearing.

1823: The first power loom in the United States began operation in a mill in Southbridge, Massachusetts.

1839: Erastus B. Bigelow perfected the first power-driven loom that could weave carpeting. A continuation of his company to the present time is the well-known Bigelow-Sanford, Inc., New York City.

1840: William Crompton invented the first successful loom to weave fancy fabrics. The loom had a speed of 45 to 85 picks per minute dependent on the fabric construction, loom settings, et al. Along with another pioneer inventor of the era, Lucius Knowles, he established the well-known Crompton-Knowles Loom Works, Worcester, Massachusetts, now the Crompton-Knowles Corporation. Incidentally, the Draper Corporation, Hopedale, Massachusetts, and Crompton-Knowles Corporation are the two leading and largest loom manufacturers in the United States.

The famous triumvirate of Bigelow, Crompton, and Knowles, by their great efforts and inventive minds placed American weaving of cloth on a par with that done in the United Kingdom.

1843: The first worsted loom to be run in America was installed in a mill in Ballardale, Massachusetts.

SOME OTHER IMPORTANT DATES IN THE DEVELOPMENT OF TEXTILE MACHINERY IN THE UNITED STATES

1681: By this time woolen mills had been established in Rowley, Watertown, and Dedham, all in Massachusetts.

1780: George Washington visited a woolen mill in Hartford, Connecticut. He commented on the superb quality of the broadcloth made there.

1788: Bissell invented his roller gin for ginning cotton, a forerunner of the cotton gin of Eli Whitney of 1793.

1788: First cotton mill built in this country, Beverly, Massachusetts.

1789: Sea Island cotton was first planted in the United States.

1793: The cotton gin invented by Eli Whitney, Yale graduate, teacher, and tutor to the children of the widow of General Nathanael Greene, second in command to General George Washington during the American Revolution. Whitney perfected his work in ten days on the Mulberry Grove Plantation, about ten miles from Savannah, Georgia, the plantation where he was working as the tutor for the Greene children. His principles are still used in cotton gin construction to the present day. Cotton production at this time was about 140,000 pounds a year. By 1820 production was 125 million pounds annually.

1794: Byfield, Massachusetts, is known in textile history for first complete mill to be run by waterpower.

1800: Eli Whitney received a $50,000 grant from the United States Government based on dues extracted from users of the gin.

The cotton gin was the first of the four great American inventions contributing to the Industrial Revolution. The others were ring spinning frames, the automatic loom, and the sewing machine.

1804: The first wool spinning machine was put in operation at Peacedale, Rhode Island.

1804: First cotton mill in New Hampshire established at Laconia.

1806: First cotton mill established in Connecticut, at Pomfret.

1808: Scholfield, a Britisher who adopted America as his home, owned a woolen mill in Massachusetts. He was a leader in the field and President Monroe, at his Inauguration, wore a broadcloth suit made by the Scholfield mill. Broadcloth became the vogue in apparel.

1809: First cotton mill built in Maine, at Brunswick.

1812: First cotton mill established at Fall River, Massachusetts.

1812–1815: During the War of 1812, the male population in America took to wearing trousers. It was a revolt against British imperialism and the knee breeches worn by Englishmen.

1822: The first fully equipped cotton mill, from raw cotton to finished fabric, began operations in Massachusetts, at Lowell.

1823: Arnold brought out his differential motion for use on a roving frame.

1828: John Thorp, Providence, Rhode Island, conceived the idea of a ring spinning frame. In an incredibly short time he built his machine, and was granted patent rights within one year.

1831: John Sharp, Providence, Rhode Island, brought out his ring spinning frame. It was at this time that Alfred Jenks, a former apprentice to Samuel Slater, built his ring spinning frame which worked with a flyer attachment to replace the fork-type flyer of the throstle machine.

It was during this year also that the first worsted fabric for the women's wear trade appeared on the market here. Men's wear worsted did not appear on the scene until twenty years later.

1835: Richard Roberts, from experience gained from other spinning frames, is given credit as being the "Father of the Ring Spinning Frame." Ring spinning was now an accredited actuality.

1846: Elias Howe and his brother-in-law, General Nathaniel Banks, of Civil War fame, invented their sewing machine. Work on it had been done in Hudson, Palmer, and Boston, in Massachusetts. In the same year, and unknown to the others, Isaac Singer brought out his famous sewing machine. Today the Singer Manufacturing Company, the third-best-known trademark in the world, is a tribute to his great efforts, surpassed only by Coca-Cola and Kodak.

1849: First cotton mill was built in Lawrence, Massachusetts.

1854: Pacific Mills, Lawrence, Massachusetts, installed the first complete worsted machinery layout.

1861–1865: The need for uniform fabrics during the Civil War caused the rise of many woolen plants, chiefly in New England and in the Philadelphia area.

1869: Carroll devised the double-flange ring, an original Draper design and device now used by all leading ring manufacturers on spinning frames.

1878: Rabbath produced a spindle which made ring spinning of yarn practical by doubling the spinning speeds on machines.

1900–1930: There was practically no improvement nor major invention in textiles in this span of years. About 1930 came the Spanish Casablancas and the French Roth systems of long-draft spinning of yarn. American mills became interested in these systems and they were soon in vogue here. A few years later, the famed Gwaltney frame for spinning was introduced by Saco-Lowell Shops of Lowell, Massachusetts, whose present headquarters are in Greenville and Easley, South Carolina.

1965: Today with automatic doffing and long-draft large-package spinning, the greater use of direct spinning, the advent of shuttleless weaving, etc., it seems, that the textile industry is again moving forward. New concepts are springing up that could lead to realization within a decade or less of the dreamed-of fully automatic textile mill.

THE MANMADE FIBER SYSTEM

The present century has witnessed the burgeoning of the Manmade System and the Automation System. Both have supplemented the Factory System, and without them it would not have reached the pinnacle of success that it now enjoys. The first half of this century witnessed the development of the Age of Electricity, Science, Transportation, and a rise in standards of living.

[376]

The second half has seen the meteoric development of manmade fibers and of automation.

Generally speaking, the textile fibers which have been used for centuries, the natural fibers—cotton, wool, linen, and silk—have had to give way to the manmade fibers—acetate, rayon, nylon, and a host of others.

These manmade fibers, when they first came over the textile horizon, were called by many names: synthetic fibers (a poor choice), created fibers, miracle fibers, chemical fibers, test-tube fibers, specially prepared fibers, and a number of other names. The name, Rayon, did not come into vogue until 1924. Acetate was not legal until 1952.

The name, manmade fibers, is sensible and describes how these fibers are actually made—by man and his ingenuity. They are rightly classed in two categories: cellulosic fibers and non-cellulosic fibers. Only acetate and rayon are cellulosic fibers, the others are non-cellulosic.

The acceptance, demand, and uses of manmade fibers have been phenomenal and are still on the rise; their production increases with each successive year. So great has been their impact on fiber production that venerable linen and beautiful silk, formerly major fibers, do not now, even when combined, account for 1 per cent of total fiber usage, both worldwide and nation-wide. Of course, they will always be with us, but they now seem to be more or less forgotten. The great fiber, wool, from which woolen and worsted fabrics are produced, formerly a giant in the textile trade, now accounts for only 6 per cent of total fiber consumption, nationwide and worldwide. King Cotton is having his troubles, as well. In the last twenty years cotton has fallen 13 per cent, from a world total of 73 per cent to the present 60 per cent. In the same length of time, the manmade fibers have gained from 13 per cent in 1944 to 33 per cent at present. This includes cellulosic and non-cellulosic fibers.

Many factors have made the growth of manmade fibers possible. To cite only a few: con-trolled and planned fiber production, cutting wastes to a minimum; excellent research and development; fabric development and quality control; high textile testing standards for dur-ability and performance; excellent advertising plans and campaigns; educational programs in many fields; accessibility to markets; cohesion and sanity in promoting wares; and the chang-ing tastes of the public, especially toward lighter-weight garb and more changes of apparel. In addition, apparel in active and spectator sportswear, higher living standards, more leisure time, and travel by the public stimulate a constant flow of new products and new end uses. The fiber producers and textile mills have met, and will continue to meet, all challenges with which they are confronted.

CHRONOLOGICAL HISTORY OF THE RISE OF MANMADE FIBERS

The first idea with regard to making textile filaments, fibers, and yarns by chemical means was conceived by Dr. Robert Hooke in 1664. He can be considered as the "Father of the Synthetic Textile World" that came into being with considerable impact in the twentieth cen-tury. The word, "synthetic," has now been replaced by the term, "manmade," and what Dr. Hooke began is now the "Manmade Textile Fiber World."

Dr. Hooke was an English naturalist and research scientist who was born in 1635, the son of a minister. He studied at Cambridge and Oxford universities. Living in the time of Oliver Cromwell and Charles II, he was a close friend of Samuel Pepys (Peeps), the diarist of the era, and knew many persons of affluence and prominence. Dr. Hooke built a microscope which, up to that time, was the best one developed.

In 1665, his chief interests included the development of filaments by synthesis. *Micrographia*, the book he brought out in that year, stressed the fact that it was possible to produce filaments and fibers by mechanical means. Dr. Hooke wrote as follows:

"And I have often thought, that probably there might be a way found out, to make an artificial glutinous composition, much resembling, if not full as good, nay better, than the Excrement, or whatever other substances it be out of which the Silk-worm wire-draws his clew. If such a composition were found, it were certainly an easier matter to find very quick ways of drawing it into small wires for use. I need mention not the use of such an Invention, nor the benefit that is likely to accrue to the finder, they being sufficiently obvious. This hint, therefore, may, I hope, give some Ingenious inquisitive Person an occasion of making some trials, which if successfull, I have my aim, and I suppose he will have no occasion to be displeased."

From 1664 until 1884, a span of 220 years, many scientists followed the ideas and thoughts expressed by Dr. Hooke. In the latter year Count Hilaire de Chardonnet, Besançon, France, unveiled his famous nitrocellulose filament and fiber, the first truly synthetic or manmade textile fiber that had commercial value. Some of the more outstanding scientists who tried to make Dr. Hooke's ideas a concrete actuality included René de Réaumur, Friedrich Gottlob

Keller, George Audemars, Dr. Schweitzer, Sir Joseph W. Swan, Dr. Weston, and Naudin and Schutzenberger. Each person improved on the work of his predecessors, but until the discovery of nitrocellulose by de Chardonnet, none was successful. Its demise occurred in 1934.

1889: At the Paris Exposition, de Chardonnet showed many articles made from his nitrocellulose yarn, and wide acclaim was afforded him and his findings.

1890: L. H. Despaissis perfected the cuprammoninum (Bemberg) method of producing yarn by artificial means, now known as rayon.

1892: The viscose-solution method of making yarn was patented by three British scientists, C. F. Cross, Clayton Beadle, and E. J. Bevan.

1893: Edward D. Libbey produced the first glass fiber; a glass dress was shown at the World's Fair in Chicago during the year.

1898: C. H. Stearn and C. F. Topham received patents and the rights to produce viscose filament on a commercial basis in England.

1903: Platinum was first used in the manufacture of the spinneret, the device by which solutions are forced through small openings or orifices on their way to be solidified into yarn. At present, they are made from a combination of platinum and iridium, alloys of gold, and stainless steel.

1904: Samuel Courtauld built and set in operation the first rayon plant in England.

1911: The American Viscose Company, now a division of the FMC Corporation, began production of viscose rayon in Marcus Hook, Pennsylvania.

1918: Courtaulds, Ltd., began the manufacture of Fibro, a viscose rayon staple fiber that is still in demand throughout the world.

1919: Henri and Camille Dreyfus, brothers from Basel, Switzerland, then working in England, offered the first acetate yarn for sale.

1924: Kenneth Lord of the fabric firm of Galey & Lord, now a unit in Burlington Industries, Inc., coined the word, "Rayon." This name replaced a host of misleading terms such as artificial silk, fiber silk, Glos, and milkweed silk.

Production of acetate yarn was begun in this country under the aegis of the Dreyfus Brothers, now the Celanese Corporation of America, in Amcelle, Maryland.

1926: Dr. C. M. A. Stine began his intensive and exhaustive research on polymers for E. I. du Pont de Nemours & Co., Inc., Wilmington, Delaware. Thirteen years later, because of his findings, nylon appeared on the market.

1927: Du Pont began its production of commercial rayon which, by this time, was receiving good acclaim from the apparel trades.

1929: Dr. Wallace A. Carothers of Du Pont, working from the findings by Dr. Stine begun in 1926, perfected polymerization of molecules by condensation and the determination of the structure of high-molecular-weight compounds. These findings made the introduction of nylon inevitable and Dr. Carothers was the recipient of the patents for nylon for the Du Pont Company.

1931: Estron acetate fiber announced by Eastman Chemical Products, Inc.

1934: Cordura, the high tenacity tire yarn made of rayon, announced by Du Pont.

1937: Vinyon, a product of American Viscose Corporation, made its debut.

1938: Zelan, a water repellent, announced by Du Pont.

1939: Announced in 1938, nylon hosiery came on the market on May 15 following a two-year period of try-out of the stockings in and around Wilmington, Delaware. These stockings proved to be a sensation to the female population of America. Vinyl upholstery also made its appearance during this year.

1940: Saran base product announced by the Dow Chemical Company, Inc., Midland, Michigan.

1941: Celanese Corporation of America announced its Fortisan, a super-strong saponified rayon with great dimensional stability. Tereylene polyester fiber discovered by Dr. Whinfield, England. He had developed it from his knowledge of the work done by Dr. Carothers of Du Pont. Shortly after the announcement the patent rights were purchased by Du Pont.

1943: Elastic-type Vinyon brought out by American Viscose Corporation.

1946: Fiber V, now known as "Dacron" polyester fiber, announced by Du Pont.

1947: Helanca Patent Corporation, Wattwil, Switzerland, brought out the first commercial stretch yarns.

1948: "Orlon" acrylic fiber now being produced by Du Pont.

1949: Dynel modacrylic fiber introduced by Union Carbide Corporation.

1951: Chemstrand Corporation, a division of the Monsanto Company, Inc., commenced production of nylon.

1953: American Enka Corporation began nylon production. "Teflon" tetrafluoroethylene fiber made its debut with Du Pont.

1954: Avron, formerly Avisco XL, rayon announced by American Viscose Corporation. Zantrel, a high wet-modulus rayon in staple form came into the market; now a product of American Enka Corporation.
1956: Verel modacrylic fiber announced by Eastman Chemical Products, Inc.
1957: Creslan acrylic fiber unveiled by American Cyanamid Company, Inc.
1958: Tyrex, Inc., began to market its Tyrex yarn, a "Super-2" high-tenacity rayon tire cord. Nylon 501 carpet yarn announced by Du Pont. Kodel polyester fiber was brought out by Eastman Chemical Products, Inc.
1959: The first of the Spandex fibers, Lycra, announced by Du Pont. Golden Caprolan, nylon tire yarn, announced by Allied Chemical Corporation.
1960: Fortrel polyester fiber produced by Fiber Industries, Inc., Shelby, North Carolina; Eastman Chemical Products, Inc., by this time was producing Verel modacrylic fiber, and its Estron 50 and Estron 75. Celanese Corporation of America began production of Arnel, a triacetate fiber, and American Enka announced its Blanc de Blanc, an extra-white nylon fiber, while Du Pont contributed its Antron with a trilobal cross-section nylon, and "Teflon" TFE-fluorocarbon fiber. Avlin, formerly Fiber 40 and RD 100, introduced by American Viscose Corporation; Vycron polyester fiber placed on the market by Beaunit Corporation; and Chemstrand Corporation began its licensing program for A-Acrilan acrylic fiber. Chemstrand also announced its Cadon, a multilobal cross-section nylon, FRN Nylon, and its carpet yarn, Cumuloft, a staple fiber. The Dow Chemical Company, Inc., began production of Rovanna, a microtype Saran, while Minnesota Mining & Manufacturing Co., Inc., developed its Scotchgard, a water repellent. Reeves Brothers, Inc., New York City, began promotion for its polypropylene bristles for use in brushes, and Prolene polypropylene fiber was announced by Industrial Rayon Company, a division of Midland-Ross Corporation.
1961: Lycra, the first spandex fiber, was put on the market. Shortly thereafter it was followed by Vyrene spandex fiber of United States Rubber Company, Inc. Spunbonding was announced by Du Pont at the end of the year.
1962: Herculon polypropylene in bulked filament, staple, and tow developed by Hercules Powder Company, Inc. Du Pont brought to the market its "Teflon" FEP-fluorocarbon fiber.
1963: Spandelle, a spandex fiber, was put in production by Firestone Synthetic Fibers Company. Tyweld, an adhesive-treated rayon, came out under the aegis of Industrial Rayon Company, Midland-Ross Corporation.
1964: "Cantrece" nylon hosiery was promoted by Du Pont, along with its "Reemay," a spunbonded polyester structure.

AUTOMATION

There are hundreds of definitions for automation, some serious, others facetious. The word is misunderstood, confusing, fearsome, and at times even awe-inspiring.

Automation may be defined as the science of operating or controlling a mechanical process by highly automatic means, such as by electrical devices. Without automation, obsolescence is sure to result. The word is not new since it can be stated that any device which makes the task of man easier is a form of automation. Thus, the wheel, the lever, the rocking chair, hand tools, the steam engine, the arithmetic machine of Pascal in the seventeenth century, De Forest's electronic valve of 1907, and John Bardeen's transistor of 1948 are all examples. It has taken many centuries for automation to gain maturity from its early beginnings to the present time.

The Industrial Revolution may be considered as the beginning of modern automation. The first machines to become automated were the carding machine, the spinning frame, and the weaving loom. From these three examples, automation has evolved through the genius of inventors, predominantly English, who laid the foundation for modern technology and material progress.

In the modern world, the term was first heard, with many misgivings, in the 1850's. Automation was at this time very limited in scope and not very specific in application for providing better and easier means to do certain parts of man's work. In the early 1960's automation became a household word, spread rapidly, received much attention in the press, and seemed to take on a glamour that attracted people to it. Many wanted to know about its good points, its bad points, and how it might affect our social, political, and economic standards, as well as our living standards.

The concept has now reached the point where it seems that everything is or can be automated. The benefits from automation have spread rapidly, increased the welfare of man, and substituted devices and machines that aid him in conserving not only his energy and strength, but also that of animals. The word now has a specific meaning and has gotten away from the general meaning which it seemed to connote a few years ago. Several things have contributed to the rise of automation. To mention only a few: research and development, quality control, the rise in specific, detailed technology (textile and otherwise), costing, increased production; mass production, assembly lines, uniform sizes, job specialization; engineering and imagineering, new ideas and new concepts, new products, new end uses, computation, and, in general, the speeding up of almost everything, so it seems. Automation, of course, is here to stay and people are now beginning to see that it has something positive to offer to mankind and the growing world population. Skeptics are coming around to the point that automation is a help and not a hindrance. As time goes on, the population sees that it will not, in the long run, do away with jobs but will increase them. Any student conversant with the history of texiles, or any other major field of endeavor for that matter, realizes that the great inventions and progress made in a particular field in the last twenty years are fantastically phenomenal. Automation has contributed much to this material progress.

As has been mentioned before, there are three oustanding men who helped to develop automation, all of whom lived and worked more than 150 years ago:

1. James Watt: In 1784 Watt brought out his steam engine with its flyball governor which kept the steam flow constant with the varying loads, a continuously self-acting engine. He used centrifugal force to move the whirling fly-balls into position to cut the back throttle of the steam engine so as to keep the machine operating at a fairly constant speed. It took, however, more than one hundred years to eliminate inefficiencies because of the time lag and the factor of oscillation in the mechanical linkage.

2. Oliver Evans: In 1790, the Evans Flour Mill in Philadelphia combined a number of prior inventions, including a conveyor belt with buckets attached to it and Archimedean screws, to grind grain automatically. The mill was automated to the extent that the grain was unloaded from boats, conveyed through the milling operation to the containers which were then loaded onto boats, without any human handling. Only one attendant was required to supervise the entire operation. His contemporaries were excited about his ingenuity but were also fearful of the economic results that might accrue from his greatly increased output of grain and the effect it might have in eliminating workers in the field.

3. Joseph M. Jacquard: This great genius, after several years of research and work, brought out the famous loom which bears his name. Working in Lyons and Paris, he began about 1792 to make progress with the ideas for his loom. The Jacquard loom is considered to be one of the greatest examples of automation ever produced; at that time it was the last word in automation. By means of a set of cards every warp yarn in the loom could be controlled and raised or lowered at will. The cards were cut on a card-punching machine and holes were punched in them in accordance with the motif or pattern decreed by the fabric designer. One method was: where a hole was made in the card, the warp end would rise; where there was not any hole the warp end would remain as is, or be lowered to form the bottom of the warp or loom shed. Thus, when the set of cards was mounted in the head-motion of the loom and the loom began to weave fabric it was merely a matter of telling the machine what to do. His loom, still one of the greatest inventions of all time, has served as the source from which card-punching machines have been developed in all phases of automated industry.

Automation embraces a great many facets in its rapid progress. It includes design, plant, and production engineering; instruments, controls, drives, handling devices, and sensing and measuring devices, all of which are aided by the works done by electrical, electronic, hydraulic, pneumatic, and mechanical instruments, and machines.

To show the progress of one company since its founding, herewith is given the record of the Saco-Lowell Shops, Easley, South Carolina, now a Division of the Maremont Corporation, Chicago, Illinois. Automation for many years has been at the forefront of this company's thinking, production, research, and development.

1811: The Saco Iron Works, Saco, Maine, founded; a step-parent of the Saco-Lowell Shops.

1813: Francis Cabot Lowell founded the Boston Manufacturing Company, Boston, Massachusetts. A mill was built in nearby Waltham to spin yarn and to weave cloth. Production began in 1814.

1818: "The Little Waltham machine shop" had outgrown its basement room where machinery was made and was installed in a new building. This mill was the first one of the company which, at that time, was more interested in making cloth than machinery.

1823: The newly formed Merrimack Manufacturing Company bought for the sum of $75,000 all the Waltham patent rights and privileges and the plant was located in East Chelmsford, Massachusetts, where machinery sales increased rapidly. During the year another link was forged when the Elliott Manufacturing Company was built on the banks of the Charles River in Newton Upper Falls, Massachusetts. Otis Pettee, a village mechanic, was named superintendent, and as was traditional at the time, set up his shop to build the machines required to make the cloth. In 1832, Pettee founded his own company which prospered; additions to the plant were made in 1835–36. The next five years, thanks to what is now known as automation, saw East Chelmsford grow from a village of about two hundred people into a town of 2,500 persons. Within a few years the name of the settlement was changed to Lowell.

1825: The next move for the Waltham Machine Shop came when it was transferred to the Locks and Canal Company, in East Chelmsford, which in 1845 became known as the Lowell Machine Company. As a result of this transaction, fabric production and the machine shop were divorced.

1837: From this time to midcentury, the formative years of Saco-Lowell, there were the establishment of the Lowell Machine Shops, the Saco Water Power Company, and Otis Pettee & Company. Following the Civil War, Lowell Shops further expanded, and this meant prosperity for many years.

1887: The Pettee Machine Shop Division built the first revolving flat card in this country, one that reigned supreme here for seventy-five years.

1897: The Saco Water Power Company merged with the Pettee Machine Works to form the Saco & Pettee Machine Shop, a merger of two major machinery units.

1905: Because of rather poor conditions and outlook at this time, and with business in a decline, Robert F. Herrick bought a majority of the company stock. Mr. Herrick bought a 20 per cent share. Other purchasers included one fifth by Whitin Machine Works, Whitinsville, Massachusetts, one fifth by Saco & Pettee, another fifth, it is thought, by Draper Company, Hopedale, Massachusetts, and the last fifth was split among Howard & Bullough, Fales & Jenks, Mason Machine Works, and the Woonsocket Machine Company, Woonsocket, Rhode Island. Within a month of this transaction, Lowell bought the A.T. Atherton Machine Shop and the Kitson Machine Company, thereby effecting control over the output of preparatory machines which none of the seven new owners had previously been able to build successfully.

1911: Mr. Herrick and an associate, for more than two million dollars, acquired control of the Kitson and Lowell Shops.

1912: This year was the actual beginning of the career of the great Saco-Lowell Shops when a merger was effected among the shops in Lowell and Newton, Massachusetts, and Saco, Maine.

1919: Saco-Lowell acquired the Pawtucket (Rhode Island) Spinning Ring Company.

1924: The company unveiled its Tunstall Two-Side Combing frame. It was designed to increase production in less floor space and was founded on an automation principle that to the present time remains unchallenged.

1926: The company promoted the well-known LeBlan-Roth System. This method of drafting is done by a single apron, the purpose of which is to obtain continuous contact with the stock along the length that is subject to drafting action. Control of the fibers and resistance to drafting is exercised by the pressure set up by the control rolls, which keep the roving, as it passes forward from the back roll in continuous contact, under slight pressure, with the apron. This arrangement was an advanced automation concept.

1927: In a reorganization of the facilities of the company, the separate stages of picking operations were combined into a single operation and to do this, the Single-Process Picker was manufactured.

1929: With the Depression here and abroad setting in, a consolidation of facilities was begun. The Lowell plant had outgrown its usefulness and was liquidated while the Kitson plant was closed. Activities were now centered in Newton, Massachusetts, and in Biddeford-Saco, Maine. In 1932 the Newton plant was abandoned and the facilities in Saco and Biddeford were expanded and completed.

Prior to World War II, the company established its Research and Development Department to improve its own standing and to better face competition in the field of textile machinery. This group was crystallized into a well-knit organization to promote further interest, increase the ability to cope with ever-present problems, and to give a close look to automation with regard to combining some of the individual operations in yarn manufacture into a single or joint operation.

1944: The company brought out its New Era ® spindle that was widely accepted in the trade.

1948: During this time the exodus of textile companies and concerns from New England to the South was at its height. Many of the venerable textile centers in New England had become deserted villages, because of the hegira from there. The company acquired a plant in Sanford, North Carolina.

1952: Introduction of the Gwaltney Spinning frame, named for the Director of Research, Eugene Gwaltney. Known as the SG-1 Spinning frame it was considered the last word in spinning equipment. Many new concepts in all phases of yarn manufacture were now being studied by all companies with automation being given much attention.

1955: The Versa-matic ® four-delivery drawing frame was announced. It had a delivery speed of three hundred feet per minute and is the pace-setter for the high-speed drawing of today.

1957: Saco-Lowell had been studying closely since 1930 the ever-changing conditions in the textile industry. The company had been successful but it was aware that more success would come with research, development, and automation. At this time the textile industry was changing rapidly. The South was now the textile empire in this country. Many of the old-time, long-established concerns had been liquidated. Foreign competition was one of the main reasons for this toll among many of the New England institutions. Labor conditions there were chaotic and unsettled. Mergers were frequent, and combinations ran into millions of dollars.

New textile fibers began to be introduced. Only the alert, up-to-the-minute companies could survive. The manmade fiber kingdom revolutionized the entire industry. Many of the fibers could be used alone or in blends and their manipulation was of concern to all manufacturers, especially machinery manufacturers. A machinery revolution was inevitable, and automation played a major role in it. The industry was confronted with new yarns, fabrics, finishes, end uses, etc. Companies had to take close account of stock to learn where they stood, and to decide what to do about the future. Plants that were still in New England had to decide whether to try to weather the storm there or move South where conditions were more congenial. Saco-Lowell decided to expand its Southern facilities and by the end of the year had established a second plant in North Carolina, at Jonesboro. In addition, it planned to erect headquarters and a new plant in Easley, South Carolina, to handle its increased business.

1958: By midyear the textile-machinery building in Biddeford, Maine, was closed and all production was being done in the South. The ordnance department in Saco, Maine, was retained and fully modernized; its Research and Development Department is now considered to be one of the best in the textile industry.

Automation was further advanced when the company brought out its new concept in fiber drafting, the MagneDraft ® Drafting System. This was acclaimed as a great milestone, and is considered by many to be the best method available.

1959: The Research and Development Center was opened in Clemson, South Carolina.

1960: Another milestone in the history of the company was the acquisition of controlling interest by the Maremont Corporation, Chicago, Illinois. Maremont was originally a blacksmith shop when it began business in 1877. It was a major company in the wagon-building business until the advent of the gasoline-powered machine, the automobile. For many years interested in diversification, Maremont has always been known for its capable management. The merger of Saco-Lowell with Maremont has done much for both parties.

During this year the Rovematic ® roving frame to process cotton, worsted, and manmade fibers was unveiled. The company already had two great spinning systems in operation, the Gwaltney and the MagneDraft ® drafting systems. When this frame was announced more than one million dollars had been spent for tooling, and it made conventional roving frames obsolete.

1961: The new Marathon ® Spinning Ring was now ready for production, the first and only ring with electro-polished finish. By this time the company was making an impact in the international market, and the new spinning ring became a favorite of the trade throughout the world.

The DuoCard and Multiple Cards, developed on the principles of automation, marked a new concept in carding fibers.

1962: Introductions this year included the Model 140 Comber frame, the high-speed Two-Delivery Versa-matic ® drawing frame, and the Spinomatic ® Spinning Frame, three machines that are highly regarded throughout the world.

Saco-Lowell became interested in the Continuous Automated Spinning System developed by Toyobo-Howa Textile Engineering Company, Ltd., of Japan. A licensing agreement was consummated with this company so that this system could be adapted to manufacturing conditions in the United States.

The new plant in Easley, South Carolina, was completed and was named the W.

Frank Lowell Plant in honor of the retiring president. The giant plant, in addition to the manufacture of roving and spinning frames, spindles, travelers, top and bottom rolls, and twisters and winders, also houses the executive, administrative, sales, engineering and accounting departments, along with the advertising and public relations divisions. It is a complete textile facility in every sense of the word, and automation has been most important in the conception and realization of the present quarters.

1963: The 150th anniversary of the company, one of the truly great concerns in the field of textile machinery, was celebrated this year. It reached its apex, despite lean years at various times, because of thorough research, development, and automation. Saco-Lowell now has more employees than ever before and disproves completely the idea that automation throws people out of work.

Thus, in the last half of the present century there are three great systems which have aided man to achieve ascendancy in business and manufacturing in this complex world. Our material prosperity is now at the greatest zenith ever reached by man, based on his machinery, money, management and methods, mill engineering, manipulation, millwrighting and maintenance, marketing, and merchandising. All these aid man in his quest for success, for higher standards of living, and, supposedly, for a better world.

The Factor System, the Manmade Fiber System, and the Automation System have made the vast textile industries what they are today. And, instead of causing a loss in manpower, automation has actually increased the number of positions open to the artisans of today.

Linked with automation is the word, *cybernetics*, which implies the scientific study of those methods of control and communication common to living organisms and machines.

Cybernetics comes from a Greek root which means "helmsman." The term is applied to the analyses of the operations of devices and machines of many types. Automation and cybernetics, more or less combined in their present usage, cover the utilization of machine production without any human effort being applied. Obviously, the action is that of repetitive chores or continued work-effort.

On the other hand, people do have to work to eat and live, and eat and live to perform work. This comes to the point of work versus labor, the on-the-job, people-to-people action and response. It is a case of production by way of machines, actually jobs versus work and effort. People must work so as to provide buying power. People are, generally speaking, active by nature with a desire to work. Thus, automation and cybernetics have caused a revolution. In the two centuries since the beginning of the Industrial Revolution, there have been unsettled conditions temporarily but, all told, it did not take people long to realize that automation and cybernetics were decidedly positive rather than negative. In the eighteenth century carding machines, spinning frames, and weaving looms caused considerable chaos and unrest as well as loss of work among the artisans when they were first introduced. In time, however, these conditions were alleviated and things returned to normal.

The following group of inventions and their developments show that the numbers of workers increase after the initial fears and misgivings have vanished: the mower and reaper; vulcanization of rubber; steam-cylinder printing press; elevator; typewriter; railroad airbrake; airplane and space travel; telephone; radio and television; computers and communications; and a host of other inventions that could be mentioned.

Thus, in our material progress through the many centuries to the present day, it has been demonstrated that automation and cybernetics are here to stay and will be a blessing rather than a curse.

Text on the Saco-Lowell Shops from *The 150th Anniversary Bulletin* of Saco-Lowell Shops, October, 1963; kindness of Mr. Allen F. Barney, editor, and Director of Advertising and Public Relations for Saco-Lowell Shops, a Division of Maremont Corporation, Greenville, South Carolina.

Founding Dates of Some of the Major Textile Companies and Allied Industries in the United States in the Nineteenth Century

1802: E. I. du Pont de Nemours & Company, Inc., Wilmington, Delaware.
1812: Saco-Lowell Shops, Lowell, Massachusetts (now the Maremont Corporation, Easley, South Carolina).
1813: J. P. Stevens & Company, Inc., North Andover, Massachusetts, and New York City.
1816: Draper Corporation, Hopedale, Massachusetts.
1816: B. F. Gladding & Company, Inc., South Otseco, New York.
1816: Rocky Mount Mills, Inc., Rocky Mount, North Carolina.
1816: James Lees & Sons Company, Inc., Bridgeport, Pennsylvania.

1817: Atkins & Pearce Mfg. Company, Inc., Cincinnati, Ohio.
1820: H. W. Butterworth & Sons Company, Bethayres, Pennsylvania.
1823: Atkins, Haserick & Company, Boston, Massachusetts.
1825: Cranston Print Works, Inc., Cranston, Rhode Island.
1831: Noone Mills, Peterborough, New Hampshire.
1831: Whitin Machine Works, Whitinsville, Massachusetts (White Consolidated Industries, Inc., Cleveland, Ohio).
1832: Davis & Furber Machine Company, Inc., North Andover, Massachusetts.
1832: Rodney Hunt Machine Company, Orange, Massachusetts.
1832: The Kendall Company, Walpole, Massachusetts.
1834: Curtis & Marble Machine Company, Worcester, Massachusetts.
1838: Cheney Brothers, Inc., South Manchester, Connecticut.
1839: Indian Head Mills, Inc., Nashua, New Hampshire; New York City.
1840: J. & P. Coats (R.I.), Inc., Pawtucket, Rhode Island.
1843: Collins & Aikman Corporation, New York City.
1843: Kent Manufacturing Company, Clifton Heights, Pennsylvania.
1844: Brownell & Company, Inc., Moodus, Connecticut.
1844: Pepperell Mfg. Company (now the West Point-Pepperell, Inc.), Boston, Massachusetts.
1845: Graniteville Company, Graniteville, South Carolina.
1845: Trion Division, Riegel Textile Corporation, New York City.
1846: Stevens Linen Associates, Inc., Webster, Massachusetts.
1847: James Hunter Machine Company, Inc. (Division of Crompton-Knowles Corporation), North Adams, Massachusetts; Worcester, Massachusetts.
1850: Bates Manufacturing Company, Inc., Lewiston, Maine.
1850: Levi Strauss & Company, Inc., San Francisco, California.
1850: Fletcher Industries, Cheltenham, Pennsylvania.
1850: Mount Vernon Mills, Inc., Baltimore, Maryland.
1851: January & Wood Company, Inc., Maysville, Kentucky.
1852: C. G. Sargent's and Sons Corporation, Graniteville, Massachusetts.
1856: Paul Whitin Corporation, Gilberville, Massachusetts.
1856: Fruit of the Loom, Inc., Providence, Rhode Island.
1857: Talbott Mills, Inc., North Billerica, Massachusetts.
1858: Bemis Bro. Bag Company, Boston, Massachusetts.
1858: Shuler & Benninghofen, Hamilton, Ohio.
1863: Industrial Equipment Corporation, Holyoke Machine Co., Holyoke, Massachusetts.
1864: The Clark Thread Company, Newark, New Jersey.
1864: Thomas Taylor & Sons, Hudson, Massachusetts.
1865: Coats & Clark, Inc., New York City.
1865: Deering Milliken, Inc., New York City.
1865: Lacon Woolen Mills, Lacon, Illinois.
1865: Millville Manufacturing Company, Inc., Millville, New Jersey.
1865: J. & H. Clasgens Company, Inc., New Richmond, Ohio.
1865: The William Carter Company, Inc., Needham Heights, Massachusetts.
1865: Scott & Williams, Inc., Laconia, New Hampshire.
1866: Howard Brothers Mfg. Co., Inc., Worcester, Massachusetts.
1866: C. H. Masland & Sons, Inc., Philadelphia and Carlisle, Pennsylvania.
1866: Charles S. Tanner Co., Inc., Providence, Rhode Island.
1866: Veeder-Root, Inc., Hartford, Connecticut.
1867: Benjamin Hay Co., Inc., Cincinnati, Ohio.
1867: Ponemah Mills, Taftville, Connecticut.
1868: Chas. W. House & Sons, Inc., Unionville, Connecticut.
1868: Virginia Mills, Inc., Swepsonville, North Carolina.
1869: Muscogee Manufacturing Company, Columbus, Georgia.
1869: The Manhattan Shirt Company, Inc., New York City.
1870: Gudebrod Brothers Silk Company, Pottsville, Pennsylvania.
1872: Morgan Cotton Mills, Inc., Laurel Hill, North Carolina.
1873: Cleveland Mills Company, Lawndale, North Carolina.
1873: Whitinsville Spinning Ring Company, Inc., Whitinsville, Massachusetts.
1876: Bibb Manufacturing Company, Inc., Macon, Georgia.
1876: The B.V.D. Corporation, New York City.
1876: The B. Kuppenheimer & Co., Inc., Chicago, Illinois.
1876: John P. King Manufacturing Co., Inc., Augusta, Georgia.
1877: Chatham Mfg. Co., Inc., Elkin, North Carolina.

1877: Henrietta Mills, Henrietta, North Carolina.
1879: Johnson & Johnson, New Brunswick, New Jersey.
1880: Clifton Mfg. Co., Inc., Clifton, South Carolina.
1880: Utica & Mohawk Cotton Mills, Inc., Utica, New York.
1880: Nelson Knitting Company, Inc., Rockford, Illinois.
1880: Shuford Mills, Hickory, North Carolina.
1880: United States Testing Company, Inc., Hoboken, New Jersey.
1880: Warner & Swasey Co., Inc., Cleveland, Ohio.
1881: Janesville Cotton Mills, Inc., Janesville, Wisconsin.
1881: Ledbetter Mfg. Co., Inc., Rockingham, North Carolina.
1881: Riverside Mills, Augusta, Georgia.
1882: Dan River Mills, Inc., Danville, Virginia.
1882: The Columbia Mills, Inc., Minetto and New York City, New York.
1882: Newberry Mills, Inc., Newberry, South Carolina.
1882: The Pacolet Mfg. Co., Pacolet, South Carolina.
1882: Callaway Mills, Inc., La Grange, Georgia.
1883: Massasoit Co., Inc., Laurelton, New Jersey.
1883: Proctor & Schwartz, Inc., Philadelphia, Pennsylvania.
1883: Superior Yarn Mills, Inc., Mount Holly, North Carolina.
1883: Cashmere Corporation of America, Cleveland, Ohio.
1885: Cluett, Peabody & Co., Inc., New York, New York.
1885: Bigelow-Sanford Carpet Company, Inc., Amsterdam and New York City, New York.
1885: M. Lowenstein & Sons, Inc., New York City.
1887: Birch Brothers, Inc., Somerville, Massachusetts.
1887: Alester G. Furman Co., Inc. (textile brokers), Greenville, South Carolina.
1887: H. F. Livermore Corporation, Boston, Massachusetts.
1887: Hart, Schaffner & Marx, Chicago, Illinois.
1887: Munsingwear, Inc., Minneapolis, Minnesota.
1887: Cannon Mills Company, Inc., Kannapolis, North Carolina.
1887: L. B. Lockwood Co., Inc., Cleveland, Ohio.
1888: Robert Reis & Co., Inc., New York City.
1889: Rock River Cotton Co., Inc., Janesville, Wisconsin.

Source: *America's Textile Reporter*, weekly magazine since 1887, 286 Congress Street, Boston 10, Massachusetts.

How Textile Fabrics Received Their Names

Although most words can be traced to their origin and roots, there seems to be no group of words with a more interesting geographical and historical background than the fabric names which are common in the textile industry.

For example, silk originated in China, linen in Egypt, cotton in India, and wool in Mesopotamia—the so-called "Big Four" natural fibers that have served mankind from time immemorial as the basis for the manufacture of textiles for use in apparel, as decorative and home fabrics, and as industrial cloths. Their development down through the ages and their true meanings in the present world of textiles are both interesting and intriguing.

France leads all nations in textile-fabric names, especially since the founding of the silk industry there in the early decades of the sixteenth century by Francis I, king of France (1515–1547). To the present day he is still known as the "Father of the Silk Industry" in textile circles. It was Francis who revived the denier coin as the unit used to figure the yarn size or count of silk yarn, a coin that had lapsed into oblivion after the death of Julius Caesar, over fifteen hundred years before the time of Francis I. All silk and manmade yarns are spoken of in terms of the denier count at present. Francis set up the silk industry in Lyons, St. Etienne, and other centers in France as well as establishing Paris as the fashion center of the couturier for women —positions these cities still retain today.

About 250 years after the reign of this great leader, another Frenchman, J. M. Jacquard, brought out the famous loom that bears his name. This loom placed France in the forefront in the manufacture of beautiful fabrics—damask, brocade, brocatelle, tapestry, and other decorative, high-quality materials. Several hundred fabrics have originated in France, and many of these are still important staple fabrics of the present day.

A host of nations throughout the world have contributed to the names and origins of textile materials. Among the leaders who have made the greatest contributions, in addition to France, are England, Scotland, Italy, India, and China. England and Italy rank as outstanding in fabric origins and names, very likely because of their distinguished, centuries-old tradition and interest in textiles.

The following list, while only partial, should be of interest to the reader as it reveals the worldwide scope of the great textile industry from fiber to fabric, to finish, to fashion:

CHINA

CANTON CREPE: It is made of silk from the Canton area and is identified by its crepe weave, a derivation of the plain weave, in which certain raisers are left out of the weave so as to make small floats in the goods to give it a pebbled effect and feel. The yarn is of high twist, which adds to its wearing quality and ability to resist friction and chafing.

CANTON FLANNEL: Identified by its nap on one or both sides, it is a medium-to-heavy-weight cotton goods; made from a three-up and one-down, or a four-up and one-down, right-hand twill.

CANTON SILK: It was first made in Canton, one of the oldest silk areas in the world. Made with a satin weave, the fabric has long served as a popular staple dressgoods throughout the world.

CHINA SILK: When applied to a fabric, it is any lightweight fabric made of silk produced in China; much of the goods is very flimsy, and the textures and qualities have wide variance.

CREPE DE CHINE: A very fine, lightweight silk made with a crepe weave, usually made with raw-silk warp and crepe-twist silk filling alternating with 2-S twist and then 2-Z twist. Usually piece-dyed or printed.

HABUTAI: Meaning "soft" or "spongy," it is an appropriate name for the fabric commonly made on hand looms in China and Japan; it is heavier than its counterpart, China silk fabric, which it resembles in other respects.

NANKEEN: It is named for the ancient city of Nankin, where the cloth was first woven on hand looms with cotton yarn in warp and filling. Usually made with local cotton, which has a natural yellowish tint, or dyed a buff or yellow color if made from other cottons.

PONGEE: From the Chinese word *pun-ki*, which means "woven in one's home," it is made from wild or Tussah silk in the natural or ecru color of the filament; it is very uneven in yarn and texture and noted for its many nubs and slubs in the yarn.

SATIN: It was first made from silk and woven in satin weaves, either in warp effect or in filling effect. The original fabrics were called *sztun*, until the Renaissance, when the Italian silk manufacturers changed the term to *saeta*, which implies a "hair or bristle," since the fabrics showed a hairline and glossy surface effect.

SERES: From the Greek *Sēres*, an East Asian people, probably the Chinese, who were known as silk makers by the Greeks and Romans. The word "sericulture" means the production of silk by cultivating silkworms.

SHANTUNG: It comes from the province of this name. It is native reeled silk, full of many types of imperfections. At times, the more uneven and nubbier the goods, the better it was supposed to be. Shantung is still a reigning favorite in the women's wear dressgoods trade.

SILK: From the Old English *seole*, which was probably derived from the old Slavic *shelkŭ*. It is also thought that the term is a contraction of *seres*, the ancient name for an East Asian people who grew silkworms and made silk. *Seres*, in time, was contracted into *sei*, and later, into silk. (*See* SERES.)

ENGLAND

ALBERT CLOTH: A doublecloth, woolen overcoating of the dressy type. The construction adds considerable weight to the material to provide more warmth to the wearer. Has an appealing smooth surface (face) effect. A velvet collar is always a distinctive asset to the coating. Named for Prince Albert (1819–1861), the German prince husband of Queen Victoria (1819–1901).

ANACOSTA: High-texture and high-quality worsted dressgoods, made in Great Britain. Filling texture is higher than warp texture. Piece-dyed cloth.

AXMINSTER: A popular low-priced carpeting first made in Acksminster. Not a yard of it, however, has been made there for many years; but there are several world carpet centers that make this floor covering. Axminster is now being rapidly replaced by tufted floorcovering.

BAIZE: Coarse, long-napped, woolen cloth that has been made in Great Britain for many centuries. Such materials were dyed "bay" or a brownish red color. Hence the name, which is a corruption of the plural of "bay." Baize, at one time, was made thinner and finer in quality than the modern fabric of this name and was used in clothing.

BEDFORD CORD: This sturdy, excellent-wear cloth was first made in Bedford, England, and it is also claimed by New Bedford, Massachusetts, where the cloth was produced as early as 1845. Although now made from several fibers and combinations of fibers, the original worsted cloth with its distinctive cords in the warp direction was first made to simulate corduroy, which originated in France—*cord du roi*, "cord of the king." Cotton Bedford cord is supposed to have been made in Bedford, England, at the time the "Louis kings" were reigning in France in the seventeenth century. Popular today in riding habits and uniform fabric.

BLANKET: This cloth is named in honor of the man who first used it as a covering for warmth and sleeping purposes. Thomas Blanket (Blanquette). He was a Flemish weaver who lived in Bristol, England, in the fourteenth century. The cloth is made of wool, worsted, or cotton, or by combining these fibers in varying percentages in the construction. Material is heavily napped and fulled. Used for bed covering, robes, steamer rugs. An essential cloth to people in the temperate zone.

BOX CLOTH: Really a coarse Melton used for the overcoating trade. Cloth is very heavy. Made into the formal type of garment. Repels water.

BRITISH SHEETING AND SHIRTING: These staple British products have more sizing than comparable fabrics made in the United States.

CASSIMERE: Suiting and trousering material of various compact weaves and color effects. Popular staple cloth. Hard-twisted yarn is employed. Often made with worsted warp and woolen filling. Can be made with a cotton warp with worsted or woolen filling. Cassimere is rather lustrous, harsh in feel, and light or medium in weight. Shines with wear. May be classed as a low-grade serge.

CHALLIS: First made in India from cotton (*see* INDIA: Challis), the first fabric of this type to be made from worsted or fine woolen yarn was produced in England in 1830. Challis is a soft, lightweight fabric, made in plain weave, of medium construction, and it may be dyed or printed. Can also be made from hair-fiber yarns mixed with wool or worsted yarn. One popular staple is made from silk or nylon warp and worsted filling. This rather inexpensive fabric is used much in women's and childrens' dressgoods, comforters, counterpanes, robes, and spreads.

CLAY: Class of staple worsted cloth, as to weave and construction, made famous by J. T. Clay of Rastrick, Yorkshire, England. The weave is a three-up and three-down right-hand twill. Texture is usually low. The cloth has been greatly imitated, and now the term is common rather than distinctive. Imitation is the sincerest form of flattery; the imitation of the genuine cloth proves this to be true.

CORONATION CLOTH: Made its debut at the time of the coronation of King Edward VII, in 1901. It comes in wool or worsted fabric and has "an unfinished finish," which means that there is a napped effect on the face which may, according to the finish given, be compact or rather straggly in appearance. Solid-ground colors are used and there are single-yarn woven lines in the warp direction, set about one inch apart. Metallic yarns are used for decoration in this fabric.

COTTON: In the English language, it is merely the anglicized form of the Spanish word *godon*.

COVERT: Twilled, lightweight overcoating cloth. Usually made of woolen or worsted yarn with two shades of color—say, a medium and a light brown. Cloth was first used as a hunting fabric and it is very durable. The name is derived from a similar term in connection with field sport. Covert is very rugged and stands the rigors of wearing very well. A highly desirable cloth that gives a smart appearance to the wearer. The material is a staple stock-dyed fabric.

CRAVENETTE: Registered name given to a celebrated rainproofing process for woolen and worsted apparel cloth by a Bradford, England, manufacturer named Wiley. For want of a better name he named it after the street in which he lived, Craven Street in London. The process was invented about one hundred years ago, and while exceptionally durable in its application, it is understood not to be a chemical-saturation treatment. Cravenetting is particularly effective on cloths of well-balanced weave construction.

DOILY: First made by a man named Doyley, this linen napkin was made in the era of Queen Anne of England (1707–1714).

DOMET: Household material obtaining its name from the term "domestic"—home. Also spelled dommet, domett.

FEARNAUGHT: English overcoating of the cheviot group. Cloth is heavy in weight, and the filling yarn aids in obtaining the well-known, characteristic shaggy face finish of the fabric. Much shoddy and other reworked fibers are used in making the cloth.

FLANNEL: Loosely woven cloth of simple weave which the dull finish tends to conceal. Cloth is found in standard blue and in fancy effects, chiefly in stripe form. Material is used for suitings, uniform cloth, outing material, and night wear. Flannel cloth originated in Wales. There is considerable variance in weight and texture in this cloth.

GLENGARRY: An English tweed cloth of the homespun and tweed group. Made from woolen yarns of the "hit-and-miss" type. This cloth admits of the use of much waste stock.

GUN CLUB CHECKS: Men's and women's wear dressgoods used for street and sportswear. Three colors of yarn are used in making the cloth. The warp and filling make a natty combination in the cloth. Men's-wear cloth may have a smaller check than women's-wear cloth. Men's-wear cloth could be laid out as six blue, six brown, six green in warp and filling arrangement. Women's-wear cloth could be constructed as follows: twelve light-brown, twelve dark-brown, twelve green in warp and filling.

HENRIETTA: Dressgoods that vary somewhat in detail. Some of the material is like cashmere cloth, other cloth is of the salt-and-pepper type. One of the popular cloths of years ago and not much in use in recent years. Cloth comes in the white state or may be piece-dyed. Used in children's clothing. Weight ranges from seven to fourteen ounces. Named for Henrietta Maria, the queen and consort of Charles I (reign 1625–1649) of England.

HOMESPUN: Originally an undyed woolen cloth spun into yarn and woven in the home with the rather crude machinery used by the peasants and country folk the world over. The industry came to the fore in the British Isles and then spread to the Continent. Owing to the substantial appearance and serviceable qualities, homespun is imitated to great extent on power looms today.

JERSEY: Either woven or knitted, it first appeared on the island of that name, one of the English Channel islands. First used by fishermen, the back of the goods was often napped to provide extra warmth to the wearer. The jersey of today is much different from the original fabric.

KERSEY: Originated in Kersey, near Hadleigh, Suffolk County, England. The present kersey cloth is heavily fulled or milled and made of woolen yarn, has a high-lustrous nap and a "grain" face. In southern districts of this country there is a cheap type of cloth that is a "union," but is sold as kersey. Kersey when compared to a beaver is fulled more, has a shorter nap and higher luster. The weight of the cloth runs from fourteen to twenty-four ounces per yard. Face finish weaves have to be used so that the ultimate finish will be acceptable to the trade. The cloth gives good wear and is of the dressy, conventional type. Found in blues, browns, blacks, and all popular shades.

KERSEYMERE: A fancy woolen cloth on the order of worsted cassimere. The name would tend to indicate that such cloth is a product of the mills along the waterways of Kersey, England. As there are no meres or lakes in the vicinity of this town, it is more probable that the term is simply a variation of "cassimere."

LINSEY-WOOLSEY: Cloth made of linen and woolen yarn. Cotton may be used instead of linen. Either stock is always the warp. Animal fibers always are the filling. Cloth is of loose structure, coarse, and often highly colored. It originated in England and was much in use in the Colonies at one time. It is more or less obsolete now. A little of the cloth finds use by the rural folk in outlying districts.

MELROSE: Double-twill cloth of silk and wool, named for Melrose on the Tweed River in Scotland.

MELTON: Sister cloth of kersey. There are four cloths in the group—beaver, kersey, melton, and broadcloth. Melton is a heavily felted, hard, plain, face-finished cloth. It is used for riding, box-driving, hunting cloth, and in overcoatings. One of the most serviceable cloths for outerwear. In garment making, melton in lighter construction is used as "under-collar cloth." The name of the cloth is said to be that of the originator of the material, but very likely it comes from the famous Melton Mowbray fox-hunting area of Leicestershire, England. In its group of cloths, melton is fulled the most, has the shortest nap. It is not a laid nap, and cloth is dull in appearance and non-lustrous. Double shearing is given in finishing so as to give the cropped appearance that is one of the distinguishing marks of the fabric. There are many grades of melton, dependent on the type of trade for which it is intended.

MELTONETTE: Women's wear cloth of very lightweight melton.

MERCERIZATION: Discovered by John Mercer in 1844 quite by accident—one of the greatest phenomena of all time and a great boon to the finishing of cotton fabrics. Cotton yarn and fabric, because of this accidental discovery, will show a silken-like, permanent luster that will last for the life of a fabric or garment; the fabric so treated will become stronger, and only about seven-tenths as much dyestuff is needed to dye mercerized goods (as compared with dyeing non-mercerized fabrics). Done in a cold bath of caustic soda, at a strength of about twenty-five to forty-five degrees (Twaddle thermometer), mercerizing can be performed at ordinary room temperature. John Mercer was a calico dyer and interested chiefly in the affinities of dyestuff for fabric rather than in fabric development.

NORFOLK SUITING: At one time very popular in this country with its pleats and belted-suiting effect, it came into being in the county of this name.

OXFORD MIXTURE: Usually a color effect in dark gray noted in woolens and worsteds. The degree of shade is governed by the mixed percentages of black and white stocks used. Mixing takes place prior to the carding and spinning of the yarn. Its reference to Oxford, England, has suggested calling the lighter-weight mixture cloths by the name of Cambridge, the rival university of Oxford. Oxford and Cambridge are the two oldest universities in England and are known all over the world. The colors of the schools are dark-blue and light-blue respectively, hence the use of dark and light oxfords or grays under those two names. In this country much gray cloth is given the name of Oxford.

PRIESTLEY: A well-known English worsted that is found in the better types of clothing stores. Made by the English manufacturer Priestley.

PRUNELLA: Originally a fine-twilled worsted fabric used for shoe and gaiter tops, the material derives its name from the fact that plum color or purple was a favorite shade used.

QUEEN'S MOURNING, THE: A black fabric with a white hairline; was a contemporary of coronation cloth which was noted in this country some years ago. The fancy yarns were red, white, and blue, and the cloth went under the name of "Inauguration Cloth."

TATTERSALL: A cloth that has its cycles of popularity, a rather gaudy-checked or block-effect material whose name comes from the famous horse auction rooms of London owned by Tattersall. It is believed that the ideas for the cloth were taken from the horse blankets, which were usually made in check effects. Made today with woolen, worsted, or mixture yarns, it is much used in vests and sportcoats.

VICTORIA LAWN: Very-high-quality cotton fabric named for Queen Victoria of England.

WEST OF ENGLAND: Woolen cloth of high reputation made in Leeds, Bradford, and Huddersfield, in the West Riding of England. Cloths that come from this Yorkshire district are referred to as "West of England" cloth.

WORSTED: Goes back to the day of William the Conqueror, 1066. The story goes that when he came to Britain he noted that the peasants were manipulating woolen fibers with a type of card or comb, a process used to work the fibers into a sliver and slubbing form so that they could be hand-spun into a yarn. William became much interested in the work, and not knowing what to call it, and since he had "worsted" the people by conquest, he called the area Worsted. In due time, the finished yarn was given this name as well, and the village of Worsted,. where he is supposed to have observed the workers doing their carding and combing, is in Norfolk County. About 1340, fabric of this name was being made in Suffolk County, England. Worsted fabric, as it is known today, did not become a winner in the trade until the 1890's, but it is still a favorite today for business, travel, and conventional wear.

FRANCE

AMIENS: The fabric originated in the city of that name is a hard-twist-yarn worsted made with a twill weave. It is either solid in color or can be produced in small novelty patterns.

ARMURE: A name for weaves showing small interlaced designs of chain armor, which was popular for military equipment during the Crusades.

ASTICOTINE: French woolen material, light in weight. Fulled considerably, it has good stretch and elasticity in both warp and filling.

BARATHEA: Fine-textured material of broken filling character. Made of silk warp and woolen or worsted filling. Other combinations may be used. High-quality stock is used to make this cloth. Used as mourning materials and in cravat cloth. Cloth is generally black.

BARÈGE: A silk-and-wool veiling first made in Barèges, France.

BATISTE: Named for Jean Baptiste, a French weaver who lived in Cambrai and first produced the cloth noted for its fine yarns, high texture, and softness. Yarns are of cotton or linen; a staple fabric for many decades.

BEIGE: A popular shade, it is the French term for natural, or natural color.

BOLCHÉ: Shirting material used by the clergy of southern Europe. A plain-weave cloth made of good stock and left in undyed state.

BOUCLÉ: From the French, it means "buckle" or "ringlet." Staple suiting fabric on the order of a worsted cheviot with drawn-out, looped-yarn construction. These yarns give a "ring appearance" to the face of the cloth. Also made in cottons. Bouclé yarn is very popular in the knitting trade. There are many types of this yarn to be found in this part of the textile business.

BOURETTE: From the French, meaning "hairy in appearance." The cloth has this rather hairy appearance; the yarn is interspersed with nubs to give the special effect.

BOURRÉ: A rough-faced fabric of the crepon group deriving its name in the same manner as bourette.

BROCADE: From the French, meaning "to ornament." Brocades are very rich, expensive, decorative materials.

BROCATELLE: On the order of brocade—the fabric was first made with raised-wool figures on a silk background.

BROCHÉ: Another name for a hairline or pin-stripe fabric—the name implying that the single color of the goods is broken up and decorated by a stripe.

CAMBRIC: A very fine, thin, lightweight cloth of cotton or linen, about which it has been stated that the "greatest thread was not even the size of the smallest hair." The old Flemish name for cambric was Kameryk. Cambrai, incidentally, was the city in France where the American soldiers in World War I received their baptism of fire, some of the engineers who went to France with General Pershing in May, 1917.

CANICHE: Comes from the French word for "dog" and implies a fabric made with a curly face finish. Present-day poodle cloth, brought out a few years ago by Lesur of Paris, is a development of caniche.

CHAMBORD: Woolen yarn, mourning cloth, which may contain cotton or silk fibers. The cloth has a ribbed appearance and the size of the ribs vary in diameter.

CHAMBRAY: Cotton-staple material first made in Cambrai, France. Made of white-cotton warp and colored filling.

CHENE: From the French, meaning "shiny, bright, having a sheen."

CHENILLE: Cloth of a fluffy or fuzzy face which simulates the fur of the caterpillar. From the French, meaning "caterpillar."

CHIFFON: From the French word for "rags of the flimsy type," it has been used to signify veiling and sheer fabrics of the soft, diaphanous type known for high yarn twist to give strength to the goods.

COCKLE, COCKEL: From French, *Coquelle*, meaning "cockle shell," the name is given to a distorted or shriveled effect on fancy cloths. This is the result of uneven scouring and fulling in finishing. Cockling may also be caused by improper tension on yarn in weaving, or lack of uniform quality in the raw material used. Several novel ideas have been advanced for the correction of this detriment to cloth.

CORDUROY: Made its debut during the reigns of the Louis kings of France, it means "cord of the king," a fabric much used by the outdoor servants and lackeys in the halcyon days of France. Noted for its rugged construction and good wear, the material is still very popular at present.

COTE CHEVAL: This is a corded cloth in France used for riding-habit material and uniform cloth for officers. *Côte* means "ribbed or lined," *cheval* means "horse," hence the name for the cloth. It has the grosgrain effect broken at intervals with a short stop to produce a striped appearance that is slightly rounded and may be compared to the ribs noted on the horse.

COUPURÉ: Comes from the French verb which means "to cut through." The term is applied to pile fabrics of several types which have been cut and clipped to give the desired effect.

CREPE: From the Anglicized French word *crêpe*. Originally a mourning cloth that showed a crimped appearance in fine silken material which got its derivation from the Latin term *crispus*, which means "curled." The cloth, when black, is much used in clerical circles. Light in weight, strong, and well-constructed worsted material. It is of superior quality and is made with a minutely wrinkled surface in imitation of the silken tissue of crinkled appearance. Now made from all major textile fibers.

CREPE DE CHINE: Cloth made of a China silk with a crepe-weave construction. France has been greatest producer of it for years.

CREPE DE LAINE: The latter word is French for "wool." The cloth is a thin lightweight dress-goods fabric, made with plain weave, or a crepe weave. Material is of the sheer variety.

CREPON: The French word means "to make crisp"; hence, materials having a crisp finish made from a crepe weave.

CRETONNE: Named for the village by this name in Normandy; made from osnaburg gray goods, the cloth is strong, unglazed in finish, and may be plain or printed on one or both sides.

DELAINE: In French it means "of wool." Wool of this name signifies that the stock is of the merino type; the highest-grade, finest, and best wool obtained anywhere in the world. The delaine-wool center in this country is in Ohio.

DENIM: Was first made in de Nimes or Nimes. This rugged, compact cotton fabric gives excellent service and is still popular all the way from work clothing to evening wear. It is made with right-hand or left-hand twill constructions, usually in the latter weave, which affords quick recognition as to the face of the fabric.

DRAP D'ÉTÉ: From the French, it means "cloth of summer." Used in evening wear and very popular as a staple with the clergy, it is a thin, lightweight, fine, high-count woolen or worsted cloth. It is now also made in blended yarns, such as contain nylon, "Dacron," "Orlon," etc. A rather expensive fabric, but it does afford excellent service.

EMPRESS CLOTH: Hard-twisted cotton warp and worsted filling cloth of the repp family. Popular in the middle of last century and first worn by the ever prominent Empress Eugénie (1826–1920). The cloth was all the rage during her era. A two-up and one-down twill is used on the face construction. A rib weave is used for the back structure.

EPINGLE: Its name taken from the word for "pin," the fabric was developed by the French about four centuries ago. A distinctive fabric first made with silk yarn and now with acetate, rayon, or worsted, this fine corded dressgoods with alternating large and small ribs gives an effect of pin points in its pebbled effect, which is aided by the use of contrasting or harmonizing yarns.

EPONGE: The French word for "sponge," the term is applied to a group of cloths which are very soft or spongy in feel and used to some degree in women's wear dressgoods. Fabrics of this name are usually rather porous in texture, which make them ideal for summer wear.

ETAMINE: Implies a bolting fabric or a sifting cloth, and the word implies a dressgoods material which has porous areas in it such as noted in leno or doup fabrics, mock leno cloths, and "cloth that breathes," a term rather popular in advertising goods of this character. Etamine is usually lighter in weight than eponge.

FELT: Derived from the rolling and pressing of a pulpy mass of wool fibers, hair fibers, or fur fibers into a matlike form. The term means "to mix and to press into shape," a contraction of the German *falzen*. Felt is said to have been known to wandering tribes who evolved the art of making it long before spinning and weaving were invented. The patron saint of the felt industry is St. Feutre of Caen, France; while on long trips he placed wool in his sandals to relieve foot pain. He noticed that the serrations or scales peculiar only to wool fibers, aided by heat, pressure, and moisture, interlocked and formed a matted layer of wool fabric. Thus felt was born as we know it today.

FOULARD: Means "silk handkerchief," and the fabric still serves this purpose as well as being a popular fabric used in the neckwear trade, dressgoods, and scarves.

FOULÉ: The term given to fabrics which have been shrunken in the finishing operations. The verb form means "to full or to shrink," hence the English term "fuller"—one who fulls or shrinks textile fabric.

GAUFRÉ, GAUFFRÉ: Means puffed or waffled suggestive of honeycomb or waffle material that is so much in demand for women's-wear summer dressgoods in cotton and manmade-yarn materials.

GLACÉ: The term applied to a smooth finish applied to certain fabrics; from the French for "iced" or "icy."

GRENADINE: While of Italian and Spanish origin, it was developed on a large scale by the French weavers in Lyons. Originally the meaning implied an outercovering, cape, or cloak made with bellshape lines. Present-day grenadine is a dress fabric made with open-gauze weave with hard-twisted yarn; stripes and checks may be obtained by cramming the yarn in some places and skipping reed dents in other areas to give the desired gauzy effect. Made from most of the major textile fibers.

GRISSAILLE: French for "gray or grayish." Warp and filling have contrasting black and white threads that give grayish appearance to the cloth.

GROSGRAIN: Originated in the Middle Ages and gained popularity in France when silk yarn was used to make the goods noted for the pronounced filling-rib effect. The term means a large or thick grain line in the filling direction of the goods; grosgrain is said to be "bengaline cut to ribbon width."

HONEYCOMB: Also known as waffle cloth, the term comes from the French, *nid d'abeille*, "a bee's nest," hence the application to the raised lines seen in the goods.

JACONET: A thin cotton fabric somewhat heavier than cambric; the face of the material is given a glazing treatment to produce high luster. East Indian in origin, the French developed the fabric by making stripe and check motifs in the goods, an improvement over the original goods.

JACQUARD: The name given to fabrics in which elaborate motifs are woven into the goods—brocades, damasks, brocatelles, tapestries, napery fabrics, neckwear, and so on. Named for the inventor of the loom which weaves the material—Joseph Jean Marie Jacquard, 1752–1834. He invented and perfected his looms between the years 1801 and 1810. Jacquard was a friend of Napoleon, and the latter pensioned him for his contributions to the French textile industry. Jacquard was one of the greatest contributors to the textile industry of all time.

JEAN: A twill-woven cotton with an undressed finish, a lining fabric which was first produced in Caen, a city known to our soldiers in the Normandy beach landings in 1945. Jean is made with a three-harness twill in warp effect or filling effect, some right-hand twill and some left-hand twill. Both types are popular staples in the trade.

LAWN: Comes from the city of Laon, a few miles from the textile center of Rheims. Originally used for garments worn by the clergy, present-day lawn is a lightweight cotton or linen fabric of the better grade, usually made of combed cotton yarn.

LENO: Also known as doup-woven cloth, it is known for its open-work face which resembles lace. The term is applied to fabrics which are constructed on the principle of "cross-weaving," in which two sets of harnesses—standard and skeleton—are used to make the warp ends cross each other in weaving. Marquisette is an example of doup-woven fabric. This method of weaving is supposed to have originated in or near Laon, and the material, in some circles, has been called a "cross-woven lawn," when yarns such as those used to make lawn have been used to make the fabric.

LISLE: A fine, hard-twisted cotton or linen yarn or thread used in socks and stockings. Lisle was the former name for the textile center Lille.

LONGCLOTH: A contraction of lawn, it is supposed to have been the first fabric made in a definite length in France; the original length is supposed to have been thirty-six yards. Made with carded or combed yarns, today the material belongs in the cambric-nainsook group of cottons, but it is more closely woven and somewhat heavier than these two fabrics.

LOUISINE: Was named for Louis XIV; a distinctive silk fabric with twice as many ends as picks in the construction; each pick crossed two warp ends at once to form a warp-rib effect.

MARSEILLES: A popular cotton summer-wear bed covering named for this city in France; comes in several weights and widths.

MATELASSÉ: A bed covering and dressgoods fabric recognized by its padded or pouched face effect; from the French verb *matelasser*, which means "to pad or to stuff."

MAZAMET: The name given to a type of French melton. It is the name of the city in France where the largest wool pullery in the world is located.

MÉLANGE: From the French, meaning "mixed"; hence, a fabric which shows a mixture effect. Also used to imply printed slubbings or top of worsted stock, and the name is given to the cloth produced therefrom; printed slubbing is also known as vigoureux printed.

MISTRAL: On the order of etamine, it is made with nubbed, uneven yarn to give a wavy effect in the cloth; the French term for a strong northwest wind.

MOIRÉ: Also known as watermarked, it received its name from the verb, *morrer*, "to wave." First seen on silk or mohair fabrics, the effect is also given to cottons, acetates, rayons, and comparable materials to improve the surface effect.

MOLLETON: Means melton in French. Name also given to silence cloth in cotton-goods trade.

MONTAGNAC: The registered trademark of E. de Montagnac et Fils, of Sedan. Made for a great many years, this luxury fabric is composed of wool and cashmere, the latter adding much to the appearance, feel, and beauty. The silken-like feel of the goods is one of the chief assets of this smart, dressy overcoating, which has a weight of thirty-six ounces per yard. The name means "mountain," and the cloth is ideally suited for mountain wear. Little of it is used in the United States.

MOREEN: A contraction of the verb *morrer*, "to wave." Mohair, silk, cotton, rayon, and acetate cloths are sometimes sold under this term when the watermarked effect has been applied to poplin-type fabrics.

MOUSSELINE DE LAINE: "Wool muslin" in French. This dressgoods cloth of plain weave is light in weight and made of worsted. The cloth is often printed, and qualities vary according to composition, which is often stock other than straight worsted warp and filling.

OMBRÉ: Means "shaded" in French; fabrics with stripes of various types in them often are sold under the term.

ONDÉ: French dressgoods of cotton warp and bright-colored wool filling. This cloth is supposed to have originated in Orleans. Cloth is cross-dyed, the warp and filling therefore showing different colors in the finished garment.

ONDULÉ: Another contraction from the French for "waving or shading" effects. The finish is brought about by causing groups of warp ends to be forced alternately by the ondulé reed to the right and then to the left.

ORGANDY: A plain, figured or dyed thin muslin-type cloth noted for its stiff finish, it received its name from the French, *organdi*, a word used originally to mean "book muslin." Also spelled "organdie."

ORLEANS: Made of cotton warp and bright wool filling, it first appeared in this French city well known in history. Alpaca and mohair are now used in the present-day fabric.

PANNE: Means "to flatten." The term is linked with *peluche*, the French for "plush" in many instances. Used also with velvet, panne signifies that the fabric has had the pile effect pressed flat in one direction; hence, panne velvet.

PEAU DE CYGNE: Was first made in France and because of its soft, appealing feel was given this name, which means "skin of the swan."

PEAU DE SOIE: Means "skin of silk," and the fabric was a staple until silk fabrics began to decline at the beginning of World War II.

PIQUÉ: From the French, and means "pike" or "that which pierces" and is not altered in any way. This popular cord, rib or wale fabric, should have its effect in the filling or crosswise direction in the fabric, from selvage to selvage. Today, however, the term is applied to materials with wales that run in the warp or vertical direction in the goods as well. Piqué is made with two warps and two fillings and may also have stuffer threads in addition to the binder threads used to hold the cords in place. Bird's eye piqué, waffle piqué, and Bedford cord are kindred fabrics to plain piqué, all in demand for summer wear.

PLUMETIS: A lightweight fabric made of cotton or wool which shows a raised motif on a plain background to give a feathered or plumed effect.

PLUSH: From the word, *peluche,* which means "shaggy." Pile fabrics with a pile of one-eighth of an inch or higher are known as plush; when the pile is less than this height, the cloth is in the velvet or velveteen class.

POIRET TWILL: Named for Paul Poiret, probably the most popular couturier of Paris in the 1920's. Still a staple fabric in women's-wear suiting of the better type, it is made in a steep-twill weave and has twice as many ends as picks per inch in the cloth texture.

POPLIN: Has been made for many centuries, and its name comes from the papacy. The Italians first made the fabric *papalino*, in the famous walled medieval city of Avignon, then in papal territory (1305–1370). This silk or worsted cloth was used in church vestments, and the French called it *papaline* and *papeline*. The contraction *popli* followed, and around 1800 the British called it "poplin" and used cotton to make this staple fabric.

RATINÉ: From the French, meaning "frizzy" or "fuzzy." An overcoating cloth on the order of chinchilla. Used in women's-wear coatings, ensembles, and in some dressgoods.

SANGLIER: From the French, meaning "wild boar." This dressgoods is a plain cloth of wiry worsted or mohair stock, closely woven and given a rough surface finish. Material is supposed to represent the coat of the boar.

SCHAPPÉ: A type of waste silk which receives its name from *hacher*—"to chop or to cut up." Schappé silk is cut into short lengths and spun into yarn on the spun-silk method of spinning; it can also be mixed or blended with other major fibers. This silk has good strength but poor, irregular luster. Pronounced "schap" in this country.

SOLEIL: The French term for "sun." Many allied types of silk fabrics are given this name since they show bright satin face effects which simulate the rays of the sun.

SOUFFLÉ: Means "puffed," and the large designs seen in crepon and other cloths are made with a raised or puffed motif and called by this name.

SUEDE: The French way of saying "Sweden" in English. Fabrics of this type are closely woven, or knitgoods napped and sheared to produce a very soft, appealing nap on the goods; simulates leather of this name.

TAMISE: Is a close-mesh fabric first made of silk and wool and now manmade yarns. The name comes from the French for "sieve"; hence the fabric is of the diaphanous type such as marquisette, voile, or organdy.

TERRY CLOTH: Received its name from the verb *tirer*, "to pull out." Turkish toweling is the original fabric, and the pile is made so that the loops are drawn through a foundation and remain uncut. The pile effect may be on one or both sides.

TOWEL: Derived from the word *toille*, a linen fabric. Originally spelled *touaille*, the towel cloth of today is still usually made from linen, but much cotton toweling is also made.

TRICOT: Means "to knit," and the fabric can be woven or knitted to go along with the demands of fashion. Fine, vertical lines are seen on the face, while crosswise ribs are noted on the back of the material.

TULLE: First made in Toul, it is a very fine, soft, machine-made net. Hexagonal meshes are a feature of the material, used in veils and bridal gowns. Silk and nylon fabric of this type, despite open-mesh construction, is strong, rugged, and gives excellent service.

VELOUR: Is merely the French term for "velvet." The term today has a double meaning—a cut-pile cotton fabric on the order of cotton velvet, or a material with a raised or napped finish. Velour can also imply pile fabrics in general, a very broad term at present. From the Latin *vellosus*, meaning "hairy." Knit velour is a popular staple.

VIGOGNE: The French way of saying "vicuña," which is the most expensive textile fiber today. Vicuña coats, incidentally, have sold for as much as $1,000 per garment, while the fabric has sold for as high as $150 a yard. The animal of this name lives at heights of five thousand feet or higher in the Andes Mountains of South America, chiefly in Peru.

VIGOUREUX: A popular method used to print worsted tops for use in high-grade suiting fabric. The word means "strong," and worsteds of this type are always a staple in the trade since they give excellent service to the wearer. Also spelled *vigoreux.*

ZIBELINE: Comes from the French for "sable," the fur-bearing animal found in Russia. Fabric of this name is made to resemble this fur, which is rather long; the cloth has a pronounced shaggy, hairy-faced appearance. Qualities vary to considerable degree in the women's coating trade.

INDIA

BANDANNA: Means "to tie" or "bind." Cloth of this name was colored by the Indian natives by dip-dyeing or by tie-dyeing to produce a mottled effect. The fabric at present is usually dyed by the resist method or the discharge method of printing, while some of the goods, in accordance with the motif, is direct-printed. Bandanna prints may or may not be clear and clean in pattern and looks.

BENGALINE: First made in India by the use of silk yarn in the warp and cotton yarn for the cross-rib effect filling to produce the cord. Now made from all major textile fibers.

BENGAL STRIPES: Named for the province in India, these are distinctive stripe effects in which several colors are observed. Neckties, ribbons, dressgoods, and regimental stripes are some examples of multicolored stripe effects.

CALICO: One of the oldest staple fabrics known to mankind, it was first made in Calicut, the seaport town in the southwest area of the Madras province on the Malabar Coast.

CASHMERE: The cloth was first made from the downy hair of goats of the Vale of Kashmir. Indian commercial cashmere cloths are found in overcoatings, suitings, and vestings. Cloth is made of fine wool that may be mixed with hair fibers. Soft finish is noted in the fabric. In an all-hair fiber cloth, the material is made into the famous, well-known, highly desirable shawl cloths.

CHALLIS: comes from *shalee*, which means "soft to the touch." It is made from cotton and is a cloth in demand all over the world at the present time. Cotton challis was colored by hand methods which are today known as direct, resist, or discharge methods of printing.

CHINTZ: From the word meaning "spotted." Indian chintz was colored by painting or staining the motif onto the goods; the fabrics were made to give a multicolored effect that was bizarre or conservative, still true in the fabric of this name at the present time.

CHUDAH: Named for the Indian plant noted for its brilliant green colorings. The color today is also known as Kelly Green, a vivid shade. Also spelled *chuddah, chuddar.*

COTTON: First known in India about 3,000 B.C., it was considered very rare and precious; India is supposed to be the home of cotton. In A.D. 502, a Chinese emperor ascended his throne arrayed in a cotton robe. In the seventh century, the plant was classed as a garden flower. And cotton is still king in America today, the universal textile fiber for all mankind.

DORIAN: Originally a striped muslin first made in India, still a staple in many world centers.

GINGHAM: Comes from the word, *ging-gamp*, which signified a cotton fabric of the East Indies made with stripes, cross-stripes, or barred effects—a variegated cloth. Still a most popular cloth, it is now made from woolen, worsted, and manmade yarns, as well as from cotton.

INDIA LINEN: A very fine linen first made in India.

INDIAN LAWN: Known as Indian linen as well, it has been made for over four thousand years in India. Fabrics of this name in museums are noted for their particularly fine yarn counts, evenness of weaving, and zephyr weight.

KHAKI: From the Hindi, meaning "dusty." Cloth is made in cotton, wool, worsted, and linen, and with combinations of these fibers. Cloth first gained prominence when it was taken as the standard color for uniform cloths of the British army in all parts of the empire. Since then, other nations have adopted the color. It is an ideal shade for field service. Fabric has limited use in civilian dress. Some trousering and riding breeches are made with that color.

MADRAS: Still one of the most popular of shirting fabrics, it originated in this Indian province. Extant fabrics were made with the varied stripe effects which make the fabric ideal for shirting purposes.

MULL: A soft, limp, pliable cloth that is really a lightweight muslin; seems to be superseded by lawn, longcloth, cambric, and voile.

[394]

BOMBAZINE: It comes from the Latin *bombycinum,* which means "fabric of a silken texture." One of the oldest fabrics known to mankind, it has gone through many changes from the original cloth. Originally, it was an all-silk material, then, around 1830, when it became popular in Great Britain, a silk warp and worsted filling was used. Present-day goods are made from any of the major textile fibers, alone or in blends, or with a warp of one type of yarn and a filling of another type, such as a cotton warp and acetate or rayon filling. A simulated fabric is now made with an all-cotton warp and filling. When dyed black, bombazine is much used for mourning fabric. Its attractive low price causes it to be one of the popular export fabrics sent to all parts of the world. Today this fabric, while still bombazine, is given other names to suit some particular purpose or whim.

CRASH: From the Latin, *crassus,* it means "coarse," typical of the material of today—a rough, irregular surface caused by the use of thick, uneven yarns. Osnaburg is the gray goods for crash made of cotton; other types are made from acetate or rayon-staple stock, and linen.

DOUPPIONI: Meaning "two," when applied to silk cocoons, it indicates that two or more cocoons have nested together; when they have been reeled, an irregular, coarse, double filament results. The Italians have been very adept in the manipulation of this yarn, which can be used in present-day fabrics such as nankeen, pongee, shantung, and other cloths which use irregular, slub-type yarn. Douppioni silk yarn is now simulated in acetate and rayon yarn made from the staple fibers.

DRILL: From the Latin *trilex,* meaning "three threads."

FLORENTINE TWILL: Received its name from this Italian city. First made as a silk fabric used for dressgoods, an eight-end satin weave in a twill-effect arrangement was used. Plain, figured, or stripe effects were used to give contrast in the material which, in addition to its use in dressgoods, found favor in vestments and vesting fabrics. Cotton warp and mohair filling were used in the lower qualities.

ITALIAN CLOTH: A broad term and one which signified a smooth lining material, was known during the Middle Ages; made of all cotton with a five-shaft, filling-effect weave in either a satin weave or a twill weave. Usually piece-dyed black or brown, the fabric is now made with acetate or rayon yarn, in addition to the cotton cloth for which there is still demand in the apparel trade.

LACE: It comes from the Latin *loquens,* which means "to make a knot, snare, or noose"; corrupted into the present term. Real or handmade lace is produced by a needle and known as point or needlepoint lace, or on a pillow with bobbins and pins, as in the case of bobbin or pillow lace, and at times by crocheting or by knotting or tatting. Machine-made lace manipulates the threads to produce the effects observed in real lace.

LINEN: From the Latin *linum,* it broadly refers to any yarn or fabric made from flax fibers. Italy was known for its linens during the Renaissance, since much had been learned in the manipulation of flax into linen fabric from extant linen fabrics made in Egypt.

MESSALINE: Named for the wife of the Emperor Claudius, Messalina, this fine silk fabric was compactly woven and noted for its high-sheen finish. This cloth was made on a five-end satin weave and had all the characteristics of peau de cygne, which was made on an eight-shaft weave. Both fabrics were popular in the silk trade from the turn of the century until World War II, when acetate and rayon fabrics of similar nature replaced them.

MILANESE FABRIC: Known as a warp-loom knitcloth made on the Milanese loom, usually from acetate, nylon, rayon, or silk yarns. This very fine fabric is named for the city of Milan.

ORGANZINE: It comes from the Italian and means "twisted silk"; the term for the silk warp in a material.

SERGE: From the word *sercia,* which means "silken"; the Spanish term is *xerga.* Originally made in Italy and Spain, the cloth was made with a small twill weave, usually a two-up and two-down right-hand twill construction. Serge of today is a light-to-medium-weight worsted fabric of good texture, even yarn, and clear face finish; made with the same weave as the silk fabric.

SICILIAN: First made on the island of Sicily, cotton warp and mohair filling were used for this lining fabric, which is still popular at present when made from these or other yarn combinations. Another fabric of the same name, also made in Sicily, used silk warp and woolen filling in which the rather bulky crosswise threads formed a rib effect in the material; a dressgoods cloth.

TARLATAN: First made from linen warp and wool filling, it was a coarse, stiff, heavily sized cloth named *Tarlantana,* a Milanese term for fabrics of this type. Now resembles buckram and crinoline.

VELVET: First made with a short, dense pile woven from silk warp, at present the term is applied to cloths made partly from silk, acetate, or rayon, and partly of other materials, as well as to goods made entirely of other yarns. Velveteen is a filling-pile fabric and is often confused or mistaken for velvet, a warp-pile-effect material. Incidentally, corduroy is a filling-pile-effect weave cloth. Velvet received its name from *vellute*, which implies a wooly feel to the touch as in the case of that noted on a hide or a pelt. The use of silk warp and woolen filling improved the hand of the goods, and cloth of this type was made from time to time. The pile effect in velvet may be cut or uncut. Also made from some manmade yarns today.

VELVETEEN: A simulation of true velvet, it may be made of acetate, rayon, or cotton, with a plain-weave construction on the back. The cloth may be wax-treated to improve the luster, and the finished product may be piece-dyed or printed on a dyed background.

VENETIAN: Named for the city of Venice, it is a warp-faced sateen stronger and heavier than ordinary sateen cloth, which is always made of cotton yarn. Eight-end satin weaves are used to make this lining material which closely resembles Italian cloth used in linings. Venetian is given a mercerized or a Schreinerized finish to enhance the luster.

VOILE: A corruption of the word *vela*, which implies "a covering, curtain, or sail." This staple is now made of silk, cotton, acetate, nylon, rayon, or worsted yarns.

SCOTLAND

BANNOCKBURN: The name comes from the village of that name, about twenty-five miles from Glasgow. This obvious tweed center unveiled this distinctive, typical British cloth by the use of single and two-ply yarn, with the latter of contrasting colors. The excellent-wearing cloth is much used for suitings and topcoating and to some degree in sportwear. Bannockburn is the site of the famous Battle of Bannockburn, where Robert Bruce of Scotland defeated the English and assured Scotland its independence from England for many years. This battle took place in 1314, and Scotland and England were not joined as one nation until 1603.

CHEVIOT: Rough woolen suiting and overcoating cloth. Similar to cassimere in construction. The name is derived from the fact that hardy wool from the Cheviot Hills of Scotland is used in making the cloth.

Today the cloth is made from either a plain or a twill weave. Many other cloths use cheviot wool but are not classed as cheviot cloth. True cheviot is very rugged, harsh, uneven in yarn, does not hold a crease, and sags with wear. It is a good "knock-about" cloth and ideal for sportswear. May be piece- or stock-dyed and has the tendency to shine with wear. In quality, the material ranges from low to high, and it is made on hand or power looms. A genuine British cloth.

HARRIS TWEED: Considered as the last word in genuine tweed cloth this cloth comes from the Harris and Lewis Islands off the northwestern coast of Scotland, the home of Clan MacLeod. These tweeds give excellent wear and command a good price. The material has characteristics of its own, even to the well-known and advertised "peat-bog order" that the cloth takes on in the processing in the home in the course of construction. This is the tweed par excellence and is imitated more than any other popular staple material. The hand-loom production is small, but power-loomed production is large. Trademark of The Harris Tweed Association, Ltd.

HEATHER MIXTURE: Tweeds, homespuns, and cheviots that have flake yarn, or some similar fancy yarn in them. The cloth seems to have a rather multicolor appearance because of the yarn used.

HOMESPUN: Refers to fabrics originally made in the home, and Scotland was one of the foremost centers where hand-woven woolens were made. The advent of the factory system with its men, material, machinery, and money seriously cut down the production of these fabrics. Homespun should be made of a plain weave, but Donegal "homespun," while made of a plain weave, is bought and sold as Donegal Tweed. This Irish fabric is made from coarse yarns with the warp being grayish white or of self-color, and the filling a color blend with specks of red, blue, green, and orange in the yarn.

MELROSE: First made in a silk and wool dressgoods cloth named for this town on the Tweed River, Scotland. Little of the fabric is seen today.

PAISLEY CLOTH: Used for coverings and shawls. Originated in Paisley, this characteristic worsted fabric is made with scroll designs all over the material. Colors run from red through to brown, with spots of other colors to enhance the design. The medley of color in this cloth is often very attractive. Genuine paisley is expensive.

[396]

SCRIM: A low-textured cotton which received its name from the fact that the reduced texture in the goods caused the material to become "scrimpy or skimpy"; hence the contraction into "scrim." Used for curtains, bunting, buckram; cheesecloth when bleached and given a heavy starching is called scrim.

SHETLAND: Overcoating cloth used for storm coats, ulsters, reefers. The cloth is rough and shaggy and has a tufted face. Made of the harsh, rugged wools of the sheep that come from the Shetland Islands. Other wools are now used in making the popular shetland suiting fabric, which is in the small family with homespun, tweed, and cheviot.

TWEED: Very popular staple used for overcoating, topcoating, and suiting fabric. Tweed originated in the homes of the peasants in the vicinity of the Tweed River, which separates England from Scotland. The first cloth was woven on hand looms. Today, hand-loomed tweed is a highly desirable fabric and brings a good price.

TWILL: In this sense the name given to cloths that show a twill-weave construction on the face of the material. In short, twill cloth shows a diagonal or bias effect on any material in regular repeat formation. From the Scotch *tweel*—"to make a diagonal effect." There are many varieties of twill—right-hand, left-hand, broken, herringbone, twilled baskets, baskets-in-twill effect, steep, reclining, even and uneven, single and double, braided, entwining, etc.

MISCELLANEOUS

ABA: A wool or hair fiber or combination-stock material used by peasants in southern Europe and Asia. Material is coarse and thick and has considerable felting given in finishing.

ALMA: A mourning fabric, has been known among the Egyptians for many centuries; made from cotton or linen and dyed black or purple.

ANACOTE: Central-European worsted serge with smooth sheen and finish. Small twill weave used in making the material. Cloth has demand among the religious orders, and also finds a market in regular trade.

ASTRAKHAN: Spelled in a variety of ways. It is a pile cloth of coarse structure that shows an interesting, curly face. Gives appearance of natural fur. The product originally came from the state of Astrakhan, Russia. The curly, looped effect resembles that noted in Persian lamb.

KNITTED ASTRAKHAN: In popular demand today, it is lower in cost than the woven article. The cloth, as a substitute, is found in the fur trade for coatings and is popular in winter wear. People who cannot afford real astrakhan buy the woven or knitted cloth of that name and become "the slaves of fashion," always noted in the world of women and their fashions in apparel.

AUSTRIAN CLOTH: One of the finest woolen and worsted fabrics to be found anywhere today. Made in Austria for many years, the fabric is made from the highest grades of merino wool obtainable, either Austrian, Silesian, or Botany Bay, Australian wool; finds use in evening clothes for men and in diplomatic circles.

BALBRIGGAN: Balbriggan in Ireland is where the first bleached hosiery was made. Also used for other purposes today, the fabric is a lightweight, plain-stitch knitted cotton cloth with a napped back.

BERBER: A lightweight, satin-faced fabric, made of all silk or of a cotton back and a silk face; it came into prominence at the turn of the century, when the famous English General Gordon of Khartoum defeated the Berber tribes in his campaign against the Mahdi in North Africa. The late Sir Winston Churchill, incidentally, served in this campaign under General Gordon.

BIAZ: A cotton or linen dressgoods still popular in the area where it was first made, Asia Minor. The cotton cloth simulates the more expensive linen fabric. Has been a staple cloth for many centuries.

BREECHES: Comes from the word *briges*, which was a loose, trouserlike garment worn by the peasant folk of Ireland, a forerunner of the knickers of a later age.

BUCKRAM: Received its name from Bokhara in southern Russia, where it was first made; a stiff, firmly starched cotton fabric such as scrim, cheesecloth, or tobacco cloth, and heavier than crinoline. Used for belt and skirt lining, in the millinery trade, and in bookbinding.

BUNTING: From the German *bunt*, which means variegated or gay-colored, characteristic of it today. A popular fabric used for decorative purposes.

BURLAP: From the Danish *boenlap*, a protective fabric that withstands hard usage. India for centuries, has been its greatest producer of fiber.

CADET CLOTH: The standard blue-, gray- or indigo-, and-white mixture, made of woolen yarn, as decreed by the United States Military Academy at West Point, New York. Other public and private institutions use this or similar cloth. Heavy in weight, durable, rather boardy in feel, it is an excellent outdoor cloth. The material is of double-cloth construction. The texture is very compact and the material heavily fulled and carefully finished.

CANVAS: Obtained from *canabis* or *cannabis,* the botanical name for "hemp." Canvas fabric is more or less synonymous with duck today.

CARACUL: Merely one of the ways of spelling karakul, a broadtail sheep of unknown origin found in Bokhara in southern Russia. The glossy, black fur is taken from the young lambs known as Persian lamb, broadtail, astrakhan, karakul. Fabric of this name is a simulation of the genuine fur and may be knitted or woven.

CARMELITE CLOTH: Named in honor of the Carmelite Order of the Roman Catholic Church. Plain-weave, low-texture, woolen cloth that is given considerable fulling. Somewhat resembles woolen bunting. Used as garb; a quality fabric.

CASTOR: The fur on the beaver is sometimes called by this name, hence its application to fabrics which resemble this fur.

CHEVRON: Broken-twill and herringbone weaves give a chevron effect such as seen on military uniforms to denote service. Chevron designs are popular in suiting fabrics and topcoating.

CHINCHILLA: A material simulating the rough, wavy fur of the rare Spanish animal of this name. Incidentally, there are only a few dozen genuine chinchilla fur coats in the world today; the price of one may reach as much as $30,000.

COBURG OR COBOURG: A lining and dressgoods material made from a two-up and one-down right-hand twill. Warp is cotton, filling is worsted. May be piece-dyed or printed. Named for Coburg, Germany.

CONVENT CLOTH: Use is obvious. The cloth is made of crepe weave to give it a pebbled effect. Light in weight, it was first made from wool warp and silk filling; much is now made from fiber-blended cloths.

DAMASK: Figured fabric, originally made in silk, that came to us from China via Damascus in Asia Minor. Marco Polo, in his travels of the thirteenth century, speaks of the material and gives an interesting tale about it. Damask has been made for centuries and is one of the oldest and most popular staple cloths to be found today. Damask belongs to the group embracing brocades, brocatelles, and Jacquards. The cloth is made from cotton, linen, wool, worsted, silk, rayon, etc. Used for tablecloths, napkins, doilies, runners, interior decoration, wall coverings, and furniture covering. Elaborate designs are possible, for damask is made on the intricate Jacquard looms, where it is possible to give vent to the whims of the designer of these cloths.

DIAPER FABRIC: Originally made of silk with small square or diamond effects. First made in d'Ypres, Belgium, a city of memories to the American soldiers in World War I. The word *diaspron,* from the Greek, means "small-figured," but present-day diaper fabric, well known in many households, received its name from "cloth of d'Ypres" which has been contracted into the English word "diaper."

DIMITY: Comes from the word *dimitos,* "a double thread." This lightweight staple cotton comes in plain construction or may be made in a derivation of the plain weave in which bars, cords, or stripes are used to add to the appearance. Of Greek origin.

DUCK: From the Danish word *doek,* a cotton cloth used by sailors in the summer; first made for use in caps and pantaloons. Now has many other uses.

EOLIENNE: Takes its name from the Greek *Aeolus,* the god of the winds. The cloth is a lightweight, zephyr fabric and may be classed as a very fine poplin. First made of silk warp and worsted filling, it is now made with acetate, rayon, or cotton.

FORESTRY CLOTH: Used by the United States Government for uniform cloth, overcoatings, trouserings, knickers, shirts, blouses, etc. The cloth is olive-drab in color and is made from a twill weave. Made of worsted, wool, cotton, mixes, etc., this cloth is used essentially in the Forestry Service of the nation, but is likewise utilized by some other departments. In short, the name is nothing more than another term for khaki cloth.

FRIEZE: Heavy woolen overcoating with a rough, fuzzy, frizzy face. Cloth is said to have originated in Friesland, Holland. Irish frieze has an established reputation. Cloth ranges from twenty-two to thirty or more ounces per yard. Much used in times of war as overcoating for soldiers. The grade and quality varies considerably. The average army frieze is made of cheap stock, is stock-dyed, harsh and boardy in feel, has many flecks in it and is not any too serviceable. A composition of frieze could be 67 per cent of three-eighths wool and 33 per cent of shoddy and reworks. Much adulteration is given the cloth, hence the wide variance as to the quality.

FUSTIAN: Was a low-quality, coarse cotton cloth first made in the Fustat, the ghetto area outside the city of Cairo. The Egyptians used a double-cloth construction to make the cloth, which, despite the fact that it was regarded as an inferior material, gave long wear. Some better-grade goods were made from linen. The fustian of today has changed much from the original cloth and implies, as a generic term, the rather high-pick, heavy cotton goods on the order of beaverteen, corduroy, doeskin, moleskin, and velveteen.

GALATEA: A left-hand cotton twill fabric used in childrens' sailor suits and play clothes, an old standby for many years. The name comes from the sea nymph of Greek mythology.

GAUZE: First used for netting and veiling, it was given to the world by the city of Gaza, Israel. Present-day fabric is open mesh, loose in construction, and plain or doup-leno weaves are used. Cheesecloth and tobacco cloth are current examples of gauze.

GOTON: Means "cotton" to the Egyptians.

GRANADA: From Latin, *granum* via the Italian, *granito*. In English the term means "grained" or "grainy," "rough" or "pebbly." Named for the city in Spain, where it is still a popular staple. It is a fine, face-finished fabric, usually made of worsted or suitable fibers that will blend with it. Broken effects in weave construction provide the granular pattern. Used in suiting and coating fabrics.

HONEYCOMB: A raised effect noted on cloth made of worsted yarn. Material is used as dress-goods and suiting cloth. The appearance of the fabric resembles the cellular comb of the honey bee. The material is often called "waffle cloth," in the cotton trade. The high point on the one side of the cloth is the low point on the other side.

HUCK, HUCKABACK: A strong cotton or linen cloth; the name comes from the German *huckepack*, meaning "peddler's wares." Literally, it means "piggyback."

JESUIT CLOTH: Suiting material of plain-weave construction worn by the members of the Society of Jesus, founded by Ignatius of Loyola with Papal approval in 1540. This coarse fabric is dyed black and is made from hard-twisted yarn. There is considerable call for this cloth among religious orders throughout the world.

LACE: The Latin word *loquens* meaning a "knot" or "noose," has been corrupted into lace.

LONGCLOTH: Contraction from lawn cloth.

MALINES: One of the oldest and best known of laces, nets and silk fabrics, diaphanous in nature. Named for this venerable city of Belgium.

MERINO: (The Spanish word *merino* signified roving from pasture to pasture, said of sheep. Originally from the Latin *major* "greater." A very fine quality of wool of the so-called merino sheep of Spanish origin, hence a cloth of such material. The term "merino" is now applied also to knitted woolen fabrics, notably undergarments constructed of yarns with an admixture of cotton to prevent shrinkage in laundering.

MOHAIR: From the Arabic *Mukhayyar*, a goat's hair fabric. Called "mockaire" in medieval times. A glossy lining cloth in both plain weave and twills, in dyed or natural colors, made from the hair of the Angora goat of Asia Minor. It is made of domestic fibers, also of adulterated stock.

MOMMY CLOTH: The name given to the linen or cotton fabric used to encase dead persons in Egypt. Many mummies are still extant and may be seen in any number of museums throughout the world. The yarn used was very fine in diameter and high in yarn count; the fabric was made of plain weave and it was left in the unbleached state. Spelled in several ways.

MOSCOW: A heavy, stiff, boardy, cumbersome overcoating peculiar to Russia, really a bulky frieze fabric that is most difficult to use in cut-fit-trim. Named for the city of Moscow.

MUSLIN: First made in Mesopotamia, homeland of the Turkish peoples. *Mosul* or "muslin" is now a generic term which covers a host of cotton cloths, from sheers to heavy sheetings. Another meaning of muslin is that it is a pure starched or back-filled finish material with a dull, thready or clothy effect, used as a printcloth. Muslin and muslin sheeting are genuine staples used throughout the world today.

MOZAMBIQUE: Named for the island off the east coast of Africa, it is a fabric of the grenadine type made with large floral effects in relief to form the motif, a staple decorative fabric. Originally made of silk, it is now available in rayon, acetate, and other manmade fibers, as well as in silk, which is still used in the more costly fabrics.

NUN'S VEILING: Used as religious garb with some little call in the dressgoods trade. Cloth is all-worsted, all-silk, worsted and silk, etc. The fine, sheer types made are dyed black or brown in the piece, but other colors are given when there is a call for the material in the dressgoods trade. Fabric shines with wear. This cloth, when used by laymen, is made into dresses, cloaks, kimonos, and babies' coatings.

OSNABURG: The base fabric from which cretonne is made, it is named for the city in Germany. Much foreign matter in the cloth is readily apparent.

PANAMA: The name sometimes given to small basket weaves such as a 2-2, 3-3, 4-4. Some embroidery canvas is known by this term, a cloth made for many years on hand looms in Panama. The name is also given to the straw plaiting used by the makers of Panama hats, which, curiously enough, are not made in Panama but in Ecuador.

PERCALE: Comes from the word *parfalah,* which describes a cloth made in Persia for many centuries. Noted for its fine texture, smooth finish, and small printed motifs on the cotton fabric. This staple is probably the most popular cotton print goods on the market today; sheeting of percale is also exceedingly popular at present. Often called calico.

QUOTON: The Arabic term for "cotton," it is a derivation of the Indian term for cotton, *goton.*

SAXONY: A broad term today, it was first applied to the merino wool of Germany, one of the best of the wools obtainable anywhere. It also is the name for a quality knitting yarn and a luxury-type men's overcoating fabric. Named for the province in Germany, Saxony is a popular name to designate fabrics such as a Saxony flannel, Saxony carpet, Saxony cord.

SARSENET: From the Arabic, meaning a "silk veiling or net." Used in the veiling and millinery trades today.

SEBASTOPOL: A twill-faced, heavy overcoating which originated in this well-known city fortified by the Russians and captured by the French and the English during the Crimean War, 1855.

SEERSUCKER: From the Persian (Iranian) word *shirushakar,* meaning "puckered, blistered or shriveled surface." It is made with stripes alternating with plain or crepe ground weaves. The base ends in the fabric are under loom tension, while those that give the puckered effect are woven with a slack tension. Another method of obtaining the effect is to print the cloth in stripes with a preparation that will resist the action of caustic soda. Thus, when the goods are passed through the concentrated caustic-soda solution, the imprinted stripe areas will shrink to give the appearance of puckered or blistered stripes. This cloth is called plissé.

SHAWL: Originally a floor covering and a contraction from *sald,* the Sanskrit term for "floor," whence comes the name.

SILESIA: Smooth-finish lining fabric originating in Silesia when it belonged to Austria. It is also the name for Austrian merino wool, one of the best wools in the world.

SULTANE: Silk and wool fabric made with a twill weave and given a rough finish without any shearing or singeing. The name comes from sultana, the "first" wife of the sultan.

SWISS: Permanent finish given to many quality cotton cloths. An excellent durable finish that was first brought out in Gallen (St. Gall), Switzerland. The term itself denotes excellent fabric finish.

TABBY: A plain weave; the name originated from a street of that name in old Baghdad.

TAFFETA: One of the oldest fabrics known to man; originally made of silk and noted for its smooth surface, even texture, and slight crosswise rib, the Persians called it *taftan.* The plain weave used to make it is still, in some circles, called the tabby weave. Taffeta was being made in the fourteenth century, and France was making the material prior to this time and called it *taffetas.* Its first use was for linings in rich, luxurious mantle fabrics. Then it developed into dress fabrics, at first worn in court circles. The goods are now made from about all of the major textile fibers. Much of the goods today are moiréd in this form-concealing fabric.

TARTAN PLAID: A conventionalized, multicolored fabric, the outstanding material of which is kilt fabric. Plaids are used for blankets, robes, many types of dressgoods, neckwear, ribbon, silks, etc. This cloth was given to the world by the well-known Scotch clans Campbell, Cameron, MacPhee, Stewart, Douglas, MacDonald, MacPherson, MacTavish, etc. In woolens and worsteds, in subdued effects, it has use in suiting cloth. The word, formerly spelled *tartanem,* was borrowed from the English, who took it from the Spanish term *tiritana.* The Spaniards gave this name to colored cloths as far back as the thirteenth century. The Scots have capitalized on tartans more than any other nation and the general belief is that these plaids were Scottish in origin. The Gaelic term is *breacan.* It takes about seventeen yards of material to make a complete kilt outfit for an adult. The material is most interesting, and a study may be made of the symbols and meanings of the plaids by enterprising students interested in the subject. Two-up and two-down twill weaves are used in construction.

THIBET: Used in heavy suitings for cheap grades of jersey trouserings. Piece-dyed and given clear finish, it runs from twelve to thirty ounces per yard in weight. Wool, worsted, shoddy, and waste fibers are used in making the several qualities on the market. Broken weaves are employed in the construction, and the filling is usually double—a face filling and a back filling. A soft and smooth plain-finished face, woolen or part woolen fabric, it is usually piece-dyed for suitings or overcoatings. Genuine Thibets are made from the fleece of the mountain sheep of Thibet (usually spelled Tibet).

ULSTER: Heavy overcoating cloth, loosely woven with warp of right-hand twist yarn, and filling of left-hand twist yarn. All types and kinds of fibers are used in the material, de-

SURE CARE SYMBOLS

Follow these symbols to WASH or DRY-CLEAN and IRON your clothes or home furnishing with satisfactory results. Look for the labels with these simple guides to happier washdays.

	B use bleach carefully	**DC**	
you may wash by machine or by hand	do not use bleach	may be dry-cleaned	do not dry-clean
wash by hand	do not wash	may be ironed	do not iron

RECOMMENDED WASH TEMPERATURES:

160°	hot water with any soap or detergent	**H**	hot iron
120°	medium-hot water with any soap or detergent	**M**	medium-hot iron
105°	warm water with mild soap or mild detergent	**C**	cool iron
CW	use cold water; it lessens the danger of staining and shrinkage	**S**	steaming iron
WS	wash separately; it lessens the danger of staining and shrinkage	**L**	little or no ironing

DD	drip dry	**SD**	spin dry	**DF**	dry flat
TD	you may tumble dry		**LD**	hang on line to dry	
DR	dry rapidly (for example remove excess moisture between towels)				

HERE ARE HOW THESE SYMBOLS MIGHT LOOK ON LABELS; WHAT THEY TELL YOU.

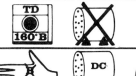

Wash by machine or by hand in hot water with any soap or detergent. Use bleach carefully. Tumble dry. Do not dry-clean. Iron with hot iron.

Wash by hand in warm water with any soap or detergent. Do not bleach. Dry clean. Little or no ironing.

Wash by hand in lukewarm water with mild soap or detergent. Do not bleach. Dry rapidly. Dry clean. Do not iron.

These are the permanent SURE CARE© Symbols. Keep them at hand so you can refer to them for washing and dry-cleaning of all your clothes and other fabric products.

©N.R.M.A. 1960, R. H. MACY & CO., INC.

Courtesy of the National Retail Merchants Association. Sure Care Symbols created and developed by Ephraim Freedman, Chairman, Technical Committee NRMA and Director of Macy's Bureau of Standards.

NIP		WET	
PULL		Water	
RESTRAIN		Soap	
PRESS		Oil	
STRIKE AGAINST		DRY	
STRUCK BY		COOL	
PLACE		HEAT	
Can		ROTATE Wind	
Ball		Unwind	
Quill		TWIST	
Section Beam		SHEAR	
Loom Beam		NAP	
Dye Kettle Spool		CUT	
Jack Spool		CLEAN	
Cloth Roll		DOFF	
DEPOSIT		WIND—as for lap	
TRANSFER		BOBBIN Wind	
MEASURE QUALITATIVE		Spin	
MEASURE QUANTITATIVE		Piece-up	
CONTROL MECHANICAL		DETACH	
CONTROL ELECTRICAL		TRANSFER THROUGH RESTRAINT	
TUMBLE		INTERMITTENT FEED	
DRAFT		FOUR DOUBLINGS	
CONDENSE			

The above symbols were conceived by the late Professor E. R. Schwarz, Graduate Textile Department, Massachusetts Institute of Technology, Cambridge, Massachusetts. They were introduced to the textile world by Mr. C. J. Monego of the Quartermaster Research and Engineering Laboratories, Natick, Massachusetts. Dr. Stephen J. Kennedy, Director of Research for the Quartermaster Department, and Mr. Monego very kindly granted permission for the use of these symbols in this book.

pendent on the quality of the cloth wanted. May be piece-dyed or stock-dyed for mixed effects. The long nap given the cloth in finishing is pressed down. Material is good for cold, stormy winter weather. Fabric weight is from twenty-four to thirty ounces. Originated in Ulster County, Northern Ireland.

VICUÑA: A cloth that finds use in overcoatings for special and conventional occasions. The material gets its name from the fine woolly fur of the vicuña, a native of the Andes Mountains in South America. The vicuña belongs to the llama and alpaca group. Genuine vicuña overcoating is scarce in this country. Japan is the greatest user of the fiber. The imitation or commercial cloth called vicuña is produced by giving to certain staple and semistaple cloths of wool a small admixture of vicuña fibers. The fibers make for the soft, silken-like feel and finish noted in the fabric. The fur of the vicuña is difficult to obtain, and there is a law that the animals must not be shot when found. The story of the animal resembles that of the American buffalo or bison. Too much slaughtering brought about a great decrease in the production. The vicuña is found in mountain areas five thousand feet above sea level. Peru is the homeland of vicuña.

WHIPCORD: This rugged, steep twill fabric made with high-twist yarn gets its name from the fact that the material simulates the lash of a whip.

WOOL: From Wolle, the German word for "wool fleece." Vilna, on the Baltic Sea, obtained its name because of the business carried on there in wool.

YARD: A thirty-six-inch length in America. The English yard is a standard established by the government, indicated by two marks on a metal rod embedded in the masonry of the House of Parliament in London. The American yard, which is 1/100,000 of an inch longer than the English yard, is not fixed by government standard. The foot of today, which measures twelve inches, is supposed to have been the length of the foot of James I (reign 1603–1625). Cloth is usually sold by the yard.

ZEPHYR: Originally a lightweight worsted yarn of good quality. Fabric made of the yarn was also known as zephyr. Today many lightweight cottons and manmade yarn materials are advertised as zephyr to attract attention to the sheerness or lightness of the material. The name is derived from Zephyrus, the Greek term for light west wind.

Source: *American Fabrics Magazine*, Doric Publishing Co., Inc., 24 East 38th Street, New York City.

SYNTHETIC RUBBER YARNS AND OTHER PRODUCTS

ACRYLIC RUBBER:
Acrylon BA 12, Acrylon EA 5 of Chemical Division, Borden Co., 350 Fifth Ave., New York City.
Hycar 4021 (PA-21) of B. F. Goodrich Chemical Co., 3135 Euclid Ave., Cleveland, Ohio.

BUTADIENE RUBBER—ACRYLONITRILE POLYMERS:
Butaprene of Xylos Rubber Co., Division of Firestone Tire & Rubber Co., Akron, Ohio.
Chemigum of Chemical Division, Goodyear Tire & Rubber Co., Akron, Ohio.
Herecol N 33 of Heresite Chemical Company, Manitowoc, Wis.
Hycar 1014, 1041, 1042, 1043, and 1072 of B. F. Goodrich Chemical Co., Cleveland, Ohio.
Nitrex, Paracril of Naugatuck Chemical Division, United States Rubber Co., 1230 Sixth Ave., New York City.
Polysar Krynac of H. Muehlstein & Co., 60 E. 42nd St., New York City.
Tylac (lattice) of Chemical Division, International Latex, Playtex Park, Dover, Del.

BUTADIENE RUBBER—METHYL VINYLPYRIDENE COPOLYMERS:
Philprene of Rubber Chemicals Division, Phillipps Chemical Co., Bartlesville, Okla.

BUTADIENE RUBBER—STYRENE COPOLYMERS:
Ameripol of Gulf Chemicals, Inc., 3121 Euclid Ave., Cleveland, Ohio.
ARSC Polymers of American Synthetic Rubber Corp., 500 Fifth Ave., New York City.
Baytown Masterbatches of United Rubber & Chemical Co., Charlestown, W. Va.
Buna Rubber of Copolymer Rubber & Chemical Corp., Baton Rouge, La.
FR-S of Synthetic Rubber and Latex Division of Firestone Tire & Rubber Co., Akron, Ohio.
Gentro of Chemical Division of General Tire & Rubber Co., Akron, Ohio.
Polyco of Chemical Division, Borden Co., Inc., 350 Fifth Ave., New York City.
Polysar S, Polysar S-50, Polysar Kryflex 200, S-X-371, SS-250, Polysar Krylene, Krylene NS 1, Krynol 651, Krynol 652 of H. Muehlstein & Co., 60 E. 42nd St., New York City.
S-Rubber of Synthetic Rubber Sales Division, Shell Chemical Corp., Torrance, Calif.
Synpol of Naugatuck Chemical Division, United States Rubber Co., Inc., New York City.

CHLOROPRENE RUBBER:
Neoprene (Types AC, C-G, GN-A, KNR, GRT, S, W, WHV, WRT, and WX) of Elastomer Chemical Dept., E. I. du Pont de Nemours & Co., Inc., Wilmington, Del.

CHLOROSULPHONATED POLYETHYLENE:
Hypalon of E. I. du Pont de Nemours & Co., Inc., Wilmington, Del.

FLUORINATED RUBBER:
KEL-F Elastomers of Jersey City Chemical Division, Minnesota Mining & Manufacturing Co., Jersey City, N. J.
3M Brand Fluoro-Rubber 1F4, Fluorochemical Division, Minnesota Mining & Manufacturing Co., St. Paul, Minn.
Viton A of Elastomer Chemical Department, E. I. du Pont de Nemours & Co., Inc., Wilmington, Del.

ISO BUTYLENE POLYMERS:
Vistanex of Enjay Co., Inc., 15 W. 51st St., New York City.

[403]

POLYISOBUTYLENE RUBBER:
  Enjay Butyl, GR1 of Enjay Co., Inc., 15 W. 51st St., New York City.
  Hycar 2202 of B. F. Goodrich Chemical Co., Cleveland, Ohio.
  Polysar Butyl of H. Muehlstein & Co., 60 E. 42nd St., New York City.

POLYSULPHITE RUBBER:
  Thiokol (Types A, FA, ST) of Thiokol Chemical Corp., 780 N. Clinton Avenue, Trenton,
  N. J.

SILICONE RUBBER:
  G-E Silicone Rubber of Silicone Products Dept., General Electric Co., Waterford, N. Y.
  Silastic of Dow-Corning Corp., Midland, Mich.
  Union Carbide Silicone Rubber of Silicones Division, Union Carbide Corp., 30 E. 42nd St.,
  New York City.

URETHANE RUBBER:
  Adiprene C of Elastomer Dept., E. I. du Pont de Nemours & Co., Inc., Wilmington, Del.
  Genthane S of Chemical Division, General Tire & Rubber Co., Akron, Ohio.

SELECTED LIST OF SEMITECHNICAL AND TECHNICAL BOOKS ON TEXTILES FOR YOUR LIBRARY

TITLE	AUTHOR	PUBLISHER
American Fabrics Magazine	Staff	Doric Publishing Co., Inc., 24 East 38th Street, New York City
Apparel Manufacturing Analysis	Jacob Solinger	John Wiley & Sons, Inc., 605 Third Avenue, New York City
Calculations, Yarn and Cloth	L. H. Jackson	Textile Book Publishers, Inc., 257 Park Avenue South, New York City
Cellulose; The Chemical That Grows	William Haynes	Doubleday & Company, Inc., Garden City, New York
Chemistry & Dyeing Textile	Olney	Spaulding Co., Boston, Massachusetts
Costume, The Book of	Davenport	Crown Publishers, 419 Fourth Avenue, New York City
Cotton, Growing	Cardozier	McGraw-Hill Book Co., 330 West 42nd Street, New York City
Cotton Handbook, American	Merrill, Macormac, Mauersberger	Textile Book Publishers, Inc., 257 Park Avenue South, New York City
Cotton, Heritage	M. D. C. Crawford	Fairchild Publications, Inc., 7 E. 12th Street, New York City
Dictionary, Modern Textile	George E. Linton	Meredith Press, Inc., 60 East 42nd Street, New York City
Diderot Pictorial Encyclopedia of Trades & Industry	Denis Diderot	Dover Publications, Inc., 180 Varick Street, New York City
Dress, How to Look and	Garson	McGraw-Hill Book Co., 330 West 42nd Street, New York City
Fabric Defects	J. B. Goldberg	J. B. Goldberg, Textile Consultant, 11 West 42nd Street, New York City

TITLE	AUTHOR	PUBLISHER
Fabrics, Focus on	Dr. Dorothy S. Lyle	National Institute of Drycleaning, Inc., Silver Spring, Maryland
Fashion, The Woman In	Langley Moore	Batesford, Ltd., London, England
Finishing, Textile	March	John Wiley & Sons, Inc., 605 Third Avenue, New York City
Handbook of Textile Fibers	Dr. Milton Harris	John Wiley & Sons, Inc., 605 Third Avenue, New York City
Handbook of Industrial Fabrics	Ernest R. Kaswell	Wellington Sears Co., 111 West 40th Street, New York City
Handbook of Textile Fibers (Natural and Manmade)	J. Gordon Cook, Ph.D.	Merrow Publishing Company, Ltd., Watford, Hirts, England
Index to Manmade Fibers of the World	Peter Lennox-Kerr	Harlequin Press, Ltd., Manchester, England
Lace and Embroidery, The Story of	D. E. Schwab	Fairchild Publications, Inc., 7 E. 12th Street, New York City
Man-Made Textile Encyclopedia	J. J. Press, Editor	Textile Book Publishers, Inc., 257 Park Avenue South, New York City
"Mercury" Dictionary of Textile Terms	Staff of "Textile" Mercury	Textile Mercury, Ltd., 41 Spring Gardens, Manchester 2, England
Mode in Costume, The	R. Turner Wilcox	Charles Scribner's Sons, Inc., 597 Fifth Avenue, New York City
Nylon Technology	Karl Inderfurth	McGraw-Hill Book Co., 330 West 42nd Street, New York City
Printing, Textile	Fred F. Jacobs	Chartwell House, Inc., 280 Madison Avenue, New York City
Rayon Technology	Staff Members	American Viscose Company, 1617 Pennsylvania Blvd., Philadelphia, Pennsylvania
Rug and Carpet Book, The	Mildred O'Brien	McGraw-Hill Book Co., 330 West 42nd Street, New York City
Sewing Machine Book, Singer	Mary Brooks Picken	McGraw-Hill Book Co., 330 West 42nd Street, New York City
Tailors, Textiles For	House of James Hare Staff	House of James Hare, Ltd., London, England
Textile Design, Advanced	William Watson	Longmans Green Company (David McKay Co., Inc.), 750 Third Avenue, New York City
Textile Design and Color	William Watson	Longmans Green Company (David McKay Co., Inc.), 750 Third Avenue, New York City

TITLE	AUTHOR	PUBLISHER
Textile Fibers, Structure of	A. R. Urquhart & P. O. Howitt	Textile Institute, Manchester, England
Textile Fibers, Yarns, and Fabrics	Ernest R. Kaswell	Reinhold Publishing Company, Inc., New York City
Textile Fibers, Sixth Edition of	Matthews and Mauersberger	John Wiley & Sons, Inc., 605 Third Avenue, New York City
Textile Materials, Identification of	Staff of Textile Institute	Textile Institute, Manchester, England
Textile Testing	Skinkle	Lowell Technological Institute, Lowell, Massachusetts
Wool Handbook, American	Von Bergen and Mauersberger	Textile Book Publishers, Inc., 257 Park Avenue South, New York City
World Encyclopedia of Textiles	Editors of *American Fabrics Magazine*	Prentice-Hall, Inc., Englewood Cliffs, N.J., and Doric Publications, Inc., 24 East 38th Street, New York City

LASTRILE: A manufactured fiber in which the fiber-forming substance is (1) a hydrocarbon, such as natural rubber, polyisoprene, polybutadiene, copolymers of dienes and hydrocarbons of amorphous (crystalline) polyolefins; (2) a copolymer of acrylonitrile and a diene (such as butadiene) composed of not more than 50 per cent but at least 10 per cent by weight of acrylonitrile units; (3) a polychloroprene or a copolymer of chloroprene in which 35 per cent by weight of fiber-forming· substances are composed of chloroprene units. The term "Lastrile" is the seventeenth generic term decreed by the Federal Trade Commission, Washington, D.C., March, 1966. Lastrile falls into category (2), above. The first sixteen generic terms for Manufactured Fibers became effective March 3, 1960.

DAILY CASH PRICES ON TEXTILE COMMODITIES

Textiles and Fibers

Cotton, one in. mid Memphis lb	.2925	.2925	.3075
Print Cloth, 64x60 38½ in. NY yd	.16½	.16½	.16
Print Cloth, 80x80 39 in. NY yd	.21½	.21½	.20¼
Sheetings, 56x60 40 in NY yd	.20¼	.20¼	.20
Burlap, 10 oz. 40 in. NY yd	.1705a	.1655	.1325
Wool, fine staple terr. Bstn, lb	1.30	1.30	1.24
Wool Tops, NY lb	1.740n	1.725	1.620
Rayon, Satin Acetate NY yd	.25	.25	.27½

Index

Tergal, 278
Tetoron polyester fiber, 278
Tex system for designation yarn number, 354-356
Textile bibliography (specific breakdown of subject areas), 318
Textile commodities, daily cash prices, 406
Textile Distributors Association, 189-193
Textile Economics Bureau, Inc., 318
Textile Fiber Products Identification Acts, extracts from, 345-354
Textile Inventions:
  Early nineteenth century, 369
  Eighteenth century, 369
Textile library, your, 404-406
Textile manufacture, periods in, 369
Textile Organon, 318
Textured Yarn Company, Inc., 285
Textured yarns:
  advantages of, 283
  definition of, 280
  high-bulk, 283
  names of some major, 283-285
  some uses of, 285
Texturizing, 283, 284
Thermoplastic, 250
Thermoplastic plastics:
  acrylic type, 300
  cellulosic type, 300
  definition of, 250, 299
  nylon thread type, 301
  polyethylene types, 301
  polystyrene type, 301
  vinyl type, 301
Thermoset, 250
Thermosetting plastics:
  casein type, 300
  cast phenolic type, 300
  definition of, 250, 299
  melamine plastic type, 300
  molded phenolic type, 300
  polyester type, 300
  urea type, 300
Tire fabric, rayon, 225
"Toramomen," 278
Tow, definition of, 250
Trade customs and definitions for the rayon, nylon, and silk converting industry:
  finished goods, 190
  gray goods, 189
Trade names, 303-318
Transparent:
  rayon, 225
  silk, 178
  velvet, 235
Travis (Darvan), 255-256
Tricolette, rayon, 223
Tricot, 138
Tricotine, 138
Triple sheer, rayon, 226
Tropical, 138
Trousering, 138
Tulle:
  rayon, 226
  silk, 178

Tussah, 180
Tussah in linen-like fabrics, 181
Tussah silk fabrics:
  douppioni, 180
  drapery, 180
  Nankeen, 181
  Nankin, 181
  rajah, 181
  shantung, 181
  shantung suiting, 181
  tussah, 181
  tussah in linen-like fabrics, 181
  velvet, 181
Tweeds, 132
Tweeds, major types of, 138-139
Twill lining, acetate, 236
Twill, rayon, 226
Tycora, definition of, 285
Tyrex, definition of, 278
Typewriter ribbon, 78

Ulster fabric, 139
Ulstron, 278
Unfinished wool, 124
Uniform cloth, 140
Union Carbide Corporation, 256, 265
Union cloth, 140
Urethane foam, 270, 271

Vegetable fibers:
  abaca, 96-97
  coir, 97
  Cuba bast, 97
  hemp, 96-97
  henequen and sisal, 96
  Japan mulberry, 97
  jute, 93
  New Zealand flax, 97
  pineapple, 97
  ramie, 93
  rope, 97
  straw, 97
Velour, 140
Velvet:
  rayon, 226
  silk, 179
  tussah, 181
Velveteen, cotton, 78
Velvet, types:
  bagheera, 179
  chiffon, 179
  ciselé, 179
  cut or beaded, 179
  faconné, 179
  Lyons, 179
  nacré, 179
  transparent, 173, 235
Verel:
  chemical test, 264
  definition of, 264
  properties of, 264
  uses of, 264
Vertical imperfections, 192
Vicuña:
  fabric, 149
  fiber, 145

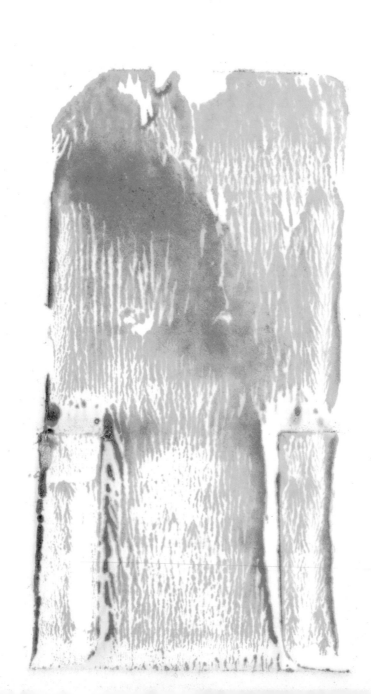